Flora of the East Riding of Yorkshire

Hull University Press

HUMBERSIDE
COUNTY COUNCIL

Flora of the East Riding of Yorkshire

by

F.E.Crackles B.Sc., M.Sc., F.L.S.

Edited by
Dr R.R. Arnett

HULL UNIVERSITY PRESS
HUMBERSIDE COUNTY COUNCIL
1990

© Eva Crackles 1990

British Lending Library Cataloguing in Publication Data

Crackles, Eva
    Flora of the East Riding of Yorkshire.
    1.Yorkshire.   East Riding. Plants.
    I. Title   II. Arnett, R.R. (Roger R)
    581.94283

    ISBN 0-85958-487-9

Photo-typesetting (10 and 12 point Times) by the School of Geography and Earth Resources, University of Hull.

Printed by V. Richardson & Sons Ltd.,
Brekkes Buildings, Wm. Wright Dock, Hull, HU3 4PA.

Contents

Part One

Foreword

What has been described as a peculiarly British product, the 'local *Flora*', has had an extremely chequered history, enjoying steep rises and falls in popularity governed by a wide range of factors, both socio-economic and scientific. Rarely, however, have they been as fashionable as they are today, and never have they been so important. They are uniquely suited to providing an accurate, up-to-date survey of the flora of a region set in an historical background. Such surveys are becoming increasingly essential data-bases in an age of ever-accelerating environmental destruction, as they will enable at worst a planned pattern of damage and at best a selective programme of conservation. Their extremely local nature ensures a most productive combination of regional expertise, pride and responsibility.

Considering the fact that most English counties and vice-counties possess reasonably modern *Floras*, and that Yorkshire has a particularly long history of intensive study by many devoted and knowledgeable field botanists, it seems extraordinary that there have been no authoritative *Floras* produced for almost 90 years. The present volume has started to rectify this situation, as it covers South-East Yorkshire, one of the five vice-counties into which Yorkshire was divided last century for plant recording purposes. No-one else has the knowledge or credentials of the author, Eva Crackles, that make her the ideal person to write this *Flora*, which is an enormous tribute to her knowledge and skill resulting from a life-time of field-work in the area.

The *Flora* follows, broadly, what has become a familiar and successful pattern in this sort of publication over the past 30 years or so. The introductory chapters cover historical, topographical, ecological and distributional characteristics, and Miss Crackles has wisely persuaded an expert, Roger Arnett, to contribute a chapter on geology and soils. In addition to all this and to the main part of the *Flora* (the systematic account) there are 465 maps indicating the presence or absence of selected species in each of the 2 x 2 km 'tetrads' of the vice-county. Transparent overlays are provided for these maps, allowing them to be interpreted in terms of a range of topographic and ecological parameters.

Clearly the *Flora* will immediately become the authoritative and indispensable source of floristic data concerning the East Riding. Its users will quickly come to realise their indebtedness to Eva Crackles. With any luck, botanists in other vice-counties of Yorkshire will soon become so envious that they will seek to remedy their disadvantage by preparing their own *Floras*.

Professor C.A. Stace
Professor of Plant Taxonomy
School of Biological Sciences
The University of Leicester
February 1990

Preface

The East Riding of Yorkshire is an interesting area affording unusual research opportunities for the botanist. It has the advantage of possessing clearly defined topographical areas and great physical diversity supporting a great variety of habitats. Within the region are areas of intense agricultural and commercial activity and vegetation changes are taking place at an increasing rate. The various effects of human activity on the flora of the area are of more than local interest. Such interference has resulted in both the destruction and creation of habitats, the gain and loss of species and the creation of disturbed and intermediate habitats which have favoured hybridization.

The position of the East Riding in the British Isles also gives its flora an added interest. Many species are at or near the limit of their climatic range. Some are at the northern and some at the southern edge of their range in the British Isles. Thus there is the opportunity for studying the distribution and frequency of a number of species for which climatic factors are critical.

The only previous *Flora of the East Riding of Yorkshire* was by J.F.Robinson and published in 1902. Since that time, there have been major advances in the study of taxonomy, particularly of critical taxa, and the approach to fieldwork has become more ecological. In addition, motorised transport has enabled the area to be explored with much greater thoroughness. As in most recent local *Floras*, tetrad distribution maps are included. An innovation is the presentation of distribution maps of 250 species in sets relating to habitat, the species of the same or generally similar type of habitat being placed in one set; maps of established aliens are also placed together. In addition, transparent overlays permit the reader to compare species distribution with that of important environmental factors.

I have lived in the area for all but two years of my life and have studied the vegetation of the East Riding of Yorkshire in detail since 1950, as a spare time activity until retirement from teaching in 1978 and subsequently more or less full time. In 1980 the Leverhulme Trust awarded a Research Fellowship making a generous grant to cover expenses for two years of fieldwork and herbarium research.

Eva Crackles
March 1990

List of Figures

List of Plates (Centre-fold)

Acknowledgements

It is my first duty to express my gratitude to the Press of my University and to Humberside County Council for agreeing to publish the *Flora of the East Riding of Yorkshire*.

Both the University Press and I are indebted to Roger Arnett for producing camera-ready copy of the text for the printers, likewise to Richard Middleton who has put the data for the tetrad distribution maps onto computer and has produced the maps by laser printer at the University. Keith Scurr of the School of Geography and Earth Resources, also of the University of Hull, drew Figures 1 - 5. The colour photographs, in the book and on the dust wrapper, were taken by the author with the exception of Plates 8 and 11 by Dr M. Thompson, Plate 12 by the late P.L. Gravett and Plate 35 by Mrs M. Payne. We are also grateful to Roland Wheeler-Osman, the University photographer, who has given valuable advice.

I am indebted to Professor C.A. Stace who read the manuscript and made valuable comments and suggestions and to D.H. Kent who also commented on the work and in particular for up-dating the Latin names.

I am grateful to the following who have helped me in a variety of ways during the preparation of the work for publication: Miss A. Braithwaite, Mrs P. Dunning, G. Hylands, C. Unwin and Dr M. Visvalingham.

In addition I wish to thank a number of personal friends and organisations for generous donations towards the publication costs: Beverley Naturalists' Society; Botanical Society of the British Isles, Welch Bequest Fund; Cartographic Information Research Group, University of Hull; Council for the Protection of Rural England, North Humberside Branch; Mrs J.E. Duncan; Ferriby Conservation Society; Mr J. Fryer; Goole and District Natural History Society, in memory of Mollie Withers who contributed records to the *Flora*; Mrs D.E. Haythornthwaite; Hull City Council; South Holderness Countryside Society; Mrs R. Suddaby; Wharfedale Naturalists' Society; York and District Field Naturalists' Society; Yorkshire Naturalists' Union; Yorkshire Wildlife Trust.

Grateful thanks are due to the many landowners and tenant farmers who have, over many years, granted permission to myself and other botanists to examine the vegetation on their land.

I wish to place on record my thanks to all those who have provided plant records and in particular to those who have collected records for the tetrad maps in unworked and often botanically unrewarding areas. My indebtedness to Professor Good for his major contribution to our knowledge of the East Riding flora and to other recorders is expressed more fully at the end of Chapter III. I am also indebted to those many referees and specialists who have determined or confirmed the identification of critical or unfamiliar taxa including aliens; their names are given in the text.

I would also like to acknowledge my debt to the late Percy Gravett who patiently taught me to take good photographs.

Eva Crackles
March 1990

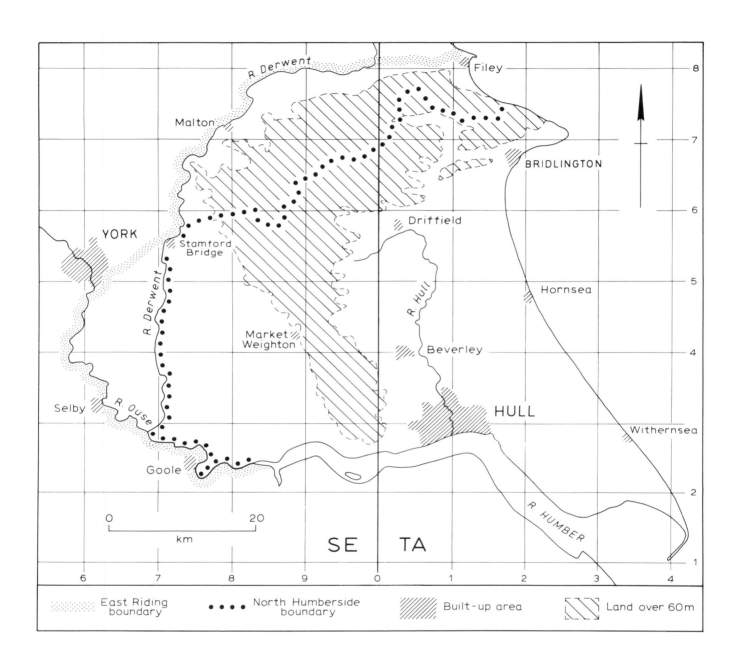

Figure 1   The East Riding of Yorkshire

Part One

I

The East Riding of Yorkshire

1 Definition of the area

The Flora covers the Watsonian vice-county of S.E.Yorkshire (v.c. 61) as shown in the maps in its pages. The region almost coincides with the former administrative county of the East Riding of Yorkshire (Figure 1). Most of the area now forms part of the county of Humberside with the remainder lying within North Yorkshire.

2 Topography and history of the area

For descriptive purposes, the East Riding of Yorkshire is subdivided into four areas, each possessing a distinctive physical environment. These regions are shown in Figure 2, and are used throughout Part Two of the *Flora* where the distributions of individual plant species are described.

i) Upper Derwentland

The Vale of Pickering is a broad flat valley extending some thirty miles inland from Filey, that part of the valley which is in v.c. 61 lying to the south of the R. Hertford. Adjacent to the river, there are extensive peat lands, with their ings and carr place-names, while along the base of the wolds there are large areas of sand. In the Late-glacial and early Post-glacial periods, the vale was the site of Lake Pickering, one of Yorkshire's largest lakes, impounded by ice and morainic debris at its eastern end and collecting water from the surrounding hills.

The site of a Mesolithic lake dwelling was discovered at Star Carr in the parish of Seamer, just outside the v.c. 61 boundary. The vegetational history and archaeology of the region surrounding the lake was determined initially through pollen analysis by Walker and Godwin (Clarke, 1954) and later by detailed stratigraphic investigation (Schadla-Hall and Cloutman, 1985). During Zone V of the Post-glacial period, reedswamp extended across what had been open water. The Fen Sedge (*Cladium mariscus*) spread particularly rapidly at that time suggesting that the climate was warm in summer and free from severe frosts in winter. By Zone VI, overgrowth of the lake site by reedswamp was complete. No transition to acid bog has been recorded and this suggests a slowly, but continuously, rising watertable.

For thousands of years, the lake site was a sodden marshy tract slowly filling with peat to a depth of nine to eighteen feet and inhospitable in character. The R. Hertford river was cut, in 1807, to drain the peatlands; more drainage schemes were to follow and are still undertaken so that only a few marshy areas now remain.

The tract of sands and gravels occurring along the base of the escarpment represents glacial outwash material which was re-sorted by streams and rivers (Foster, 1985). Between Sherburn and Flixton the sand has been widely quarried for building purposes, the resulting pits now being utilised for a variety of purposes. The famous Ganton Golf-links are in this area. A second considerable area of sand occurs further to the west at Wintringham.

Glacial drift, in the form of the Seamer moraine, blocked the eastern end of Lake Pickering so that the level of the lake rose as it received melt water. The enormous flow of water through the gap south of Malton cut the Kirkham Gorge. The R. Derwent now meanders through this valley which is still well-wooded except for the site of Howsham Wood, which has been largely cleared. There is also a significant amount of permanent pasture and marsh by the river, between Malton and Howsham Bridge.

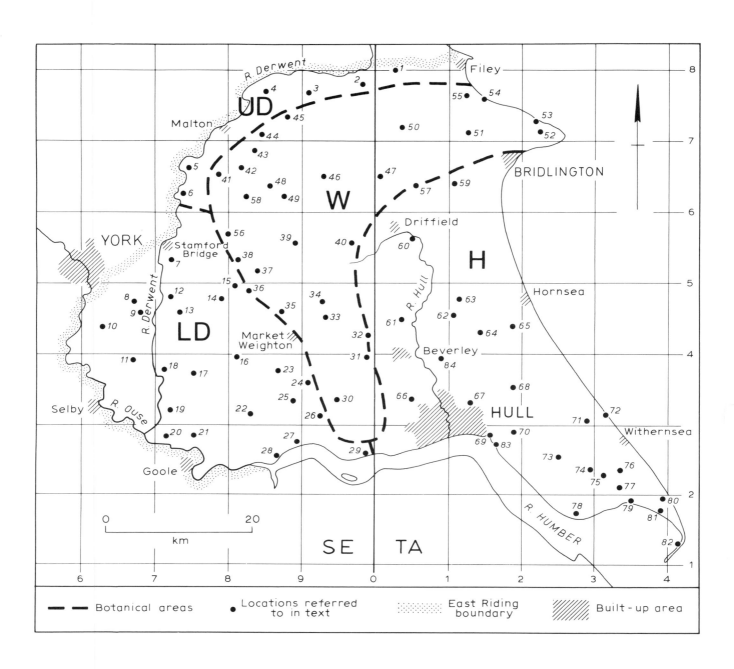

Figure 2   Botanical Areas and Key Locations

Key to Figure 2.

Botanical Areas

UD	=	Upper Derwentland
LD	=	Lower Derwentland
W	=	Wolds
H	=	Holderness

Reference numbers for locations indicated on Figure 2:

	Upper Derwentland		**Wolds**		**Holderness**
1	Flixton	42	Birdsall	61	Arram
2	Ganton	31	Bishop Burton	63	Brandesburton
6	Howsham	56	Bishop Wilton	59	Burton Agnes
5	Kirkham	49	Burdale	68	Burton Constable
4	Scampston	41	Burythorpe	66	Cottingham
3	West Heslerton	32	Cherry Burton	80	Easington
		47	Cottam	65	Great Hatfield
	Lower Derwentland	48	Cowlam	70	Hedon
14	Allerthorpe	34	Enthorpe	76	Hollym
20	Asselby	52	Flamborough	73	Keyingham
27	Broomfleet	50	Fordon	81	Kilnsea
18	Bubwith	38	Great Givendale	62	Leven
10	Escrick	51	Grindale	84	Meaux
28	Faxfleet	39	Huggate	75	Patrington
17	Foggathorpe	57	Kilham	83	Paull
16	Holme upon Spalding Moor	33	Kipling Cotes	64	Rise
21	Howden	33	Londesborough	71	Roos
8	Langwith	37	Millington	69	Salt End
7	Low Catton	45	North Grimston	79	Skeffling
13	Melbourne	36	Nunburnholme	82	Spurn Head
25	North Cave	55	Reighton	78	Sunk Island
23	North Cliffe	44	Settrington	67	Sutton on Hull
29	North Ferriby	46	Sledmere	72	Tunstall
24	North Newbald	54	Speeton	60	Wansford
15	Pocklington	40	Tibthorpe	77	Welwick
22	Sandholme	53	Thornwick Bay	74	Winestead
11	Skipwith	30	Weedley		
26	South Cave	48	Wharram		
12	Sutton upon Derwent	43	Wintringham		
9	Wheldrake				
19	Wressle				

3

ii) The Vale of York (Lower Derwentland)

The Vale of York is a predominately flat area, the varied surface of which reflects a complicated history of events occurring during and after the Late-glacial period. The ice sheet, which filled the vale, retreated northwards in stages marked by the York and Escrick moraines, two crescentric ridges. The latter, rising abruptly from the flat plain and composed of mixed sands and clays, extends from Stamford Bridge southwards by Wilberfoss to Wheldrake and Escrick and is joined to the York moraine by a sinuous ridge of gravel which was probably formed subglacially. South of the Escrick moraine, normal drainage to the east was blocked by ice or boulder clay across the Humber Gap between North and South Ferriby, resulting in the formation of Lake Humber which occupied all the adjacent low-lying land. The retreat of the ice and the breaching of the Ferriby moraine eventually led to the loss of the lake, leaving many areas swampy and ill-drained. A residual swamp, similar to Askham Bog to the south-west of York, appears to have prevailed at Heslington until at least the early part of the last century. The large numbers of carrs and ings throughout the vale testify to widespread persistence of surface water.

Salt-marsh originally extended from near the junction of the R. Ouse and R. Derwent eastwards to the foot of the wolds near Brough in a belt up to four miles wide and it was subject to regular flooding by the tidal waters of the Humber estuary.

North of the salt-marsh were tracts of carr, of which the largest was Walling Fen extending as far north as Holme upon Spalding Moor and Market Weighton. Streams, rising as springs from the foot of the wolds to the east, poured water into Walling Fen, whilst from the west the R. Foulness carried not only chalk-spring water from its source, but also water gathered as it meandered across the vale in a great curve. Walling Fen thus received a large influx of water all the year round. As the only outlet was to the south by a small tidal creek known as Skelfleet, the slight gradient and tidal water combined to hold back the fresh waters of the carr itself.

Much of the rest of the Vale of York was drained by the R. Derwent which rises in the moorlands of North Yorkshire and enters the vale after a long and circuitous course. The flat-floored valley of the river was several feet below the general level and was flooded annually on account of its slight gradient and the large volume of water carried by the river. The main tributary of the R. Derwent within the vale is Pocklington Beck, a chalk-fed stream, whose waters are often held back by the height of the main river. The three main water courses were so over-loaded that the surrounding countryside remained generally water-logged on both sandy and clay soils. Before the artificial drainage of the area, only the few low hills such as those of Holme, Newton and Wheldrake can have been completely free of water-logging.

Drainage of the carrs began in medieval times and is well documented by Sheppard (1966). Wallingfen Common included meres and adjacent carrs which were flooded for between three and ten months each year. In the edition of Camden's *Britannia,* published in 1789, a lake of one hundred acres or more is described as being present on Walling Fen until after the middle of the eighteenth century and to have been subject to flooding by salt-water from the R. Humber. Two lakes, Oxmardike and Yapley Marrs, are shown on the map of the County of York by Thomas Jefferys, published in 1775. The position of the former Oxmardike Marr, but not its extent, is indicated on the 1953 edition of the 1: 25,000 Ordnance Survey map and was to the east of the Oxmardike level crossing, whilst Yapley Marr was located to the north of the present village of Newport.

The Market Weighton Canal was cut through Walling Fen between 1772 and 1782, for the purposes of navigation and drainage. It was used to transport tiles and bricks from the works at the newly created village of Newport. The drainage improvement was not as great as envisaged because, as a result of commercial interests, water in the canal was kept above the agreed level. Consequently the lowest tracts, such as the site of the old Oxmardike mere, suffered frequent flooding. Navigational activities along the canal thrived until the mid nineteenth century when the opening of the York to Market Weighton and Market Weighton to Beverley railway lines led to a decline in water-borne traffic. Improvement in drainage of the carrs was still slow to follow.

The Pocklington Canal, cut from near Pocklington to the R. Derwent in 1814, followed Pocklington Beck along much of its course and remained separate from the drainage channels.

Extensive areas of sand formed the former commons, now greatly reduced in number and extent by being brought into agricultural use or afforested.

Much of the vale is now intensively cultivated, but some marshy areas still persist and there are ponds apparently on the sites of former meres. Ponds may also occur on the sandy areas, where marl has been extracted from beneath the surface and spread on the fields (Palmer, 1966).

With the creation of a barrage in 1975 at the point where the R. Derwent joins the R. Ouse, tidal water is now generally excluded from the lower Derwent valley thereby controlling the regular inundation of adjacent ings or water-meadows. It is claimed that the water-meadows which form the Derwent Ings Site of Special Scientific Interest (SSSI) may suffer as a result of such artificial control (Warburton, 1978).

iii) The Wolds

The Yorkshire Wolds form a crescentric area of high ground sweeping round from the R. Humber at Hessle to Flamborough Head (Figure 1), where they end in the magnificent cliffs of Bempton and Flamborough which at their highest point form a perpendicular precipice rising some 400 feet above the sea. The area consists of hills of characteristic rounded outline where surface drainage is at a minimum. There are steep escarpments to the north and west but a gradual dip slope to the east merges into the lowlands of Holderness. The word *Wolds* can be used to describe the region concerned or the type of country in that area, when the first letter is in the lower case throughout the *Flora*.

The Wolds are dissected by a large number of often sinuous valleys, running in a variety of directions and sometimes interconnected to form a complex system. Most of these valleys are now dry, but may have been excavated or modified in the Late-glacial period when the chalk was still frozen and large quantities of water were available. The valleys are floored by flint gravel except for the Great Wold Valley, extending from Duggleby to Rudston and Bridlington, which is probably pre-glacial in origin (Versey, 1971) and through which the Gypsey Race runs intermittently.

A narrow belt of Jurassic rocks forms foothills to the Wolds on their western side. Strong springs occur at the base of the chalk along the escarpment. Within the chalk itself, much of the water runs towards the middle of the syncline and may emerge in springs. Some of the springs arise here and there along the line Bridlington to Driffield to Beverley.

During the Late-glacial, there was a tundra type of vegetation on the Wolds similar to that currently found in northern Scandinavia. Eventually, forests spread in from the south, first of Birch, then Pine and as the climate became warmer mixed Oak, but the Wolds remained in part clear of woods. Mesolithic people were perhaps already clearing forest (Flenley, 1987a), a process which gained momentum in Neolithic times as man made room for his homes and fields with the introduction of agriculture. Early farmers overworked the land so that it became impoverished, forcing them to clear further areas of forest. Grazing animals prevented the regeneration of woodland on redundant fields so that deforestation had a lasting effect upon the landscape (Dent, 1987).

As late as the seventeenth and early eighteenth centuries, there were extensive hedgeless sheepwalks and frequent often extensive rabbit warrens, but Harris (1987) suggests that these were only part of the pre-enclosure scene. In most areas of the Wolds there was an open field system in which there were also large areas of arable, but land usage in these open fields varied in both space and time and the grasslands of the sheep walks were of varying age. The landscape was largely treeless. Gorse was common but its growth was controlled as it was in demand for fuel.

The landscape was transformed after Parliamentary enclosure by the planting of hedges and the reorganisation of farms. The sides of some steep valleys were planted with trees; small areas of ancient woodland remained. By 1870, most land on the Wolds was under the plough, except for steep valley sides which in the main remained as grassland, as most do to this day, although with modern machinery the ploughing out of steep valley sides is possible. There was much poor farming until the last century when the Sykes family and others introduced improved farming methods. The Wolds are now intensively cultivated; much wheat and barley is grown, but also turnip and other crops. Sheep farming continued to be important particularly on the high wolds until recent times, reduction in sheep grazing coinciding with the loss of rabbits owing to myxomatosis.

iv) Holderness

> *Lordinges, ther is in Yorkshire, as I gesse*
> *A marshy contree called Holderness*   Chaucer

Holderness is a plain of boulder clay, interspersed with considerable quantities of gravel and sand, deposited by ice in late glacial times. In the hollows of the hummocky impervious boulder clay surface there were many pools and lakes. The largest lakes, such as Hornsea Mere, Hornsea Old Mere, Lambwath Mere and Skipsea Mere, occurred in major, elongate depressions, probably marking the location of former valleys in the buried chalk surface (Flenley, 1987a).

As the ice finally withdrew, the R. Hull resumed its course southwards. Initially, its waters were provided by surface runoff from the seasonally frozen chalk uplands to the west, but as the climate continued to improve, underground drainage was re-established and the river was then fed by powerful springs arising near Driffield. In the lower valley, erosion was sufficient to remove much of the boulder clay almost down to the chalk bedrock, so that the topographic gradient of Holderness was reversed and the water in the newly developing drainage channels flowed westwards into the R. Hull system.

The initial colonisation of the drier parts by a tundra vegetation was followed by the development of woodland, first Birch, then Birch and Pine, followed by Hazel and Elm, Alder and Elm and eventually Alder and Oak (Beckett, 1981). Within the overall trend of climatic amelioration, several small reversals are indicated by the pollen record, with tree cover generally reaching a maximum some 7000 to 5000 years ago, when the clays of Holderness were probably covered with dense oak forests. From that time, man's impact on the landscape increased with forest clearance, agricultural development and primitive attempts at drainage and reclamation.

Eventually four main types of land surface could be distinguished (Sheppard, 1956):
1. Scattered well-drained gravel mounds.
2. Low-lying silt lands along the R. Humber.
3. Boulder clay lands with fairly dry areas but also numerous marshes and meres.
4. Peat lands which were difficult to drain.

By the fifteenth century there were compact villages, open fields and few woods on the clay lands, but still many meres, extensive marshes and sluggish streams. The often swampy, water-logged peat lands supported a tangle of fenland vegetation and were crossed by a few ditches and navigation channels; some parts dried out sufficiently to provide pasture for sheep and cattle in the summer months. These fenland areas, named carrs since Danish times, were mainly in the R. Hull valley. They played an important part in a rural economy providing reeds for thatching, rushes for floor covering, fish and fowl to supplement the diet as well as peat and turf for fuel.

The history of the drainage of Holderness is given by Sheppard (1956, 1958 and 1966). The northern part of the R. Hull valley remained relatively unchanged until the main drainage scheme of 1764 had its effects. Much of the valley was flooded for several months each year and the meres, variable in extent, represented the remains of flood water which lingered in the lowest parts throughout the summer. There is evidence that in some parts of the area, succession to woodland was permanently kept in check by continuous water movement (Crackles, 1977). There was still a small string of lakes at Tickton and Leven in 1775 (Sheppard, 1958) and it was established that the Leven Canal, cut in 1802, passed through two former meres or their sites (Crackles, 1968). During the course of time all the meres of Holderness became silted up or drained and reclaimed with the exception of Hornsea Mere, which remains the largest lake in Yorkshire.

Extensive areas of gravel, notably near Keyingham and Brandesburton, have been excavated and the resulting pits, usually at least partially water-filled, provide valuable wild-life habitats. Some have been used as rubbish tips, two for water ski-ing, while others are being re-excavated.

Along the coast, the boulder clay cliffs are currently being eroded at an alarming rate with annual losses of up to six feet being recorded (Pringle, 1985). Since Roman times, the coastline has retreated many miles and some thirty villages have been lost to the sea (Sheppard, 1912). The westward migration of the coast has also caused the growth and destruction of successive sand spits at the south east corner of Holderness (De Boer, 1964). Spurn Point, the current example, may be in imminent danger of becoming an island, having been breached on four occasions in recent years. Deposition of silt and clay along the northern foreshore of the Humber estuary led to the reclamation of land which began in the late seventeenth century. The history of Sunk Island is given by Allison (1976).

II

Geology and Soils

by Dr R. Arnett
School of Geography and Earth Resources, University of Hull

A comparison of the two maps displaying solid and surficial geology (Figures 3 and 4) reveals an immediate contrast. The solid formations, although highly simplified in Figure 3, demonstrate a relatively straightforward pattern. Easterly dipping strata expose increasingly younger rocks from the Triassic (230 M. years) in the west of the region, to Upper Cretaceous (90 M. years) in Holderness. A general description of the geological background to the area is provided in the relevant volume of the British Regional Geology series (Kent, 1980), with more detailed information available in Rayner and Hemingway (1974). The surficial geology however, reveals a complicated pattern of gravels, sands, silts, clays and peats deposited by ice, water and wind over the past 18000 years (Figure 4). As the soils which have developed in this overblanket of sediment reflect both the solid and surficial geologies, a description of both phases is appropriate.

1 Solid geology (Figure 3)

The western third of the region, from the R. Ouse to the base of the Yorkshire Wolds, is excavated in soft red sandstones and marls of the Triassic period. The older unit, Bunter Sandstone, outcrops to the west and in the valley of the R. Derwent, and takes the form of a fine-grained sandstone usually deep red in colour although occasionally grey or mottled. Within the sandstone, intercalations of siltstone or mudstone are common. Although composed mainly of quartz and a heavy mineral assemblage dominated by the iron mineral ilmenite, there is a significant feldspar fraction which, when subjected to chemical weathering, may be transformed into secondary clay minerals. Rounded, iron-rich sand grains and the presence of feldspar indicate that these sandstones were deposited in a semi-arid continental environment with extensive dry phases alternating with fluvial activity, while the presence of bedding structures signifies shallow water deposition in ephemeral river systems. This susceptibility to chemical weathering, combined with a poor cementation of the quartz grains, has rendered the sandstone liable to subaerial erosion, a feature common to Triassic sedimentary rocks elsewhere in England and Wales. The Vale of York has its counterparts in the Vales of Eden and Clwyd, in Cumbria and north Wales respectively.

East of the R. Derwent, and lying unconformably over the Bunter Sandstone, is the Keuper Marl, representing a change from a sand-dominated continental environment to a clay-rich system in which the sediments reflect alternating marine and continental sources. 'Marl' is a chemical precipitate produced when clay-sized particles are eroded from an adjacent land mass and deposited in hypersaline water, where coagulation of the clay into silt-sized units produces a mudstone or siltstone. The sediments were subject to periodic dessication, producing the red coloration so typical of these rocks. With the approach of Jurassic deltaic conditions, the Upper Trias is characterised by more regular marine incursions, and the marls along the eastern boundary of the Keuper in Figure 3 incorporate alternating sandstones and shales. All the Triassic rocks are masked by a variable cover of late Quaternary deposits, except to the south-west of Market Weighton where marls and sandstones emerge to form the low hill at Holme upon Spalding Moor.

The Jurassic rocks of East Yorkshire outcrop in a band of variable width around the base of the chalk escarpment (Figure 3). This variability reflects the presence of the 'Market Weighton Upwarp', an unfolded block perhaps 20 kilometres in length, which did not subside at the same rate as adjacent sedimentary basins to the north and south. Consequently, the deposition of Jurassic strata, shales, sandstones, calcareous gritstones and clays, was thin over the block, but increased markedly towards the north and south. As Figure 3 demonstrates, the entire sequence of Jurassic rocks to the north of Market Weighton may be less than one kilometre wide, increasing in width and thickness towards the Vale of Pickering and the Humber estuary. The presence of this 'upwarp' has not merely affected the total width of the Jurassic strata, but also the proportion of the Wolds escarpment occupied by these beds. South of Market Weighton, shales and sandstones of the Lower and Middle Jurassic become increasingly significant (Figure 3) but have little effect on the shape of the overlying escarpment.

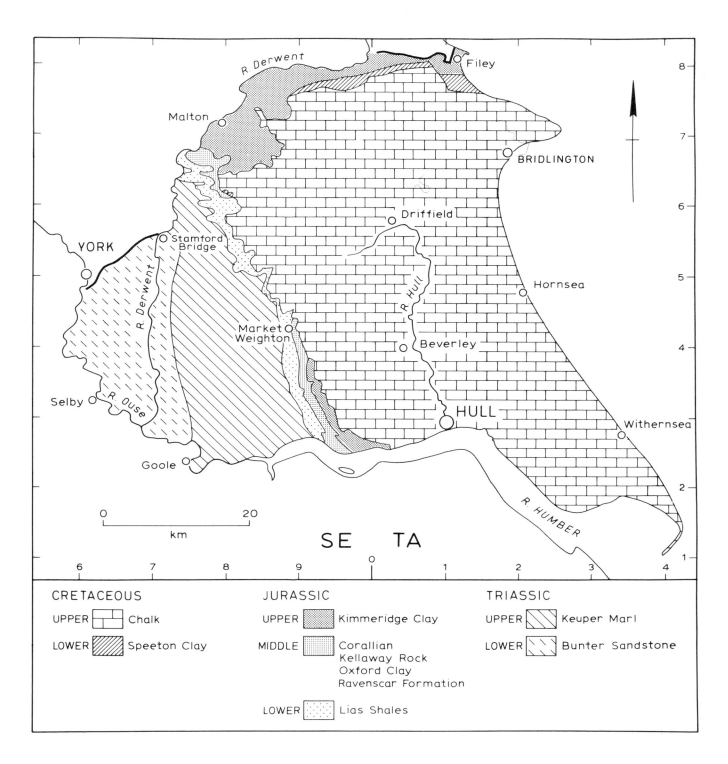

Figure 3   Solid Geology

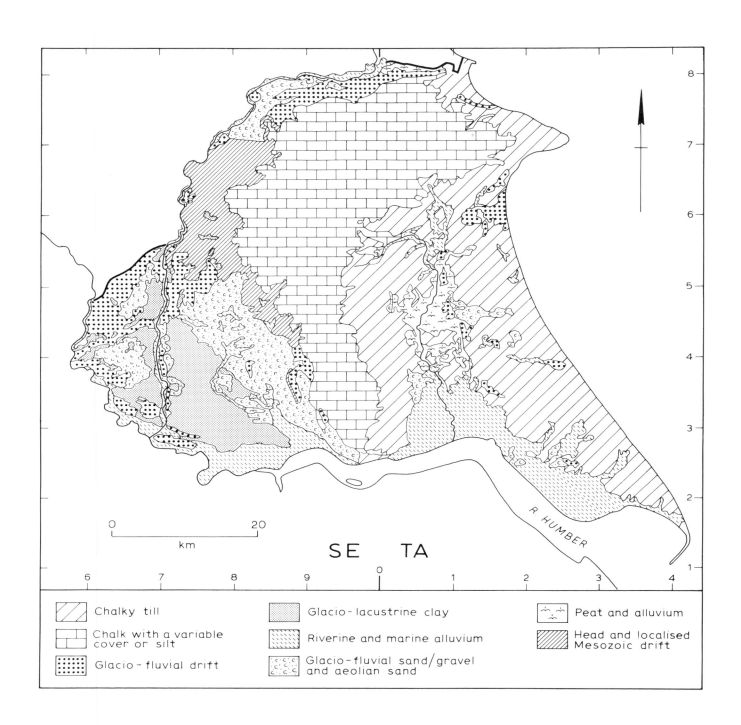

Figure 4   Surficial Geology

A prominent topographic 'bench' between North Cave and South Cave clearly locates the Jurassic outcrop, but within it, the various lithologies are poorly differentiated (Lewin, 1969). To the south and south east of Malton however, Jurassic rocks form an integral part of the lower escarpment, with separate benches being identified with particular strata. Localised faulting in this area causes additional complications to relationships between geology and topography. The northern escarpment is underlain by more argillaceous rocks, Kimmeridge Clay in the west and Speeton Clay (Lower Cretaceous) in the east, both of which have induced considerable landslipping in the overlying chalk.

The base of the Wolds escarpment, from the Humber estuary round to Filey, represents a zone of major hydrogeological contrast, where permeable and porous chalk overlies Jurassic shales and clays whose capacity to absorb and transmit water is greatly reduced. The result is a line of springs emerging at or close to the junction, often associated with major dry valley systems excavated into the escarpment face. The seasonal regime and chemical quality of these hydrological resurgencies have important implications for plant distributions.

Apart from Speeton Clay, no major outcrops of Lower Cretaceous rock occur in the East Riding. The Upper Cretaceous chalk rests unconformably on a variety of Jurassic strata along its western and north western margins and upon Speeton Clay in the north. Lower Chalk, outcropping along the face of the escarpment, is a hard nodular formation containing numerous marl bands. Above this, the flinty Middle Chalk occupies the crest and upper parts of the Wolds dipslope, while the more massively-bedded Upper Chalk is not exposed until well down the dipslope, before finally vanishing beneath the Quaternary deposits of Holderness. At the present coastline, solid chalk lies approximately 30 to 35 metres below mean sea level (Catt, 1987).

2 Surficial geology (Figure 4)

The variety of surficial deposits overlying the solid strata in East Yorkshire directly reflects the changing physical environments which have succeeded one another over the last 18000 years, from the late Devensian glacial maximum, referred to as the Dimlington Stadial (Rose, 1985), to the present time. The mineral and organic sediments mapped in Figure 4 vary in thickness from a few millimetres on the higher parts of the Wolds, to over 35 metres in Holderness. Even on the highest parts of the Wolds, where deposits have either been totally removed or incorporated into the chalk, the influence of Quaternary events remains discernible.

At its maximum extent, late Devensian ice completely surrounded the Yorkshire Wolds with one possible exception to the south of Malton where the high chalk uplands give way to the Howardian Hills running westwards along the southern edge of the Vale of Pickering. In the Vale of York the main source for the ice was north west England, crossing the Pennines via Stainmore and augmented by small confluent glaciers moving out of Swaledale, Wensleydale, Nidderdale and Wharfedale. Drift deposited by this ice was composite in origin, including red sandstones and marls derived from Triassic rocks underlying the vale, Jurassic material exposed along the flanks of the North Yorkshire Moors and Howardian Hills, and Magnesian Limestone from the western margins, in addition to more distant erratics transported from the Lake District, Pennines and Vale of Eden.

Although the ice remained stationary at the Escrick moraine for some considerable time, there is evidence of at least one surge southwards towards Doncaster, where gravels rich in Carboniferous erratics have been described (Gaunt, 1976). Much of the till deposited by this ice has been either eroded or buried by later deposits and that which remains has been extensively modified by subsequent glacio-fluvial processes. As Figure 4 reveals, it now covers large areas to the south east of York and in the valleys of the R. Ouse and R. Derwent.

Late Devensian ice from the North Sea also penetrated into the Vale of Pickering, although there is considerable controversy as to its maximum extent (Foster, 1985). Apart from peat and alluvium in the valley of the R. Hertford inland from Filey, the deposits fronting the northern wolds escarpment are a mixture of sands, gravels and loamy clays, mapped by the Soil Survey of England and Wales as 'Glacio-fluvial Drift' (Jarvis *et al*, 1984), but being rather different in origin and composition to those materials similarly classified and described in the Vale of York. The Vale of Pickering sediments have been much more extensively modified and resorted, to give discrete formations of

11

sands and clays rather than composite till.

Figure 4 distinguishes between the 'Chalky Till' of Holderness and its counterparts in the Vales of York and Pickering. As it appears on the surface, the former has undergone far less alteration, and remains a stiff, blue/brown boulder clay largely in the form in which it was deposited. A second differentiating feature is indicated by its name, in that it includes a considerable amount of chalk and flint incorporated from the Cretaceous bedrock beneath. Although described as 'Chalky Till', the transporting glacier was two-tiered in form. A lower unit, originating from southern Scotland and Northumberland, deposited 'Skipsea Till' throughout Holderness, with the amount of chalk and flint within the clay matrix increasing from north to south (Catt, 1987). The upper unit, described by Madgett and Catt (1978) as 'Withernsea Till', has a Tees valley source and is present only in south-west Holderness, where it lies on top of the Skipsea unit and from which it is distinguishable by a deeper red coloration and a reduced assemblage of chalk erratics. The latter results from a lack of direct contact between Withernsea Till and the underlying bedrock.

Immediately prior to the ice advance in Holderness, a thin layer of silty loess was deposited over much of the coastal area and the Yorkshire Wolds, probably derived from glacial outwash deposits exposed by low sea levels in the North Sea basin. Simultaneously, outcropping chalk strata were subjected to a severe periglacial climate which produced large quantities of frost-shattered rubble. A mixture of this chalk debris and silty loess now blankets the Wolds, forming an almost continuous cover over the southern section, but becoming thinner and less complete on the high wolds further north. Over these exposed interfluve areas, subsequent erosion has removed a large proportion of the finer material and deposited it in adjacent valleys.

Within that part of the Vale of York included in the East Riding, there is evidence for at least two levels of proglacial Lake Humber. Gaunt (1981) has proposed a high level lake (+33m O.D.) which existed for only a short period at the glacial maximum, when drainage through the Humber was blocked by Skipsea till ice. Apart from scattered sands and gravels along the margins of the Wolds escarpment however, little evidence remains. At a lower level (+8m O.D.), the evidence is rather more substantial, presumably representing a lengthy stillstand of ice at the Escrick moraine to the north, and either ice or moraine still preventing any outlet to the Humber (Gaunt *et al.*, 1971).

The glacio-lacustrine deposits associated with this lake are indicated in Figure 4, covering much of the low-lying topography to the west and particularly east of the R. Derwent, and consisting of up to 20 metres of laminated clay. When the lake did eventually drain, the morainic plug in the Humber gap prevented incision by the proto Ouse and its tributaries, and aeolian activity reworked much of the glacial, lacustrine and fluvial sediments, producing thick lines of dunes and coversands which now mask most of the surface between the old lake margin and the Wolds escarpment. A similar reworking of outwash sands may also have occurred in the Vale of Pickering (Foster, 1987) and central Holderness (Furness, 1985).

The morainic surface of Holderness included several discrete deposits of glacio-fluvial sands and gravels, most of which are too small to be individually identified on Figure 4, but which have a significant effect on soil development and hence on the distribution of plant communities. In addition, the uneven topography and disorganised drainage pattern led to the formation of numerous small lakes in which clay and peat accumulated (Flenley, 1987b). Most of these have now been drained and reclaimed (Sheppard, 1957), with Hornsea Mere being the last major survivor.

Deposits classified in Figure 4 as 'Head and localised Mesozoic drift' occur along the base of the Wolds escarpment particularly associated with the Triassic marls and Jurassic clays, shales and sandstones. These local argillaceous sediments have been mixed with chalky 'head' deposits, a combination of chalk rubble and aeolian loess, which soliflucted down the face of the escarpment under an earlier periglacial climate.

The plug of glacial moraine in the Humber gap, which had earlier prevented the rivers in the Vale of York from eroding into the soft fluvial and lacustrine deposits, was finally removed and incision took place down to -20m O.D. (Gaunt, 1981).

By 7000 BP, sea level had already risen to -9m O.D. and fine alluvium was being deposited in the valleys of the R. Ouse and R. Derwent and in Walling Fen. In the Vale of Pickering, similar deposition occurred in the valleys of the upper R. Derwent and R. Hertford, and also in the R. Hull valley in Holderness. Marine and riverine alluvium continue to accumulate along fluvial and estuarine systems, the latter encouraged by two artificial practices. The first is 'warping' (Heathcote, 1951) where silt-laden waters are allowed to flood on to adjoining land at high tide, before being drained off as the water level falls. The level of the land surface is thereby raised and the soils receive a regular addition of nutrient-rich sediment. The second process is direct reclamation as exemplified by Sunk Island in the lower Humber estuary, where levees are constructed to prevent flooding and the enclosed land is artificially drained.

The lower estuary also possesses East Yorkshire's only extensive area of active sand dunes. Spurn Head extends out into the Humber from a boulder clay root at Kilnsea, although its continued existence remains precarious as erosion on the seaward margins increases annually.

3 The soil system

Soil is the medium whereby vegetation communities are linked directly to the underlying geology, whether solid or surficial, which forms the major reservoir for plant nutrients. In particular, texture and mineralogy, which are closely controlled by the parent material, affect the moisture retention and nutrient status of the soil, which in turn partially determine the plant species which may develop. In some cases this parent material is derived directly from weathering of the subjacent bedrock, but more usually it develops from surficial deposits which may be totally dissimilar from the underlying solid strata. In East Yorkshire, both extreme situations occur, from complete control by solid chalk in parts of the Wolds, to absolute dependence on surficial sediments in the Vale of York, with every intermediate gradation.

Irrespective of whether this raw material originates from solid or surficial sources however, soils develop into parent material and not on it, so that many of the primary sedimentological characteristics are retained, particularly in the early stages of pedological development. The processes by which parent material becomes broken down into smaller fragments are collectively known as 'weathering' and are usually subdivided into 'mechanical' and 'chemical' components. In the former case, original material is fragmented by agencies such as expansion and contraction induced by freezing and thawing, by heating and cooling or by wetting and drying, plus the physical stresses induced by the penetration of rooting systems along lines of weakness in the bedrock. In each of these cases the mineralogy of the fragments remains identical to that of the original material, so that for soils developing in mechanically weathered rocks or sediments, the types of mineral present will accurately reflect their sources.

In contrast, rocks or sediments containing minerals which are susceptible to chemical weathering, may produce soil minerals which are different from their original sources. Many rock minerals are attacked by substances dissolved in rainwater, in particular carbon dioxide derived from the atmosphere or organic acids released from decaying vegetation, and to a lesser extent from the oxides of sulphur and nitrogen associated with airborne pollution. The action of these dilute acids is to detach the more readily soluble substances such as calcium, potassium and magnesium, and to retain them in the soil solution from where they become either a source of nutrients for plants, or are leached downward through the soil profile and eventually into the groundwater. A second important plant-related conversion associated with chemical weathering is the alteration of some primary rock-forming minerals, particularly feldspars, to secondary clay minerals such as kaolinite or montmorillonite. The physical and chemical properties of these clays are very different from those of their primary counterparts, particularly with regard to their moisture and nutrient status.

During weathering, quartz grains which are highly resistant to chemical alteration, are released into the soil matrix as the cement which binds them together in the original rock is removed. Although chemically inert, such particles play an important role in maintaining the soil's porosity and thereby encouraging the free flow of air and water through the system. Weathering processes therefore have a strong influence on plant growth. Firstly they determine the type and amount of nutrients available in the soil solution, and secondly they control soil texture, the relative proportions of sand, silt and clay, which in turn affects the speed and direction of water movement and hence the availability of this nutrient store to the rooting systems.

Whereas the linkages between geology and the plant community are clearly evident through a soil's texture and mineralogy, the organic fraction reveals less direct, but equally important influences. Soil organic matter is derived from the decomposition of plant and animal residues, and is continually being broken down, re-synthesized and mineralised through the activity of micro-organisms. Much of this material is in a transitory state and requires continuous replenishment. On a weight basis the organic component is small, between 2 and 6%, but its importance to the soil ecosystem is considerable. Firstly it acts as a granulation agent, assisting in the formation of a stable structure and thereby encouraging aeration. Secondly, organic matter is in itself an essential source of plant nutrients, particularly phosphorus, nitrogen and sulphur, all derived from the mineralisation of complex organic compounds. Thirdly, the organic fraction markedly enhances the water-holding capacity of soil and thus reduces the risk of moisture deficits. Soil textures dominated by sand and coarse silt such as those in the southern part of the Vale of York, have a low natural moisture retention capacity, and if little organic matter was present, plant growth would be highly restricted. Fourthly, humus, the stable end product of decomposition and microbial resynthesis, has the ability to retain those nutrients which are released into the soil solution by weathering, and which would otherwise be leached downwards in the profile beyond the range of plant rooting systems. Finally, organic matter is the main source of energy for soil organisms, both plant and animal, without which biochemical activity would almost cease.

How is this important soil component linked to the underlying rock or sediment ? The quality of organic matter returned to the soil depends upon the type of vegetation. Plant communities which demand large amounts of mineral nutrients, extract the necessary elements from the soil solution, incorporate them into biomass, and finally return them to the soil for re-cycling. Other communities on the other hand, are composed of plants with a low nutrient demand. They require fewer minerals for growth and return less when they die. Through its nutrient status therefore, the organic fraction reflects the availability of such minerals from the inorganic parent material with which it is associated.

4 Soil development

Soil formation is a complex process resulting from the interaction between four environmental variables, two of which - geology and the organic element - have already been introduced, with the other two being the effects of climate and topography.

At both macro and micro scales, the climatic parameters of precipitation, temperature and evapotranspiration have a direct impact on the rates at which soil-forming processes operate. Topography, or the shape of the landsurface, performs a similar function by controlling drainage and the speed and direction of water movement through the soil ecosystem. High upland areas or steeply sloping environments are usually associated with distinctive soils either because of excessively free drainage or because erosion has denuded much of the original cover. Valleys or topographic depressions tend to be characterised by deeper soils with abundant or excessive supplies of moisture as precipitation percolates into hollows from surrounding slopes.

One additional factor in the soil equation is time itself, as the chemical and physical properties of any profile are affected by the length of time over which the processes of weathering and organic accumulation have been operating. As described earlier, the last major ice advance in East Yorkshire occurred *circa* 18000 years ago, and represents an important starting point for soil development. Most pre-glacial soils have been either eroded, re-worked or transported to new locations through the agencies of ice, water and wind. Many soils however are considerably younger than this date, starting to develop naturally as alluvium was deposited along the estuarine or fluvial channels, as meres became silted up, or when sand dunes became stabilised by vegetation. The very earliest stages of soil formation are currently in evidence along the Humber estuary as alluviation continues to raise the land surface to a height above the water-table where colonising vegetation is capable of providing a thin protective cover. When man the agriculturalist appeared on the scene, drainage and reclamation schemes also initiated soil development in previously waterlogged areas.

14

5   The nature of the soil cover

Due to the relatively short time period over which East Riding soils have been developing, the influence of parent material remains very strong. The soils displayed in Figure 5 reflect to varying degrees the solid and surficial geologies in Figures 3 and 4. In the Vales of York, Pickering and Holderness, soil patterns are closely associated with surface deposits, to the almost complete exclusion of the underlying strata. In only two areas throughout the region are soil types linked directly with pre-Quaternary rocks, these being the Yorkshire Wolds themselves and along the base of the Wolds escarpment.

Over the Yorkshire Wolds, soils are generally thin, silty and calcareous, but there is sufficient depth of material to support plant growth, this latter being rather surprising given that the chemical weathering of chalk should leave little in the form of an insoluble residue. Undoubtedly the calcareous properties reflect the adjacent bedrock, itself highly shattered and disturbed by frost action immediately prior to and during the last ice advance. A source for the water-retentive silt however is less straightforward. If it did not originate from weathering of the chalk, a likely alternative, based upon mineralogical and textural analysis, is wind blown material derived from the North Sea basin (Catt, 1982).

A second area where solid geology clearly affects soil properties is along the base of the Wolds escarpment, where two underlying components are significant. Firstly, the movement of silty chalk rubble down the steep face of the scarp has extended the zone of calcareous soils westward over the Jurassic strata beneath. The clays and shales of the Lias and Oxford systems have been modified by the addition of calcium-rich deposits from the chalk above. Secondly, around the north west corner of the escarpment, between Stamford Bridge and Malton, the glacial drift is very thin and local in origin, so that the influence of underlying Triassic marls and Jurassic sandstones is increased, the former producing clay soils which are very different from their counterparts in Holderness and the Vale of York, and the latter generating loamy, calcareous soils of high natural fertility.

Elsewhere throughout East Yorkshire, the influence of solid strata is masked by surficial deposits. Within the Vale of York, laminated clays reveal the extent of former Lake Humber, coversands mask the area to the east of the R. Derwent, while drift forms the uneven topography to the south east of York. Across this general pattern, the R. Ouse and R. Derwent have superimposed ribbons of alluvium.

Throughout Holderness the basic parent material is Skipsea Till, a compact boulder clay containing numerous chalk and flint fragments. Two other deposits are noteworthy excluding the marine alluvium currently forming around margins of the estuary. One is the large area of peat and alluvium in the central Hull valley and the second consists of thick deposits of sand and gravel associated with the former ice cover. North of the Wolds, the valleys of the upper R. Derwent and R. Hertford present a similar association of sands, gravels, clays and peat, together with recent alluviation. In each of these areas the soils derive their basic chemical and physical characteristics from the underlying sediments.

The soil pattern displayed in Figure 5 however, also reflects the influence of topography, as local relief and drainage accelerate or retard the soil forming processes, even within one type of parent material. Again the major contrast is between the chalk uplands and the surrounding vales. In the Yorkshire Wolds, a high relief and permeable geology have accentuated the pedological differences between the steep slopes and exposed interfluves on the one hand, and deep sheltered valleys on the other. Fine textured material has been eroded from the former areas leaving thin, stoney, moisture-deficient soils, and deposited in the valleys where the resultant profiles are thicker, more moisture retentive and possessing a higher nutrient status. These denudation processes were much more active under a glacial or periglacial climate when the chalk would have become seasonally impermeable as a result of permafrost, thereby promoting surface runoff and enhancing erosion. Even today however, agricultural practices are accelerating the transfer of fertile topsoil from the upland chalk areas down into the valleys.

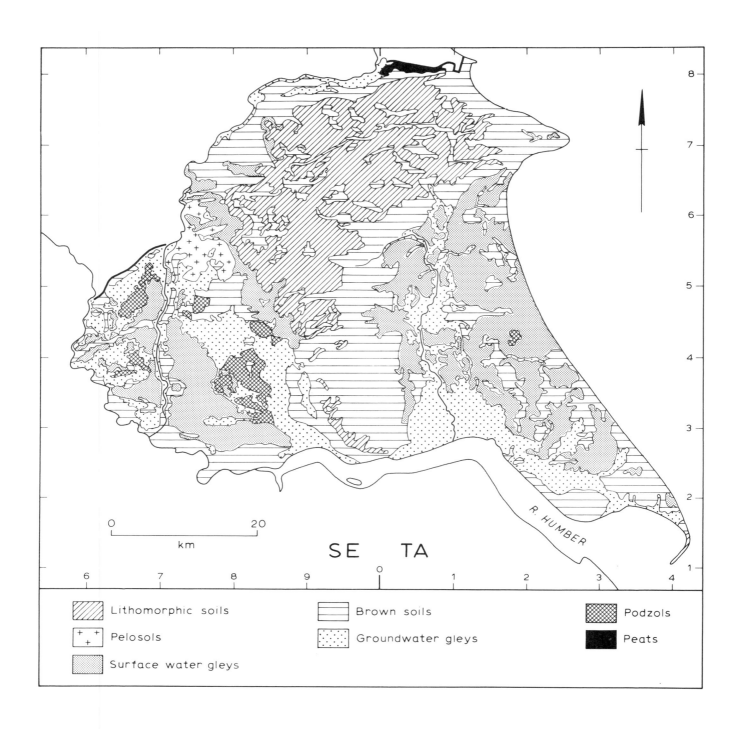

Figure 5   Major Soil Types

In the surrounding vales, altitude and relief are less extreme, but even here local variations in topography can induce major differences in soil type. Irrespective of parent material, if the ground surface is close to the water-table, the effects on soil formation and plant growth are immediate. The reduced diffusion of oxygen into and carbon dioxide out of the ecosystem favour the development of a totally different suite of soil micro-organisms, and the anaerobic conditions associated with gley soils become apparent. These groundwater gleys occur extensively in the low-lying areas adjacent to the Humber estuary and in the major river valleys (Figure 5).

At marginally higher elevations, gleying remains an important soil characteristic, caused not by the presence of groundwater, but resulting from the very low permeabilities of clay-rich parent materials whether they be of glacial or lacustrine origin, or weathered from argillaceous bedrock. Rainfall collecting on the surface of these soils is unable to percolate rapidly downwards, leading to reduced aeration in the upper parts of the profile, particularly in the vicinity of plant rooting systems. The distribution of these 'surface water gleys' or 'stagnogleys' is closely associated with low-lying areas of Skipsea Till in Holderness and glacio-lacustrine clay in the Vale of York (Figures 4 and 5). It must also be remembered that in many parts of the region, soils which would be classified naturally as groundwater or surface water gleys, may have had their properties altered through the agricultural practices of drainage or reclamation.

With further elevation of the land surface above the water-table and a more permeable parent material, free drainage accelerates the soil formation and provides an environment less restrictive to plant growth. In sandy areas, drainage may become excessive and podzolic soils tend to form, resulting from nutrient deficient parent material, intensive leaching and rapid mineralisation of organic compounds. Such soils occur in the coversand areas of the Vale of York wherever the local relief is sufficient to allow free drainage.

Optimum conditions for plant growth occur wherever free soil drainage exists, but sufficient clay and organic material are necessary to provide regular supplies of water and minerals. Soils with such characteristics are classified in Figure 5 as 'Brown Soils' and occur in both calcareous and non-calcareous environments usually in fine and medium-textured parent materials.

6 Soils of the East Riding

The soil distributions mapped in Figure 5 are based upon a classification developed by the Soil Survey of England and Wales (Avery, 1980). The system is hierarchical in that each level is differentiated on the basis of specific soil properties, these being very general at the highest level - the 'Major Soil Group' - , but becoming increasingly specific down to level four - the 'Soil Series'. Figure 5 maps the spatial distributions of the Major Soil Groups, which are classified on the basis of their dominant pedogenic characteristics. Although the Soil Survey recognises ten such divisions, only seven are extensively represented in East Yorkshire. In the sections which follow, each Major Group is described along with the most important 'Soil Associations' into which it is subdivided. A 'Soil Association' is the mapping unit adopted for the 1: 250 000 Soil Map of England Wales (Soil Survey of England and Wales, 1983), and defined as an area of similar or associated soil types which is given the name of the dominant soil series. For further information on any Soil Association, or its component series, readers should consult the Regional Bulletin published in conjunction with the above map (Jarvis *et al*, 1984).

Lithomorphic Soils

As the name implies, these soils display close affinites with the parent material. The soil-forming processes have been sufficiently active to produce a mineral-organic topsoil, but no clearly defined subsoil. The 'A' horizon grades directly into bedrock, stony rubble or unaltered sedimentary material. The lack of a thick subsoil, or 'B' horizon, is due either to an insufficient period of soil formation, or to the presence of some local environmental condition which prevents its development. Lithomorphic soils in Figure 5 are restricted to the higher and steeper parts of the Wolds, where their development is retarded by the lack of insoluble residues from the chalk and exacerbated by continuous downslope erosion.

These brown silty rendzina soils of the Andover Association vary in depth depending on the thickness of loess incorporated into the chalk rubble. As Figure 5 illustrates, they occupy the interfluve and plateau areas, while more fully developed Brown soils occur in the intervening valleys. Although porous and permeable, the Andover soils do not suffer from the level of droughtiness that one might expect from such a thin deposit. The chalk rubble itself is capable of adsorbing considerable volumes of water, and where highly shattered, this moisture is extractable by plants (Jarvis, 1973). Where much of the fine silt and comminuted chalk has been eroded from the steeper slopes however, the resulting shallow rendzinas are severely moisture deficient. Under natural conditions all these soils are alkaline with moderate levels of organic matter, but deficient in phosphorus, potassium and magnesium.

As the altitude and relative relief both decrease from north to south within the Wolds, the distribution of these lithomorphic soils becomes more restricted to exposed ridge crests and finally to the steeper parts of the west-facing escarpment adjacent to the Humber estuary (Figure 5).

Brown Soils

Soils in this group have developed significant topsoil and subsoil horizons, but display no gleying or waterlogging features in the top 40 cm. Within the group, subdivision is based upon the texture and origin of the parent material. On the Wolds, wherever the silt cover is locally thick or supplemented by colluvium moving off the steeper valley sides, brown calcareous earths of the Panholes Association replace the thinner rendzinas, providing a higher nutrient status, reduced moisture deficit problems and greater physical support for vegetation.

A second area of Brown Soils is associated with the chalky till of Holderness, wherever free drainage permits unrestricted profile development. The boulder clay in which they are developing is only slowly permeable however, and many of the deeper subsoils may possess variable signs of gleying. Although calcareous at depth, the profiles may be neutral or slightly acidic in the rooting environment.

Within Holderness there are two areas where Brown Soils are extensively developed. Firstly along the lower chalk dipslope (Figure 5), where the till cover is thinner and the topography sufficiently elevated to allow free drainage. These soils of the Burlingham Association skirt the edge of the Holderness plain from the Humber round to Flamborough Head and on towards Filey. In southern Holderness, a more undulating topography permits Brown Soils to form on better drained sites, assisted in this area by a more heavily weathered, open-structured boulder clay (Withernsea Till) and a slightly drier climate. In central and northern Holderness, Brown Soils only occur where topography or parent material facilitate free drainage.

Where parent material is coarser, usually derived from glacio-fluvial sands or sandy river alluvium, uniform brown sands of the Newport Association develop. They occur extensively along the northern flanks of the Wolds from Malton to Filey and on the higher sandy terraces of the R. Ouse between Goole and Selby and the R. Derwent below Stamford Bridge. Relief varies from gently to moderately sloping and the soils suffer extensively from wind and water erosion. Being very freely drained, they are also prone to drought during the summer months.

Within the East Riding, the York and Escrick moraines cross the Vale and provide localised areas of higher, hummocky relief. The morainic debris has been partially reworked by glacial meltwater, and the soil parent material is a mixture of loam, clay and sand. Although classified as brown earths (Bishampton Association), within the Brown Soil Major Group, they do possess a clay enriched subsoil which reduces permeability. The undulating topography and relatively high altitude however, reduce any tendency towards waterlogging.

Brown earths occur extensively in the middle Derwent valley to the south and east of Malton. Where the drift is derived from local Jurassic sandstones, the soils are coarse textured, loamy and naturally acidic (Rivington Association), although as they are used extensively for cultivation, lime and fertilisers are regularly applied. Where the underlying strata are limestones rather than sandstones, such as between North Grimston and Malton, the brown earths become more calcareous (Aberford Association), with a higher nutrient status and greater natural agricultural potential.

There are two other groups of Calcareous Brown Soils mapped in Figure 5, both affected by seasonal waterlogging, but insufficiently so to be classified as gleys. The first includes fine silty soils of the Blacktoft Association which have developed in marine alluvium around Sunk Island in the lower Humber estuary and adjoining the R. Ouse from Selby down to Goole. In the latter area the soils were largely formed in the nineteenth century by the practice of 'warping' where controlled artifical flooding was encouraged to promote the deposition of silt. Drainage dykes were linked to the main river by 'clew gates' which only opened at low tide (Palmer, 1966). Sunk Island was similarly reclaimed in the last century when a series of artificial embankments were constructed linking the 'island' with the mainland. Within these boundaries, controlled flooding induced additional sedimentation and pumping maintained low groundwater levels. Although classified as calcareous brown earths, these soils and their warp equivalents around Goole, would probably be defined as lithomorphic soils or gleys under natural conditions.

The second group of Calcareous Brown Soils (Landbeach Association) occurs in localised patches around the eastern, northern and western margins of the Yorkshire Wolds where thin drift overlies chalky, glacio-fluvial gravels. Subsoils are again affected by groundwater, but usually below 40 cm, thereby not affecting their classification as 'brown' rather than 'gley' profiles. The main areas for these soils are between Pocklington and Ellerker on the west, and between Cottingham and Beverley on the east. Soils with very similar properties are developed in gravels to the south of Brandesburton in central Holderness, although here the parent materials are non-calcareous.

Pelosols

This Major Soil Group includes those profiles described as non-alluvial clayey soils that crack deeply during dry seasons but are only slowly permeable when wet. The only major difference between this group and the Brown Soils described previously is that the moisture properties of Pelosols vary considerably between winter and summer. In the East Riding, their occurrence as the Worcester Association is limited to an area east of Stamford Bridge, where the thin drift is locally derived from underlying Triassic mudstones. The clay-rich subsoil causes significant waterlogging in winter and surface erosion by water may be a problem. Deep cracks created by dessication in the summer accentuate the moisture deficit, because any light rain which does fall, moves rapidly into the subsoil rather than being retained in the rooting zone.

Podzols

To be classified in this Major Group, soils must exhibit 'a podzolic B horizon', a subsoil layer containing amorphous mineral and organic compounds which have been translocated from higher in the profile. Under natural conditions they would also possess a surface layer of unincorporated acid organic debris, overlying a bleached horizon from which organic components, iron and aluminium have been removed. Where such soils are under cultivation, the original morphology of these upper horizons may have been largely destroyed.

In East Yorkshire, podzols have developed extensively in the Vale of York, usually on fine, sandy material overlying glacio-lacustrine clay. The Holme Moor Association occurs on elevated positions perhaps related to the crests of ancient sand dune sequences, described in the earlier section on surficial geology (Matthews, 1971). Although the sand is highly permeable, the presence of clay at depth does lead to seasonal waterlogging, so that at lower elevations in the dune sequence, similar soils would be classified as gleys rather than gley podzols. Under natural conditions these soils support a heathland vegetation community which returns an acidic litter to the surface, beneath which, the presence of a thin iron pan further reduces subsoil permeability. Ploughing has largely removed this impervious layer however, allowing cultivated plants to penetrate deeper in search of moisture. With a sandy texture and a low moisture retention capacity, the topsoils are subject to seasonal drought, while the systematic removal of hedgerows increases the susceptibility to wind erosion particularly in Spring. Figure 5 identifies isolated patches of these soils adjacent to the York and Escrick moraines, with more extensive occurrences around Pocklington and Holme upon Spalding

Moor. Only one area of significance is mapped in Holderness, around the village of Great Hatfield, where small outcrops of sand rise above the boulder clay plain.

Surface water Gley Soils

Many of the soils described as Brown Soils in Holderness and the Vale of York, possess subsoil properties indicating some degree of waterlogging or restricted drainage. Where such characteristics are more extensively displayed and where the source of the water is percolation from the surface rather than the presence of a regional water-table, the soils are classified as surface water gleys, or 'stagnogleys'. They occur extensively in lowland sites on both sides of the Yorkshire Wolds, wherever the parent material is sufficiently argillaceous to restrict the free movement of water.

Holderness gives its name to that soil association covering most of the central and northern areas of the coastal plain. These are slowly permeable, fine textured soils developing in chalky Skipsea Till and glacio-fluvial drift. Although the till is usually clay dominated, lenses of sand and gravel are common and there is a high stone content, including erratics originating from Scotland, Scandinavia and northern England. Profiles are rarely strongly gleyed, although regular mottling in the upper 40 cm. distinguishes them from Brown Soils of the Burlingham Association which occupy the more elevated, better drained sites. Seasonal waterlogging caused by low permeabilities are their characteristic features, and artificial drainage is necessary if continuous cultivation is required. Only a few areas of permanent pasture remain undrained and even here the micro-topography caused by ancient 'ridge-and-furrow' cultivation prevents excessive waterlogging. The spreading of animal slurry on these poorly permeable soils has a detrimental effect on surface water and ground water quality and the pollution hazard is always present.

A second area of stagnogleys occurs along the base of the west-facing escarpment from Market Weighton to the east of Stamford Bridge (Denchworth Association), where the parent material is local till derived from the subjacent Jurassic clays. Again the subsoils are very slowly permeable, and the gleying is increased by the addition of soil water moving laterally off the adjacent escarpment. Naturally acidic at the surface, the pH of Denchworth soils increases with depth, and the mineral complement is particularly deficient in phosphorus.

A third extensive area of surface water gleys occurs in the southern part of the Vale of York, on both sides but mainly to the east of the R. Derwent (Figure 5). This is the Foggathorpe Association developing in the glacio-lacustrine clays of former Lake Humber. Intensive gleying and seasonal waterlogging restricted land utilisation to permanent pasture until the 1960s, when extensive under-draining occurred. Scattered throughout this area are small elevated patches of glacio-fluvial and windblown sand which are too small to be identified on Figure 5, but which form 'islands' for the location of farms and villages.

Groundwater Gleys

Where extensive subsoil waterlogging is caused by fluctuations of the water-table rather than an impermeable parent material, Groundwater Gleys are the Major Soil Group. In the lower sections of the R. Hull valley and along the northern bank of the Humber estuary, soils of the Wallasea Association are widely distributed (Figure 5). Artificial embankments are necessary to prevent regular flooding, and when the groundwater levels are controlled, the soils are nutrient-rich and intensively cultivated.

Ribbons of alluvial gley soils are developed in riverine alluvium along the rivers Ouse, Derwent and Hull (Fladbury Association). Characteristically they are deep, grey-brown soils with regular mottling throughout the profile. In backswamps and other localised depressions, peaty or thick humic topsoils are generated and waterlogging is a constant feature. Even with under-draining, excess water is a problem and the land is mainly under permanent pasture. One variant of this group is found in the upper valley of the R. Hull, where fluvial deposits are intercalated with chalk gravel. These soils of the Frome Association are a complex mixture of loams, silts and clays in a gravel matrix, some calcareous and others not, but all affected by gleying to some degree. A second subgroup is found in the central sections of the Hull valley, where marine alluvium is associated with fen peat. Peaty humose soils intercalate with horizons of pure peat, silt and sand in a very complex pattern.

Sandy gleys are widespread in the low-lying areas along the eastern margins of the Vale of York. Although these sands of the Everingham Association are highly permeable, the underlying glacio-lacustrine clay maintains a high regional water-table. Prior to drainage, these soils were waterlogged almost to the surface, but are now intensively cultivated and require regular treatment with lime and fertilisers. A weak structure and a low natural organic fraction render these soils liable to wind erosion in the early part of the growing season.

Peat

Apart from small areas of humose soil associated with alluvium in the central Hull valley, the only extensive zone of peat occurs along the embanked and straightened course of the R. Hertford in the Vale of Pickering (Figure 5). The Adventurers' Association comprises amorphous and semi-fibrous peat soils mixed with reed and sedge peat containing wood fragments. With adequate pumping to remove excess water, these peats produce fertile, nutrient-rich soils, but draining does provide some problems. With oxidation and dessication, the peat shrinks and this natural wastage is accentuated by wind erosion and the danger of fire caused by the local burning of stubble.

7 Summary
This chapter has attempted to describe the pattern of soils which has developed in the widely differing environments of Yorkshire's East Riding, paying particular attention to those characteristics which affect the growth of vegetation. Without doubt, the two most important variables are the nature of the parent material in which the soils are forming, and proximity to the local water-table. Within these general constraints, the natural processes of soil formation have been strongly influenced by agricultural practices. It remains only to re-emphasise that the maps shown in Figures 3, 4 and 5 are highly generalised and should be treated with caution when interpreting the distribution patterns of individual plant species.

III

The Study of the Flora

The first known East Riding record is for Scurvy Grass (*Cochlearia officinalis*) 'by the seaside at Hull' in the famous *Herball* of John Gerard published in 1597.

Thomas Johnson (1600 or 1604 -1644), who published a 2nd edition of Gerard's *Herball* in 1633 which was described by Ray as '*Gerardus emaculatus*', was born at or near Selby (Kew & Powell, 1932). He was apprenticed to an apothecary in London and eventually set up business in Snow Hill. He visited relatives and friends in his native county in 1626, recording three species for specific localities, two of these being first British records: Water Soldier (*Stratiotes aloides*) in ditches at Rotsea and Giant Bellflower (*Campanula latifolia*) on the banks of the R. Ouse 'as I went from Yorke to visite Selby the place whereas I was borne being ten miles from thence' (Gerard, 1633).

Another notable visitor was **John Ray** (1627 - 1705), the eminent naturalist and theologian, who passed through East Yorkshire on horse-back in 1661 visiting Hull, Beverley and Selby, a journey planned to visit great churches and cathedrals and 'giving little opportunity for the study of the flora' (Lankester, 1846). Marsh Gentian (*Gentiana pneumonanthe*) was seen 'on many heathy grounds' in Yorkshire, but only two species were recorded for specific localities in the East Riding. The Common Pink was observed in great plenty on the top of the walls of the south blockhouse in the garrison at Hull. Lankester (1846), the editor of Ray's *Second Itinerary,* suggests that the plant meant was *Dianthus caryophyllus* or *D. plumarius*, but it seems more likely that it was Sea Pink (*Armeria maritima*) which still occurs on salt-marshes by the R. Humber and is known to have occurred 'near the garrison' at Hull in the eighteenth century (Whytehead in ms.). Caraway (*Carum carvi*) was also noted: 'We observed in a close near the town called Granswick, great store of *Carum*. It grows in many places about this town ...'. Judging from the position of this observation, in the account of the day spent in Hull, I believe that the translation of Ray's statement which was originally in Latin, should read: 'We observed in a close called Grangewick, near the town a great store of Carum. It grows in many places about this town ...'(i.e. Hull). There was a close called Grangewick of considerable antiquarian interest just outside the Myton Gate of Hull, then fortified.

To Edmund Gibson's edition of Camden's *Britannia* (1695), Ray contributed county lists. Besides Caraway the only other species given for East Yorkshire is *Lysimachia thyrsiflora*. However this record is in error; it was for Leckby Carr in the former North Riding (v.c. 62), being found there by Matthew Dodsworth, Rector of Sessay.

Thomas Knowlton (1691 - 1781) is the first East Riding resident to leave plant records. Previously head gardener to James Sherard at the famous gardens at Eltham, Kent, he came to Londesborough as head gardener to the Duke of Burlington in 1726 and died at Londesborough. In letters to Dr Patrick Blair and Samuel Brewer, he gives 13 East Riding records (Henrey, 1986), of which nine were first vice-county records. He undoubtedly introduced many plants to Londesborough and it is impossible to know which plants given for this locality in Baines' *Flora* (1840) are naturally occurring. Knowlton was noted nationally for his interest in the native flora and the Cape genus *Knowltonia* related to *Helleborus* was later named after him.

Revd William Whytehead (1729 - 1817), vicar of Atwick, near Hornsea, from 1756 to the time of his death, compiled a manuscript herbal which was handed down in the family and obtained for the University of Hull in 1957. William believed it was the proper function of a man of God to instruct his parishioners in the medical use of plants. In the old book, he had included a snippet of the plant, notes on where it occurred, together with its remedial and harmful qualities compiled from several printed herbals. The manuscript contains records for 74 species, most of them first vice-county records and including plants now unknown or rare in the area (Good, 1959). The majority of the records are for the Hornsea district but there are many for scattered East Yorkshire localities.

Robert Teesdale F.L.S. (*c.* 1740 - 1804), whose important contribution is much better known, was a gardener at Castle Howard, in the North Riding, until 1775 when he became a partner in a firm of seedsmen in the Strand, London. Teesdale became a member of the Linnean Society and he read two papers to the Society, one in 1792 and one in 1798, which were later published in the Society's Transactions. The first paper: *A Catalogue of the more rare plants which grow wild in the neighbourhood of Castle Howard* (Teesdale, 1794) gives specific East Riding localities for a few species only (Crackles, 1967), but including some important records. The second paper, *A Supplement to the Plantae Eboracenses* (Teesdale, 1800), contained about 140 records for the vice-county, mainly for Hull, Cottingham and Beverley. Teesdale's visits to the area were made between 1790 and 1796 and he was frequently accompanied 'in the field' by Lt Col Machell with whom he stayed. Teesdale's contribution is important in that he identified a number of *Carex* and *Potamogeton* species and other critical taxa at a time when few botanists can have had knowledge of them. Illustrations of Red Pondweed (*Potamogeton alpinus*) and Various-leaved Pondweed (*P. gramineus*) in *English Botany*, by J. Sowerby and E. Smith, 1790 - 1814, were drawn from specimens collected near Beverley by Teesdale. His observations concerning aquatic and marsh species near Beverley are particularly valuable as the area was drained within the next 50 years. Described as a most acute and indefatigable observer, Teesdale was justifiably honoured by the genus *Teesdalia* being named after him. All but one of the records by T. Knowlton in Teesdale's second paper are those of **Thomas Knowlton** F.L.S. (1757 - 1837), grandson of the earlier botanist.

Lt Col Christopher Machell (1747 - 1827) lost an arm whilst serving with the British Forces in the American War of Independence. He came to reside at Beverley in 1789 and his leisure time was devoted to the study of Natural History. He seems to have been a knowledgeable local botanist but we would know little about him except for the writings of Teesdale. It was Machell who showed Teesdale *Carex* x *axillaris* at the sides of ditches at Beverley and Marsh Stitchwort (*Stellaria palustris*) in marshes in the same area and the specimen of Milk Parsley (*Peucedanum palustre*) from Beverley in the York Museum was collected by Machell.

Seven species of flowering plants are given for East Yorkshire in Gough's edition of Camden's *Britannia* (1789), the editor having 'enlisted the help of some young friends'. The additional records, repeated in Camden (1806), which Robinson (1902) erroneously believed to be attributable to Ray, are for Bee Orchid (*Ophrys apifera*), Greater Spearwort (*Ranunculus lingua*), Water Soldier (*Stratiotes aloides*) and Sand Couch-grass (*Elymus farctus*). The record for *Cotyledon lutea* was an error. The reason for Robinson's misconception is that in the copy of the 1806 edition of 'Camden' in the Hull City Library the preface is missing.

Henry Baines (1793 - 1878) was a gardener, first at Halifax and then in his native city of York working for Messrs Backhouse. He became sub-curator of the York Philosophical Society, 1829 - 1870. In 1840 he published his *Flora of Yorkshire*, an important early contribution to the knowledge of Yorkshire Botany. There are numerous additional East Riding records, but regrettably the dates of records of uncommon species and the names of recorders are not given. Mr Baines acknowledges the help received from a number of botanists including **David Smith,** the Curator of Hull Botanic Gardens, who supplied a list of plants for the Hull area and **Oswald Allen Moore** (1818 - 1862) who no doubt also supplied East Riding records. I am indebted to Peter Skidmore of Doncaster Museum for records made by Moore in his copy of Baines' *Flora*, now in possession of Mr L. Smith of Doncaster. This list contains 76 records mainly for Heslington Fields near York and for the Bridlington area. Mr Moore became Hon. Curator of Botany for the Yorkshire Museum (1840 - 1862).

Mr Skidmore also supplied a list of records for 26 species made by **Henry Payne**, most for 1835 - 1837, and mainly for localities near York.

John Gilbert Baker (1834 - 1920) published *A Supplement to Baines' Flora of Yorkshire* in 1854 which for the East Riding mainly added records overlooked by Baines, 40 in all. There are several records by the well-known British botanist **Charles Cardale Babington** (1808 - 1895), mainly for Hull. Baker, a notable botanist was a draper at Thirsk, becoming first assistant at Kew Herbarium in 1866 and keeper from 1890 - 1899. He was author of the North Riding *Flora*.

George Norman (1824 - 1882), a merchant of Hull, was listing plants of the Hull area from 1845 for some 20 years. Many of his records appeared in Robinson's *Flora,* several of them being first records for the vice-county.

Henry Ibbotson (1814 - 1886), a school master at Mowthorpe near Castle Howard, was born at nearby Ganthorpe as was Richard Spruce with whom he botanized in his youth. He published *The Ferns of York* in 1884 which included records for Langwith Wood and other East Riding localities.

Robinson in his *Flora* (1902) acknowledged the contributions of many botanists active in the second half of the nineteenth century; I shall mention the more important of them.

Matthew B. Slater J.P., F.L.S. (1830 - 1918) lived in Malton all his life and was a friend of Richard Spruce. A very knowledgeable botanist, he contributed a good list of the rarer plants occurring in the northern part of the East Riding. His botanical notes, in circulars giving details of Yorkshire Naturalists' Union Excursions to localities well known to him, are invaluable.

James Fraser Robinson (1857 - 1927) came from Northumberland to Hull to take up an appointment as headmaster. He was a founder member of the Hull Scientific Club which became the Hull Scientific and Field Naturalists' Club. After 17 years of field work and with the help of members of the local society, he compiled *The Flora of the East Riding* published in 1902. It contains records for numerous species not previously recorded for the vice-county. Whilst the *Flora* contains records for all parts of the East Riding, the field work carried out by the author and his helpers was concentrated in the area within a 20 miles radius of the then Borough of Kingston upon Hull; this needs to be borne in mind when interpreting the author's remarks on the frequency of species. Robinson was an active member of the Yorkshire Naturalists' Union and continued to report on botanical matters in the Society's publications for some years after the publication of the *Flora.*

William Norwood Cheesman (1847 - 1925) was a draper at Selby and a highly respected citizen of that town. Better known as a mycologist, he knew the countryside near to Selby, including Riccall and Skipwith Commons, very well and contributed numerous records to the *Flora.*

Henry John Wilkinson (1859 - 1934) lived in York most of his life, working for Messrs Terry, being appointed Secretary, then Manager and finally becoming a director of the firm (1914 - 1934). He was President of the York and District Field Naturalists' Society on four occasions. He was appointed Hon. Curator of Botany of the Yorkshire Philosophical Society in 1892 and Vice-President in 1916. He compiled a *Catalogue of British Plants in the Herbarium of the Yorkshire Philosophical Society*, in which he also added a historical account of the herbarium with biographical notes about its contributors. A number of his own specimens from Skipwith Common and elsewhere are mentioned in the catalogue and he contributed numerous records for the York area for the *Flora.*

Joseph Jewison Marshall (1860 - 1934) was a pharmaceutical chemist, first at Market Weighton and later at Beverley; he left Yorkshire in 1919. He compiled the list of mosses and liverworts for Robinson's *Flora,* but also contributed records for vascular plants for the Market Weighton area; one wishes he had been more specific concerning localities.

Charles Waterfall F.L.S. (1851 - 1938) came to Hull in 1896 and was an active member of the Hull Scientific and Field Naturalists' Club until 1910 when he moved to Chester. His contribution to Robinson's *Flora* was a major one. He was also an active member of the Botanical Society and Exchange Club and many of his herbarium sheets for v.c. 61 have found their way into national herbaria. His herbarium was presented to the Botanical Department of Sheffield University. E.S. Marshall named *Epilobium* x *waterfallii* (*E. hirsutum* x *E. palustre*) in his honour.

Joseph Beanland (1857 - 1932) was an annual visitor to the Howden district and contributed numerous records for a corner of the vice-county otherwise largely unworked.

Thomas Petch B.A., B.Sc. (1870 - 1948) was born at Hornsea and educated in Hull. Whilst teaching at King's Lynn, 1900 - 1904, he spent his long summer vacations at Hedon where his mother was living. During this period he made some important discoveries, particularly of uncommon species occurring along the R. Humber. From 1905 he worked in Ceylon as a Government mycologist, eventually founding the Tea Research Institute there and becoming its Director. The mycologist, Dr Ramsbottom described him as one of the greatest naturalists he had been privileged to know. He died at King's Lynn where he lived during retirement.

I am indebted to Mrs J. Payne for records made by the following members of the York and District Natural History Society in the early part of the twentieth century : **William Ingham** (1854 - 1923) who was associated with education at York as lecturer, school inspector and finally as education officer; **William Bellerby** (1852 - 1936), a timber merchant and **Harry Britten** (1870 - 1954).

In 1910 **Hugh Bernard Willoughby Smith** M.B., F.R.C.S. (1879 - 1948) presented a herbarium of 600 sheets to the Beverley Municipal Museum. He was born at York and went to school in Pocklington. His plant collection was made mainly between 1895 and 1901 whilst he was a medical student, mainly at the London Hospital. The herbarium which is now in the Hull Museum contains but few East Yorkshire specimens, all for Pocklington and Bridlington.

The publication of the *Flora* (1902) stimulated further botanical activity. An *addendum* appeared in the *Hull Scientific and Field Naturalists' Club's Transactions* in 1903 (vol. *3*, 98 - 100). Then came short botanical notes more or less annually in the Hull Society's *Transactions*, (1904 - 1909) including a list by J.J. Marshall mainly for Market Weighton in 1908.

The Yorkshire Naturalists' Union, as a union of affiliated societies covering the whole of the county, came into being in 1877. Plant records have been published usually annually in *The Naturalist* throughout much of the Union's history as have reports of excursions. Until 1968 a printed circular was produced before each excursion; some of the notes compiled by experienced botanists who had explored an area over the years are most valuable.

Sadly, much information collected in the first 40 years of this century was lost by enemy action in June, 1943 when the Hull Municipal Museum was destroyed. Among herbaria housed in the museum was the important collection of J.F. Robinson and 800 sheets collected by James William Boult (1847 - 1924).

The Adventive Flora of the East Riding of Yorkshire by A.K. Wilson which was published in 1938 contains records mainly for Hull docks and some for the Olympia Oil Mill Sidings at Selby.

A Supplement to the Yorkshire Floras by F.A. Lees, edited by C.A. Cheetham and W.A. Sledge was published in 1941. This includes 140 East Riding records.

In 1953 came the publication of *The Natural History of the Scarborough District*, edited by G.B. Walsh and F.C. Rimington, which contains numerous records for the northern part of the vice-county.

During the latter half of the 1950s, botanists throughout the British Isles were busily engaged in collecting records for the Distribution Maps Scheme, organised by the Botanical Society of the British Isles. Information was collected for all species on a ten km square basis. The resultant *Atlas of the British Flora* (Perring and Walters, 1962) enables one to see the local distribution of a species in the context of its British distribution. During this period, Professor Good built up a substantial herbarium of v.c. 61 material at the University of Hull. In addition, Professor Good and the present author compiled A *Hand-list* of the Flora of the East Riding of Yorkshire which however remained unpublished. Records for specific localities collected for the *Hand-list* are incorporated in the present work and I am indebted to Professor Good for his major contribution to the botanical knowledge of the area.

In 1970, a scheme for collecting records on a tetrad (2 x 2 km) basis was launched by myself and Dr D. Shimwell. All authentic post-1950 records assignable to a specific tetrad have also been used, my own records from 1950 onwards forming an essential basis for the scheme. It was recognised from the outset that the scheme was over-ambitious as there are 848 tetrads, at least in part, in v.c. 61 and that help available was likely to be inadequate (Crackles, 1974 a). However, the scheme had potentialities which a less ambitious one lacked. Although it has been impossible to get adequate coverage of all tetrads, the scheme has resulted in the amassing of a vast amount of information which would have been impossible otherwise. I believe coverage has been good for semi-natural habitats and the main pattern of distribution of species therein has emerged.

Many botanists have made some contribution to the tetrad records as indicated in the list of recorders given in the introduction to Part Two of the *Flora*. The following have supplied more or less complete tetrad lists for at least one ten km square: Mrs M. Clark, E.B. Matthews and E.H. Wear and other members of the Hull Natural History Society.

The Yorkshire Naturalists' Union has continued to hold one excursion in each Yorkshire vice-county each year. These excursions are attended by naturalists with varying expertise from all parts of Yorkshire. In addition, the Botanical Section of the YNU has for a number of years arranged a meeting in v.c. 61 for the express purpose of covering an under-worked area.

In recent years also, officers of the Nature Conservancy Council have carried out extensive surveys, notably of chalk grassland, water-meadows by the R. Derwent and of Pocklington and Leven Canals. In addition, the Humberside County Council commissioned a wide-ranging botanical survey of the Flamborough Headland. I am indebted to officers of these organisations for making the results of this work available to me.

IV

Habitats

1 Chalk and limestone grassland and bare chalk

Grazing by rabbits of grassland on chalk and limestone has been greatly reduced during the past 35 years as a result of myxomatosis. Sheep grazing has also been less extensive in the same period. Consequently there has been a remarkable spread of Tor-grass (*Brachypodium pinnatum*) and Upright Brome (*Bromus erectus*) as well as of both Hawthorn (*Crataegus monogyna*) and Gorse (*Ulex europaeus*). Nevertheless a recent survey carried out by the Nature Conservancy Council shows that there are still numerous hillsides with an appreciable extent of species-rich grassland.

The composition of the grassland is affected by latitude, nature of the subsoil, aspect, steepness of slope, the history of management and undoubtedly chance has also played a part.

The true calcicoles are confined to the Wolds or almost so and occur on a thin well-drained soil overlying chalk or limestone and are almost invariably found on slopes and may be absent altogether from northerly-facing slopes.

The south-facing slopes usually have the greatest number of true calcicoles and almost all the rarest ones in the vice-county e.g. Squinancywort (*Asperula cynanchica*), Horseshoe Vetch (*Hippocrepis comosa*), Autumn Lady's-tresses (*Spiranthes spiralis*), Perennial Flax (*Linum perenne* subsp. *anglicum*) and Spring Cinquefoil (*Potentilla tabernaemontani*) are found on such slopes or south-westerly-facing shoulders. The first three of the last mentioned species are classified by Matthews (1955) as of the Continental Southern Element as also are Yellow-wort (*Blackstonia perfoliata*) and Bee Orchid (*Ophrys apifera*) and all are at or near the northern edge of their range. Yellow-wort is more likely to be found in the south of the Wolds and usually on bare chalk where competition is at a minimum. Bee Orchid is more widely spread, but rarely in the grass sward except in the southern wolds or near the coast.

Species of chalk grassland have different European distributions. Common Rock-rose (*Helianthemum nummularium*) is classified by Matthews (1955) as belonging to the Wide Element, Wild Thyme (*Thymus praecox* subsp. *arcticus*) to the Oceanic Northern Element, while Crested Hair-grass (*Koeleria macrantha*) is of the Oceanic West European Element. The Continental Northern Element is represented by the Purple Milk-vetch (*Astragalus danicus*) and Autumn Gentian (*Gentianella amarella*). Members of Matthews' Continental Element occurring in this habitat are Dwarf Thistle (*Cirsum acaule*) and Knapweed Broomrape (*Orobanche elatior*), both of which are uncommon in the vice-county. The most widely distributed species of the Continental Southern Element is the Pyramidal Orchid (*Anacamptis pyramidalis*).

The chalk valleys are of many different shapes and sizes and their slopes of differing aspect. In some areas there are complex valley systems as in the vicinity of Millington.

Almost all Wolds hillsides are privately owned and are an integral part of a farm so that permission to examine them should be obtained. A road or public footpath often passes along the bottom of a valley, but it is comparatively rare for a right of way to cross chalk grassland. One extensive south-facing bank near Fordon is a Site of Special Scientific Interest (SSSI) which is managed by the Yorkshire Wildlife Trust. It is noted for its abundance of Purple Milk-vetch as well as having all the usual chalk-loving species.

On some Wolds grassland, particularly on northerly-facing slopes or near the bottom of slopes, are a number of species which also occur on grassland away from the Wolds and which appear to require more moisture than the true calcicoles. Such species are believed to indicate the presence of deposits overlying the chalk and include: Pignut (*Conopodium majus*), Hoary Ragwort (*Senecio erucifolius*), Pepper-saxifrage (*Silaum silaus*), Devils'-bit Scabious (*Succisa pratensis*) and Zigzag Clover (*Trifolium medium*). There are also one or two species normally found on ill-drained soils, notably Marsh Thistle (*Cirsium palustre*) and Tufted Hair-grass (*Deschampsia cespitosa*). At least one extensive north-facing slope is dominated by the calcifuge Heath Bedstraw (*Galium saxatile*), whilst other calcifuges e.g. Tormentil (*Potentilla erecta*) occur here and there, possibly where there is local leaching.

Characteristic chalk grassland species are still to be found on some roadsides in the chalk grassland belt of the Wolds. On the roadside bank of the minor road as one proceeds from Millington pastures towards Huggate there is an abundance of Bloody Crane's-bill (*Geranium sanguineum*) with Greater Knapweed (*Centaurea scabiosa*), Saw-wort (*Serratula tinctoria*) and other calcicoles.

Some disused railways also provide a refuge for numerous chalk-loving species. Marjoram (*Origanum vulgare*) occurs in quantity along stretches of the Cherry Burton to Market Weighton line and Large Thyme (*Thymus pulegioides*) occurs on the track at Weedley and elsewhere.

Species only found on bare chalk, notably Red Hemp-nettle (*Galeopsis angustifolia*) and Basil Thyme (*Acinos arvensis*) are found mainly on chalk scree on steep hill sides and on the sides of railway cuttings.

Many of the numerous chalk pits which occur on the Wolds have been used as rubbish tips or otherwise lost to nature. However pits with interesting plant associations still survive. Jefferson (1984) lists thirty chalk pits with the total number of species found in each. Wharram and Kipling Cotes quarries are Sites of Special Scientific Interest and are managed by the Yorkshire Wildlife Trust. Species found in at least 20% of the pits examined include:

> Pyramidal Orchid
> Hairy Rock-cress (*Arabis hirsuta*)
> Clustered Bellflower (*Campanula glomerata*)
> Common Spotted-orchid (*Dactylorhiza fuchsii*)
> Fern-grass (*Catapodium rigidum*)
> Autumn Gentian
> Common Rock-rose
> Crested Hair-grass
> Marjoram
> Salad Burnet (*Sanguisorba minor* subsp. *minor*)
> Small Scabious (*Scabiosa columbaria*)
> Wild Thyme

Among the rarer species found in at least one or two quarries are:

> Purple Milk-vetch
> Woolly Thistle (*Cirsium eriophorum*)
> Northern Marsh-orchid (*Dactylorhiza purpurella* Steph. form B)
> Viper's-bugloss (*Echium vulgare*)
> Fragrant Orchid (*Gymnadenia conopsea* subsp. *conopsea*)
> Bee Orchid
> Hawkweed Oxtongue (*Picris hieracioides*)

2 Grassland and open communities on sand

Robinson (1902) stated that large sandy commons were a characteristic feature of the Vale of York. He specified eight good examples, all of which were noted resorts of botanists and other naturalists. Only one of these, Skipwith Common, survives as predominantly heath land. 724 acres of the common have been designated as a SSSI which is managed by the Yorkshire Wildlife Trust. The main vegetation types are dry and wet heath, bog, ponds and woodland in which Birch and Scots Pine predominate; Oak and Willow are also common. Heather (*Calluna vulgaris*) and Purple Moor-grass (*Molinia caerulea*) are dominant over large areas with Mat-grass (*Nardus stricta*) locally abundant. On damper areas Cross-leaved Heath (*Erica tetralix*) occurs, often in quantity, together with Deergrass (*Trichophorum cespitosum*) and in two or three places Marsh Gentian (*Gentiana pneumonanthe*). In wet areas by the ponds, Common Cottongrass (*Eriophorum angustifolium*) is often dominant. Round-leaved Sundew (*Drosera rotundifolia*), Broad-leaved Cottongrass (*Eriophorum latifolium*), Marsh Cinquefoil (*Potentilla palustris*) and Marsh Violet (*Viola palustris*) also occur.

Allerthorpe Common, consisting of approximately 525 acres was an exceptionally fine area, greatly valued by naturalists. There were expanses of heath and much Birch scrub with some Pines; the heath, marsh, bog, rides and drains supporting a vegetation appreciably more varied than that of Skipwith Common. There is some calcareous influence on parts of the common, such species as Fragrant Orchid (*Gymnadenia conopsea* subsp. *conopsea*) and Early Marsh-orchid (*Dactylorhiza incarnata*) having occurred. In the early 1960s, the Lord of the Manor and the commoners agreed to sell their rights to the Forestry Commission. Larger drains were constructed and the area planted with conifers, except for some twelve acres, which are managed by the Yorkshire Wildlife Trust. Many of the species formerly found on both dry and damp habitats still occur, mainly on the forest rides. These include most of the rarer vice-county species recorded for the common:

> Meadow Thistle (*Cirsium dissectum*)
> Oblong-leaved Sundew (*Drosera intermedia*)
> Round-leaved Sundew
> Bell Heather (*Erica cinerea*)
> Petty Whin (*Genista anglica*)
> Marsh St John's-wort (*Hypericum elodes*)
> Common Wintergreen (*Pyrola minor*)
> Allseed (*Radiola linoides*)

Three of these species have recently turned up on the common, years after they were thought to have been lost. In addition, Chaffweed (*Anagallis minima*), a species believed to be extinct in the vice-county, was recently found on a forestry ride. May Lily (*Maianthemum bifolium*) has been known on the common only since 1981 and may be a recent introduction. Marsh Gentian is believed to have been completely lost; one small colony was within the YWT reserve but was near the new main drain and was lost as the area dried out.

Other large areas of heath have been ploughed out or have been afforested by the Forestry Commission or privately, so that only small areas remain. Some of the characteristic species of both dry and wet habitats have survived on rides of woodland on Langwith Common and Houghton Moor and small areas of heath and bog have survived on South Cliffe Common.

Staxton and Flixton sand pits provided a haven for many sand-loving species. Unfortunately most of these pits have now been put to other uses. However the following species which are uncommon in the vice-county are still to be found at the edges of sandy fields, on waste places or in sandy lanes as in the Wintringham, West Heslerton and Ganton areas:

> Bur Chervil (*Anthriscus caucalis*)
> Dense Silky-bent (*Apera interrupta*)
> Changing Forget-me-not (*Myosotis discolor*)
> Prickly Poppy (*Papaver argemone*)
> Knotted Clover (*Trifolium striatum*)

3 Grassland on clay and loam

In most parts of the vice-county, unimproved pasture on clay and loam is rare, the vast majority of meadows and pastures having been ploughed, drained and re-seeded or treated chemically or converted to arable. A meadow bright with Cowslips or even Buttercups is now a rarity. Such meadows were common place in the early part of this century and such species as Adder's-tongue (*Ophioglossum vulgatum*), Green-winged Orchid (*Orchis morio*) and Yellow-rattle (*Rhinanthus minor*) were common members of their vegetation.

Much unimproved pasture which survives is on ill-drained soils in Lower Derwentland or on former carr land in Holderness. A considerable area of permanent grassland survives on Flamborough Head and the coastal belt of Filey Bay.

Good indicators of unimproved grassland in lowland areas, on the soils under consideration are: Meadow Barley (*Hordeum secalinum*), Great Burnet (*Sanguisorba officinalis*) and Pepper-saxifrage (*Silaum silaus*). Species-rich neutral grassland survives by the R. Derwent, but rarely, as on a bank inconvenient to plough and in parts of fields otherwise marshy. Species recorded in such pastures include:

> Common Spotted-orchid (*Dactylorhiza fuchsii*)
> Heath-grass (*Danthonia decumbens*)
> Fragrant Orchid (*Gymnadenia conopsea* subsp. *conopsea*)
> Bitter-vetch (*Lathyrus montanus*)
> Adder's-tongue
> Green-winged Orchid
> Betony (*Stachys officinalis*)
> Lesser Stitchwort (*Stellaria graminea*)

4   Woods and hedges

As the climate became warmer during the Post-glacial period, closed Birch forest gave way to mixed Oak woodland, especially Pedunculate Oak (*Quercus robur*) and English Elm (*Ulmus procera*), over the greater part of dry land. Small-leaved Lime (*Tilia cordata*) and Hazel (*Corylus avellana*) were also important constituents of such woodland (Clark, 1971). Alder (*Alnus glutinosa*) and Willows (*Salix* sp.) were the chief components of woods in wetter areas. Ash (*Fraxinus excelsior*), which forms woods on the Wolds, appeared comparatively late in the Post-glacial and was probably favoured by forest clearance undertaken by prehistoric man (Godwin, 1956). Beech (*Fagus sylvatica*) grows well on the Wolds, but is not usually regarded as native north of the R. Humber. However the presence of White Hellborine (*Cephalanthera damasonium*), Green-flowered Helleborine (*Epipactis phyllanthes*) and Yellow Bird's-nest (*Monotropa hypopitys*), all under Beech in the southernmost part of the Wolds, suggests that the tree may be native in this region. Robinson (1902) expressed a similar view based on the fact that *Petuaria*, the Roman name for Brough, means 'Beech groves'.

The area that was the East Riding of Yorkshire is now only sparsely wooded. There is little historical evidence of ancient woodland surviving.

Burton Bushes on Beverley Westwood is believed to be at least 200 years old and may be a remnant of an ancient forest. The following species occur in the proportions stated; 50% Pedunculate Oak, 16% Silver Birch (*Betula pendula*), 10% Ash and 8% Field Maple (*Acer campestre*) (Boatman, 1971). Amongst other species present are Beech, Lime (*Tilia* x *vulgaris*), Crab Apple (*Malus sylvestris*) and Hornbeam (*Carpinus betulus*). The variety of trees and shrubs, the scarcity of Hazel and the fact that Holly (*Ilex aquifolium*) is the most important shrub favour the view that the wood was not planted. At least three herbaceous species present indicate an ancient woodland site: Wood Anemone (*Anemone nemorosa*), Wood-sorrel (*Oxalis acetosella*) and Yellow Pimpernel (*Lysimachia nemorum*).

Documentary evidence suggests that the dominant trees in ancient woodland on the Westwood as elsewhere on the lower wolds and along the western escarpment were Pedunculate Oak and Ash (Harris, 1971).

Settrington woods 'some of which survive in modified form, can be traced back to the sixteenth century' (Harris, 1961). It is significant that Settrington Wood is the only East Riding locality for Alternate-leaved Golden-saxifrage (*Chrysosplenium alternifolium*), a primary woodland species.

Millington Wood, an ancient Ash wood on the Wolds, was taken over by the Forestry Commission in 1959 when Ash and Beech were the only trees present. Most of the area was clean felled and replanted with a mixture of deciduous trees and some conifers, but a compartment of young Ash was retained. In addition to some of the more usual, more or less exclusive woodland species e.g. Ramsons (*Allium ursinum*) and Wood Anemone, a number of species occur which are rare or uncommon in the vice-county:

> Baneberry (*Actaea spicata*)
> Nettle-leaved Bellflower (*Campanula trachelium*)
> Lily-of-the-valley (*Convallaria majalis*)
> Woodruff (*Galium odoratum*)
> Toothwort (*Lathraea squamaria*)

Herb-Paris (*Paris quadrifolia*) was present in some quantity in 1965 and may still occur. All these species are indicators of primary woodland i.e. woodland occupying a site which has probably been continuously wooded throughout the historical period, or virtually so. Since 1985, Millington Wood has been owned by the Humberside County Council which intends to manage it for its amenity value as well as for nature conservation. It is hoped that the area of Ash will be extended, particularly in clearings where the rarer woodland species occur and may be at risk as a result of undue water-loss.

Of East Riding woods, those of Kirkham Hall grounds have the greatest number of primary woodland species. These include the following rare or very uncommon vice-county species:

> Baneberry
> Moschatel (*Adoxa moschatellina*)
> Toothwort
> Hairy Wood-rush (*Luzula pilosa*)
> Great Wood-rush (*L. sylvatica*)
> Wood Melick (*Melica uniflora*)
> Herb-Paris
> Hard Shield-fern (*Polystichum aculeatum*)

Other primary woodland species which are rare in the vice-county are: Greater Butterfly-orchid (*Platanthera chlorantha*) and Wood Vetch (*Vicia sylvatica*).

Other woods which have at least one of the uncommon primary woodland species already mentioned are: Deepdale, Bishop Burton; Little Wood, North Newbald; Beckhead Wood Plantation, Great Givendale; Hanging Fall Wood, Sledmere; Bratt Wood, Nunburnholme; Pocklington Wood; Tibthorpe Low Wood; Spel Howe Plantation and Sutton Wood.

Much planting of trees followed Parliamentary enclosure, so that large acreages of woodland were created on the Wolds and some in the Vale of York as on Houghton Moor and on Holme upon Spalding Moor. Other woodlands in Lower Derwentland were successors of older woodland as at Escrick, Kexby and Wheldrake (Allison, 1976, 159). Large scale planting was rare in Holderness, but did occur at Rise, Burton Constable and Winestead. At Rise some of the herbaceous species present indicate a continuity of woodland on the site.
These are:

> Yellow Pimpernel
> Wood-sorrel
> Soft Shield-fern (*Polystichum setiferum*)
> Hart's-tongue (*Phyllitis scolopendrium*)
> Sanicle (*Sanicula europaea*)

Three primary woodland species occur in Wheldon's Plantation including Wood Millet (*Milium effusum*).

Woodland in Lower Derwentland is usually of a different nature from that on the Wolds and in Holderness. Silver Birch and Pedunculate Oak are the natural dominants. Climbing Corydalis (*Corydalis claviculata*), Foxglove (*Digitalis purpurea*) and Honeysuckle (*Lonicera periclymenum*) are characteristic of the woods of this area. In dykes of some woods in Lower Derwentland, coniferous and otherwise, Hard Fern (*Blechnum spicant*) and more rarely Lemon-scented Fern (*Oreopteris limbosperma*) can still be found. Sutton Wood and North Cliffe Wood are two woods in Lower Derwentland which have a number of primary woodland species and to some extent resemble woods on the Wolds. Species present in both include: Hairy Wood-rush, Wood Millet, Yellow Pimpernel and Wood-sorrel. Purple Small-reed (*Calamagrostis canescens*), given by Peterken (1974) as a primary woodland species, occurs at the western side of North Cliffe Wood and Herb-Paris has occurred. Species confined to woods on acid soils e.g. Climbing Corydalis and Hard Fern also occur in this wood which is now owned by the Yorkshire Wildlife Trust.

Much tree-felling occurred during both world wars, involving both older woodland and post-enclosure plantations. Since the Second World War there has been large-scale planting of conifers, notably in the Vale of York and locally on the Wolds as at Wintringham. Such woods have little or no ground flora, although some species of interest may survive on rides. Forestry Commission woodland at Wintringham is notable for the large quantity of Yellow Bird's-nest which occurs there.

During the 1960s hundreds of miles of hedges were destroyed as agricultural practices changed. Nevertheless considerable stretches of hedge remain, many containing several species of tree and shrub. Boatman (1980) examined 117 stretches of mixed hedge and calculated the percentage of each species in hedges in each of the areas, Vale of York, Wolds and Holderness. 32 species of shrub and tree were recorded and details of the distribution of the 25 most frequent ones presented. There is a strong similarity between the composition of Holderness and Wolds hedges. Sixteen species were common to both areas and for most of these the percentage occurrence was similar. The commonest species occurring in both areas are Hazel, Hawthorn (*Crataegus monogyna*), Ash, Blackthorn (*Prunus spinosa*) and Elder (*Sambucus nigra*). Hawthorn is usually the dominant species in hedges in all parts of the vice-county. Field Maple was found in a high percentage of Holderness hedges and in over one-third of those on the Wolds. Dogwood (*Cornus sanguinea*) is fairly frequent in both areas whilst Buckthorn (*Rhamnus catharticus*) was recorded for 50% of Wolds hedges but in few of those elsewhere.

More species of tree and shrub were recorded for hedges in the Vale of York than for those of either Holderness or the Wolds. The commonest species were Hawthorn, Ash and Pedunculate Oak. Five species, namely Alder, Silver Birch, Downy Birch (*Betula pubescens*), Broom (*Cytisus scoparius*) and Rowan (*Sorbus aucuparia*) were found only in this area. Both species characteristic of wet soils e.g. Alder, Birch and Rusty Willow (*Salix cinerea* subsp. *oleifolia*) and those characteristic of well-drained acid soils e.g. Silver Birch, Broom, Rowan and Gorse (*Ulex europaeus*) occur.

Areas where species-rich hedges are most frequent are known to have been formerly well-wooded. Mixed hedges were difficult to find on the Wolds and were mainly on the fringes, including the Jurassic escarpment. This may be related to the fact that large open fields were common on the Wolds and were enclosed comparatively late.

5 Aquatic and marsh habitats

i) Vale of Pickering (Upper Derwentland)

The R. Hertford is at present cleaned out very frequently and aquatic plants are scarce. However interesting aquatics occur in the ditches and streams of the area. The most notable of these is Whorl-grass (*Catabrosa aquatica*) with Lesser Water-parsnip (*Berula erecta*) and Water-violet (*Hottonia palustris*) also occurring. Cyperus Sedge (*Carex pseudocyperus*) was formerly recorded by a dyke near the river.

In September 1971, a fine area of fen was found on Flixton Carrs, not far from the Star Carr excavation site. The following species were at least locally frequent:

> Long-stalked Yellow-sedge (*Carex viridula* subsp. *brachyrrhyncha*)
> Carnation Sedge (*C. panicea*)
> Blunt-flowered Rush (*Juncus subnodulosus*)
> Purple Moor-grass (*Molinia caerulea*)
> Marsh Lousewort (*Pedicularis palustris*)
> Black Bog-rush (*Schoenus nigricans*)
> Saw-wort (*Serratula tinctoria*)

The locally rare Marsh Helleborine (*Epipactis palustris*) and Grass-of-Parnassus (*Parnassia palustris*) were also present. Unfortunately the area was drained and cultivated by the next summer. The above list however is valuable in giving an indication of the former riches of the area. Some characteristic fen species can still be found in remaining marshy areas, mainly in Flixton and Flotmanby Carrs.
Such species include:

> Star Sedge (*Carex echinata*)
> Long-stalked Yellow-sedge
> Gipsywort (*Lycopus europaeus*)
> Purple-loosestrife (*Lythrum salicaria*)
> Fen Bedstraw (*Galium uliginosum*)
> Common Meadow-rue (*Thalictrum flavum*)

ii) Vale of York (Lower Derwentland)

Each of the East Riding rivers presents different conditions, reflected as differences in their aquatic and marsh vegetation. Unlike the R. Hull, the R. Derwent has its main catchment area outside the vice-county and there is less calcareous influence. In the R. Derwent are species widespread in the vice-county and others which are restricted in their distribution. River Water-crowfoot (*Ranunculus fluitans*), dominant in stretches of the river, is restricted to it, whilst Perfoliate Pondweed (*Potamogeton perfoliatus*) has only been found here and in the R. Foulness in recent years. The R. Foulness, fed by springs arising at the foot of the wolds, also had an abundance of Yellow Water-lily (*Nuphar lutea*), Arrowhead (*Sagittaria sagittifolia*) and Broad-leaved Pondweed (*Potamogeton natans*), the presence of the latter pointing to the slower flow of this river. Some stretches of this formerly very attractive river are now heavily polluted and some aquatics have been lost.

The flat valley of the R. Derwent is several feet below the general level of the land and is frequently flooded because of the large volume of water carried by the river from its source. The water-meadows adjacent to the river below Low Catton owe their fertility to regular winter flooding carrying silt over the land. They have continued to be highly valued by farmers and this is the all-important factor in their survival. Traditionally the water-meadows have been cut for hay or used for summer pasture; few have been ploughed and re-seeded. Characteristic species of the water-meadows include:

> Sneezewort (*Achillea ptarmica*)
> Smooth Brome (*Bromus racemosus*)
> Slender Tufted-sedge (*Carex acuta*)
> Brown Sedge (*C. disticha*)
> Water Horsetail (*Equisetum fluviatile*)
> Ragged-Robin (*Lychnis flos-cuculi*)
> Creeping-Jenny (*Lysimachia nummularia*)
> Water Mint (*Mentha aquatica*)
> Tubular Water-dropwort (*Oenanthe fistulosa*)
> Narrow-leaved Water-dropwort (*O. silaifolia*)
> Great Burnet (*Sanguisorba officinalis*)
> Marsh Ragwort (*Senecio aquaticus*)
> Pepper-saxifrage (*Silaum silaus*)
> Marsh Stitchwort (*Stellaria palustris*)
> Common Meadow-rue (*Thalictrum flavum*)

Round-fruited Rush (*Juncus compressus*) is more rarely found, but may be present in quantity.

The ditches of the water-meadows are also an important habitat. Species occurring in or at the edge of them include: Water-plantain (*Alisma plantago-aquatica*), Bladder-sedge (*Carex vesicaria*) and Fine-leaved Water-dropwort (*Oenanthe aquatica*) with the following species occurring less frequently:

Small-flowered Winter-cress (*Barbarea stricta*)
Large Bitter-cress (*Cardamine amara*)
Water-violet (*Hottonia palustris*)
Purple-loosestrife (*Lythrum salicaria*)
Gipsywort (*Lycopus europaeus*)
Greater Water-parsnip (*Sium latifolium*)

Small areas of permanent marsh occur by the R. Derwent, mainly north of Stamford Bridge, and in four of these Wood Club-rush (*Scirpus sylvaticus*) occurs in its only vice-county localities. Most markedly fenland associations occur near to Malton containing such species as:

Lesser Water-parsnip (*Berula erecta*)
Long-stalked Yellow-sedge (*Carex viridula* subsp. *brachyrrhyncha*)
Fen Bedstraw (*Galium uliginosum*)
Mare's-tail (*Hippuris vulgaris*)
Blunt-flowered Rush (*Juncus subnodulosus*)
Bogbean (*Menyanthes trifoliata*)
Greater Spearwort (*Ranunculus lingua*)

The Pocklington Canal, cut early in the nineteenth century and remaining separate from the drainage channels, is an important aquatic habitat. Species present include: Flat-stalked Pondweed (*Potamogeton friesii*), Shining Pondweed (*P. lucens*) and Yellow Water-lily, whilst Fat Duckweed (*Lemna gibba*) is locally abundant. Notable species occurring at Walbut Lock include: Narrow-leaved Water-plantain (*Alisma lanceolatum*), Lesser Water-parsnip, Flowering-rush (*Butomus umbellatus*) and Fan-leaved Water-crowfoot (*Ranunculus circinatus*) with Lesser Water-plantain (*Baldellia ranunculoides*) also occurring here and at Sandhill Lock where Soft Hornwort (*Ceratophyllum submersum*), a rare southern species, occurs in its only Yorkshire station. Nearer to Pocklington, Opposite-leaved Pondweed (*Groenlandia densa*) is abundant.

Between the canal and the Pocklington Beck is a series of meadows which are species-rich as a result of flooding and traditional management by hay cropping. The plant communities present show similarities to those of the R. Derwent water-meadows: Marsh Stitchwort and Smooth Brome occur and, of the sedges present, Brown Sedge and Bladder-sedge are particularly abundant. However fenland species which are absent or rare in the valley of the R. Derwent occur including : Early Marsh-orchid (*Dactylorhiza incarnata*), Slender Spike-rush (*Eleocharis uniglumis*), Fen Bedstraw, Marsh Pea (*Lathyrus palustris*) and Bogbean.

Remnants of fen vegetation occur on the site of the former Walling Fen, most notably in the vicinity of Oxmardike and Broomfleet. Ponds on either side of the Hull to Goole railway line are believed to have inherited their aquatic and adjacent marsh vegetation from the former Oxmardike Marr and its surrounds. The most significant species here include:

Lesser Water-plantain
Whorled Water-milfoil (*Myriophyllum verticillatum*)
Parsley Water-dropwort (*Oenanthe lachenalii*)
Greater Water-parsnip
Greater Bladderwort (*Utricularia vulgaris*)

A fine marsh near Broomfleet House has unfortunately been partly drained. Species formerly occurring here in some quantity included: Meadow Thistle (*Cirsium dissectum*), Early Marsh-orchid and Southern Marsh-orchid (*Dactylorhiza praetermissa*). A few plants of the last species still persist.

The Market Weighton Canal was cut through Walling Fen. Greater Tussock-sedge (*Carex paniculata*) occurs by the canal near to Broomfleet in its only locality in Lower Derwentland. Also significantly, Tufted-sedge (*Carex elata*), Water Dock (*Rumex hydrolapathum*) and Arrowhead formerly occurred by the canal near the Land of Nod with Opposite-leaved Pondweed occurring in an adjacent dyke.

Further north evidence of former fenland is to be found in ponds and drains as at Sandhill, Burshill and Hasholme; species occurring include:
> Lesser Water-parsnip
> Trifid Bur-marigold (*Bidens tripartita*)
> Flowering-rush (*Butomus umbellatus*)
> Mare's-tail
> Gipsywort
> Purple-loosestrife
> Unbranched Bur-reed (*Sparganium emersum*)

At the western edge of North Cliffe Wood, Purple Small-reed (*Calamagrostis canescens*), Water-violet, Gipsywort, Purple-loosestrife and Water Dock occur, seemingly on a former lake site (Allison, 1979). Purple Small-reed also occurs on Allerthorpe Common and in a wood at Hasholme.

iii) Holderness

There is a variety of aquatic habitats in Holderness: the R. Hull and its feeder streams, Hornsea Mere, lakes in private estates and ponds and drains of varying size and age. Remnants of species-rich fen occur, mainly by the R. Hull, by Hornsea Mere and by Leven Canal.

There was little investigation of the meres and marshes of the river valley before much of the area was effectively drained. In the seventeenth and eighteenth centuries, Water-soldier (*Stratiotes aloides*) was plentiful in the R. Hull valley at least locally north and south of Beverley and it is of interest that it has recently been found in a borrow-pit in the area (Crackles, 1982). White Water-lily (*Nymphaea alba*) occurred on Leven Carrs in the eighteenth century. Robert Teesdale (1800) recorded the plants of marshes and dykes near to Beverley in the 1790s. Marsh Pea (*Lathyrus palustris*), Milk-parsley (*Peucedanum palustre*) and Lesser Tussock-sedge (*Carex diandra*) occurred abundantly near Beverley at that time. Species recorded by Teesdale which are not now known in the vice-county are: Creeping Marshwort (*Apium repens*), Various-leaved Pondweed (*Potamogeton gramineus*), Least Bur-reed (*Sparganium minimum*) and Slender Sedge (*Carex lasiocarpa*) which occurred 'in all the watery places' near Beverley. Much drainage of the R. Hull valley had taken place by the latter part of the eighteenth century and the remaining meres near Beverley and at Leven were drained before the mid-nineteenth century. Old records, mainly those of Teesdale, and the surviving remnants of fen provide a valuable glimpse of the diversely rich flora of the former extensive fenland.

a) *River Hull*

The R. Hull receives highly calcareous waters from powerfully spring-fed becks which arise in the vicinity of Driffield. The western arm of the river, the West Beck, is a SSSI. *Ranunculus penicillatus* subsp. *pseudofluitans* is dominant in the fast-flowing upper reaches of the beck and Lesser Water-parsnip (*Berula erecta*) locally so, with other species mainly or only occurring in the comparatively still water of the bays. Below Copper Hall, the West Beck is species rich, twenty-four species being recorded. River Water-dropwort (*Oenanthe fluviatilis*), which is confined to the R. Hull and is at its absolute northern limit in Britain at Driffield, is frequent below Copper Hall. Other species which are at least locally frequent in the West Beck include:
> Water Starwort (*Callitriche* sp.)
> Canadian Waterweed (*Elodea canadensis*)
> Opposite-leaved Pondweed (*Groenlandia densa*)
> Curled Pondweed (*Potamogeton crispus*)

35

Shining Pondweed (*P. lucens*)
Fennel Pondweed (*P. pectinatus*)
Arrowhead (*Sagittaria sagittifolia*)
Unbranched Bur-reed (*Sparganium emersum*)
Branched Bur-reed (*S. erectum*)

Species occurring less commonly include:
Mare's-tail (*Hippuris vulgaris*)
Fat Duckweed (*Lemma gibba*)
Spiked Water-milfoil (*Myriophyllum spicatum*)
Yellow Water-lily (*Nuphar lutea*)
Common Club-rush (*Schoenoplectus lacustris*)
Rough-fruited Horned Pondweed (*Zannichellia gibberosa*)

By contrast Foston Beck, the eastern feeder stream of the river, is far less species-rich and the common Water-crowfoot is *Ranunculus penicillatus* var. *vertumnus*, whilst the other most frequent species are Opposite-leaved Pondweed and Spiked Water-milfoil. The Horned Pondweed present is *Zannichellia palustris*.

Flat-stalked Pondweed (*Potamogeton friesii*) occurs in the Old Howe, in Frodingham Beck and in the river below the junction of the two becks where Yellow Water-lily and Spiked Water-milfoil are frequent. Below Hempholme Lock, it is more difficult to record the aquatics present.

Reedswamp, often several yards in width, occurs along the west bank of the river for most of the stretch between Hull Bridge and Hempholme Lock. Beds of reedswamp are mainly dominated by Reed Sweet-grass (*Glyceria maxima*) and more locally by Great Willowherb (*Epilobium hirsutum*), Reed Canary-grass (*Phalaris arundinacea*) and Bulrush (*Typha latifolia*). Other characteristic species of the reedswamp associations include:
Wild Angelica (*Angelica sylvestris*)
Marsh-marigold (*Caltha palustris*)
Hemp-agrimony (*Eupatorium cannabinum*)
Meadowsweet (*Filipendula ulmaria*)
Yellow Iris (*Iris pseudacorus*)
Purple-loosestrife (*Lythrum salicaria*)
Water Mint (*Mentha aquatica*)
Water Dock (*Rumex hydrolapathum*)
Bittersweet (*Solanum dulcamara*)
Marsh Woundwort (*Stachys palustris*)
Common Meadow-rue (*Thalictrum flavum*)

Narrow-leaved Water-plantain (*Alisma lanceolatum*), Flowering-rush (*Butomus umbellatus*), Greater Spearwort (*Ranunculus lingua*) and Common Club-rush are all uncommon vice-county species which occur here and there by the river's edge.

Reed beds occur only intermittently under the east bank but there is an important, species-rich relic of fenland reedswamp at Pulfin bend, near to Beverley. Much of the area is dominated by the Common Reed (*Phragmites australis*), whilst more local dominants include Purple Small-reed (*Calamagrostis canescens*), Slender Tufted-sedge (*Carex acuta*) and Reed Sweet-grass. The most notable fenland species recorded here are:
Fibrous Tussock-sedge (*Carex appropinquata*)
Tufted-sedge (*C. elata*)
Marsh Hawk's-beard (*Crepis paludosa*)
Marsh Pea
Yellow Loosestrife (*Lysimachia vulgaris*)
Bogbean (*Menyanthes trifoliata*)
Marsh Lousewort (*Pedicularis palustris*)

Marsh Cinquefoil (*Potentilla palustris*)
Bay Willow (*Salix pentandra*)
Marsh Fern (*Thelypteris palustris*)

Marshy areas occur by the river on both sides, more frequently near to Driffield. Species-rich remnants of fen are now few and small in extent. A number of species probably once more widespread occur in one or two localities only:

Lesser Tussock-sedge
Dioecious Sedge (*Carex dioica*)
Tawny Sedge (*C. hostiana*)
Narrow-leaved Western Marsh-orchid (*Dactylorhiza majalis* subsp. *cambrensis*)
Marsh Helleborine (*Epipactis palustris*)
Grass-of-Parnassus (*Parnassia palustris*)
Common Butterwort (*Pinguicula vulgaris*)
Marsh Fern

More frequent species of these marshes are:

Brown Sedge (*Carex disticha*)
Long-stalked Yellow-sedge (*C. viridula* subsp. *brachyrrhyncha*)
Bottle Sedge (*C. rostrata*)
Greater Tussock-sedge (*C. paniculata*)
Early Marsh-orchid (*Dactylorhiza incarnata* subsp. *incarnata*)
Fen Bedstraw (*Galium uliginosum*)
Blunt-flowered Rush (*Juncus subnodulosus*)
Ragged-Robin (*Lychnis flos-cuculi*)
Marsh Arrowgrass (*Triglochin palustris*)

Bogbean and Marsh Cinquefoil occur in quantity locally.

Many of the drains and dykes of the R. Hull valley have inherited species from the former fenland. The larger drains, notably the Barmston and Holderness drains, have an interesting aquatic flora including the following species:

Water-plantain (*Alisma plantago-aquatica*)
Opposite-leaved Pondweed
Mare's-tail
Yellow Water-lily
Broad-leaved Pondweed (*Potamogeton natans*)
Shining Pondweed
Fan-leaved Water-crowfoot (*Ranunculus circinatus*)
Arrowhead
Unbranched Bur-reed

The ancient Monk Dike is in particularly fine condition as, being well banked, it does not receive fertiliser from the fields. In some of the smaller dykes Water-violet (*Hottonia palustris*) can still be found growing in profusion and Greater Spearwort less commonly; Greater Bladderwort (*Utricularia vulgaris*) and Floating Club-rush (*Eleogiton fluitans*) have also been found, but rarely.

b) *Leven Canal*

This canal which was cut in 1802 extends due westwards from the village of Leven to the R. Hull. It inherited its vegetation from the meres and marshes of Leven Carrs (Crackles, 1968) and is an important SSSI. Aquatics present include:

Water-violet
Spiked Water-milfoil
Yellow Water-lily
White Water-lily
Shining Pondweed

37

Flat-stalked Pondweed
Fan-leaved Water-crowfoot
Greater Bladderwort

Red Pondweed (*Potamogeton alpinus*) was present in the 1950s and Whorled Water-milfoil (*Myriophyllum verticillatum*) at least until 1972.

The edge of the canal and its banks are species-rich. A prominent member of the reedswamp is Common Club-rush with the rare grass, the Narrow Small-reed (*Calamagrostis stricta*), abundant for some two hundred yards or so. Arrowhead, Flowering-rush and Mare's-tail occur locally. Other notable species present include:

Lesser Marshwort (*Apium inundatum*)
Purple Small-reed
Tufted-sedge
Greater Tussock-sedge
Bottle Sedge
Bladder-sedge (*Carex. vesicaria*)
Yellow loosestrife
Purple-loosestrife
Tubular Water-dropwort (*Oenanthe fistulosa*)
Brookweed (*Samolus valerandi*)

Both the Greater Water-parsnip (*Sium latifolium*) and the Fibrous Tussock-sedge did occur, but may have been lost.

c) *Hornsea Mere*

Hornsea Mere, the last of the Holderness lakes and the largest in Yorkshire, is not rich in aquatic species, although the locally rare Lesser Pondweed (*Potamogeton pusillus*) occurs. There are large areas of reedswamp, including extensive beds of the Common Reed, whilst more local dominants are:

Purple Small-reed
Slender Tufted-sedge
Grey Club-rush (*Schoenoplectus tabernaemontani*)
Sea Club-rush (*Scirpus maritimus*)
Lesser Bulrush (*Typha angustifolia*)
Bulrush

Species occurring in the reedswamp include: Flowering-rush, Milk-parsley, Marsh Cinquefoil, Greater Spearwort and Greater Water-parsnip.

Notable taxa found in other habitats by the mere are:

Apium repens x *A. nodiflorum*
Trifid Bur-marigold (*Bidens tripartita*)
Flat-sedge (*Blysmus compressus*)
Early Marsh-orchid
Round-fruited Rush (*Juncus compressus*)
Marsh Stitchwort (*Stellaria palustris*)

Old plants of Tufted-sedge and large beds of Greater Pond-sedge occur in the mere-side woods.

d) *Other Holderness sites*

Some gravel pits provide good habitats for aquatic species. Broad-leaved Pondweed, Shining Pondweed and the rarer Small Pondweed (*Potamogeton berchtoldii*) and Lesser Pondweed together with the Lesser Bulrush and Grey Club-rush occur in pits near Brandesburton. . Frogbit (*Hydrocharis morsus-ranae*), Whorled Water-milfoil and both Small and Lesser Pondweeds occurred, and may still be present, in the old pit at Kelsey Hill, Keyingham, which is now used for water skiing.

One of the lakes in Rise Park has a particularly good reedswamp flora with several fenland species. Small remnants of fen occur in other parts of Holderness as at Roos Bog, which takes the form of a circular morass, and is believed to be a kettle hole. Fenland species also occur in dykes and ponds, as at Hollym where Greater Water-parsnip and Greater Spearwort survive.

iv) Wolds

The Wolds is a generally dry area. However, usually small but interesting spring-fed flushes occur along the western escarpment. Infrequent to rare vice-county species which occur in such marshy areas are:

Flat-sedge (*Blysmus compressus*)
Star Sedge (*Carex echinata*)
Tawny Sedge (*C. hostiana*)
Long-stalked Yellow-sedge (*C. viridula* subsp. *brachyrrhynca*)
Few-flowered Spike-rush (*Eleocharis quinqueflora*)
Round-fruited Rush (*Juncus compressus*)
Marsh Lousewort (*Pedicularis palustris*)
Knotted Pearlwort (*Sagina nodosa*)

Near North Newbald is an important spring-fed marsh with a vegetation more reminiscent of the R. Hull marshes; the presence of the Southern Marsh-orchid (*Dactylorhiza praetermissa*) reflects its southern position. A species-rich spring-fed marsh, with many local rarities, which occurred two miles west of the Wolds, near Wintringham was included in *A Nature Conservation Review* by D.A. Ratcliffe (1977). Unfortunately the marsh has been greatly reduced in size due to agricultural reclamation but Black Bog-rush (*Schoenus nigricans*) still occurs in its only extant vice-county locality.

Springs arise from the underlying chalk in two or three places in the coastal belt of Filey Bay. Although such spring-fed marshes are small in extent, they are of some considerable botanical interest, consisting of a tussocky fen which contains several locally uncommon or rare species:

Bog Pimpernel (*Anagallis tenella*)
Dioecious Sedge (*Carex dioica*)
Star Sedge
Flea Sedge (*C. pulicaris*)
Northern Marsh-orchid (*Dactylorhiza purpurella*)
Few-flowered Spike-rush
Bristle Club-rush (*Isolepis setacea*)
Bogbean (*Menyanthes trifoliata*)
Marsh Lousewort
Common Butterwort (*Pinquicula vulgaris*)
Knotted Pearlwort

Notable aquatics in water channels fed by these springs are Whorl-grass (*Catabrosa aquatica*) and Ivy-leaved Crowfoot (*Ranunculus hederaceus*).

There are several ponds on Flamborough Head and the coastal belt of Filey Bay. The plant associations occurring at the edge of these ponds vary considerably. It is of interest that the following fenland species have been recorded by these ponds: Purple Small-reed (*Calamagrostis canescens*), Bladder-sedge (*Carex vesicaria*) and Blunt-flowered Rush (*Juncus subnodulosus*). Blunt-flowered Rush is the dominant plant by a stretch of drain in the Thornwick Bay area and Fan-leaved Water-crowfoot (*Ranunculus circinatus*) is a notable aquatic occurring in some of these ponds.

6   Coastal habitats

i)   Habitats by the R. Ouse and R. Humber

a)   *Salt-marshes*

Along the northern bank of the R. Humber, salt-marshes are mainly small and often poor in species; all are east of Hull. Three local British species occur: Grass-leaved Orache (*Atriplex littoralis*), English Scurvygrass (*Cochlearia anglica*) and Hard-grass (*Parapholis strigosa*).

Other characteristic salt-marsh species are:

> Thrift (*Armeria maritima*)
> Sea Aster (*Aster tripolium*)
> Common Scurvygrass (*Cochlearia officinalis*)
> Sea-milkwort (*Glaux maritima*)
> Sea-purslane (*Halimione portulacoides*)
> Saltmarsh Rush (*Juncus gerardi*)
> Sea Plantain (*Plantago maritima*)
> Reflexed Saltmarsh-grass (*Puccinellia distans*)
> Common Saltmarsh-grass (*P. maritima*)
> Glasswort (*Salicornia europaea*)
> Common Cord-grass (*Spartina anglica*)
> Lesser Sea-spurrey (*Spergularia marina*)
> Greater Sea-spurrey (*S. media*)
> Annual Sea-blite (*Suaeda maritima*)

By far and away the best salt-marsh occurs to the south of Welwick. It is the most extensive, exhibits a well marked zonation and is species-rich. Common Sea-lavender (*Limonium vulgare*) dominates a large area and is an impressive sight in August, this being the only North Humberside salt-marsh in which this species occurs in quantity. Other salt-marshes of note occur near Hawkin's Point and at Stone Creek. New salt-marshes are building up here and there along the R. Humber, most spectacularly in Spurn Bight as a result of the establishment of *Spartina* dominated areas. As the rate of the ebb flow decreases and silt is deposited, belts of Common Saltmarsh-grass and Sea Aster replace the *Spartina* and subsequently other species appear at the top of the salt-marsh.

Along some stretches, as at Cherry Cob Sands, there are extensive saltings in which the dominant species is Red Fescue (*Festuca rubra*) which provides grazing for cattle.

b)   *River shore west of Hull*

Extensive beds of Common Reed (*Phragmites australis*) occur locally, whilst open associations of scattered salt-marsh species occur along many stretches of river shore. Hemlock Water-dropwort (*Oenanthe crocata*), which has a predominantly western distribution in Britain, occurs in creeks by the R. Ouse, between Asselby Island and Faxfleet, where it is subject to periodic inundation; it has also been found at the base of the river bank at North Ferriby.

c)   *River bank*

On the salt-marsh side of the river bank eastwards of Welwick, characteristic littoral species include Sea Couch (*Elymus pycnanthus*), Sea Wormwood (*Artemisia maritima*) and Grass-leaved Orache. Slender Hare's-ear (*Bupleurum tenuissimum*) was an important constituent of the plant associations on the outer slope of the old bank between Paull and Patrington Haven, particularly along south-east facing sections, but has been lost from this habitat with the building of the new grass-seeded bank.

On or near the Humber bank are non-maritime species at or near the northern limit of their climatic range notably Narrow-leaved Bird's-foot-trefoil (*Lotus tenuis*), Stone Parsley (*Sison amomum*) and until recently Corn Parsley (*Petroselinum segetum*). Up to ten years ago the grassy bank particularly east of Weeton was floristically rich but has been impoverished in recent years by an insensitive grass-cutting regime.   Species still to be found include Spiny Restharrow (*Ononis spinosa*), Bristly Oxtongue (*Picris echioides*), Hoary Ragwort (*Senecio erucifolius*), Strawberry Clover (*Trifolium fragiferum*) and Smooth Tare (*Vicia tetrasperma*) with Hairy Buttercup (*Ranunculus sardous*) occurring in the damper places.

d) *Brackish aquatic and marsh habitats*

Conditions vary at the foot of the bank on its landward side. Along different stretches from Welwick eastwards are found stretches of canal, brackish pools, brackish marsh and damp grassland. Although mainly small in extent, these are important habitats for species with exacting requirements which are not found elsewhere or rarely so.

The most characteristic aquatics are: Brackish Water-crowfoot (*Ranunculus baudotii*), Fennel Pondweed (*Potamogeton pectinatus*), Beaked Tasselweed (*Ruppia maritima*) and the Brackish-water Horned Pondweed (*Zannichellia pedunculata*).   The fresh-water species Water-violet *(Hottonia palustris*) and Fat Duckweed (*Lemna gibba*) have also been noted.

At the gradually shelving edge of standing water are found several salt-marsh species, also other maritime species, notably Sea Club-rush (*Scirpus maritimus*) which forms beds in such habitats and at the edge of steep-sided drains. In the brackish marshes occur Parsley Water-dropwort (*Oenanthe lachenalii*), now very uncommon in v.c. 61, also species usually occurring in fresh-water marshes including Water Mint (*Mentha aquatica*) and Southern Marsh-orchid (*Dactylorhiza praetermissa*), which occurs in considerable quantity locally.

Distant Sedge (*Carex distans*), Divided Sedge (*C. divisa*) and Long-bracted Sedge (*C. extensa*) occur in damp grassland in one or two places at the foot of the Humber bank. Along Kilnsea Canal, cut in 1954, occur Distant Sedge and Long-bracted Sedge together with Sea Rush (*Juncus maritimus*) in quantity in its only East Riding station.

Notable maritime species which are frequent by drains behind the Humber bank are Wild Celery (*Apium graveolens*) and Sea Wormwood.
Interesting river-side meadows at North Ferriby are notable for an abundance of Divided Sedge, together with Brown Sedge (*Carex disticha*) and Great Burnet (*Sanguisorba officinalis*) which occur in quantity. They may be the last surviving examples of a habitat, once a characteristic feature of land adjacent to the R. Humber, and almost lost as a result of land reclamation and the building of flood banks.

ii) Sea coast habitats

a) *Spurn Point*

Spurn Point is a three and a half mile finger of sand lying between sea and river. Since 1960 it has been a Nature Reserve owned by the Yorkshire Wildlife Trust.

It is remarkable for the variety of habitats in a small acreage, a fact reflected in the large number of species present. 340 species have been recorded since the Second World War. Five species occur here in their only known Yorkshire locality: Suffocated Clover (*Trifolium suffocatum*) and Curved Hard-grass (*Parapholis incurva*), at their absolute northern limit in the British Isles, and *Salicornia dolichostachya, S. fragilis* and Dwarf Eelgrass (*Zostera noltii*) which occur on the mud flats of Spurn Bight. In addition several vice-county rarities occur, five in their only East Riding locality. The presence of most local rarities is due to the position and nature of Spurn, including the fact that Spurn is the only coastal sandy area of any extent in the vice-county. Spurn owes its presence to Marram (*Ammophila arenaria*) which is the principal sand binder.

Characteristic species of the river shore include: Spear-leaved Orache (*Atriplex prostrata*), Sea Sandwort (*Honkenya peploides*), Lyme-grass (*Leymus arenarius*) and Prickly Saltwort (*Salsola kali*) with Frosted Orache (*Atriplex laciniata*) being reported recently.

41

Sand Couch (*Elymus farctus*) forms fore dunes on the sea-shore whilst Sea Rocket (*Cakile maritima*) and Lyme-grass occur locally.

Open communities on sand are fewer and more localised than they were before the railway was dismantled in 1952. Nevertheless important communities still occur. Notable species on disturbed sand are:

Silver Hair-grass (*Air caryophyllea*)
Sea Rocket
Sea Bindweed (*Calystegia soldanella*)
Sand Sedge (*Carex arenaria*)
Sea-holly (*Eryngium maritimum*)
Sand Cat's-tail (*Phleum arenarium*)
Heath Dog-violet (*Viola canina*)

At the advent of myxomatosis in 1954, there were extensive areas of short turf. With the absence or severe reduction of rabbit grazing since that time, the vegetation of large areas of the peninsula has moved towards a climax with Sea-buckthorn (*Hippophae rhamnoides*) predominating. Short turf areas have decreased drastically in extent and have at times been maintained by treading and not by grazing. Short turf is still an important plant community in which the characteristic species include:

Early Hair-grass (*Aira praecox*)
Spring-sedge (*Carex caryophyllea*)
Sea Mouse-ear (*Cerastium diffusum*)
Little Mouse-ear (*C. semidecandrum*)
Common Stork's-bill (*Erodium cicutarium*)
Whitlowgrass (*Erophila praecox*)
Lady's Bedstraw (*Galium verum*)
Dove's-foot Crane's-bill (*Geranium molle*)
Early Forget-me-not (*Myosotis ramosissima*)
Buck's-horn Plantain (*Plantago coronopus*)
Knotted Clover (*Trifolium striatum*)
Rough Clover (*T. scabrum*)
Suffocated Clover
Spring Vetch (*Vicia lathyroides*)

A few calcicoles occur in the fixed dunes: Pyramidal Orchid (*Anacamptis pyramidalis*), Yellow-wort (*Blackstonia perfoliata*), Spring-sedge and Ploughman's-spikenard (*Inula conyza*); one or two others have been lost mainly due to loss of land.

A long established salt-marsh with a limited number of species occurs near the chalk bank. Sea-purslane (*Halimione portulacoides*) dominates a large area whilst the following species are at least locally frequent: Sea-milkwort (*Glaux maritima*), Glasswort (*Salicornia europaea*), Common Sea-lavender (*Limonium vulgare*) and Annual Sea-blite (*Suaeda maritima*). A nearby extensive hollow, only rarely inundated by sea water, is an unusual habitat with local rarities to match. Sea Fern-grass (*Catapodium marinum*) and Curved Hard-grass both occur in some quantity, and Sea Pearlwort (*Sagina maritima*) is in abundance. The development of a new salt-marsh along the river-side of the peninsula resulting from the build up of *Spartina* beds in Spurn Bay has already been mentioned.

Other changes which have affected the vegetation include:
a) the tremendous increase in the number of visitors since 1960, and
b) the greatly increased ravages of the sea resulting in the dramatic loss of land, notably on the seaward side of Kilnsea Warren, and particularly since 1973. Two fresh-water ponds and their adjacent marshes have been lost. There is at present a coastal belt with much bare sand and gravel on which such maritime species as Hard-grass (*Parapholis strigosa*), Reflexed Saltmarsh-grass (*Puccinellia distans*) and Lesser Sea-spurrey (*Spergularia marina*) occur and there are tidal pools

with Beaked Tasselweed (*Ruppia maritima*). Additional species have continued to arrive on Spurn, 45 since 1974, some of these being introduced by flood water early in 1978; not all introductions persist. For a full list of species recorded since the Second World War and a more detailed account of the changes since that time see Crackles 1975b, updated 1986.

b) *Holderness coast, north of Spurn Point*

Immediately to the north of Spurn, both Spiral Tasselweed (*Ruppia cirrhosa*) and Beaked Tasselweed occur in a borrow pit (Crackles, 1983b), whilst the halophytic Toad Rush (*Juncus ambiguus*) is to be found nearby (Crackles, 1986b).

The rest of the coast as far north as Bridlington consists almost entirely of clay cliffs, which are eroded away at an alarming rate and may be completely devoid of vegetation or on which a few common weeds, most notably Colt's-foot (*Tussilago farfara*) gain a temporary hold.

c) *Flamborough Head and Filey Bay*

The headland of Flamborough is bounded by spectacular chalk cliffs which are nearly vertical between Thornwick Bay and Bempton.

The grassland associations of the cliff top and slopes are variable. Boulder clay overlies much of the chalk and associations containing moisture-loving species such as Northern Marsh-orchid (*Dactylorhiza purpurella*), Tufted Hair-grass (*Deschampsia cespitosa*), Common Fleabane (*Pulicaria dysenterica*) and Hoary Ragwort (*Senecio erucifolius*) are frequent. Sometimes such species are present with xerophytic species, both calcicoles and calcifuges, no doubt reflecting the complex nature of the glacial deposits overlying the chalk in some places. The maritime influence is often strong.

Only a few calcicoles occur at all frequently, notably Pyramidal Orchid, Carline Thistle (*Carlina vulgaris*) and Burnet-saxifrage (*Pimpinella saxifraga*). Of the calcifuges which occur here and there, the most notable are Early Hair-grass, Heath Bedstraw (*Galium saxatile*) and Wood Sage (*Teucrium scorodonia*). Maritime species occurring in the grassland most frequently are Sea Pink (*Armeria maritima*), Common Scurvygrass (*Cochlearia officinalis*), Buck's-horn Plantain and Sea Plantain (*Plantago maritima*).

Drainage is often impeded so that there are small areas of marsh; notable species occurring in flushes on the cliffs are:

Northern Marsh-orchid
Grass-of-Parnassus (*Parnassia palustris*)
Common Butterwort (*Pinguicula vulgaris*)
Brookweed (*Samolus valerandi*)
Marsh Arrowgrass (*Triglochin palustris*)

Other species occurring in other wet areas on the cliffs include:

Water Horsetail (*Equisetum fluviatile*)
Hemp-agrimony (*Eupatorium cannabinum*)
Small Sweet-grass (*Glyceria declinata*)
Saltmarsh Rush (*Juncus gerardi*)
Ragged-Robin (*Lychnis flos-cuculi*)
Marsh Ragwort (*Senecio aquaticus*)

More rarely a predominantly salt-marsh vegetation occurs on the cliffs; the species present include:

Distant Sedge (*Carex distans*)
Common Scurvygrass
Sea-milkwort
Saltmarsh Rush
Sea Plantain

Common Saltmarsh-grass (*Puccinellia maritima*)
Sea Arrowgrass (*Triglochin maritima*)

The often much slipped and undulating strip of land which constitutes the cliffs from Speeton to Filey are of boulder clay. Those at Speeton face north-east and their plant associations are of hardy, mainly common species including woodland and marsh plants. Broad Buckler-fern (*Dryopteris dilatata*), Male-fern (*D. filix-mas*) and Red Campion (*Silene dioica*) are locally common as are Wild Angelica (*Angelica sylvestris*) and Common Fleabane.

From Reighton northwards Great Horsetail (*Equisetum telmateia*) dominates large areas of cliff, whilst Burnet Rose (*Rosa pimpinellifolia*) is a characteristic plant of the cliff top community, and Small-flowered Buttercup *(Ranunculus parviflorus)* may be found here on bare ground or path sides.
Bloody Crane's-bill (*Geranium sanguineum*) is a notable dominant in Primrose Valley and occurs also locally on cliff tops and cliffs. The stretch of cliff between Primrose Valley and Filey is particularly species-rich. Species occurring frequently here, at least locally are:
Wild Angelica
Glaucous Sedge (*Carex flacca*)
Wild Carrot (*Daucus carota*)
Hemp-agrimony
Bloody Crane's-bill
Great Burnet (*Sanguisorba officinalis*)
Hoary Ragwort
Saw-wort (*Serratula tinctoria*)
Zigzag Clover (*Trifolium medium*)
Grass-of-Parnassus is common in wet gullies.

Notable species occurring by ponds on the cliffs include: Water-plantain (*Alisma plantago-aquatica*), Lesser Marshwort (*Apium inundatum*), Bladder-sedge (*Carex vesicaria*) and Tubular Water-dropwort (*Oenanthe fistulosa*). Bogbean (*Menyanthes trifoliata*) dominates the site of a former large pond.

7 Railways

The construction of the railways in the last century no doubt destroyed habitats, but also created new ones which have become increasingly valued. The characteristic habitats of railways are: a) the ballast of the track, b) the grass verge, c) embankments, d) cuttings and e) brickwork of stations and bridges. Comparatively little botanical work has been done along lines in use, but many lines in the East Riding have been closed to traffic, most falling to the Beeching axe in the 1960s.

The disused lines are important from the conservation point of view. The Hull to Hornsea line in Holderness, the Beverley to Market Weighton line crossing the Wolds and the Market Weighton to Bubwith line in the Vale of York are public rights of way. Other lines passed into private ownership and some stretches have been ploughed up. Although shrubs and trees have developed along some stretches of line, the disused tracks still retain something of the character they assumed in the steamtrain days.
The ballast of the track provides a habitat where various annuals flourish. Such species include:
Silver Hair-grass (*Aira caryophyllea*)
Thyme-leaved Sandwort (*Arenaria serpyllifolia*)
Sticky Mouse-ear (*Cerastium glomeratum*)
Small Toadflax (*Chaenorhinum minus*)
Fern-grass (*Catapodium rigidum*)
Common Whitlowgrass (*Erophila verna*)
Sticky Groundsel (*Senecio viscosus*)
Biting Stonecrop (*Sedum acre*) sometimes covers large areas of ballast. Infrequent to rare vice-county species found on ballast, some in quantity locally, include:

Sea Mouse-ear (*Cerastium diffusum*)
Strapwort (*Corrigiola littoralis*)
Pale Toadflax (*Linaria repens*)
Fine-leaved Sandwort (*Minuartia hybrida*)
Sand Spurrey (*Spergularia rubra*)
Squirreltail Fescue (*Vulpia bromoides*)
Rat's-tail Fescue (*V. myuros*)

Two of the most notable species, Sea Mouse-ear and Strapwort, occur on the Hull and Barnsley line which was formerly linked to Alexandra Dock.

Railway sidings have a similar surface to that of the tracks, but are large areas showing a greater variety of conditions. The Priory Yard and Spring Head sidings in Hull have been very species-rich, but both are being at least partly built upon.

The grass verge and embankment communities differ markedly in different regions and these provide important habitats for species which may have totally or partially disappeared from the surrounding farmland.

The verges of disused lines over the Wolds are varied in character and rich in species having plant associations on both well-drained calcareous soils and on deposits over the chalk as along the private line between Burdale and North Grimston. Most Wolds grassland species are to be found on these verges including such uncommon species as Deadly Nightshade (*Atropa belladonna*), Ploughman's-spikenard (*Inula conyza*) and Knapweed Broomrape (*Orobanche elatior*). Pyramidal Orchid (*Anacamptis pyramidalis*) and Bee Orchid (*Ophrys apifera*) also occur on some stretches.

Cuttings through the chalk as at Weedley, Enthorpe and between Flamborough and Speeton as well as bare chalk along the track, provide a valuable habitat for chalk species which may be otherwise scarce in an area e.g. Long-stalked Crane's-bill (*Geranium columbinum*), Fragrant Orchid (*Gymnadenia conopsea*), Bee Orchid and Rue-leaved Saxifrage (*Saxifraga tridactylites*). Red Valerian (*Centranthus ruber*) may be abundant in such a habitat, as at Enthorpe.

The disused tracks of Holderness are also greatly valued. They provide a refuge for grassland species, now otherwise rare in the area e.g. Common Spotted-orchid (*Dactylorhiza fuchsii*) and Zigzag Clover (*Trifolium medium*). Also on these tracks are several species which have apparently otherwise always been uncommon or absent in Holderness including:

Silver Hair-grass
Kidney Vetch (*Anthyllis vulneraria*)
Small Toadflax
Mouse-ear Hawkweed (*Hieracium pilosella*)
Perforate St John's-wort (*Hypericum perforatum*)
Biting Stonecrop
Sand Spurrey (*Spergularia rubra*)

Here and there along the disused lines, as near Great Hatfield and near Asselby, are ill-drained areas or drainage ditches with aquatic and marsh plant associations.

The vegetation along railway lines still in use may differ markedly from that of disused lines due to changes of management.

The vegetation of the stations is different from that of the tracks. The supporting walls of platforms, particularly north-facing ones and more rarely the walls of coal cells provide a habitat for ferns, two species (*) being recorded which would be otherwise absent in the vice-county. Ferns recorded on station brick-work are:

Black Spleenwort (*Asplenium adiantum-nigrum*)
Wall-rue (*A. ruta-muraria*)
Maidenhair Spleenwort (*A. trichomanes*)
Lady-fern (*Athyrium filix-femina*)

45

*Brittle Bladder-fern (Cystopteris fragilis)
Scaly Male-fern (Dryopteris affinis)
Male-fern (D. filix-mas)
*Limestone Fern (Gymnocarpium robertianum)

Other species occurring somewhat rarely on station brickwork are Ivy-leaved Toadflax (*Cymbalaria muralis*) and Pellitory-of-the-wall (*Parietaria judaica*).

Some other species may also occur only in the station area and not along the track. These include wind dispersed species e.g. Oxford Ragwort (*Senecio squalidus*) and Traveller's-joy (*Clematis vitalba*), seeds of which appear to have been carried into stations by steamtrains. Also on or between platforms and in station yards are found aliens and other species uncommon in a particular region and which have apparently been introduced with freight.

8   Waste places

The history of the flora of Hull's waste places is remarkable. As a result of commercial activity, plants from various parts of the world have been introduced into the city as seed. The climatic conditions are unfavourable for most alien species so that they are transient in their occurrence. In a favourable season, they may be able to produce flowers and even ripe fruit but their seed may be unable to survive the winter. Some aliens may be repeatedly introduced. Comparatively few persist for a number of years, reproducing successfully. Some of these species may eventually spread in the city and even further afield. Examples of introduced species which are now widely distributed in the vice-county, having first become established on Hull's waste places, are given in the next chapter.

Robinson (1902) recorded numerous aliens for docks to the west of the city and plants of foreign origin continued to be recorded for waste ground on or near these docks in the early part of the century (Wilson, 1938; *Reports* of the Botanical Society and Exchange Club of the British Isles). Some species which Robinson (1902) recorded as occurring year after year or as frequent, common or even abundant have not been recorded for the city since. Such species include: *Centaurea aspera, C. calcitrapa, Glaucium corniculatum* and *Rhagadiolus stellatus*.

Wilson (1938) recorded a large number of aliens for King George Dock which was opened in 1914. He described conditions near the docks in the east of the city in the 1930s. New docks were surrounded by large areas of waste land which was only gradually brought into use for the storage of timber or for the construction of railway sidings. Rubbish from dock quays, warehouses and railway trucks were dumped on the area resulting in a prolific growth of exotic plants with 'all the cereals from Rye to Maize and Castor Oil and Sunflowers occurring'. Sooner or later all these gave way to a luxuriant growth of Fireweed (*Chamerion angustifolium*). Most of the aliens recorded early in the century originated from Europe, including the Mediterranean region. In the 1930s such species still predominated, but there were also a number of species from more distant parts, notably from North America.

Before the Second World War, the centre of Hull, particularly the Old Town, was heavily built-up and waste places were rare. The situation changed dramatically during the war when numerous bombs and many mines rained down upon the city destroying buildings and so creating waste places. By the early 1950s a number of aliens, notably White Melilot (*Melilotus alba*), Ribbed Melilot (*M. officinalis*), Oxford Ragwort (*Senecio squalidus*), Sticky Groundsel (*S. viscosus*), Tall Rocket (*Sisymbrium altissimum*) and Eastern Rocket (*S. orientale*), were widely distributed at least in the centre of the city. All of these species had previously been recorded for the docks and the bombed sites were important in allowing for their further spread.

The bombed sites with the greatest number of species of vascular plant occurred in the Old Town with the exception of one or two sites by railways. The next best sites occurred between the Old Town and the docks, both to the east and to the west. The half-mile of the ancient High St south of Alfred Gelder St was particularly rich in species, 134 species being recorded between 1950 and 1953 and 195 species in total.

Hull's ancient High St is remarkable. Narrow and winding, it follows the course of the R. Hull. In spite of the ravages of the last war, stretches of it still retain the fundamental character of the street. When treading the narrow pavements, one is hemmed in by a continuum of buildings on each side. Buildings on the east side are interrupted only by the narrow staithes leading to the quay by the river on which corn and other imports have been landed over the centuries. In the street, there are fine old merchant houses, inns, museums and warehouses, but no shops. Before the war there were warehouses of seed, corn, sack and bag merchants and of pharmaceutical chemists, those on the east side backing on to the riverside quay and built on land reclaimed from the river in the thirteenth, fourteenth and fifteenth centuries. In 1941 the Germans straddled bombs along the old harbour destroying many old buildings, including warehouses, and rendering others unsafe so that they had to be demolished.

Species recorded in the High St in the 1950s included:

a) commercially important species such as the Fuller's Teasel (*Dipsacus sativus*), Sunflower (*Helianthus annuus*), Flax (*Linum usitatissimum*) and Castor Oil (*Ricinus communis*) ;

b) species of pharmaceutical importance, for example Wormwood (*Artemisia absinthium*), Henbane (*Hyoscyamus niger*) and Opium Poppy (*Papaver somniferum*) ;

c) culinary herbs such as Dill (*Anethum graveolens*) and Coriander (*Coriandrum sativum*) and

d) fodder plants, notably Buckwheat (*Fagopyrum esculentum*).

At least half the species recorded for waste places in the High St are foreigners, many of them introduced as impurities in imported seed and including natives of East and Central Europe, the Mediterranean region, North Africa, Asia and America. Although many aliens found on bombed sites shortly after the war had previously been recorded for the docks, there were notable exceptions including: *Ammi majus, Althaea hirsuta, Brassica juncea, B. tournefortii* and *Solanum sisymbrifolium*.

Seeds found during archaeological excavations in Sewer Lane at the western side of the Old Town were found to be generally well-preserved with cotyledons intact (Armstrong, 1977). It seems that water-logged conditions in the Old Town enabled seeds of some species to remain viable for between four and six centuries. These observations suggest the interesting possibility that some of the plants found on bombed sites in the Old Town may have developed from dormant seed.

Many bombed sites, particularly in the Old Town continued to be a happy hunting ground for aliens and for native species until 1979 when Hull City Council obtained money from the Government to 'clean up' the inner city. Additional aliens found in the 1970s and later by the edge of the High St, near to the remaining seed warehouses, were mainly bird seed aliens and included: *Cannabis sativa, Carthamus tinctorius, Centaurea diluta* and several grasses including *Digitaria sanguinalis* and five *Setaria* species.

Some of the aliens found in the city are of interest being of economic importance in other parts of the world. For instance, *Brassica juncea* is cultivated in Asia as Indian or Chinese Mustard and Safflower (*Carthamus tinctorius*) is a dye plant whose seeds yield a valuable oil used for culinary purposes and for illumination.

Aliens have also been recorded from time to time on rubbish tips and on other waste places in and near the city.

Since the Second World War, areas near to warehouses on the docks have been concreted and imports have increasingly been transported in containers so that the introduction of aliens on to dock wasteland has become comparatively rare. Nevertheless dockland wastes are important urban sites, for both native species and established aliens.

The Queen Elizabeth Dock area presents a variety of habitats including railway sidings and track, fresh-water and brackish marsh and open salt-marsh vegetation on its river frontage. It is particularly notable for its Marsh-orchids. A population of about one thousand plants consists mainly of the hybrid between a rare form of the Northern Marsh-orchid (*Dactylorhiza purpurella* Steph. form B) and the Common Spotted-orchid (*D. fuchsii*) with some individuals of the rare parent also present. There is also a significant population of the Southern Marsh-orchid (*D. praetermissa*) on another part of the site.

An area between the now disused Alexandra Dock and King George Dock is regarded as being of great scientific interest by the Nature Conservancy Council. This is a unique site on account of the unusual combination of plant communities present as well as the great diversity of species. There are four species and a hybrid which do not occur elsewhere in North Humberside, also several species which are uncommon or local and others which are infrequent in the administrative county. There are several established aliens of which the most notable are Pale Toadflax (*Linaria repens*), Slender Rush (*Juncus tenuis*) and *Solidago graminifolia*. At the eastern side of the site there is a considerable area of sand, the presence of which is difficult to explain. The sand may have come out of the dock basin, but it seems more likely that it is sand that has been deposited either for use as ballast for ships or for filling sand boxes of steam locomotives, sand being carried to help with braking on slippery rails or on slopes. Part of the sandy tract is dominated by Heather (*Calluna vulgaris*), a remarkable occurrence in the city. Bilberry (*Vaccinium myrtillus*) and Cowberry (*V. vitis-idaea*) are here in their only East Riding locality. There are other species present which are characteristic of the sandy soils of Derwentland, but are absent or uncommon elsewhere. These species are : Pill Sedge (*Carex pilulifera*), Wavy Hair-grass (*Deschampsia flexuosa*), Fine-leaved Sheep's-fescue (*Festuca tenuifolia*) and Narrow-leaved Sorrel (*Rumex tenuifolius*). There are fine populations of the rare form of the Northern Marsh-orchid and of the Common Spotted-orchid. Other notable species on the sandy area are Wood Small-reed (*Calamagrostis epigejos*), Heath Wood-rush (*Luzula multiflora*), Sand Spurrey (*Spergularia rubra*) and Hare's-foot Clover (*Trifolium arvense*). Noteworthy species on cindery parts of the site are Purple Small-reed (*Calamagrostis canescens*) and Rat's-tail Fescue (*Vulpia myuros*)

Uncommon or infrequent vice-county species which occur on this site and on Queen Elizabeth Dock are Yellow-wort (*Blackstonia perfoliata*), Viper's-bugloss (*Echium vulgare*), Blue Fleabane (*Erigeron acer*), Bee Orchid (*Ophrys apifera*) and Great Mullein (*Verbascum thapsus*).

Waste places in other parts of the vice-county provide a refuge for the characteristic species of an area as well as allowing for the spread of aliens. Species rarely recorded for the East Riding have been found on disused air fields, for example Yellow Bartsia (*Parentucellia viscosa*) and Sulphur Cinquefoil (*Potentilla recta*) at Elvington and Pocklington respectively.

V

The Distribution of Flowering Plants and Ferns

1 Introduction

The purpose of this chapter is to give some guidance in interpreting the distribution maps.

Maps constructed on a tetrad basis reveal patterns of distribution, many of which were not anticipated. The distribution of a species may be seen to relate to a particular type of soil or physical feature which can be mapped on the same basis. Climatic factors may have an effect on the distribution of some species, particularly of those which are at or near the northern or southern edge of their range or mainly occur in the wetter western parts of Britain.

The maps often reveal unexpected features showing that soil and other preferences are more complicated than the botanical literature suggests or that more than one factor is playing a part in determining the distribution of a species. Factors interact and the presence of one factor may compensate for the lack of another. Chance also plays a part; a species may not occupy all the potentially suitable sites.

The maps give no information concerning the abundance or otherwise of a species in any one place. Squares on a map indicate that the species has been found in the tetrads indicated, but take no account of the number of plants present within them.

It should be borne in mind that the flora is constantly changing, whilst the collection of information has of necessity taken place over a number of years. The distribution maps refer to all post-1950 records, whereas some species have become much rarer in recent years so that the maps over-state their present distribution to a greater or lesser extent. Conversely, other species have spread rapidly in the same period and are still doing so, with the result that their distribution maps soon become out of date. Decreases have been most marked in the case of some arable weeds, for example Corn Buttercup (*Ranunculus arvensis*) whilst increases are most noticeable in the case of some alien species. Changes of frequency are recorded in the text, but it must be remembered that the present distribution of a species is only one stage in its history. It was appreciated from the outset that maps of common species of particular habitats, for example marshes and woods, would be as useful to the future historian as place-name maps are to us.

A selection of the distribution maps is presented in sets, determined mainly on ecological grounds. The sets of maps are arranged habitat by habitat in the same order as adopted in this chapter as detailed in the 'Contents' of the *Flora*. It was considered instructive for the reader to be able to compare the distribution patterns of species within the same or broadly similar types of habitat. In the case of species in any particular set, one factor is likely to be predominant in determining their distribution, but other factors may also play a significant role. In the present chapter, attention is drawn to some distribution patterns and, where appropriate, an interpretation may be offered. It is hoped that the presentation of maps in sets will stimulate interest and promote further thought and investigation. Maps of species included in the sets are arranged in alphabetical order of Latin names, whilst those for other species are given in taxonomic order after the sets of maps.

The distribution maps are important not only in showing where species occur, but also in revealing significant gaps in distribution. Water Avens (*Geum rivale*) for instance is seen to be absent from most of Holderness, and although the reasons are not fully understood, high winter temperatures may prove to be limiting factors (Perring and Walters, 1962). Other species are found to be absent from coastal areas.

As an aid to interpreting the maps, transparent overlays are provided to show the distribution of factors which may be significant. They are produced on the same scale as the species distribution maps, and are to be found in a pocket at the end of the volume. The overlays include :

1. Chalk and limestone	2. Altitude
3. Sand and gravel	4. Clay
5. Rivers, canals and lakes	6. Springs
7. Disused railways	8. Built-up areas

2 Species of grassland and other unshaded terrestrial communities

i) Calcareous grassland and bare chalk (Maps 1 - 28)

Maps presented in this section are of species occurring entirely or mainly on the Wolds. Most true calcicoles of grazed grassland are seen to be mainly distributed in a belt of variable width along the western side of the Wolds and curving around the northern escarpment to Flamborough Head. Most of these species also occur in the Cowlam valley (10 km grid square 96) and again on high ground south of the Gypsey Race between Driffield and Bridlington. Some of the species most widely distributed within this zone are Crested Hair-grass (*Koeleria macrantha*), Common Rock-rose (*Helianthemum nummularium*) and Wild Thyme (*Thymus praecox* subsp. *arcticus*), all being hardy species occurring on slopes of all aspects. This zone includes most of the unploughed grassland and the highest parts of the Wolds. Some calcicoles e.g. Woolly Thistle (*Cirsum eriophorum*) and Purple Milk-vetch (*Atragalus danicus*) are found mainly north of Pocklington.

Other species with a similar distribution to that of species of grazed calcareous grassland are Tor-grass (*Brachypodium pinnatum*) and Woolly Thistle, neither of which depend on grazing, also Basil Thyme (*Acinos arvensis*) and Red Hemp-nettle (*Galeopsis angustifolia*) which are only found in open communities on the chalk. The distributions of these last two species and of Majoram (*Origanum vulgare*) are slightly modified by local spread along railways. Almost all uncommon chalk grassland species are confined to the previously mentioned belt. A few calcicoles also occur rarely on gravels in Holderness and some on fixed dunes at Spurn Head.

Some species included in this section are more widely distributed. This may be because they are taller and more deep-rooted, for example Greater Knapweed (*Centaurea scabiosa*), or have a more efficient dispersal mechanism as in the case of the Pyramidal Orchid (*Anacamptis pyramidalis*) or are less exclusively calcicolous, as exemplified by Salad Burnet (*Sanguisorba minor* subsp. *minor*) and Hoary Plantain (*Plantago media*). Burnet-saxifrage (*Pimpinella saxifraga*) also occurs away from the Wolds, but rarely, as on the disused railways of Holderness.

ii) Sand and gravel (Maps 29 - 50)

Species included in this section are found mainly on sand or gravel, and being calcifuges are intolerant of calcareous soils. Most of these species are found only or mainly in Lower Derwentland, although some also occur on sand in the Vale of Pickering, usually somewhat rarely, and some on Spurn Point. The distribution of many of these species has undoubtedly been reduced by loss of habitat.

Loose Silky-bent (*Apera spica-venti*) is more widely distributed in Lower Derwentland than most calcifuges as it occurs on arable land as well as on roadside verges. Maps of species confined to sandy arable, or almost so, notably Bugloss (*Anchusa arvensis*) and Amsinckia (*Amsinckia intermedia*) are presented in the set of arable weeds.

Some species are even more widely distributed. Common Stork's-bill (*Erodium cicutarium*), for instance, is found in a variety of habitats on suitable soils in both Derwentland and Holderness. Heath Bedstraw (*Galium saxatile*) which is also a strict calcifuge, occurs widely, while Early Hair-grass (*Aira praecox*) occurs on glacial deposits overlying chalk on the cliffs of Filey Bay as well as in sandy areas.

Silver Hair-grass (*Aira caryophyllea*), a characteristic plant of sandy districts, is also frequent along disused railways in Holderness and its distribution map is included in the section on railways. Sand Spurrey (*Spergularia rubra*) also occurs on disused lines and sidings in Holderness, but rarely.

iii) Grassland species on clay and loam (Maps 51 - 58)

Species in this set frequent a variety of soils which are neither very acid nor strongly calcareous, although their distributions are likely to have been greatly reduced by the ploughing out of permanent grassland.

The distribution patterns of those species which are believed to prefer clay soils : Great Horsetail (*Equisetum telmateia*), Bristly Oxtongue (*Picris echioides*), Hoary Ragwort (*Senecio erucifolius*) and Zigzag Clover *(Trifolium medium)* do not coincide at all closely with each other or that of clay as shown on the overlay provided. However, other factors may be involved. Bristly Oxtongue, classified by Matthews (1955) as of the Southern Oceanic Element, is at the northern edge of its range in the East Riding. This is reflected in its somewhat localised distribution, with a marked preference for areas near to the R. Humber and the sea coast. Great Horsetail occurs mainly on clay over chalk, particularly at the head of small coombs on the Wolds. The tetrad map shows it to be locally frequent at the western edge of the Wolds and along the coast, where it occurs on cliffs. Zigzag Clover and Hoary Ragwort occur on Wolds grassland as well as on Holderness clay, with the last mentioned species being the only member of this group which is frequent in Lower Derwentland.

Meadow Crane's-bill (*Geranium pratense*) is seen to be locally common on the Wolds particularly at the western side and to be scarce in Holderness and Perring and Walters (1962) suggest that too high a winter temperature may be limiting.

3 Species of wood, scrub and hedge (Maps 59 - 94)

The distributions of some woodland species, for instance Ramsons (*Allium ursinum*), Wood Anemone (*Anemone nemorosa*), Wood-sorrel (*Oxalis acetosella*) and Sanicle (*Sanicula europaea*), are good indicators of the distribution of older woods or their former sites. These species seem to have little or no ability to colonise young plantations. The indications are that older woodland is most frequent on the Wolds.

Wood Speedwell (*Veronica montana*) and Early Dog-violet (*Viola reichenbachiana*), which seem only to occur in older woodland, are almost confined to woods on calcareous soils. In contrast, Climbing Corydalis (*Corydalis claviculata*) is restricted to woods and plantations on the sandy soils of Lower Derwentland.

Some likely primary woodland species, those thought to occur only in ancient woods or on their sites, are seen to occur mainly in the Cottingham - Beverley area (GR 54.03), to a greater or lesser extent near Kirkham (GR 54.76) and to be very uncommon elsewhere. These species are Opposite-leaved Golden-saxifrage (*Chrysosplenium oppositifolium*), Yellow Pimpernel (*Lysimachia nemorum*) and Wood Millet (*Milium effusum*).

Broad Buckler-fern (*Dryopteris dilatata*) and Three-nerved Sandwort (*Moehringia trinervia*) are examples of species which are widely distributed in woods, including young plantations.

The distribution map of Primrose (*Primula vulgaris*) is included in this section, although the species also occurs on dyke sides and coastal cliffs and on the sites of felled woodland. The map shows some resemblance to that of woodland place-names (Smith, 1937) and the occurrence of Primroses outside woodland may indicate its survival on former wooded sites. Its incidence in the East Riding bears no resemblance to its distribution pattern in Dorset (Good, 1944). The most important advantage gained by woodland species is protection from water loss, and their survival outside this habitat appears to depend on water supply and their ability to conserve moisture. In Dorset, Primroses were found to occur in both woods and hedges on heavy soils in most areas, and also on mixed soils and some limestones in regions of heavy rainfall. Where the species occurs on light soils in Dorset, it is in woodland situations only.

The distribution of Red Campion (*Silene dioica*) in the East Riding shows some resemblance to that of Primrose in Dorset. It occurs in woods and hedges on the clay soils of Holderness except near the R. Humber and the sea coast, whilst on the lighter soils of the Wolds it occurs only in woodland or in the shade of over-hanging trees. On the lighter soils of Derwentland, Red Campion is scarce. Honeysuckle (*Lonicera periclymenum*) frequents woods on the sandy soils of Lower Derwentland but is mainly in hedges on the clay soils of Holderness.

Deadly Nightshade *(Atropa belladonna)* is seen by its map to be locally frequent in the south of the Wolds and also to occur in the vicinity of Garrowby. Elsewhere the species appears to be bird-sown.

4 Species of various aquatic and marsh habitats

i) Open water (Maps 95 - 118)

Maps showing the distribution of aquatics need to be interpreted taking into account the habitat requirements of the various species (Haslam, Sinker and Wolseley, 1975). Not merely the chemical properties of the water, but also depth, rate of flow and the nature of the substrate in the case of rooted species, all play a part in determining distribution patterns.

Some species occur in the East Riding only in rivers, maybe in one particular river e.g. River Water-dropwort (*Oenanthe fluviatilis*). Species requiring highly alkaline waters such as Opposite-leaved Pondweed (*Groenlandia densa*) and Unbranched Bur-reed (*Sparganium emersum*) are seen to be mainly in the R. Hull valley. Other species, for instance Lesser Water-parsnip (*Berula erecta*), Mare's-tail (*Hippuris vulgaris)* and Shining Pondweed (*Potamogeton lucens*) may be present in highly alkaline waters but are seen to be more widely distributed.

Most of the species mentioned in the previous paragraph occur in a range of aquatic habitats, but some including Shining Pondweed, Yellow Water-lily (*Nuphar lutea*) and Arrowhead (*Sagittaria sagittifolia*) are confined to larger waters, and their distribution maps should be compared with the overlay showing rivers, lakes and canals.

Many species, perhaps once more widespread in the lakes and pools of former fenland areas, now survive in ponds, dykes and canals both in Holderness, mainly in the R. Hull valley, and in Lower and Upper Derwentland. Rigid Hornwort (*Ceratophyllum demersum*), Water-violet (*Hottonia vulgaris*) and Spiked Water-milfoil *(Myriophyllum spicatum)* are good examples. Fine-leaved Water-dropwort (*Oenanthe aquatica*) is now mainly in Lower Derwentland, in ponds, also in dykes in the water-meadows. But it is said to have been formerly 'common in muddy dykes of Holderness' (Robinson, 1902) and should, I believe, be regarded as one of those fenland species which were originally more widespread.

The map of Whorl-grass (*Catabrosa aquatica*) shows it to occur mainly along the spring lines, demonstrating that it is chiefly in channels and streams which are spring fed.

Broad-leaved Pondweed (*Potamogeton natans*) is predominantly a still water species frequenting non-acidic waters of a suitable depth, and is seen from its map to have a wider distribution than most fenland species. With regard to free-floating species of still water, Common Duckweed (*Lemna minor*) is the most widespread. Ivy-leaved Duckweed (*Lemna trisulca*) is seen to be somewhat infrequent, for reasons which are not immediately evident.

Bog Pondweed (*Potamogeton polygonifolius*) is the only species given in this section which requires acid conditions, and as such is confined to Lower Derwentland.

ii) Reedswamp (Maps 119 - 134)

Maps presented in this section are of species which occur mainly at the edge of open water, usually forming more or less extensive beds. Several factors are likely to have a bearing on their distribution. They differ in their nutrient and pH requirements and in conditions which they tolerate. Some can occur at a much greater depth than others, while some differ in their toleration of water movement and fluctuations in water level (Haslam, Sinker and Wolseley, 1975). The maps reveal many different distribution patterns, not all of which can be readily explained.

Slender Tufted-sedge (*Carex acuta*) which requires a constantly high water level is seen to occur mainly in the valleys of the R. Hull and R. Derwent.

Some species occur in former fenland areas. Of these, Tufted-sedge (*Carex elata*), Bottle Sedge (*Carex rostrata*), Greater Pond-sedge (*Carex riparia*) and Water Dock (*Rumex hydrolapathum*) are most frequent in the R. Hull valley but are also present elsewhere in Holderness and in parts of Derwentland. The Water-plantain (*Alisma plantago-aquatica*) is also widespread in the former fenland areas but is also locally frequent in the valley of the R. Derwent. Lesser Pond-pedge (*Carex acutiformis*) and Water Horsetail (*Equisetum fluviatile*) also exhibit a wider distribution than typical fenland species.

Reed Sweet-grass (*Glyceria maxima*) shows a tendency to occur by the larger waters and its distribution map should be compared with the overlay giving the position of rivers, lakes and canals. The map of Common Reed (*Phragmites australis*) reveals a distribution pattern related both to former fenland areas and to habitats where brackish conditions prevail or have prevailed.

The Grey Club-rush (*Schoenoplectus tabernaemontani*) is widespread in Holderness, although in the British Isles generally it is much more restricted to coastal areas. The most widely distributed species in this section is seen to be the Reed Canary-grass (*Phalaris arundinacea*).

iii) By various aquatic habitats; may be also in marshes (Maps 135 - 172)

Some species occur only at the edges of aquatic habitats. These include Small-flowered Winter-cress (*Barbarea stricta*) and Great Yellow-cress (*Rorippa amphibia*), both of which are seen to have a very limited distribution.

Several species in this section occur only or mainly in former fenland areas. Typical examples are Purple Small-reed (*Calamagrostis canescens*), Gipsywort (*Lycopus europaeus*), Yellow Loosestrife (*Lysimachia vulgaris*), Skullcap (*Scutellaria galericulata*), Marsh Woundwort (*Stachys palustris*) and Blunt-flowered Rush (*Juncus subnodulosus*). Greater Spearwort (*Ranunculus lingua*), an uncommon fenland species, occurs mainly in Holderness. Hemp-agrimony (*Eupatorium cannabinum*), which occurs almost entirely along ditch and stream banks, is also seen to have a fenland type of distribution.

Greater Tussock-sedge (*Carex paniculata*), which requires highly alkaline conditions where the reedswamp is at least seasonally high, is found in the upper reaches of the R. Hull and rarely elsewhere.

Some species found in former fenland areas also occur in the water-meadows by the R. Derwent, for instance Purple-loosestrife (*Lythrum salicaria*) and Common Meadow-rue (*Thalictrum flavum*). Bladder Sedge (*Carex vesicaria*), which is particularly frequent in the dykes of the Derwent water-meadows, is uncommon in Holderness.

The distribution map of Plicate Sweet-grass (*Glyceria plicata*) is of interest. The species is seen to be distributed mainly along the spring lines, being particularly frequent at the western side of the Wolds.

The more widely occurring species show marked differences in their distribution patterns. The Common Valerian (*Valeriana officinalis*) is notably concentrated in the R. Hull valley. Some species including Fool's Water-cress (*Apium nodiflorum*) and Water Mint (*Mentha aquatica*) are particularly common in the upper reaches of the R. Hull valley and along the spring line to the west of the Wolds. Others such as Marsh-marigold (*Caltha palustris*) also occur frequently in the Derwent water-meadows. Celery-leaved Buttercup (*Ranunculus sceleratus*) is notably absent from the western edge of the Wolds. The commonest and most widespread species in this section is seen to be Brooklime (*Veronica beccabunga*).

The only species, included in this section, which prefers acid conditions is Marsh Speedwell (*Veronica scutellata*), and this occurs mainly in Lower Derwentland.

iv) Marsh (Maps 173 - 200)

Species included here occur only or mainly in marshes, although a few are also found by ponds or dykes and exceptionally by streams.

Species occurring mainly in former fenland areas include Early Marsh-orchid (*Dactylorhiza incarnata*), Fen Bedstraw (*Galium uliginosum*) and Brookweed (*Samolus valerandi*).
Examples of fen-marsh species which also occur in the water-meadows by the R. Derwent are Brown Sedge (*Carex disticha*) and Tubular Water-dropwort (*Oenanthe fistulosa*).

Narrow-leaved Water-dropwort (*Oenanthe silaifolia*) is confined to the Derwent water-meadows and Marsh Stitchwort (*Stellaria palustris*) mainly so.

Some species are characteristic of marshes and flushes which are spring-fed. Long-stalked Yellow-sedge (*Carex viridula* subsp. *brachyrrhyncha*) is a very good indicator of this type of habitat, occurring along spring lines to the east and west of the Wolds. Flat-sedge (*Blysmus compressus*) is also found in this habitat, mainly to the west of the Wolds. Bogbean (*Menyanthes trifoliata*) is now mainly in spring-fed areas. Ragged-Robin (*Lychnis flos-cuculi*) is seen to be particularly frequent along the spring lines as well as in the R. Derwent water-meadows.

Species requiring acid conditions may occur only in Lower Derwentland as in the case of Marsh Violet (*Viola palustris*) or mainly so, as illustrated by the Bulbous Rush (*Juncus bulbosus*). A number of species occur in acid conditions in Lower Derwentland, but are also scattered more or less frequently in other areas, usually in former fen and carrland. These species are Bog Pimpernel (*Anagallis tenella*), Common Yellow-sedge (*Carex viridula* subsp. *oedocarpa*), Common Cottongrass (*Eriophorum angustifolium*), Marsh Pennywort (*Hydrocotyle vulgaris*), Marsh Lousewort (*Pedicularis palustris*) and Marsh Cinquefoil (*Potentilla palustris*).

The distribution pattern of some species is not clear cut. Nevertheless their occurrence or otherwise in the river valleys, by canals and lakes and along the spring lines can often be ascertained, by using the appropriate overlays.

Maps of some species characteristic of marshy places are not included in this section as they also occur on apparently dry grassland on clay soils where the water-table is high. Notable examples are : Great Willowherb (*Epilobium hirsutum*), Meadowsweet (*Filipendula ulmaria*), Greater Bird's-foot-trefoil (*Lotus uliginosus*) and Common Fleabane (*Pulicaria dysenterica*). Similarly Cuckooflower (*Cardamine pratensis*) is omitted as it occurs in damp grassland as well as in marshes.

5 Coastal species (Maps 201 - 222)

Maps presented in this set are of species which occur entirely or mainly along the R. Humber or on the sea coast, although they may differ in their ecological requirements.

Salt-marshes are to be found between Salt End and Spurn Point. Characteristic salt-marsh species may be confined to these areas but some also occur along the river shore to the west of Hull and in suitable places along the sea coast.

Other species occur on the bank of the R. Humber or in brackish marshes or by dykes behind the bank. Some of these species are also seen to occur along the lower course of the R. Hull and by the Fisherman's Channel on the reclaimed Sunk Island, as do some salt-marsh species including Sea Aster (*Aster tripolium*). More rarely such species may occur inland in non-maritime habitats. For example Sea Club-rush (*Scirpus maritimus*) frequents gravel pits near Keyingham and occurs by Hornsea Mere, where Saltmarsh Rush (*Juncus gerardi*) is also found.

Coastal sand is scarce and its position is identified by the distribution of Marram (*Ammophila arenaria*) and Sand Couch (*Elymus farctus*).

Buck's-horn Plantain (*Plantago coronopus*) occurs intermittently on the R. Humber bank and cliff tops, mainly on well-drained soils.

6 Arable species (Maps 223 - 240)

Distribution maps in this section are for species occurring only on arable or chiefly so. Their distribution patterns mainly reflect soil requirements, although means of dispersal may be an important factor.

Some species, for example Fine-leaved Fumitory (*Fumaria parviflora*), Venus's-looking-glass (*Legousia hybrida*) and Yellow-juiced Poppy (*Papaver lecoqii*) occur on calcareous soils only. Of these, Fine-leaved Fumitory is seen to be very local in its distribution, while Venus's-looking-glass, uncommon at any one time, is seen to have occurred on the Wolds in a surprising number of widely scattered localities since 1950.

Several species, including Night-flowering Catchfly (*Silene noctiflora*) and Field Woundwort (*Stachys arvensis*) are observed to occur mainly on the Wolds, but not exclusively so. The fact that the latter is most often found on the chalk wolds is of interest as the species is usually found on non-calcareous soils in the British Isles (Clapham, Tutin and Warburg, 1962).

The distribution of Bugloss (*Anchusa arvensis*) shows a remarkable correlation with that of sands and gravels in both Lower Derwentland and Holderness. Amsinckia (*Amsinckia intermedia*), an American alien first recorded in the vice-county in 1964, is seen to be already widespread on the sands of Lower Derwentland. Corn Spurrey (*Spergula arvensis*) is a much more widely distributed calcifuge.

Corn Marigold (*Chrysanthemum segetum*) and Large-flowered Hemp-nettle (*Galeopsis speciosa*) occur both in Derwentland and Holderness, the former being more frequent on the sands of Lower Derwentland and the latter most frequent on the peaty soils of the R. Hull valley.

Black-grass (*Alopecurus myosuroides*) is most frequent on the clays of Holderness and most post-1950 records for Corn Buttercup (*Ranunculus arvensis*) are for these soils.

Improved methods of screening seed and changes in agricultural practice resulted in the diminution and loss of arable weeds in the first half of this century and earlier. The widespread use of herbicides, which began in the early 1950s, has had a much greater and more significant effect so that some fields may be almost barren of weeds. Some species, including Corn Buttercup which was once 'in every cornfield', are now rare. However, it is impossible to monitor all the changes and some species for which there have been few recent records may or may not have become scarce. Such species include Fine-leaved Fumitory and Narrow-fruited Cornsalad (*Valerianella dentata*). Other species such as Night-flowering Catchfly and Loose Silky-bent (*Apera spica-venti*) [Map 30],which have become rare in some parts of the British Isles, appear not to have become less common here (Crackles, 1970, 1986c).

7 Species of man-made habitats

i) Railways (Maps 241 - 246)

The railways have been instrumental in extending the range of a number of species within the county. This is particularly noticeable in Holderness where several species which frequent the railway tracks, including both calcicoles and calcifuges, are otherwise rare or absent. Maps for six such species are given in this section and their distribution in Holderness should be compared with the overlay displaying the routes of disused lines. In the case of some of these species, notably Small Toadflax (*Chaenorhinum minus*) and to a lesser extent Biting Stonecrop (*Sedum acre*), their spread along railway lines elsewhere, particularly on the Wolds can also be ascertained.

Recording of species on railways has been mainly confined to disused lines. It must be borne in mind that some sections of such lines have now been destroyed, although this is, as yet, minimal in Holderness and confined to the route from Hull to Withernsea. However the proposed construction of a permanent cycle way along the Hull to Hornsea line is likely to destroy much of the track bed along which species spread in the days of steam-trains.

ii) Walls (Maps 247 - 250)

Old walls able to provide a habitat for ferns and other characteristic species are uncommon, and a considerable proportion of them are in disused railway stations. Maps of four species confined to this habitat are included, and the distribution of each is different.

8 Established alien species (Maps 251 - 264)

A number of alien species have spread in the area, many since 1950. Several reveal a distribution pattern consistent with a spread mainly from Hull, with the concentration of records thinning out to scattered dots as distance from the city increases. For many of these species the first vice-county record was for the Hull area. Such species include : Hoary Cress (*Cardaria draba*), Beaked Hawk's-beard (*Crepis vesicaria* subsp. *haenseleri*), American Willowherb (*Epilobium ciliatum*), Oxford Ragwort (*Senecio squalidus*), Tall Rocket (*Sisymbrium altissimum*) and Eastern Rocket (*S. orientale*). In the case of any such species, the possibility of later introductions into the vice-county at other localities cannot be ruled out. There is evidence that both the garden alien Slender Speedwell (*Veronica filiformis*) and Amsinckia (*Amsinckia intermedia*) [Map 224] spread from more than one locality. The former has spread especially rapidly in the Hull area, due to the availablility of suitable sites, particularly lawns.

The occurrence of some species along the river and at the coast, notably Hoary Cress, suggests an introduction to some localities by air movements.

A scattered distribution without any appreciable concentration in any one place suggests an introduction at several different localities. Species showing such a distribution are Large Bindweed (*Calystegia silvatica*) and Tall Melilot (*Melilotus altissima*).

Policeman's Helmet (*Impatiens glandulifera*) spread mainly along the R. Ouse and R. Derwent, but has from time to time been introduced elsewhere.

VI

Conservation

Conservation is concerned with the maintenance of habitats. The aim in any region should be to retain the maximum diversity of habitats and the greatest possible variety of plant associations within each habitat, thus in turn providing support for the maximum number of animal species. Such a policy provides the variation within the natural environment which the country-lover enjoys.

If a habitat is to remain species-rich, there is the need to impede the natural succession to a climax vegetation of shrubs and trees. To maintain an existing vegetation, there is the need for the continuation of conditions which have operated in the past or to find an effective substitute for them. There is still much to be learnt about the management of habitats.

The Nature Conservancy (later the Nature Conservancy Council) was established under a Royal Charter in 1949, as a body financed by Treasury grant and responsible to the Privy Council. By the National Parks and Access to the Countryside Act (1949), the Nature Conservancy was empowered to create nature reserves and it also had the duty to inform local planning authorities of Sites of Special Scientific Interest (SSSIs). Local naturalists were invited to identify sites of exceptional value for SSSI designation.

Amongst the earliest East Riding SSSIs to be registered were Allerthorpe Common, Bishop Wilton Deepdale, Kelleythorpe marsh, Kelsey Hill gravel pits, Pulfin Bog and Spurn. I have personally been involved in recommending sites for SSSI consideration and was asked by the Nature Conservancy to carry out a botanical survey of both Pulfin Bog and Spurn as early as 1954.

Prior to the 1981 Wildlife and Countryside Act, 21 sites in the vice-county had been designated Sites of Special Scientific Interest, but such status gave no protection and even brought about their destruction or damage by directing attention to them. By the time of the 1981 Act, six sites had been removed from the list as they had been completely destroyed, and several others had been adversely affected to some extent, either through mismanagement or as a result of detrimental and destructive operations within sites or on adjacent ones. Kelsey Hill gravel pits, highly valued by local naturalists and having a remarkable flora, were used as a tip for industrial waste. A site at Wintringham comprising a spring-fed flush, a marsh and damp grassland and recognised as a type of area now rare in the British Isles (Ratcliffe, 1977) was largely drained and ploughed before becoming listed. Another example is Cottondale SSSI, the most species-rich chalk hillside on the Wolds, which was ploughed out.

The Wildlife and Countryside Act, 1981, was intended to give protection to SSSIs, but it remains to be seen how effective this will be. All sites have been under review, with some being removed from the list, the boundaries of others redrawn, and additional sites added.

East Riding SSSIs considered to be of national importance include: Salt End to Spurn Flats, including the whole of Spurn Point and all habitats between the river and agricultural land; Hornsea Mere; Leven Canal; West Beck (R. Hull) and adjacent marshes; East Dale, Fordon and Waterdale; Derwent and Melbourne Ings; Skipwith Common and Flamborough Headland.

Other Sites comprise a variety of habitats including ponds, marshes, chalk grassland, heath, chalk pits and woods. Some SSSIs are the only examples left of a particular type of habitat and clearly need effective protection.

The Yorkshire Naturalists' Trust (now the Yorkshire Wildlife Trust) was the second County Naturalists' Trust to be established, being formed in 1946. Its main function is to buy or lease pieces of land and manage them as Nature Reserves or to enter into management agreements with owners of suitable sites. The first YWT reserve in the East Riding was Spurn Point which has been owned by the Trust since 1959. Out of twelve sites now acquired by the Trust within the vice-county, all but two are SSSIs, some of these being mentioned in Chapter Four. Part of Hornsea Mere is managed by the Royal Society for the Protection of Birds and Flamborough Headland is designated a Heritage Coast. Other sites are in private hands.

The National Parks and Access to the Countryside Act, 1949, made statutory provision for the establishment of nature reserves by local authorities, but little use was made of this provision either locally or nationally over very many years. Humberside County Council and the new National Rivers Authority are committed to take into account the needs of nature conservation in the exercise of their planning and other functions. In 1982 the County Council published a policy statement relating to nature conservation and acquired Millington Wood SSSI in March 1985, for both conservation and amenity purposes. In addition, the Council also owns several disused railways and other land of conservation value, including the Hessle Country Park.

There are few sites which are managed mainly for conservation or research purposes. A nature reserve, like any other area of land, is affected by the use it receives, and both the amount and kind of use must remain within strict limits if the reserve is to continue to serve the purpose for which it was created. The large number of visitors to some sites, and the behaviour of a few, gives cause for concern. Irreversible damage to a site can so easily be inflicted from ignorance.

Recently the County Council's Countryside Section, with the help of local naturalists, has listed a very large number of sites worthy of protection. At least 200 such sites, excluding SSSIs, are believed to be of particular botanical interest. This list has been widely circulated and suggestions with regard to possible additional sites have been invited. These potential conservation areas include ponds, gravel pits, roadsides and disused railways, and all will need to be assessed as to their relative worth. It is hoped that ways will be found of protecting most of them, whether or not some become nature reserves.

Pressures on the countryside are great and always increasing and almost every type of habitat comes under threat at some time. Residential and industrial development, new road schemes and refuse disposal all have an impact on the environment. An attempt should be made to minimise the destructive effects of such development by putting forward well-reasoned arguments as to why a particularly interesting area should be avoided if at all possible.

Agriculture and forestry have done far more to change the flora of the area in the past 50 years than any other factor. There was much ploughing out of grassland during the Second World War, and after the war there followed a great revolution in farming methods. The use of the tractor replaced the horse and from the early 1950s herbicides have been increasingly used on cultivated land so that their use is now almost universal. Not only have arable weeds been destroyed with some species becoming extinct, but transport of poisonous substances by air movements has had detrimental effects on un-ploughed areas on and off the farm. The increased use of artificial fertilisers has resulted in the pollution of some rivers and drains and the contamination of groundwater supplies, as well as changing the composition of some grassland communities. Large excavators, dredgers and other machinery are with us and have had a devastating effect on the environment in some areas. Hedges have been ripped out to enlarge fields in order to accommodate combine harvesters, but they have also been removed along roadsides which would seem unnecessary. The draining and ploughing up of marsh and ill-drained grassland and the ploughing of steep chalk hillsides, both of which were previously impracticable, have resulted in the loss of many interesting habitats. Some of these activities have been aided by government grants. Although the cultivation of some reclaimed land has proved to be uneconomic and the land has later been abandoned, the scientific value of the site has been lost forever. Numerous ponds and stretches of drain have been filled in and interesting aquatic communities lost.

Afforestation, particularly the planting of coniferous woodland, has destroyed extensive areas of heathland as well as other plant communities.

Many stretches of roadside verge and river bank are cut too early in the season, or too often, eventually resulting in the loss of species. Plants flowering from June onwards have no chance to set seed before the machines are out. The cutting of a verge with flowering Bee Orchids (*Ophrys apifera*) gives particular cause for concern as five to eight years elapse before new plants flower and they do so only once.

Collecting of specimens by botanists is now minimal and usually carried out in a highly responsible way, but picking of attractive flowers such as Cowslips and Early-purple Orchids by the general public still occurs as does the illegal uprooting of plants. Both practises can in the course of time severely diminish populations.

Naturalists, notably members of the Yorkshire Naturalists' Union, play an important part in providing information about threatened sites and those being considered as SSSIs or nature reserves, also in assessing the value of sites. The ability to identify locally uncommon species, including difficult taxa, is important, as these plants are invaluable indicators of noteworthy locations. A naturalist concentrating on becoming knowledgeable on one particular type of habitat would be in the position to give invaluable service.

The accumulation of information is not enough. When habitats are being threatened or impoverished, prompt and effective action by those who have the power to influence what happens in the countryside is crucial. The sympathetic consideration of conservation issues by local authorities is essential if valuable sites are to be saved.

All who care about the natural environment have a part to play in being vigilant. The aim must be to prevent unnecessary destruction of habitats wherever and whenever threats occur.

New potentially interesting sites can be created and Kilnsea Canal is a good example. It was created after the severe flooding of 1953 by the construction of a defensive bank using material excavated from the adjacent area. The natural colonization of the canal and its banks, mainly from dormant seed, was of great interest and the plant communities, particularly those at the the edge of the water, are still noteworthy. The succession of vegetation occurring in a newly created chalk, sand or gravel pit is of scientific interest. Rare plants have been found on worked gravel areas, developing seemingly from dormant seed. A newly created pond with shelving edges presents interesting possibilities, particularly if on the site of former fen or marsh; patience may be highly rewarded.

Some of the activities now masquerading as conservation are disquieting. The creation of wild flower areas 'in the wild' gives cause for concern. Conservation is not about creating outside museums. The proper place for collections of growing plants is the Botanic Garden. Deliberate introductions can only cause confusion for those of us who record naturally occurring species and try to understand the factors which affect their distribution.

Tree planting, while desirable in itself, can destroy plant communities. The vast majority of herbaceous plants are intolerant of shade so that care should be taken not to plant trees over species-rich plant communities or over rare plants. The selected area should be surveyed in the flowering season unless the necessary information concerning the ground flora is already available.

Although loss of habitat over the past 30 years has been considerable, there are still sites of great interest in the region, notably along the coast, on the Wolds, and in the valleys of the Rivers Hull and Derwent, as well as in the rest of the Vale of York and in the Vale of Pickering.

It is the responsibility and privilege of all of us, to do all we can to conserve this rich natural heritage both for ourselves and for future generations to enjoy. The environment will continue to be subject to change. Conservation is not a once-and-for-all process, but a continous one. Vigilance, foresight, careful thought and informed action are required and will be rewarded.

Part Two

THE FLORA

The main purpose of the *Flora* is to describe the distribution of established native and alien vascular plants in the botanical vice-county of S.E. Yorks. (Watsonian v.c. 61) which almost coincides with the former East Riding of Yorkshire.

Records for the tetrad maps have been collected since 1970, but all post-1950 records which could be assigned to tetrads have been used and given as black squares; an open square indicates a pre-1950 record. In the text, details of all records are given for species which have always been uncommon. Dramatic changes in the distribution of some species have occurred since 1950 and these are indicated in the text.

PLAN

SEQUENCE AND NOMENCLATURE

Sequence and classification is based on the *List of British Vascular Plants* (ed. J.E. Dandy, 1958). Latin names are as given in the *Excursion Flora of the British Isles* (Clapham A.R., Tutin T.G. and Warburg E.F.) Edn 3, as far as is applicable and updated as necessary. Synonyms are given only where the new name may be unfamiliar or to relate to an entry in *The Flora of the East Riding of Yorkshire* (Robinson, 1902).

ENGLISH NAMES

These are as in *English Names of Wild Flowers* (Dony, J.G., Jury, S.L. and Perring, F.H. Edn 2, 1986). Other English names in use locally are also given.

FIRST RECORD

The date given is the first known record. If no date is given, the first record is an undated one in Robinson's *Flora*.

EUROPEAN DISTRIBUTION

It is instructive to relate the local distribution of a species to its distribution in Europe as a whole. Matthews (1955) classified species according to their geographical distribution. Matthews classification is given in abbreviated form for native species with a limited European distribution. Representatives of the following groups are found in the East Riding *Flora*:

1. **ME.**   Mediterranean Element :   species whose chief centre of distribution is in the Mediterranean region.

2. **OSE.**   Oceanic Southern Element :   species with their main distribution in south-west Europe.

3. **OWEE.**   Oceanic West European Element :   species almost confined to western Europe.

4. **CSE.**   Continental Southern Element :   species occurring mainly in southern and central Europe.

5. **CE.**   Continental Element :   species characteristic of central Europe, thinning out westwards.

6. **CNE.**   Continental Northern Element :   species whose main centre of distribution is in central and northern Europe.

7. **NME.**   Northern Montane Element :   species with the main centre of distribution in northern Europe, but reappearing further south but usually only in montane situations.

8. **ONE.**   Oceanic Northern Element :   species chiefly characteristic of north-west Europe.

STATUS

The status of each species in the *Flora* refers exclusively to the East Riding of Yorkshire, Watsonian v.c. 61, irrespective of the status of the species in other parts of the British Isles.

The following terms are used:

Native	A species not known to have been introduced by human agency.
Alien	A species not native in the British Isles and introduced by man intentionally or unintentionally.
Naturalised Alien	An introduced species found growing amongst native species and able to reproduce either sexually or vegetatively
Established species	An introduced species which persists, but only in the absence of competition with native species.
Introduced	Applied to a species which is not native in the vice-county, irrespective of whether it is native or not in other parts of the British Isles.
Adventive	A species not deliberately brought into the East Riding, having arrived in ballast, bird seed, grain, on freight trains, etc.
Casual	A species which does not persist, being unable to reproduce itself by sexual or vegetative means.
Denizen	An escape of cultivation growing in natural or semi-natural communities.

HABITATS

The habitats given are those in which the species has been found in v.c. 61; these may differ from those in which a species may occur elsewhere.

FREQUENCY

This is described by the terms: **very common, common, frequent, infrequent, uncommon and rare**. Those species described as uncommon are believed to occur in twelve or fewer localities at the present time and the rare ones in three or fewer localities.

LOCAL DISTRIBUTION

Except in the case of uncommon and widely distributed species, a statement is made summarising the main features of a plant's distribution. The map reference refers to the distribution maps.

RECORDS

Details of records are given for uncommon and rare species by region as follows:

U.D.	Upper Derwentland (Vale of Pickering and low ground south to Howsham).
L.D.	Lower Derwentland (Vale of York, including all low ground north to Howsham).
Wolds	The area as indicated in Figure 2.
Hold.	Holderness, taken as the whole of the area to the east of the Wolds (Figure 2).

For each record, the name of a nearby village is given and the 10 km square reference, also the date and the initials or name of the recorder. The 10 km grid squares (centrads) are numbered from their coordinates on the National Grid. All S.E. Yorks. localities are in the 100 km square 44(SE) or 54(TA). As there is no chance of confusion, the 100 km square reference is not given. Thus Holme upon Spalding Moor is given as in centrad 83 (full G.R. 44.83) and Hedon in centrad 12 (full G.R. 54.12).

61

PUBLICATIONS CITED

Nat.	*The Naturalist.* 1875 onwards. The journal of the Yorkshire Naturalists' Union.
N.H. Scarb.	*The Natural History of the Scarborough District.* Vol.1. 1953, ed. G.B. Walsh and F.C. Rimington.
O.B.G.	*Botanist's Guide through England and Wales.* 1805. D. Turner and L.W. Dillwyn.
Rep. BEC.	*Report of the Botanical Society and Exchange Club of the British Isles.* 1879 - 1948.
R. 1902.	*The Flora of the East Riding of Yorkshire.* J.F. Robinson.
SYF.	A *Supplement to the Yorkshire Floras.* 1941. F.A. Lees, ed. C.A. Cheetham and W.A. Sledge.
Trans. HSFNC.	*Transactions of the Hull Scientific and Field Naturalists' Club.* 1898 - 1919.
Trans. YNU.	*Transactions of the Yorkshire Naturalists' Union.*
Wats. Top. Bot.	*Topographical Botany.* Edn 2. 1883. H.C. Watson.
W. 1938.	*The Adventive Flora of the East Riding of Yorkshire.* A.K. Wilson.

HERBARIA CITED

Herb. BM.	Herbarium of the British Museum (Natural History), Cromwell Road, London SW7.
Herb. FEC.	Private collection of F.E. Crackles. East Yorkshire specimens of uncommon and critical taxa collected from 1950 onwards, also a comprehensive collection of grasses and sedges.
Herb. HLU.	Herbarium of the Department of Botany, University of Hull. Includes a large collection of v.c. 61 specimens mainly built up by Professor R. Good.
Herb. JBa.	Collections of British *Hieracia* by James Backhouse (1825 - 1890) in herb. BM and in herbaria of the Botanical Departments of Glasgow and Oxford Universities.
Herb. K.	Herbarium of the Royal Botanic Gardens, Kew, Richmond, Surrey.
Herb. LINN.	Herbarium of the Linnean Society, Burlington House, London.
Herb. MANCH.	Herbarium of the Department of Botany of the University of Manchester.
Herb. Scarb.	Herbarium at the Woodend Museum, Scarborough.
Herb. WAS.	Private herbarium of Dr W.A. Sledge, Leeds.
Herb. Wales	Herbarium of the Department of Botany of the National Museum of Wales, Cardiff.
Herb. York Mus.	Herbarium at the Museum of the Yorkshire Philosophical Society, York.

LIST OF RECORDERS

The following recorders are referred to in the text. The dates of former botanists are given where known ('fl.' = flourishing). The names of those who have produced more or less complete lists for more than one tetrad or have contributed to several tetrad lists are prefixed by an asterisk.

Abbot, Mrs P.	PA	Flintoff, R.J. (1873 - 1941)	RJF
Adams, D.	DA	Foggitt, J.B.	JBF
Adams, F,W,	FWA	Foggitt, T.J. (1858 - 1934)	TJF
Allison, Miss J.	JA1	Fordham, Dr W.J. (1882 - 1942)	WJF
Arnold, Dr S.M.	SMA	Fowler, Miss H.	HFo
Atkins, J.	JA	Fritchley, Mrs A.	AF
Audas, D.	DAu	Frost, H.	HF
Babington, C.C. (1808 - 1895)	CCB	Gardam, Miss P.	PG
Backhouse, J. (1825 - 1890)	JBa	Garnett, Revd P.M. (1906 - 1967)	PMG
Bannister, Mrs T.	TB	Giblin, M.	MG
Beanland, J. (1857 - 1932)	JBe	Good, Prof. R.D'O	RG
Bellerby, W. (fl. 1899 - 1913)	WB	*Gorham, J.	JG
Boatman, Dr D.J.	DJB	*Grant, D.R.	DRG
Bolton, J.	JBo	Gravett, P.L.	PLG
Boult, J.W. (1847 - 1924)	JWB	Greenacre, B.H.	BHG
Bradley, Miss F.	FB	Greenacre, G.M.	GMG
Bradshaw, Dr M.E.	MEB	Grewe, Mrs I. (fl. 1950 - 1969)	IG
Braithwaite, Miss A.	AB	Gulliver, R.	RGu
Bramley, Mrs D.	DB	Hailstone, S. (1768 - 1851)	SH
Bramley, J.R.	JRB	Hall, Mrs E.	EH
*Bray, Mrs E.	EB	Hamilton, W.	WH
Brigham, Miss W.W.	WWB	Harman, M. (fl. 1886 - 1902)	MH
Britten, H. (1870 - 1954)	HB	Hartley, C.	CH
Bromby, J.	JB	Harwood, Revd J.T. (fl. 1898)	JTH
Bulley, R. (fl. 1916 - 1938)	RB	*Haythornthwaite, Mrs D.E.	DEH
Bunce, H.O.	HOB	Hawley, R.	RH
*Burkitt, K.F.P.	KFPB	*Heafford, Miss R.M.	RMH
Burnham, A.	ABu	Hewitt, Miss S.	SHe
Chalk, Miss E.	ECha	Hickson, Miss M.	MHi
Cheesman, W.N. (1847 - 1925)	WNC	Hill, G.H. (fl. 1892)	GHH
*Chicken, E.	EC	Hope-Simpson, J.F.	JFH-S
Chicken, Mrs E.J.	EJCh	Horne, A.J.	AJH
*Clark, Mrs M.	MC	Horsman, Mrs A.	AH
Clark, Dr S.C.	SCC	Houseman, Mrs F.	FH
Cobbe, Miss A.B. (1866? - 1952)	ABC	Hughes, D. (fl. 1932)	DH
Cobbe, Miss M. (d. 1937)	MCo	Hugill, Mrs M.	MHu
Collins, R.	RC	*Hunt, J.	JHu
Comley, J.R.	JRC	*Hunt, R.	RHu
Cox, H. (fl. 1904)	HC	*Hylands, G.	GH
Cracroft, R.	RCr	Ibbotson, H. (1814 - 1886)	HI
*Crackles, Miss F.E.	FEC	Ingham, W. (1854 - 1923)	WI
Crawford, T.	TC	Institute of Terrestrial Ecology	ITE
Cross, E.R. (1866 - 1954)	ERC	*Jefferson, Dr R.	RJ
Cudworth, J.	JC	Jones, A.	AJ
Cundall, Dr R.D.	RDC	Kendall, J. (fl. 1930s)	JK
Dargie, T.	TD	Kilby, Miss. R. (fl. 1948 - 1965)	RK
Davis, H.J.	HJD	Killingbeck, J.	JKi
Deall, Miss N.	ND	Knowlton, T. (1691 - 1781)	TK
DeBoer, F.	FD	*Lambert, Miss J.	JL
DeBoer, Mrs G.	GDe	Leach, D.J.	DJL
Dickens, R.	RD	Lees, F.A. (1847 - 1921)	FAL
*Dobson, A.T.	ATD	Levis, J.D.	JDL
Dolman, G.	GD	Lewis, R.	RL
Duncan, Mrs J.E.	JD	Lucas, J.	JLu
Dunning, Mrs P.	PD	Lush, B.	BL
Ealing, Dr M.	ME	Lynn, A.E.	AEL
Fenton, K.	KF	Machell, Lt Col C. (1747 - 1827)	CM
Flint, Mrs H.	HFl	Magee, L.	LM

Marshall, A.	AM	Stather, W.H.	WHS
Marshall, J.J. (1860 - 1934)	JJM	Storey, Miss E.	ESt
Mason, S.	SM	Stubbs, F.B.	FBS
*Matthew, E.B.	EBM	Stuttard, P.	PS
McClintock, D.	DM	Tansley, Sir A.G.	AGT
McCollin, D.	DMcCo	Taylor, Sir G.	GT
*Medd, T.F.	TFM	Taylor, Dr J.M. (1886 - 1947)	JMT
Merryweather, J.	JM	Teesdale, R. (c.1740 - 1804)	RT
*Middleton, R.	RM	Tennant, D.J.	DJT
Middleton, W. (d. 1842)	WM	*Thistleton, Mrs R.	RTh
Moon, Miss B.	BM	Thompson, C.	CT
Moore, O.A. (1818 - 1862)	OAM	Thompson, E.	ET
Morehouse, Mrs E.M. (fl. 1940)	EMM	Thompson, Mrs M.	MT
Mott, T.	TM	Todd, Miss B.	BT
Mowat, Miss A.B.	ABM	Underwood, Mrs A.	AU
Nature Conservancy Council	NCC	Ungley, D.	DU
Nelson, G.A.	GAN	Usher, Dr M.	MU
Nethercoat, M.F.	MFN	Vaughan, C.	CV
Nethercoat, Mervyn	MeN	Walters, Dr S.M.	SMW
Newbold, Dr C.	CN	Washington, Miss A.	AWa
*Newbould, J.A.	JAN	Waterfall, C. (1851 - 1938)	CW
Nicholls, M.	MN	Watts, F.	FW
Norman, G. (1823 - 1882)	GN	Waugh, W.L. (fl. 1930)	WLW
Norman, Miss M.M.	MMN	*Wear, E.H.	EHW
Oliver, Miss M. (fl. 1892)	MO	Webb, D.	DW
Parsons, Dr H.F. (1846 - 1913)	HFP	Webster, G. (fl. 1896)	GW
*Pashby, B.	BP	Webster, J.	JW
Payne, E.J. (fl. 1937)	EJP	Wegener, Dr A.	AWe
Payne, H. (fl. 1831 - 1895)	HPa	Whitewell, W. (fl. 1866 - 1878)	WWh
Payne, Mrs J.	JP	Whytehead, W. (1729 - 1817)	WW
Payne, K.G.	KGP	Wiggington, M.	MW
Peacock, A.	AP	Wilkins, D.A.	DAW
Peacock, Mrs H.	HiP	Wilkinson, H.J. (1859 - 1934)	HJW
Peak, E.A. (fl. 1887)	EAP	Wilson, A.K. (fl. 1930 - 1960)	AKW
*Pellant, Mrs H.	HP	Winter, P.	PW
Perring, F.H.	FHP	*Withers, Mrs M.	MFW
Petch, T. (1870 - 1948)	TP	Woods, Revd F.H. (1850-1915)	FHW
Philip, R.H.	RHP	Worsdale, A.	AW
Porter, C.	CP	Wray, A.E.	AEW
*Priest, Miss S.	SP	*Yeates, C.S.V.	CSVY
Pratt, Revd E.	EP	Yorkshire Naturalists' Union	YNU
Purchas, Miss G. (fl. 1925)	GP	Youill, E.	EY
Reeves, W.W. (1819 - 1892)	WWR		
Rob, Miss C.M. (1906 - 1975)	CMR		
Robertson, Miss J.	JRo		
Robinson, J.F. (1857 - 1927)	JFR		
Robinson, Mrs M.	MR		
Rowntree, H. (fl. 1941)	HR		
Rushton, J. (fl. 1960s)	JR		
Sayer, M.M. (1895 - 1969)	MMS		
Schofield, J. (fl. 1899)	JS		
Shaw, G.A. (1916 - 1980)	GAS		
*Shimwell, Dr D.W.	DWS		
Shorer, Miss. S.	SS		
Simpson, G.	GS		
Singleton, F.	FS		
Slater, M.B. (1850 - 1918)	MBS		
Sledge, Dr W.A.	WAS		
Smith, A.M. (1879 - 1962)	AMS		
Smith, H. (fl. c.1860)	HS		
Smith, H.B.W (1879 - 1948)	HBWS		
Smith, W.G.	WGS		
Speck, Mrs K.	KS		
Spence, B.	BS		
Spencer, J.E.	JES		
Spooner, E.	ES		
Spruce, R. (1817 - 1893)	RS		
Stainforth, T. (1882 - 1944)	TS		

PTERIDOPHYTA

LYCOPSIDA

LYCOPODIACEAE

Huperzia Bernh.
H. selago (L.) Bernh. ex Schrank & Mart. (*Lycopodium selago* L.)
Fir Clubmoss.
Native.   Heaths.
One unspecified locality, Wats.Top.Bot., 1883 (Trans. HSFNC, 1903, *3*, 100).

Lycopodiella Holub
L. inundata (L.) Holub (*Lycopodium inundatum* L.)
Marsh Clubmoss.
Native.   Wet heaths.
One unspecified locality, Wats.Top.Bot., 1883 (R. 1902); on authority of O.A. Moore, ? Langwith Moor 64 (SYF).

Lycopodium L.
L. clavatum L.
Stag's-horn Clubmoss.   1850.
Native.   Heaths.   Rare.
L.D. Houghton Woods 83, 1935, TS, herb. FEC, conf. 1953, RG, herb. HLU.
Hold. Cottingham Common 03, 1850, GN, extinct by 1902 (R. 1902).

SELAGINELLACEAE

Selaginella Beauv.
S. selaginoides (L.) Link
Lesser Clubmoss.   1805.
Native.   Fen, marshes and moors.   Extinct.
L.D. Wheldrake Moor 64 (Baines, 1840); Skipwith Common 63, 1905, WI.
Wolds Near Newbald Springs 93, 1900, JFR (R. 1902).
Hold. Near Beverley 03 (O.B.G., 1805).

ISOETACEAE

Isoetes L.
I. lacustris L.
Quillwort.
Native.   Ponds poor in dissolved salts.
One locality only: Riccall Common 63, WNC; probably extinct by 1902 (R. 1902).

SPHENOPSIDA

EQUISETACEAE

Equisetum L.
E. hyemale L.
Rough Horsetail.
Native.
U.D. Dry woods, Kirkham 76 (Teesdale, 1800).
L.D. Bubwith 73, *c.*1887, G. Roberts (SYF). Extinct.

E. fluviatile L. (*E. limosum* L.)   Map 126.
Water Horsetail.   *c.*1845.
Native. In shallow still water at the edge of lakes, canals and ponds including water-filled gravel pits and by ditches, may be locally dominant; also in marshes in the R. Hull valley. Frequent.   Widely distributed in Holderness and Derwentland.

E. palustre L.   Map 183.
Marsh Horsetail.   1848.
Native. In marshes and by ponds; requiring moving ground water with a medium base content: many localities are along the spring line. Frequent, less common than formerly because of loss of habitat.

E. arvense L.   Map 265.
Field Horsetail.   1835.
Native. Roadside verges, railway banks, gardens, fields, waste places. Common except on the chalk.

E. arvense x *E. fluviatile* = *E.* x *litorale* Kühlew. ex Rupr.
Brandesburton gravel pit 14, 1981, F.E.Crackles, herb. FEC. May occur elsewhere where both species occur together.

E. telmateia Ehrh. (*E. maximum* auct.)   Map 51.
Great Horsetail.
Native. Damp shady places; mainly on clay soils. Locally frequent.
The tetrad map shows it is frequent at the western edge of the Wolds; it is typically at the head of small coombs or on steep slopes where it may be locally dominant. It is also locally abundant on the slopes of clay cliffs of Flamborough Head 26 and Filey Bay 17. It occurs on a shaded bank at Lowthorpe 06 and in wet woods e.g. at Settrington 87 and Howsham 76; Leys and Oxpasture Woods 86.
It is uncommon in Holderness: Kelsey Hill 22 (R. 1902) and 1950, RG; Wilfholme 04, 1970, MC; also at Kilnwick 04 and Bell Mills 05, 1970, MC where it occurs in quantity, 1985, EC.

PTEROPSIDA

OSMUNDACEAE

Osmunda L.
O. regalis L.
Royal Fern.   1836.
Native.   Wet heaths and woods.   Rare.
L.D. Langwith and Wheldrake lanes 64 'very frequent' (Baines, 1840), two plants in woods on Langwith Common, 1965, Mrs G. DeBoer; Skipwith Common 63, WNC (R. 1902) and 1970, YNU Excursion (one plant). The 'South Cliff' record (R. 1902) refers to North Cliffe Wood 83, *c.*1850, GN (Trans. HSFNC, *1*, 111), still there 1899, JJM.

DENNSTAEDTIACEAE

Pteridium Scop.
P. aquilinum (L.) Kuhn   Map 266.
Bracken.   1858.
Native. Woods, heaths, hedge-banks, road-side verges. Widespread and locally abundant, especially on the sands of Lower Derwentland; rare on shallow chalk soils.

BLECHNACEAE

Blechnum L.

B. spicant (L.) Roth [*Lomaria spicant* (L.) Desv.] Map 267.
Hard Fern.   1858.
Native. Woods and commons on acid soils, usually by dykes. Uncommon.
Most records are for Lower Derwentland.
L.D. Houghton Woods 83, 1858 (R. 1902) and 1953, RG, still present; near Selby 63, WNC (R. 1902); Allerthorpe Common 74, 1953, AKW; Bielby 74, 1953, RG; Duck Nest 83, 1955, RG; North Cliffe Wood 83, 1955, FEC, still present; Langwith Common 64, 1956, FEC, still present; Skipwith Common 63, 1957, RG; Sutton Wood 74, 1970, YNU Excursion; Fulford 64, 1980, EB.
Hold. Formerly in Birkhill Wood 03, 1900 (R. 1902).

ASPLENIACEAE

Phyllitis Hill

P. scolopendrium (L.) Newman (*Scolopendrium vulgare* Sm.)   Map 268.
Hart's-tongue.   1850.
Native. Walls, railway brickwork, woods, steep banks. Infrequent, but widely scattered.
Records include:
U.D. Kirkham Abbey 76, 1955, RG.
L.D. Lock walls, Thornton 74, 1956, RG and Faxfleet 82, 1978, FEC.
Wolds Church wall, Burton Agnes 16, 1982, EC.
Hold. Watton Abbey 04, 1957, FEC; lock wall, Princess Dock, Hull 02, 1979, FEC; railway brickwork at Burstwick 22, 1982, FEC, Patrington 32, 1983, FEC and Ellerby 13, 1984, FEC; church walls at Bridlington 16, 1983, EC.
Rarely in woods and plantations as at Thorpe Plantation 22, 1948, RL and 1983, HF; Weldon's Plantation 32, 1981, FEC and at Rise Park 14, 1982, FEC.

Asplenium L.

A. adiantum-nigrum L.
Black Spleenwort.   2nd half 18th century.
Native. Walls. Uncommon, possibly increasing.
U.D. Coal cells, West Heslerton railway station 97, 1982, FEC; Willerby churchyard 07, 1983, EC.
Wolds Old walls: Burton Agnes 16, 2nd half 18th century, WW; Bishop Burton 93, 1959, FEC; Thwing 07, 1964, FEC; Wetwang churchyard 95, 1983, EC.
Hold. Old wall Beeford 15 and Bridlington church 16, 2nd half 18th century, WW; Easington church 31, 1899, Cannon Maddock (R. 1902); Bridlington Priory 16, 1983, EC. Railway brickwork: Burstwick 22, 1958, ABM; Great Hatfield 14, 1976, SCC; Patrington 32, 1983, FEC.

A. trichomanes L.
Maidenhair Spleenwort.   Map 248.
Native. Old walls and other brickwork. Infrequent.
Post-1950 records include:
U.D. Kirkham 76, 1958, RG; coal cells, West Heslerton railway station 97, 1982, FEC.
L.D. Market Weighton Canal lock house 83, 1956, FEC; railway station, Bubwith 73, 1982, FEC and Foggathorpe 73, 1985, FEC.
Wolds Railway bridge, Eppleworth 03, 1957, FEC; Londesborough Arches 84, 1982, EC, confirming an old record (R. 1902); Hunmanby Hall 07, 1983, FB.
Hold. Watton Abbey 04, 1957, FEC; Bridlington 16, 1971, MC; railway station, Ellerby 13, 1984, FEC.

A. ruta-muraria L.   Map 247.
Wall-rue.   1850.
Native. Old walls and other brick-work. Infrequent.
Records include:
U.D. Kirkham Abbey 76, 1958, FEC; railway station, West Heslerton 97, 1982, FEC.
L.D. Bridge, Elvington 74, 1955, RG; Wholsea Lock 83, 1956, RG; wall by church walk, Hemingborough 63, 1981, YNU Excursion; Highfield railway station 73, 1982, FEC; churchyard wall, Skipwith 63, 1983, FEC; coal cell, Shiptonthorpe railway station 84, 1983, EC.
Wolds Churchyard and farm walls, Flamborough 26, 1970, MC; Londesborough Arches and churchyard wall 84, 1983, EC.
Hold. Watton Priory 04, 1957, FEC; Bridlington Priory 16, 1970, MC; old wall, Beverley and Plaxton Bridge, near Thearne 03, 1977, JA.

Ceterach DC.

C. officinarum DC.
Rustyback.   2nd half 18th century.
Native. Walls and other brickwork.
Wolds Old wall, Langton 76, 1890, MBS (R. 1902).
Hold. Nunkeeling churchyard 14, 2nd half 18th century, WW; one tuft, Beverley Bridge 04, T.Audas (R. 1902).
Extinct.

ATHYRIACEAE

Athyrium Roth

A. filix-femina (L.) Roth   Map 62.
Lady-fern.
Native. Damp woods, hedgebanks. Locally frequent in Lower Derwentland, mainly in woods; infrequent elsewhere.

Cystopteris Bernh.

C. fragilis (L.) Bernh.
Brittle Bladder-fern.
Native. Walls. Very rare.
Hold. Railway stations, Burstwick 22 and Patrington 32, 1958, ABM, herb. HLU; refound at Patrington 1984, FEC.

ASPIDIACEAE

Dryopteris Adans.

D. filix-mas (L.) Schott [*Lastrea filix-mas* (L.) C. Presl]
                                                                  Map 269.
Male-fern.
Native. Woods, hedges, on brickwork or at the foot of walls. Very common.

D. affinis (Lowe) Fraser-Jenkins (*D. borreri* Newm.)
Scaly Male-fern.   1947.
Native. Woods, walls. Rare.
L.D. Disused railway station, Foggathorpe 73, 1984, JM.
Wolds Millington Wood 85, 1964, FEC.
Hold. Weldon's Plantation, Winestead 32, 1947, RL; Oak wood, Burton Carr 16 and Fish Ponds Wood, Boynton 16, 1987, EC.

D. cristata (L.) A. Gray [*Lastrea cristata* (L.) C. Presl]
Crested Buckler-fern.
Native. Extinct ?
U.D. Kennythorpe Moor 76, MBS (R. 1902); Firby 76, 1923, GP.

L.D. Probably also Cliffe Wood 83, JJM and Skipwith Common 63 (R. 1902).

D. carthusiana (Vill.) H.P. Fuchs [*D. lanceolatocristata* (Hoffm.) Alston; *Lastrea spinulosa* C. Presl]　Map 72.
Narrow Buckler-fern.　　　　　　　　　　1888.
Native. Damp woods. Locally frequent, mainly in Lower Derwentland.

D. dilatata (Hoffm.) A. Gray [*Lastrea dilatata* (Hoffm.) C. Presl]　　　　　　　　　　　　Map 73.
Broad Buckler-fern.　　　　　　　　　1897.
Native.　Woods, copses.　Common.

Polystichum Roth
P. setiferum (Forsk.) Woynar
Soft Shield-fern.　　　　　　　　　　1947.
Native.　Woods.　Very rare.
Hold. In plantation by the sea, Holmpton 32, 1947, RL, herb. HLU; Rise Park, 14, 1982, FEC, herb. FEC.

P. aculeatum (L.) Roth [*P. lobatum* (Huds.) Chevall]
Hard Shield-fern.　　　　　　　　　　1880.
Native.　Woods, hedge banks, beck-sides.　Uncommon.
U.D. Westow 76, 1924, GP; Kirkham Abbey Woods 76, 1968, FH; Howsham 76, 1970, MC; green lane, Muston 08, 1984, DRG.
Wolds Danes Dyke 26 & 27, 1955, RG and 1970, MC.
Hold. Between Spring Head and Cottingham 03 and near Leconfield 04 (R. 1902); in Birkhill Wood 03, 1905 (Trans. HSFNC *3*, 218); Swine 13, 1932, TS; Burgany Plantation, Winestead 32, 1948, RL; Lockington 94, 1956, RG; Ellerby 14, 1957, RG.

THELYPTERIDACEAE

Thelypteris Schmidel
T. palustris Schott [*T. thelypteroides* Michx ; *Lastrea thelypteris* (L.) Bory]
Marsh Fern.　　　　　　　　　　　　*c.*1845.
Native.　Fens.　Rare.
L.D. Heslington Fields 64, *c.*1845, OAM.
Hold. Pulfin Bog 04, 1897, found with sori, 1937, AKW, scarce by 1967, FEC, still present, 1983, EHW; Kelleythorpe 05, 1904, FHW (Nat. 1904, 348), found with sori, 1935, AMS, locally abundant, 1968, FEC.

Oreopteris Holub
O. limbosperma (All.) Holub [*Thelypteris oreopteris* (Ehrh.) Slosson; *Lastrea oreopteris* (Ehrh.) Bory]
Lemon-scented Fern.　　　　　　　　1840.
Native. Mainly in woods on acid soils, usually by dykes. Rare.
All records are for Lower Derwentland: Escrick 64 (Baines, 1840); Skipwith Common 63, WNC (R. 1902) and 1959, FEC; Houghton Moor 83 (R. 1902); by dykes in Houghton Wood 83, 1962, FEC, still there; Langwith Common 64, 1956, FEC.

Phegopteris (Presl) Fée
P. connectilis (Michx) Watt [*Thelypteris phegopteris* (L.) Slosson]
Beech Fern.　　　　　　　　　　　　*c.*1845.
Native.
Given for v.c. 61 in Wats. Top. Bot., 1883 (Trans. HSFNC, 1903, *3*, 100). 'Langwith Lane, JB', in O.A. Moore's copy of Baines' *Flora*.

Gymnocarpium Newm.
G. dryopteris (L.) Newm. [*Thelypteris dryopteris* (L.) Slosson; *Phegopteris dryopteris* (L.) Fée]
Oak Fern.
Native.　Damp woods.　Rare.
Near Sledmere 96, 1897, T. Audas (R. 1902). Extinct.

G. robertianum (Hoffm.) Newm. [*Thelypteris robertiana* (Hoffm.) Slosson]
Limestone Fern.
Native.　Very rare.
Disused railway station, Foggathorpe 73 (Merryweather, 1984)

POLYPODIACEAE

Polypodium L.
P. vulgare L. *sensu lato*
Polypody.　　　　　　　　　　　　1888.
Native. Epiphytic on trees and on old walls.　Uncommon.
U.D. Firby woods 76 (Nat. 1920, 366); on trees by Moor Beck, Leavening 76, 1961, FEC.
L.D. Near Market Weighton 84, 1899 (R. 1902); wood, Storwood 74, 1957, RG, herb. HLU; on Wressle Castle 73, 1970, GAS & ET.
Wolds On old wall, Bishop Burton 93, 1959, FEC.
Hold. On old hawthorns in hedgerows: Haltemprice Lane 03 and Swine 13, GN, Routh 04, 1888 (R. 1902); at Hornsea 14, 1987, DRG.
Now divided into three species on cytological and morphological grounds including :
P. vulgare *sensu stricto* The Storwood specimen is this, as the epiphytes are likely to be;
P. interjectum Shivas Sand dunes, Spurn 41, 1978, FEC, conf. R.H. Roberts, previously recorded as *P. vulgare* L.

MARSILEACEAE

Pilularia L.
P. globulifera L.
Pillwort.　　　　　　　　　　　　1901.
Native.　Shallow, somewhat acid ponds.　Very rare.
L.D. Skipwith Common 63, WNC, found in abundance in other ponds, 1901, HRW (R. 1902), conf. 1964, TFM; near Cliffe Common railway station 63, 1921, JBF.

AZOLLACEAE

Azolla Lam.
A. filiculoides Lam.
Water Fern.　　　　　　　　　　　1978.
N. American alien.　Ponds.　Rare.
L.D. Hemingborough 63, 1977, H. & J. Flint; pond completely covered with *Azolla* and *Lemna minor* in nearly equal proportions, much reduced in quantity by 1978 (Nat. 1979, 112); near Osgodby 63, 1985, EC.
Hold. In garden pond, Beverley 03, 1979, MeN; it spread remarkably, completely covering the pond by 1980, had almost completely disappeared by 1981 and completely so by 1982.

OPHIOGLOSSACEAE

Botrychium Sw.

B. lunaria (L.) Sw.
Moonwort.   1887.
Native. Dry grassland. Very rare now.
U.D. Westow 76, c.1925, GP.
L.D. Near Brough 92 (R. 1902); near Barlby 63, WNC (YNU Circular, 1912); Riccall Common 63, 1933, D.W. Toyne; S.W. of Houghton Woods 83, TS (YNU Circular, 1943); near Allerthorpe Common 74, 1973, TFM.
Wolds North Grimston 86 (Nat. 1902, 298); Buckton cliffs 17 (Nat. 1912, 211); on chalk grassland, North Newbald 93, 1957, FEC, area later planted with conifers; Thorpe Hall 16, 1971, PG, still present.
Hold. 'On chalky and gravelly knolls in pastures' by Hornsea Mere (Teesdale, 1800), conf. 1904 (Trans. HSFNC *3*, 184); Beverley, Risby, 1887, EAP, Burn Park and Hall Ings, Cottingham 03 (R. 1902).

Ophioglossum L.

O. vulgatum L.   Map 270.
Adder's-tongue.
Native. Damp grassland, fens, open woodland; Wolds grassland, chalk pits. Infrequent and diminishing because of loss of habitats. Formerly 'common in pastures in all districts and very abundant on clayey soils' (R. 1902).
Post-1970 records :
L.D. Skipwith Common 63, 1970, YNU Excursion; grassy bank, Newton upon Derwent 74, 1979, SP.
Wolds Lowthorpe 06, 1970, EC; Tibthorpe 95, 1970, FEC; Little Wood, North Newbald 93, 1972, FEC; grassland near Thixendale 85, 1982, NCC.
Hold. Fen-marsh, Sunderlandwick 05, 1971, FEC; Holmpton 32, 1971, GH; Sunk Island 21, 1986, AJ.

SPERMATOPHYTA

GYMNOSPERMAE

PINACEAE

Larix Mill.

L. decidua Mill.
European Larch.
Introduced. Commonly planted for forestry and ornament

Pinus L.

P. sylvestris L.
Scots Pine.
Native and Denizen. Frequent.

TAXACEAE

Taxus L.

T. baccata L.
Yew.
Denizen and ? Native. Widely planted in churchyards and elsewhere.
Some fine old trees in Risby woods 03.

ANGIOSPERMAE

DICOTYLEDONES

RANUNCULACEAE

Caltha L.

C. palustris L.   Map 139.
Marsh-marigold.
Native. Water meadows, marshes, fens, ditches, wet woods; by rivers, lakes, canals, ponds and dykes. Frequent, but some loss of habitat.

Helleborus L.

H. foetidus L.
Stinking Hellebore.   1840.
Introduced. Plantations and waste ground. Rare.
Now only known at Hessle, near chalk quarry 02, 1981, Hull Nats. Excursion, confirming an earlier record 1931, AKW. Other records:
L.D. Langwith 64 (Baines, 1840); Fangfoss 75, 1956, MT.
Wolds Londesborough 84 (Baines, 1840); West Heslerton 97, 1884 (N.H. Scarb.); Sewerby 16, RJF (BEC. *6*, 1921, 370); North Grimston 86, 1944, KGP.
Hold. North Hull 03, 1912, TS (Trans. HSFNC *4*, 322); near Cherry Cob Sands 22, 1938, AKW.

H. viridis L. subsp. *occidentalis* (Reut.) Schiffn.
Green Hellebore.   1840.
Possibly native in Wolds woodland, otherwise introduced. Rare.
L.D. Wressle 73, WNC (R. 1902).
Wolds Londesborough 84 (Baines, 1840); Settrington 87, 1921, Lady Middleton; Sledmere 96, 1960, YNU Excursion; Brantingham Dale 93, 1976, JA.
Hold. Meaux Abbey 03 (R. 1902).

Eranthis Salisb.

E. hyemalis (L.) Salisb.   Map 271.
Winter Aconite.   1902.
Established alien. A native of S. Europe.
In plantations and woods. Infrequent, but in widely scattered localities. Sometimes in quantity as at Great Givendale 85, near Watton 04 and at Wassand 14.

Aconitum L.

A. napellus L. (*A. anglicum* Stapf)
Monk's-hood.   1840.
Naturalised alien. Uncommon.
U.D. Kirkham Abbey Woods 76, 1958, RG.
L.D. Ditch bank, Elvington 74 (Baines, 1840).
Wolds Plantation, Drewton Dale 93, CW (R. 1902) and persisting there; woods at Sewerby 16, Marton 26 and Boynton 16 (W. 1938); near Wauldby 93, 1939, HJD; Thwing 07, 1954, RG.
Hold. Meaux 03, 1950, IG.

Consolida L.

C. ambigua (L.) P.W. Ball & Heywood (*Delphinium ajacis* auct.)
Larkspur.
Introduced. Cornfields, waste places. Rare.
U.D. Near Ganton station 97, 1956, RG.
L.D. Cornfield, Newsholme 72 (R. 1902).
Wolds Re-surfaced quarry, Burton Fleming 07, 1970, EC.
Hold. Hull docks (R. 1902); Kelsey Hill 22, 1936, HJD and King George Dock, Hull 12, 1932-1935, AKW (W. 1938).

Actaea L.

A. spicata L.
Baneberry.   CNE.
Native. Usually in Ash woods, rarely under Beech, on both chalk and limestone; in considerable quantity in two localities. Uncommon.
Bessingdale 96, Firby and Howsham woods 76, MBS (R. 1902); refound in Howsham Wood by Revd A.B. Purchas, but later thought to be destroyed during felling (Flintoff, 1931). 'Woods near Kirkham Abbey' (Nat. 1920, 366); found in Kirkham Hall grounds 76, 1964, FEC; Folkton Brow 07, 1950 RG, still present; near Great Givendale 85, 1963, GAN; Millington Wood 85, 1964, FEC, still present; Beckhead plantation, Great Givendale 85, 1965, DA, still present; Leavening Brow 76, 1970, ATD; Bishop Burton 94, 1977, PG & EHW, still present. See also Garnett and Sledge (1967).

Anemone L.

A. nemorosa L.   Map 60.
Wood Anemone.
Native. Deciduous woods, sometimes the dominant plant over large areas; may persist on woodland sites for some years. Occasionally on roadside verges, particularly in Holderness as in the Wawne area. Common.

A. ranunculoides L.
Yellow Anemone.
Naturalised alien.   Uncommon.
Wolds Plentiful near Sewerby and Marton 16, Major Lawson (Flintoff, 1931) as well as in the churchyard, Boynton 16, RJF (W. 1938).

A. apennina L.
Blue Anemone.
Naturalised alien.   Uncommon.
Wolds Boynton and Sewerby 16, Major Lawson (Flintoff, 1931); plantation, North Ferriby 92, TS (W. 1938); Great Givendale 85, 1969, TFM.

Hepatica Mill.

H. nobilis (L.) Mill. (*Anemone nobilis* L.)
Hepatica.
Naturalised alien.
Sunderlandwick 05, Sir T. Ferens, comm. FEC, 1981.

Clematis L.

C. vitalba L.
Traveller's-joy.   CSE.   1895.
Native in Southern England, believed to be an introduction in the East Riding. Edges of woods, in hedges and in an orchard. Uncommon.
U.D. Firby Wood 76, 1958, RG.
Wolds In hedge Wold Gate, near Bridlington 16, 1895, HBWS and 1965, MC, hedge destroyed 1966-1967; Hessle chalk pits 02 and Boynton Woods 16 (R. 1902), still at Hessle; old lane Elloughton 92, 1953, RG; Settrington 87, 1985, ND.
Hold. Spring Head, Hull 02 (R. 1902); still on railway bank, Spring Head, 1982, FEC; Sunk Island 31, 1933, AEW; bombed site, Albion Street, Hull 02, 1975, FEC; at disused railway stations at Swine 13, 1978, Patrington 32, 1983 and Burstwick 22, 1984, FEC; on disused railway line near Willerby 03, 1982, FEC.

Ranunculus L.

R. acris L.
Meadow Buttercup.
Native. On long established grassland, including chalk grassland and road-sides, but avoiding acid soils. Common.

R. repens L.
Creeping Buttercup.
Native. Wet meadows, pastures, marshy ground, wet woods and as a persistent garden weed, particularly on heavy soils. Now the commonest Buttercup.

R. bulbosus L.
Bulbous Buttercup.
Native. Dry meadows and pastures on neutral or basic soils, including chalk grassland. Less common than formerly. Frequent.

R. arvensis L.   Map 234.
Corn Buttercup.   1840.
Native. Cornfields mainly, also waste places. Now uncommon and decreasing.
Several places near York (Baines, 1840). The statement 'in every cornfield' (R. 1902) may be misleading; it is impossible to know just how widely distributed the species once was; most of the post-1950 records are for Holderness. Purer seed corn, use of weed killers and other changes in agricultural practice have rendered it uncommon. On King George Dock, Hull 12, 1932, AKW (W. 1938).
Post-1970 records:
U.D. Rillington 87, 1970, RMH.
L.D. Broomfleet 82, 1978, YNU Excursion.
Wolds Thwing 07, 1970, EC.
Hold. Wawne 13, 1970, MC; near Hedon 12, 1971, GH; Burshill 04, 1972 MC; Humbleton and Garton 23, 1973, EBM; garden weed on farm site, Cottingham 03, 1983, PG.

R. sardous Crantz   Map 272.
Hairy Buttercup.
Native. Damp arable and grassland; occasionally on sand. Infrequent.
Most records for Holderness, with a tendency for localities to be on or near the coast or bank of the R. Humber. A tall form with bright yellow flowers was in abundance in a fallow field, Broomfleet 82, 1982, YNU Excursion.
Inland records include:
L.D. Arable, Harlthorpe 73, 1982, FEC & JD; by barn, Asselby Grange 73, 1986, DJL.
Wolds Calcareous arable, Driffield 05, 1982, EC.
Hold. Kelsey Hill gravel pits 22, 1955, YNU Excursion; by R. Hull, Hull 03, 1957, FEC; near Cottingham 03, 1968, DWS; on former carr land, Hollym 32, 1984 and at Roos 22, 1986, FEC.

R. parviflorus L.
Small-flowered Buttercup.   OSE.   1931.
Native. Disturbed ground and path-sides in dry places; may be erratic in appearance. Uncommon.
Wolds Skidby chalk pits, 1898 (SYF); eroded bank, North Grimston 86 and seed field, Wharram 86, 1931, YNU Excursion; cornfield, north of Filey Brigg 18, 1948, RK; on cliff top, near Reighton 17, 1968 and near Hunmanby Gap 17, 1971, FEC; Beacon Hill gravel pits and arable field, near Sykes Plantation, Flamborough Head 26, 1970, MC.
Hold. Carnaby 16, 1959, SHe; on verge of new road, Driffield 05, 1967, JR & MC; arable near Burton Agnes 16, 1970, MC.

R. auricomus L.　　　　　　　　　　Map 87.
Goldilocks Buttercup.
Native. Woods, more rarely in ditch bottoms and on road-sides. Infrequent. Said to be formerly common under hedgerows in Holderness and other areas (R. 1902).

R. lingua L.　　　　　　　　　　　Map 160.
Greater Spearwort.　　　CE.　　　　1789.
Native. Marshes, fens; by ponds and a lake and in dykes. Uncommon and local, mainly in Holderness.
In the reed beds at Hornsea Mere 14, where it has long been known (R. 1902) and here and there by the R. Hull. First record: marshes and ditches, near Beverley (Camden, 1789). Survived in dykes in the R. Hull valley as at Kelleythorpe 05, 1969, FEC and at Tophill Low 04, 1976, JB; also in a pond in former carr land, near Hollym 32, 1984, KS.
Other records:
U.D. Kirkham 76 (Baines, 1840); by stream, Kennythorpe 76, 1958, FEC; in marsh, near Westow 76, 1983, NCC.
Wolds Undercliff, near Filey 17, W.H. Cooke (Nat. 1894, 231) and YNU Excursion (Nat. 1931, 369); by pond Speeton 17, 1984, SMA.

R. flammula L.　　　　　　　　　　Map 159.
Lesser Spearwort.
Native. In marshes and dykes, by ponds and lakes; tolerant of acid conditions. Frequent.

R. sceleratus L.　　　　　　　　　Map 161.
Celery-leaved Buttercup.
Native. On mud by ponds and in ditches and in shallow water. Frequent in Holderness and Lower Derwentland.

R. hederaceus L.
Ivy-leaved Crowfoot.　　　OWEE.　　　1899.
Native. On mud and in shallow water. Uncommon.
L.D. Skipwith Common 63, 1930, RG; Heslington Fields 64, 1958, FEC & 1980, EB.
Wolds Flamborough Head 27, CW (R. 1902); Millington Pastures 85, 1965, AWe; Buckton and Speeton 17, 1973, MC.
Hold. Withernsea 32, 1899, CW, (R. 1902).

R. baudotii Godr.
Brackish Water-crowfoot.　　　OSE.
Native. Brackish dykes, canals, pools and ponds. Uncommon.
In stretches of canal and in dykes near the R. Humber bank as at North Ferriby 92, Skeffling 31 and Kilnsea 41. In ponds Kilnsea Warren 41, 1954, FEC. On the coast, near Hunmanby Gap 17, 1971, EC. Formerly near the R. Hull at Stoneferry 13, also at Salt End 12 (R. 1902). Only now known inland in Broomfleet delphs 82, 1978, FEC.

R. peltatus Schrank　　　　　　　Map 114.
Pond Water-crowfoot.
Native. Ponds, temporary pools, dykes. Infrequent; formerly 'common in Holderness' (R. 1902).
This Water-crowfoot with its large flowers is very attractive when flowering in late April and in May.

R. aquatilis L. (*R. heterophyllus* Weber)
Common Water-crowfoot.
Native. Gravel pits, ponds and drains. Uncommon, but probably under-recorded. Most records for Holderness.
L.D. Hemingborough 63, 1981, FEC; Holme upon Spalding Moor 73, 1981, JRo.

Hold. Dunswell and Cottingham 03; Hedon and Marfleet 12; Grimston Garth 23 and Withernsea 32 (R. 1902); near old mill, Withernwick 14, 1956, FEC; Cowden Lane 14, 1981, FEC and on baked mud at pond side, Hollym 32, 1981, FEC; near Aldbrough 23, 1986, FEC.

R. trichophyllus Chaix ex Villars (inc. *R. drouetii* F. Schultz)　　　　　　　　　　　Map 115.
Thread-leaved Water-crowfoot.
Native. Ponds, dykes and slow streams. Locally frequent in Holderness, particularly in the R. Hull valley and in Lower Derwentland; also in a few widely scattered localities. Probably under-recorded.

R. circinatus Sibth.　　　　　　　Map 113.
Fan-leaved Water-crowfoot.
Native. Large drains, canals and ponds. Uncommon and local, but sometimes in abundance.
L.D. In the Pocklington Canal at East Cottingwith 74, 1958, FEC, at Walbut Lock 74, 1981 and in the Bielby Arm 74, 1981, NCC; near Burnby 84, 1971, FEC; pond, Foggathorpe 73, 1987, DRG.
Hold. Dykes in Dunswell Lane 03 and in pond, Burton Constable 13 (R. 1902); Risby fishpond 03, 1953, AKW and gravel pit, Burshill 04, 1957, RG; locally common in the Barmston drain at Aike and Tophill Low 04, 1971, MC & FEC; abundant in Leven Canal 04, 1981, CN.

R. fluitans Lam.
River Water-crowfoot.
Native. Moderate to swift-flowing rivers.
Only recorded for the R. Derwent, as at Howsham Bridge 76, 1955, RG and at Elvington 74, 1973, YNU Excursion. The full extent of its distribution in the R. Derwent is not known.

R. penicillatus (Dumort.) Bab.
Stream Water-crowfoot.
Subsp. *psuedofluitans* (Syme) S.Webster [*R. pseudofluitans* (Syme) Baker & Foggitt; *R. calcareus* R.W.Butcher]
Native. Moderate to fast flowing calcareous streams.
Only known in the R. Hull; dominant in the West Beck above Wansford; frequent as a smaller form in the rest of West Beck 05 and in the R. Hull south of the junction with Frodingham Beck, at least south to Hull Bridge 04.
Var. *vertumnus* C.D.K. Cook
Native. Slow streams.
Frequent in Foston Beck 05, 1981, C. Newbold; the only known locality.

R. ficaria L.　　　　　　　　　　Map 273.
Lesser Celandine.
Native. Woods, copses, under hedges, in ditches; on grassland including roadsides and Wolds grassland; occasionally in churchyards and more rarely as a lawn weed. Common.
Three genetic races, with 4x, 3x and 2x chromosomes respectively, occur in the vice-county; plants from 96 populations have been studied and their distribution and ecological requirements recorded (Nicholson, 1983). The diploid, subsp. *ficaria* sets seed, is more light tolerant than the tetraploid and is far more widely distributed and frequent, occurring in a greater variety of habitats. Wolds grassland may be carpeted with it, as at Millington. The tetraploid, subsp. *bulbilifera*, is dependent on vegetative propagation and requires wetter conditions and is usually in shaded conditions. The triploid is rare and only occurs in the presence of both the diploid and tetraploid and is

thought to be the hybrid between them: it has been found in wooded parkland at Anlaby 02 and Hornsea 14 and at Burton Bushes 03 where the distribution of all three taxa was studied.

Myosurus L.

M. minimus L.
Mousetail.   CE.   2nd half 18th century.
Native.   Damp arable.   Rare.
L.D. Has turned up three times in recent years near the R. Derwent, at or near the edge of winter-flooding; at Aughton 73, 1935, JK, still growing plentifully in a sandy lane there, 1936, WAS (Nat. 1936, 161); 'several thousand plants' on a farm track and by gateway, Bubwith 73, 1975, ES; on dried-out mud in gate-way at Elvington 74, 1980, PS. Plants apparently develop from dormant seed and do not persist.
Hold. Near Brockham, Hornsea 14, 2nd half 18th century, WW.

Aquilegia L.

A. vulgaris L. *sensu lato*
Columbine.   1840.
Uncommon. May possibly have been native in woods on calcareous soils in some of the early recorded localities e.g. Beverley Westwood 03 (Baines, 1840), Danes Dyke 26 or 27 and Settrington 87, MBS (R. 1902). Recent records are for a variety of habitats and are thought to be for escapes of cultivation.

Thalictrum L.

T. flavum L.   Map 167.
Common Meadow-rue.
Native.   Marshes, fens; by dykes and canals.
Locally frequent in the R. Hull valley and in other former fenland areas of Holderness and of Derwentland; also in water-meadows by the R. Derwent. In drier places on the bank of the R. Humber at Blacktoft 82, Hessle 02 and in sand dunes at Spurn 41. Some loss of habitat.

BERBERIDACEAE

Berberis L.

B. vulgaris L.
Barberry.
Naturalised alien. Hedges, usually near gardens. Rare now. First planted for ornament and its edible fruits, then almost eradicated when it was found to be the host of a rust on wheat. Recent records:
L.D. Hasholme 83, 1981, DRG.
Wolds. Sledmere 96, 1969, MC.
Hold. Sunderlandwick 05, 1971, FEC.

Mahonia Nutt.

M. aquifolium (Pursh) Nutt. (*Berberis aquifolium* Pursh)
Oregon-grape.   1931.
Naturalised alien. Open woods, hedges. Infrequent, but widely distributed. Originally planted as game cover; often bird-sown.
First records are for the Wolds: Kipling Cotes 94, South Dalton 94, AEW; plantation, North Ferriby 92, 1931, AKW (W. 1938).

NYMPHAEACEAE

Nymphaea L.

N. alba L. (*Castalia speciosa* Salisb.)
White Water-lily.   2nd half 18th century.
Native and introduced. Rivers, canals, drains, lakes. Rare as a native.
U.D. Welham Springs 76, MBS (R. 1902).
L.D. Formerly in the R. Derwent (Baines, 1840).
Hold. On Leven Carrs in the latter half of the 18th century, WW. Believed to be native in Leven Canal 04, which inherited its aquatic flora from the former meres (Crackles, 1968); may also be native in drains near Whitecross, Leven, 1975, EHW. Formerly near Driffield 05 (R. 1902). Introduced at Rise Park and Hornsea Mere 14.

Nuphar Sm.

N. lutea (L.) Sm. (*Nymphaea lutea* L.)   Map 105.
Yellow Water-lily.   1866.
Native.   Rivers, streams, canals, lakes and larger drains. Frequent.
In the R. Derwent, R. Foulness, R. Hull and in drains in the river valleys; also in the Pocklington 74 and Market Weighton 83 Canals; in Staddlethorpe and Broomfleet delphs 82, 1955, RG; in Hornsea Mere 14, 1950, FEC, still present. Some loss of habitat resulting from the filling in and cleaning of drains as in the Hull area, also as a result of pollution as in the R. Foulness.

CERATOPHYLLACEAE

Ceratophyllum L.

C. demersum L.   Map 97.
Rigid Hornwort.   1878.
Native. Lakes, canals, large drains and streams, less commonly in small drains and ponds. Infrequent.
Post-1950 records:
in the Pocklington 74 and Market Weighton 82 Canals, 1980, DRG and in Broomfleet delphs 82 and other localities in Lower Derwentland. Several records for the R. Hull valley, including Frodingham Beck and the Old Howe 05, 1982, ECha and Leven Canal 04, 1953, FEC. Also in Hornsea Mere 14, 1979, FEC and lakes at Burton Constable 13 and Rise Park 14, 1971, FEC.

C. submersum L.
Soft Hornwort.
Native.   A rare species of S.E. England.
One record: Pocklington Canal at Sandhill Lock 74, 1981, C. Newbold.

PAPAVERACEAE

Papaver L.

P. rhoeas L.   Map 274.
Common Poppy.   1840.
Native. Cornfields and disturbed ground by roadsides, edges of fields, quarries, gravel pits and waste places. Common.
Once a troublesome weed in cornfields (Baines, 1840). Still common in smaller numbers. A cornfield scarlet with poppies was still a feature of the country-side thirty years ago; now occasionally a belt of scarlet may occur around a field or along an edge of it or along a recently disturbed roadside verge. The reduction in quantity is due to changes in agricultural practice.

P. dubium L.   Map 275.
Long-headed Poppy.
Native. Arable and disturbed soil on waysides, waste places, pits; mainly on sand and gravel. Frequent.

P. lecoqii Lamotte   Map 233.
Yellow-juiced Poppy.   1958.
Native? Arable fields and other disturbed ground, chalk pits; always on calcareous soils. Infrequent; almost restricted to the northern part of the Wolds.
First records: Leavening 76, 1958 and near Wharram 86, 1959, CMR.

P. hybridum L.
Rough Poppy.   1840.
Introduced. Arable and waste places.
Cornfields, near Malton and on the Wolds (Baines, 1840). The record for Malton cornfields was made by Teesdale, 1794 and could be for v.c. 61 or 62. Baker, 1854 was calling for confirmation of these early records. Also recorded for Brough 92, EAP (R. 1902).

P. argemone L.   Map 276.
Prickly Poppy.   CSE.   1798.
Introduced? Sand pits, chalk quarries, gravel pits; roadside verges, particularly those recently disturbed. Infrequent; may not persist.
Post-1950 records include:
U.D. Sand pit, Staxton 07, 1956, RG; verge of new road, Knapton 87, 1967, FH; field track, West Heslerton 97, 1986, EC.
L.D. Sand pit, North Cave 83, 1953, FEC; roadside, North Cliffe 83, 1954, FEC; gravel pit, Burnby 84, 1971, FEC & EHW; Barmby Moor 75, 1977, PA.
Wolds Chalk quarry, Leavening 76, 1958, YNU Excursion; Rudston and Nafferton 06, 1971, MC.
Hold. Gravel pit, Brandesburton 14, 1969, EC.

P. somniferum L.
Opium Poppy.   1854.
Introduced, mainly casual. Waste places. Infrequent.
Burlington Quay 16, SH (Baker, 1854); chalk pit, Hessle 02 (R. 1902). On bombed sites and other waste places in Hull, particularly in the Old Town, 1951-1978. Post-1950 records for twenty other scattered localities.

Meconopsis Vig.
M. cambrica (L.) Vig.
Welsh Poppy.   1840.
Established alien. Rare.
Wolds Introduced Londesborough 84 (Baines, 1840).
Hold. Kilnsea 41, 1970, FEC; Hornsea 14, 1978, RH.

Glaucium Mill.
G. flavum Crantz
Yellow Horned-poppy.   CSE.   1798.
Native. A maritime plant, usually on shingle. Very rare.
Hornsea 14 and Bridlington Quay 16 (Teesdale, 1800). One plant on sand by road at Spurn 41, 1978, brought in by winter flooding and persisting.

Chelidonium L.
C. majus L.   Map 277.
Greater Celandine.   1840.
Established alien. Hedgebanks, waste places; mainly near villages. Infrequent.
Formerly grown for its valued medicinal properties. Lost

from most of the localities given in Baines (1840) and Robinson (1902); has decreased markedly in the last thirty years.

FUMARIACEAE

Corydalis Medic.
C. claviculata (L.) DC. (*Neckeria claviculata* N.E.Br.)
                                                  Map 70.
Climbing Corydalis.   OWEE.   1878.
Native. Woods on acid sandy soils. Infrequent but sometimes in quantity locally.
Only in Lower Derwentland. Still in Houghton Woods 83 and on Langwith Common 64 where it has been known since 1878 (R. 1902), also on Allerthorpe Common 74, 1984, YNU Excursion.

C. lutea (L.) DC. (*Neckeria lutea* Scop.)
Yellow Corydalis.   1840.
Introduced and naturalised on old walls. Rare.
L.D. On old garden wall, Water Fulford 64, WWh (R. 1902); Wressle Castle 73, 1950, FEC.
Wolds Londesborough 84 (Baines, 1840).

Fumaria L.
F. muralis Sond. subsp. **boraei** (Jord.) Pugsl. (*F. boraei* Jord.)
Common Ramping-fumitory.
Doubtfully native.   Very rare.
Skipwith 63, 1878, HFP, YNU Trans. 1878. Extinct.

F. officinalis L.   Map 278.
Common Fumitory.
Native. Arable fields, gardens, waste ground. Common.

F. parviflora Lam.   Map 228.
Fine-leaved Fumitory.   CSE.   1943.
Native. Corn and turnip fields on chalk. Uncommon and very local on the Wolds; most records for 07.
Records include: Staxton 07, 1943, YNU Excursion; cornfield Kelleythorpe 05, 1949, RL; Wharram 86, 1950, YNU Excursion; turnip field, Fordon 07, 1957 & 1968, FEC; Cowlam 96, 1960, YNU Excursion; Weaverthorpe 97, 1966, FEC; Thwing 07, 1970, EC; near Potter Brompton 97, 1986, YNU Excursion.

CRUCIFERAE

Brassica L.
B. oleracea L.
Wild Cabbage.
Introduced. King George Dock, Hull, Hull 12, 1933, AKW (W. 1938); bombed sites, Hull 02 & 12, 1950-1953, FEC.

B. napus L.
Rape, Swede.   1903.
Casual. Waste places. Infrequent.
Hold. Hull docks 02, 1903, CW and King George Dock, Hull 12, 1932, AKW (W. 1938); frequent on waste places in the Hull area since the 2nd World War. Several other scattered records which may include records for relics of cultivation. The cultivation of an early-flowering strain, Oil-seed Rape, has become common and it is sometimes seen in quantity along some roadsides.

B. rapa L.
Wild Turnip.
Alien. Waste places. Infrequent.
Records include:
L.D. By R. Derwent at Breighton 73 and Elvington 74, 1970, FEC.
Hold. Hull docks 02 (R. 1902); King George Dock, Hull 12, 1932, AKW (W. 1938); Kilnsea Warren 41, 1932, RG; rubbish tip, Hessle 02, 1946, AKW; bombed sites, Hull 02 & 12, 1950-1953, FEC; cliff top, Tunstall 33, 1954, RG. Records may refer to the wild stock of Turnip or various relics and rejects of cultivation.

B. nigra (L.) Koch (*B. sinapioides* Roth)
Black Mustard.
Alien. Waysides and waste places. Infrequent.
Hold. Drainsides, near Hull (R. 1902); King George Dock, Hull 12, 1934, AKW; bombed sites, Hull 02 & 12, 1950-1953, FEC.
Recorded for sixteen scattered tetrads since 1970.

Sinapis L.
S. arvensis L. (*Brassica sinapistrum* Boiss.)
Charlock.
Native. Field borders, weed of arable and gardens, waste ground, disturbed roadsides. Common on chalk and clay, less-so elsewhere. Formerly common in cornfields; forty years ago some fields were a sheet of yellow. Seeds remain long dormant.

S. alba L. [*Brassica alba* (L.) Rabenh.]
White Mustard.
Introduced. Cultivated fields, waste places, disturbed waysides.
Formerly much cultivated on the rich alluvium bordering the R. Humber as on Sunk Island 21. Infrequent now.

Diplotaxis DC.
D. muralis (L.) DC. Map 254.
Annual Wall-rocket.
Alien. Waste places on a variety of soils.
Said to be formerly common (R. 1902), but Hessle and Hull were the only localities mentioned. Uncommon now; mainly in the Hull area; still in Hessle chalk pits 02, 1974, JKi.
Other records:
Wolds Southburn 95, 1978, EBM.
Hold. Mappleton 24, 1957, KF; Spurn 41, 1958, RG and later; railway stations at Cottingham 03, 1958, RG and Arram 04, 1969, MC; on disused railway line, near Hollym 32, 1984, KS.

D. tenuifolia (L.) DC.
Perennial Wall-rocket.
Established alien. Old walls, waste places. Rare.
U.D. Kirkham Abbey 76, MBS (R. 1902).
Wolds Skidby chalk pit 03, 1937, AKW.
Hold. In quantity on Spurn Point 41, 1958, MMN, still present.

Raphanus L.
R. raphanistrum L.
Wild Radish.
Native? Arable, waste places, disturbed roadsides. Widely distributed and locally frequent.

[**R. maritimus** Sm.
Sea Radish.
Native. Drift line and cliffs.
The record for Bridlington etc. (Baines, 1840) 'frequent in cornfields' refers to *R. raphanistrum*.]

R. sativus L.
Garden Radish.
Introduced. Waste places. Uncommon.
Hold. King George Dock, Hull, 1935, AKW (W. 1938); Hull bombed sites, 1950-1953, FEC.

Crambe L.
C. maritima L.
Sea-kale. OWEE.
Native. On coastal sand.
Hold. On the coast from Bridlington to Hornsea (Baines, 1840); Sand le Mere 33, HS. Extinct (R. 1902).

Rapistrum Crantz
R. rugosum (L.) All.
Bastard Cabbage. 1899.
Alien. Waste places. Uncommon.
Hull docks, 1899, CW and King George Dock, Hull 12, 1934 and later, AKW (W. 1938); under the Humber Bridge, Hessle 02, 1983, EHW.

Cakile Mill.
C. maritima Scop.
Sea Rocket. 1729.
Native. On disturbed coastal sand. Uncommon.
On the seashore at Spurn 41 and sometimes in quantity on the peninsula. On sandy parts of the R. Humber bank near Skeffling and Easington 31; on Hessle foreshore 02, 1985, EHW. Here and there on the sea-coast: Barmston Drain end 15, 1955, RG; dunes at Fraisthorpe and Auburn 16, 1970, MC.

Lepidium L.
L. sativum L.
Garden Cress.
Introduced, mainly casual. Waste places. Uncommon.
Hold. West Dock, Hull 02, 1902, CW; King George Dock, Hull 12, 1934, AKW (W. 1938); Hessle refuse tip 02, 1947, AKW and Hessle foreshore 02, 1947, RG.

L. campestre (L.) R. Br.
Field Pepperwort. 1840.
Native. Arable, waste places, gravel and sand pits; always on well-drained soils. Uncommon and usually in small quantity. Probably once locally frequent as an arable weed: 'in cultivated fields on poor sandy soils' (Baines, 1840); 'in cornfields frequent' (R. 1902).
Post-1950 records:
U.D. Muston 07, 1956, TFM; Wintringham 87, 1969, EC.
L.D. Skirpenbeck 75, 1956, MT.
Hold. Leven 04, 1951, RG; Kelsey Hill 22, 1951, FEC; on Hedon Rd, Hull 12, 1953, FEC; Barfhill Covert 04, 1956, RG; Wawne 13, 1972, FEC; Foston 05, 1978, EC; Burshill 04, 1983, FEC; King's Mill, Driffield 05, 1985, ND.

L. heterophyllum Bentham
Smith's Pepperwort. OWEE.
Native. Arable, waste places. Rare.
Hold. Near Beverley 03, 1956, RG.

L. ruderale L.
Narrow-leaved Pepperwort.   1840.
Established alien.   Waste ground, cliffs.   Uncommon.
L.D. Brough 92, CW (R. 1902); Olympia Oil Mill Sidings,
Selby 63, 1937, WAS.
Wolds 'On the cliffs from Filey to Bridlington' (Baines,
1840) where it was possibly native; by roadside near R.
Humber, North Ferriby 92, 1987, FEC.
Hold. Near Humber at Marfleet 12 and abundant on Hull
docks (R. 1902); near Bridlington 16, 1931, JRB; Salt End
Common 12, 1931, AKW (W. 1938); bombed sites, Hull
12, 1952, FEC; King George Dock, Hull 12, 1953, FEC;
disused tip, east Hull 13, 1963, EC; disused railway station,
Swine 13, 1978, FEC.

L. latifolium L.
Dittander.   1903.
Native?   Waste places.   Rare.
Hold. Hull docks, 1903-1904, JFR and West Dock, Hull
02, 1906, CW (W. 1938); occurred in great quantity on
waste ground by Barmston Drain, Bridlington Ave, Hull
02, 1977, FEC, and on site of recently filled-in drain near
R. Hull, Witham, Hull 12, 1978, FEC; also on bombed site,
Clifton St, Hull 02, 1978, FEC.

Coronopus Zinn
C. squamatus (Forsk.) Aschers. (*C. ruellii* All.) Map 279.
Swine-cress.   1840.
Native. Waste ground, especially trampled places such as
gateways and paths; usually in small quantity. Mainly on
clay. Somewhat infrequent.
On pavements: 'in the streets of Beverley' 03 (Baines,
1840); between paving stones, Fulford 64, 1981, EB.

C. didymus (L.) Sm.
Lesser Swine-cress.   1970.
Alien.   Uncommon.
Most records are for disturbed ground near the R. Humber;
may not persist.
U.D. Field track, Knapton 87, 1986, EC.
L.D. Footpath, Blacktoft jetty 82, 1970, RTh; disused
railway station, Eastrington 83, 1976, FEC; persistent
garden weed, Fulford 64, 1980, EB.
Hold. In quantity, the Citadel, Hull 12, 1973; by Humber
bank, Kilnsea 41, 1977, EP and by Humber Dock, Hull 02,
1982, FEC.

Cardaria Desv.
C. draba (L.) Desv. (*Lepidium draba* L.)   Map 252.
Hoary Cress.   1902.
Established alien. Roadsides; waste places, including Hull
bombed sites; docks; R. Humber foreshore. Locally fre-
quent, particularly in the Hull area.
Early records:
L.D. Fulford 64, 1927, GP; Cawood 53, 1941, WAS.
Hold. Near Hull docks (R. 1902); plentiful near the R.
Humber shore and docks, Hull, 1935, AKW; Stoneferry 13
and near Cottingham 03, RG (W. 1938); on bombed sites
and other waste places, Hull 02 & 12, 1950, FEC and on the
foreshore at Hessle 02 and North Ferriby 92, 1950, FEC;
Spurn 41, 1954, FEC, still present.
Later recorded scattered localities include:
Wolds Flamborough Headland 26, 1964, AWe and 27,
1984, SMA.
Hold. Hornsea 24, 1969, MC.

Iberis L.
I. amara L.
Wild Candytuft.   CSE.
Native.   Disturbed soil on chalk.   Rare.
Railway bank, west of Enthorpe station 94, 1958, RG and
persisting.

Thlaspi L.
T. arvense L.   Map 280.
Field Penny-cress.   1798.
Doubtfully native. Arable land, waste places. Locally
frequent, particularly on the Wolds.

Teesdalia R.Br.
T. nudicaulis (L.) R.Br.   Map 49.
Shepherd's Cress.   CE.   1820.
Native. Arable and waste places on sand. Very rare now;
all records for Lower Derwentland; probably always
uncommon.
Langwith Moor 64, 1820, W. Middleton, last record 1890
(TFM, YNU Circular 1965); Woodhouse Moor, Pockling-
ton 85; near Holme upon Spalding Moor 83 (Baines, 1840);
Market Weighton 83, 1890, JJM (herb. Scarb. Mus.);
Dryham, 83, 1907, JFR; near Bielby 74, *c.*1930, GN;
Allerthorpe Common 74, 1927, YNU Excursion and 1953,
AKW; Barmby Moor 74, 1972, FEC; near Wilberfoss 74,
1983, RJ.

Capsella Medic.
C. bursa-pastoris (L.) Medic. (*Bursa Bursa-pastoris*
Weber)
Shepherd's-purse.
Native. Common everywhere on cultivated land and dis-
turbed soil on waste ground and waysides.

Cochlearia L.
C. officinalis L.   Map 207.
Common Scurvygrass.   ONE.   *c.*1845.
Native. On the drier parts of salt-marshes and on cliffs.
Infrequent on salt-marshes and the R. Humber shore, west
to Faxfleet 82; locally frequent on the cliffs of Flambor-
ough Head.

C. danica L.
Danish Scurvygrass.   ONE.   1881.
Native. On sandy and rocky shores and banks near the sea.
Rare.
Wolds Bempton cliffs 17, 1947, ME (N.H. Scarb.).
Hold. Hornsea 24, 1881, YNU Excursion (R. 1902).

C. anglica L.
English Scurvygrass.   ONE.   1912.
Native. Salt-marshes from Stone Creek 21 to Spurn 41, but
local.
Hold. Welwick 31, 1912, JFR (SYF) and 1958 FEC, still
there; Spurn 41, 1958, Hawkin's Point 21, 1963, Skeffling
31, 1981 and Stone Creek 21, 1983, all, FEC. Formerly 'at
Marfleet' 12 (SYF).

C. anglica x *C. officinalis* = *C.* x *hollandica* Henrard
Plants with characters intermediate between the above two
species occur at the upper part of some salt-marshes e.g. at
Welwick and may be this hybrid.

Lunaria L.
L. annua L.
Honesty.
Garden escape.   Uncommon.

L.D. Near Hemingborough 72, 1981, YNU Excursion.
Wolds. Near Foxholes and Burton Fleming 07, 1982, HP;
near Bridlington 16, 1982, NCC.

Alyssum L.
A. alyssoides (L.) L. (*A. calycinum* L.)
Small Alison.   1854.
Alien. Clover fields and other arable; waste places. Not
persistent (Baker, 1854). Rare.
U.D. Sand pits, Staxton 07, 1942, ERC (N.H. Scarb.).
L.D. Heslington Fields 64, JBa (Baker 1854); Market
Weighton 84, JJM (W. 1938).
Wolds Cornfields at South Cave 93 and Welton 92, CW
(R. 1902); Wharram 86, 1950, CMR.
Hold. West Dock, Hull 02, 1908, CW (W. 1938).

Lobularia Desv.
L. maritima (L.) Desv.
Sweet Alison.
Introduced. Seed found in archaeological excavations,
Sewer Lane, Hull (Armstrong, 1974) suggest it was grown
in Hull in the 15th - 17th centuries.
Hold. Hessle tip 02, 1939, AKW; Brigham roadside 05,
1957, RG; near lifeboat cottages, Spurn 41, 1964, FEC;
soon disappearing; disused railway station, Cannon St,
Hull 02, 1978-1979, FEC. Plants at Hull and Spurn were
dwarf, small-flowered and much less conspicuous than the
cultivated plant.

Erophila DC.
E. verna (L.) Chevall. (*E. vulgaris* DC.)   Map 281.
Common Whitlowgrass.
Native. On all well-drained soils: sand, gravel, chalk and
on railway cinders in open plant communities; on walls.
Locally frequent in Lower Derwentland, on the Wolds and
on the gravels of the R. Hull valley; rare in the rest of
Holderness.

E. praecox (Stev.) DC.
Native. Plentiful on the sand of Spurn Point 41, 1981, FEC.
Further critical work on the Whitlowgrasses is desirable.

Armoracia Gilib.
A rusticana Gaertn., Mey. & Scherb. (*Cochlearia
armoracia* L.)
Horse-radish.   1798.
Introduced. Cultivated for the condiment prepared from
the roots and widely naturalised in Great Britain. Waste
places. Infrequent, but widely distributed; locally frequent
in the Hull and Beverley areas.

Cardamine L.
C. pratensis L.   Map 282.
Cuckooflower.
Native.   Wet meadows and marshes.   Common.

C. amara L.   Map 283.
Large Bitter-cress.   1792.
Native. Wet places, stream sides, ditches, wet woods.
Uncommon and local.
U.D. Kirkham 76 (Teesdale, 1794) and 1978, FEC;
Burythorpe 76, 1958, FEC; Firby, 76, 1981, YNU Excur-
sion.
L.D. Near Howden 72, JBe, (R. 1902); near R. Ouse,
Asselby Island 72, 1971, DWS; in dyke near Sutton Wood,
1973, YNU Excursion; near Fulford 64, 1981, EB.
Hold. Figham Common 03 (Trans. HSFNC, 1906, *3*, 300);
Tophill Low 04, 1979, DRG.

[*C. amara* x *C. pratensis* = *C.* x *ambigua* O.E. Schulz
Puzzling plants found near Gibraltar Farm by the R. Hull,
1897 and formerly recorded (R. 1902) as *C. pratensis* var.
dentata was believed to be this hybrid (Trans.HSFNC , *3*,
300); still present 1910. There is only one British record for
this unlikely hybrid.]

C. impatiens L.
Narrow-leaved Bitter-cress.
This is a very local native of Great Britain in shady woods
chiefly in the west of Britain. 'On the churchyard wall at
Londesbro' (Baines, 1840); thought to have been intro-
duced by T. Knowlton senior who knew it at Fountains
Abbey (Henrey, 1986). A single plant by chalk stream,
Londesborough 84, 1980, RM.

C. flexuosa With.   Map 284.
Wavy Bitter-cress.
Native. Wet woodland; moist shady places. Infrequent.
Mainly in the R. Hull valley and locally near the R.
Derwent. Can be seen on wood rides in Burton Bushes,
Beverley 03 and in Danes' Dyke 26.

C. hirsuta L.   Map 285.
Hairy Bitter-cress.
Native. Bare ground, gardens, grassland, waste places,
walls. Locally frequent; may be under-recorded.

Barbarea R.Br.
B. vulgaris R.Br.   Map 286.
Winter-cress.
Native. Banks of rivers, streams, drain banks; damp
hedgebanks and roadsides. Locally frequent; much less
common than thirty years ago.

B. stricta Andrz.   Map 136.
Small-flowered Winter-cress.   1969.
Native. Sides of dykes, drains, streams, canals and rivers.
Very infrequent. Presumably previously over-looked; may
be increasing.
Records include:
L.D. Near the R. Ouse at Stillingfleet 54, 1975 and on
Fulford Ings 64, 1979, TFM. In the R. Derwent valley:
Stamford Bridge 75, 1969, MC; Aughton Ings 63 & 73,
1972, FEC & CMR; near Sutton Wood 74, 1972 and
Bubwith Ings 73, 1977, TFM. By the Market Weighton
Canal, near Broomfleet and on the R. Humber bank, Faxfleet
82, 1978, FEC.
Hold. Locally in the R. Hull valley at Arram Beck 04, 1969,
MC & JR and at Tophill Low 04, 1970, MC & FEC; Wawne
Common 13, 1972, FEC; by the R. Humber, Spurn 41,
1979, HF1 & AF.

Arabis L.
A. caucasica Schldl.
Garden Arabis.
Garden escape.   Uncommon.
Wolds Railway embankment, Hunmanby 07, 1978, BP.
Hold. On railway, near Bridlington 16, 1977, railway land
survey, ITE.

A. hirsuta (L.) Scop.   Map 3.
Hairy Rock-cress.   1798.
Native. Mainly on grazed chalk grassland or on bare chalk,
chalk pits. Somewhat infrequent and usually in small
quantity.
On other soils:

L.D. Brough Cockle Pits 92, 1939, AKW; by Market Weighton Canal 83, 1954, FEC; on sand, Houghton Woods Lane 83, 1953, FEC.
Hold. Gravel pits, near Brandesburton 04 & 14, 1969, YNU Excursion.

Nasturtium R.Br.

N. officinale sensu lato   Map 158.
N. officinale R.Br. [*Rorippa nasturtium-aquaticum* (L.) Hayek]
Watercress.
Native. In streams and ditches and spring-fed flushes. Common.

N. microphyllum (Boenn.) Reichb. [*Rorippa microphylla* (Boenn.) Hyland.]
Narrow-fruited Watercress.
Native. In streams and wet places. Frequent.

N. officinale x *N. microphyllum* = *N.* x *sterile* (Airy Shaw) Oefel.
Hunmanby Gap 07, 1955, RG; Elmswell 05, 1968, FEC.

Rorippa Scop.

R. sylvestris (L.) Bess. [*Nasturtium sylvestre* (L.) R.Br.]
                                                              Map 163.
Creeping Yellow-cress.   1840.
Native. By rivers, ditches and ponds; in water-meadows. Infrequent.
Mainly by the R. Hull, R. Derwent and R. Ouse, where water stands in winter. More rarely on drier places as on the filled-in Queen's Dock, Hull 12, 1951, FEC.

R. palustris (L.) Bess. [*Nasturtium palustre* (L.) DC.]
                                                              Map 287.
Marsh Yellow-cress.
Native. By ponds and drains and in marshy ground, especially where water stands only in winter. Infrequent but widely distributed.

R. amphibia (L.) Bess. [*Nasturtium amphibium* (L.) R.Br.]   Map 162.
Great Yellow-cress.   1840.
Native. By rivers, canals, ditches and ponds. Locally frequent in the R. Derwent valley; uncommon elsewhere. Said to be formerly common in Holderness dykes (R. 1902).

Hesperis L.

H. matronalis L.
Dame's-violet.
Naturalised alien. Hedgerows, waste places, roadsides. Infrequent, but widely scattered.

Erysimum L.

E. cheiranthoides L.
Treacle Mustard.   1900.
Alien. Waste places. Uncommon; mainly in the Hull area.
U.D. Near Kirkham 76, 1958, YNU Excursion.
L.D. Olympia Oil Mill Sidings 63, 1931, WAS; near Cawood 53, 1941, YNU Excursion; Elvington 74, 1960, RC; roadside, Allerthorpe 74, 1975, EC; by Pocklington Canal 74, 1980, RGu.
Hold. West Dock, Hull 02, 1900, CW (W. 1938); Stoneferry (R. 1902); Hessle 02, 1927, GP (W. 1938); two bombed sites, Hull 02, 1951 and rubbish tip, Hull 13, 1953, FEC; Kelleythorpe 05, 1969, MC.

Cheiranthus L.

C. cheiri L.
Wallflower.
Established alien. Old walls. Rare.
The plants on the Friary wall, Beverley are probably of early origin and thought to be the wild species.
L.D. Church walls, Howden 72 (R. 1902).
Hold. Old walls, Beverley 03 (R. 1902); still on Friary wall, Beverley, FEC; disused chalk pit, Beverley Westwood 03, 1912, JFR.

Alliaria Scop.

A. petiolata (Bieb.) Cavara & Grande [*Sisymbrium alliaria* (L.) Scop.]   Map 288.
Garlic Mustard.
Native. Hedgerows, wood margins. Widely distributed and locally common.

Sisymbrium L.

S. officinale (L.) Scop.
Hedge Mustard.
Native. In hedgebanks, by roadsides, on waste places, in arable. Common.
Var. *leiocarpum* DC. is the common plant on Hull's waste places, docks and railway sidings.

S. orientale L. (*S. columnae* Jacq.)   Map 263.
Eastern Rocket.   1902.
Established alien. Native of S. and S.E. Europe, N. Africa and the near East. Waste places, docks, bombed sites, gravel pits, railway sidings, sides of pavements. Locally frequent in the Hull area; otherwise infrequent. Very common on Hull docks by 1902 (R. 1902).
Other early records:
L.D. Olympia Oil Mill Sidings, Selby 63, WAS (W. 1938); Cawood 53, 1941, YNU Excursion.
Hold. King George Dock, Hull 12, 1934 and allotments, Springhead 02, 1935, AKW (W. 1938); Spurn 41, 1946, WAS. Established on 33% of Hull bombed sites by 1953, being frequent in all central areas of the city; has persisted on any suitable site remaining. Recorded North Ferriby 92, 1950 and Leven 04, 1953, FEC.
Has been recorded in several widely scattered localities in the vice-county increasingly since 1958; most of these records have been published in *The Naturalist* in botanical reports.

S. altissimum L.   Map 262.
Tall Rocket.   1903.
Established alien. Native of E. Europe and the near East. Docks, bombed sites and other waste places, rubbish tips, railway sidings, more rarely on arable.
Early records:
L.D. Olympia Oil Mill Sidings, Selby 63, WAS (W. 1938); Cawood 53, 1941, YNU Excursion.
Hold. Hull docks, 1903, CW; King George Dock, Hull 12, 1932, AKW; Ings Road, Hull 13, 1933, AEW. Established on 14% of Hull bombed sites by 1953, being frequent in the Old Town and East Central areas. Still present in the Old Town, Hull in the 1970s and later found elsewhere in the city and surrounding areas, including Beverley 03.
Uncommon elsewhere:
L.D. On arable, North Cave 83, 1953, FEC; Brough Haven 92, 1969, MC; Barmby Moor 74, FEC; Eastrington 72, 1976, YNU Excursion.
Hold. Spurn Point 41, 1954 & 1970, FEC; Keldgate, Beverley 03, 1977, JA; R. Humber bank, Easington 31, 1983, FEC.

Arabidopsis (DC.) Heynh.
A. thaliana (L.) Heynh. [*Sisymbrium thalianum* (L.)
Gay]   Map 289.
Thale Cress.
Native. Arable and waste places on well-drained soils,
disused railways and sidings. Locally frequent on the
sandy soils of Lower Derwentland.
Uncommon elsewhere including:
Wolds Settrington railway station 86, 1984, DEH.
Hold. Kelsey Hill gravel pits 22, Kilnsea Warren 41 (R.
1902); Priory Yard Sidings, Hull 02, 1983, FEC; disused
railway, Hollym 32, 1984, FEC.

Camelina Crantz
C. sativa (L.) Crantz
Gold-of-Pleasure.   1798.
Alien. Casual. Arable, waste places. Rare now.
U.D. Staxton 07, 1941, HR (N.H. Scarb.).
L.D. Heslington Fields 64, 1835 (O.B.G.).
Wolds 'On the wolds' (Baines, 1840); near Weaverthorpe
97, 1851, J. Slater, herb. Scarb. Mus.; Everthorpe quarry
93, 1955, RG.
Hold. Among clover at Eske 04 (Teesdale, 1800); abun-
dant near to Hull docks (R. 1902); University College
grounds, Hull 03, 1930, RG; Hessle refuse tip 02, 1943,
AKW.
Var. *foetida* Bridlington 16, FAL (R. 1902).

Descurainia Webb & Berth.
D. sophia (L.) Webb ex Prantl (*Sisymbrium sophia* L.)
Flixweed.   1799.
Native? Disturbed ground, sand pits; often on sand.
Uncommon.
U.D. Sand pits, Heslerton 97, 1956, RG; Ganton 97, 1957,
FEC; sandy lane, Wintringham 87, 1957, FEC, still pres-
ent; Staxton 07, 1971, MC.
L.D. Banks of the Market Weighton Canal, 1836 (Baines,
1840); Wholsea Lock 83, 1956, RG; Burnby 84, 1971,
FEC & EHW; near Sandholme 83, 1974, EHW; near
Pocklington 74, 1984, YNU Excursion.
Wolds Near Flamborough lighthouse 27, c.1845, OAM
(Baker, 1854); Langtoft 06, 1971, MC.
Hold. Bridlington 16, 1799, SH (R. 1902); common near
the Hull docks, 1899-1901 (R. 1902); bombed sites, Hull
02, 1981, FEC.

RESEDACEAE

Reseda L.
R. luteola L.   Map 290.
Weld.
Native. Disturbed ground, especially on chalk, chalk quarries, gravel pits; waste places, arable. Widely distributed
and frequent, particularly on the Wolds. May turn up in
great quantity on newly disturbed ground. Used as a dye
plant in medieval times.

R. lutea L.   Map 291.
Wild Mignonette.
Native. Disturbed ground especially on chalk, chalk pits,
edges of arable, waste ground, railway banks. Common on
the Wolds, infrequent elsewhere. Occurs in the Hull area,
mainly on railway sidings and dock reserves.

R. alba L.
White Mignonette.
Introduced. Established on a roadside near Broomfleet 82,
1978, YNU Excursion.

VIOLACEAE

Viola L.
V. odorata L.   Map 292.
Sweet Violet.
Native. Wood borders, scrub, hedgebanks, roadsides, mainly
on calcareous soils.
The white-flowered form is locally frequent as on roadsides
near Warter 85. Frequent on the Wolds, infrequent elsewhere. Lost from many hedgebanks by destruction of the
habitat and use of herbicides, perhaps most particularly in
Holderness where it is said to have been formerly very
common (R. 1902).

V. hirta L.   Map 28.
Hairy Violet.   1840.
Native. Grassland on chalk and limestone and in open
woods. Frequent on the Wolds, mainly on chalk grassland.

V. hirta x ***V. odorata*** = ***V.*** x ***permixta*** Jord.
Near Sledmere 96, 1963, FEC; near Tibthorpe 95, 1967,
FEC; Brantinghamdale 93, 1979, FEC.

V. riviniana Reichb.   Map 293.
Common Dog-violet.
Native. Woods, hedgebanks, grassland; on a variety of
soils, if not wet. Not frequent on chalk grassland, occurring
occasionally on northern slopes. Widely distributed and
locally common.

V. reichenbachiana Jord. ex Bor. (*V. sylvestris* auct.)
                                                        Map 94.
Early Dog-violet.
Native. Woods on chalk and limestone, rarely under
hedges. Locally frequent on the Wolds.
Occurs in the YWT reserve at Great Givendale; under the
Yew hedge by the church path at Warter where it has
probably been planted. Formerly recorded on gravel near
Hornsea Mere CW (R. 1902).

V. canina L. subsp. *canina* (*V. ericetorum* Schrad.)
Heath Dog-violet.   1901.
Native. Heaths and dunes. Rare.
L.D. Allerthorpe Common 74, 1937, GAN & WAS (SYF);
Tilmire 64, 1984, EB.
Wolds Welton 92 (R. 1902); Deepdale Plantation, Bishop
Burton 94, 1985, EHW.
Hold. Spurn Point 41, CW (R. 1902), still present, 1986,
FEC.

V. canina subsp. *canina* x ***V. lactea*** Sm. = ***V.*** x ***militaris***
Savouré
Spurn 41, CW (BEC 5, 1919, 642).

V. palustris L.   Map 200.
Marsh Violet.   CNE.   1836.
Native.
Wet acid places, including wood clearings and paths.
Uncommon and only in Lower Derwentland.
Langwith Common 64, 1836, HPa; Houghton Woods 83,
1953, RG & 1962, FEC; Skipwith Common 63, 1954, RG;

Bunny Hill 83, 1955, RG; Sutton Wood 74, 1961, FEC; Snake Hall 83, 1981, YNU Excursion.
Formerly in Holderness at Hall Ings, Cottingham 03 (R. 1902).

V. tricolor L. subsp. *tricolor* (including *V. lloydii* auct. & *V. lepida* auct.)   Map 240.
Wild Pansy.
Native. Cultivated ground, both on sand and chalk. Infrequent.

Subsp. *curtisii* (E. Forst.) Syme
Native. Dunes and grassy places near the sea. Rare.
Roadside, Spurn 41, 1971, TD.

V. arvensis Murr.   Map 294.
Field Pansy.
Native.
Cultivated and waste ground. Widely distributed and locally frequent.

V. arvensis x *V. tricolor*
U.D. Arable field, Wintringham 87, 1958, PG, det. Kew & 1986, EC.
Wolds Octon Grange 07, 1977, EC.

POLYGALACEAE

Polygala L.
P. vulgaris L.   Map 23.
Common Milkwort.
Native. Chalk grassland, chalk pits. Frequent.
The tetrad map shows the species to be present throughout the belt of chalk grassland in the west and north of the Wolds, also in the Cowlam valley 96 and between Risby and Beverley 03 and in scattered localities between Driffield and Bridlington.

P. serpyllifolia Hose (*P. serpyllacea* Weihe)   Map 44.
Heath Milkwort.   1938.
Native. Heaths, roadsides; only on sand. Uncommon and local.
L.D. Cliffe Common 83, 1954, FEC; near Low Plantation, Holme upon Spalding Moor 83, 1954, FEC; Skipwith Common 63, 1954, RG; Houghton Moor 83, 1957, FEC; Allerthorpe Common 74, 1962, FEC; Duck Nest 83, 1981, YNU Excursion.
Hold. Hall Ings, Cottingham 03, 1938, AKW, herb. HLU.
There has been much confusion between the two *Polygala* sp.; the remark in Robinson (1902) under *P. serpyllacea* applies to *P. vulgaris*. The record for grassy terraces, Hornsea Mere 14 (Nat. 1926, 280), presumably on gravel, may have been correct.

HYPERICACEAE

Hypericum L.
H. androsaemum L.
Tutsan.
Introduced.
Wolds Londesborough 84 (Baines, 1840).
Hold. Winestead 22 and between Holmpton and Patrington 32, 2nd half 18th century, WW. Extinct.

H. perforatum L.   Map 245.
Perforate St John's-wort.
Native. Grassland, including roadsides, particularly on calcareous soils, open woods, chalk pits, railway tracks and sidings, gravel pits. Locally common on the Wolds; infrequent in Lower Derwentland. Frequent along disused railways in Holderness, otherwise scarce there; it was formerly described as uncommon in Holderness (R. 1902).

H. maculatum Crantz (*H. dubium* Leers)
Imperforate St John's-wort.
Native. Damp places.
Given as occurring in v.c. 61, Wats.Top.Bot., 1883 (Trans. HSFNC *3*, 1903, 93). Extinct.

H. maculatum x *H. perforatum* = *H.* x *desetangsii*
Lamotte
Grassy places. Uncommon.
L.D. Water Fulford 64, 1969, TFM; near Broomfleet 82, 1980, FEC; disused railway station, near Harswell 84, 1987, FEC.
Hold. On roadside near Arnold 13, 1979, FEC; Kilnsea Warren 41, 1984, JRC & MN.
It occurs in the absence of both parents in at least four of these localities. It has recently been found that this fertile hybrid has been spreading in Yorkshire along the railways unnoticed; it may occur on more railway lines in v.c. 61 (Crackles, 1988).

H. tetrapterum Fr. (*H. quadratum* Stokes)   Map 147.
Square-stalked St John's-wort.
Native. By rivers, canals, ponds, ditches and in marshes. Common.

H. humifusum L.   Map 40.
Trailing St John's-wort.
Native. Heaths, wood rides, sandy fields; only on non-calcareous soils. Infrequent and local.
Mainly in Lower Derwentland as on Allerthorpe and Skipwith Commons.
Rare elsewhere:
Wolds Formerly in clearing at southern end of Long Plantation, North Ferriby 92, 1945, FEC; on drift on north facing slope, Millington 85, 1953, FHP; Butterwick Whins 97, 1965, EC.
Hold. Formerly in Birkhill Woods 03 (R. 1902); Bygot Wood 04, 1971, FEC & MC; the Moors, Burton Constable 13, 1988, YNU Excursion.

H. pulchrum L.   Map 295.
Slender St John's-wort.
Native. Woods and grassland. Infrequent, but widely distributed; usually in small quantity.
In several localities on acid soils in Lower Derwentland e.g. on Allerthorpe Common 74. Usually considered a calcifuge, it occurs here and there on the Wolds with characteristic chalk grassland species e.g. near Cowlam 96, 1957, FEC, still present; Staxton 07, 1957, FEC; West Lutton 96, 1964, FEC. Rare in Holderness: old terrace of Lambwath Stream, Withernwick 04 and Birkhill Woods 03 (R. 1902); Weldon's Plantation, Winestead 32, 1966, YNU Excursion; Rise Park 14, 1971, FEC; Turtle Hill Wood 16, 1984, EC.

H. hirsutum L.   Map 296.
Hairy St John's-wort.   CNE.
Native. Wood rides and damp grassland, mostly on basic soils; railway banks, chalk quarries. Locally frequent, mainly on the Wolds. Rare in Derwentland and in Holderness east of the R. Hull valley.

H. montanum L.
Pale St John's-wort.   CE.   1893.
Native.   Open woods and scrub on chalk.   Rare.
Wolds Filey 18, 1893 (Nat. 1894, 231); Hessle chalk pit 02, 1908, CW (Trans. HSFNC, *4*, 104); Elloughton Dale 92, 1920, JFR & 1979, EHW; Brantingham Dale 93, 1982, NCC; disused railway, near Wharram 86, 1985, EC.

H. elodes L.
Marsh St John's-wort.   OWEE.   1810.
Native. Beside ponds and in other wet places on acid soils. Rare.
L.D. Langwith 64 and Heslington 64, 1810, WM (herb. York Mus.); Skipwith Common 63, 1840, HI, possibly still present; at junction of two drains, Allerthorpe Common 74, 1959, FEC, refound on the common, 1988, EHW.

CISTACEAE

Helianthemum Mill.
H. nummularium (L.) Mill. (*H. chamaecistus* Mill.)
                                                Map 16.
Common Rock-rose.   1840.
Native. Grazed grassland on chalk and limestone; usually on hillsides, on all aspects; chalk pits. Common in the grazed grassland belt of the Wolds.
Formerly on gravel in Holderness e.g. at Brandesburton 14 (R. 1902), still there 1955, RG.

TAMARICACEAE

Tamarix L.
T. angelica Webb
Tamarisk.
Established alien.
On Spurn Point 41, 1974, FEC.

CARYOPHYLLACEAE

Silene L.
S. vulgaris (Moench) Garcke (*S. cucubalus* Wibel)
                                                Map 297.
Bladder Campion.
Native. Roadsides, field borders, chalk grassland and scree; waste places, chalk quarries; mainly on calcareous soils. Locally common on the Wolds; infrequent in Lower Derwentland; uncommon on gravel in Holderness; in quantity on dockland reserves in Hull 12.

S. uniflora Roth (*S. maritima* With.)
Sea Campion.   ONE.   1798.
Native. Seaside, Hornsea 24 (Teesdale, 1800), doubt was cast upon this record (R. 1902). Patches of this species occurred on the river-side of Spurn Point 41 after winter flooding, 1978, JC & FEC. It has occurred as a casual on Hull docks: King George Dock and the Victoria Dock, 12, 1923, JFR and Alexandra Dock reserve 12, 1979, FEC.

S. conica L.
Sand Catchfly.
Native.
In cornfields, Driffield 05, 1858, HI, herb. Whaley, Bradford Museum. No later record.

S. dichotoma Ehrh.
Forked Catchfly.
Alien.   Waste places and arable.   Rare.
U.D. Staxton 07, 1942, ERC; arable, near Kirkham 76, 1958, YNU Excursion.
Hold. Hull docks (R. 1902); King George Dock, Hull 12, 1935, AKW (W. 1938).

S. gallica L. (*S. anglica* L.)
Small-flowered Catchfly.   CSE.   1945.
Alien?
Sandy and gravelly places usually. Said to be formerly 'common in cornfields', although only five localities were specified (R. 1902). Not known now.
U.D. Sand pits, Staxton 07, 1940, ERC (N.H. Scarb.).
L.D. Langwith 64, 1845, CCB and Heslington Fields 64 (Baker, 1854); Market Weighton JJM (R. 1902).
Wolds South Cave 93, JFR (R. 1902).
Hold. Hornsea 14, CW (R. 1902); King George Dock, Hull 12, 1933, AKW (W. 1938).

S. noctiflora L. [*Melandrium noctiflorum* (L.) Fr.]
                                                Map 235.
Night-flowering Catchfly.   1840.
Native. Cornfields and other arable, mainly on calcareous soils; more rarely on waste places.
Described as 'rare, in sandy cornfields' at the beginning of the century: Heslington 64, 1840, OAM; Sandholme 83, JBe (R. 1902); Market Weighton 83, JJM (Trans. HSFNC, 1909, *4*, 105). Now locally frequent on the Wolds, scarce elsewhere. On waste places in Holderness: Bridlington 16 and Hull docks (R. 1902); rare on bombed sites, Hull 02 & 12, 1951, FEC; King George Dock, Hull 12, 1953, FEC.

S. dioica (L.) Clairv. (*Lychnis dioica* L.)   Map 90.
Red Campion.
Native. Woods, copses, hedge banks; avoids acid habitats. In hedgerows and woods on the heavy soils of Holderness, becoming scarce near the R. Humber and the coast. In woods and under over-hanging trees only, on lighter soils. Scarce in Lower Derwentland. Decreasing in quantity as a hedgerow plant, believed to be due to the failure of pollination with the increasing use of insecticides.

S. latifolia Poiret subsp. **alba** (Mill.) Greuter & Burdet
[*Lychnis alba* Mill.; *Silene alba* (Mill.) E.H.L.Krause]
                                                Map 298.
White Campion.
Native. Hedgerows, borders of cultivated fields, waste places. Very common in some areas; infrequent in Holderness, perhaps avoiding the cold heavy clay soils.

S. latifolia subsp. **alba** x **S. dioica** = **S** . x **hampeana** Meusel & Werner
Infrequent, but widely distributed, usually one or two plants only. Recorded for 27 tetrads, usually where the parental species grow close together, often on disturbed soil; sometimes in the absence of at least one parent. May be somewhat over-recorded; it is important not to rely entirely on flower colour but to look at calyx teeth which are intermediate in length and shape and with glandular hairs as in *S. latifolia* subsp. *alba*.

Lychnis L.

L. flos-cuculi L.   Map 188.
Ragged-Robin.
Native. Wet meadows including water meadows by the R.
Derwent; in marshes and fens; wet woods as in Low Wood,
by Hornsea Mere 14. Frequent along the spring lines,
scattered elsewhere; scarce in Holderness except in the R.
Hull valley.

Agrostemma L.

A. githago L. [*Lychnis githago* (L.) Scop.]
Corncockle.   1840.
Alien.   Cornfields and dock wastes.
'In cornfields, a troublesome weed' (Baines, 1840); corn-
fields, Bridlington 16, 1898, HBWS; sparingly in corn-
fields at Rise 14 and more plentiful on dock wastes, Hull (R.
1902); 'fairly sprinkled about' at Market Weighton, 1908,
JJM (Trans. HSFNC , 1909, *4*, 105).
Later records:
U.D. Burythorpe 76, 1926, GP; Staxton 07, 1943, WAS;
Wintringham 87, 1957, FEC.
L.D. 'Seldom seen now, but abundant in sandy cornfields,
Allerthorpe' 74, 1931, WAS (SYF); Barmby Moor 74,
1939, GAN; North Cave 83, 1945 & 1953, FEC; Fangfoss
75, 1956, CT.
Wolds South Cave 93, 1931, FS; Sherburn 97, 1946 -
1947, JFH-S.
No record since 1957.

Dianthus L.

D. deltoides L.
Maiden Pink.   CE.   1792.
Native.   On sand.   Rare.
'About Scampston' 87 (Teesdale, 1794). Later recorded as
Rillington (SYF), confirmed, 1956, RG. The species
continued to flourish when the area was planted with
conifers, between young trees and on grassy rides, 1957,
FEC; not found, 1964. Skipwith Common 63, 1977, TFM.

D. barbatus L.
Sweet-William.
Garden escape.
Sand pit, Staxton 07, 1958, MMN.

Vaccaria Medic.

V. hispanica (Miller) Rauschert (*V. pyramidata* Medic.;
Saponaria vaccaria L.)
Cowherb.
Alien.   Casual.   Uncommon.
L.D. Near Olympia Oil Mills, Selby 63, 1920, JBF.
Wolds Garden weed, Hunmanby 07, 1973, comm. EC.
Hold. Cornfield, Driffield 05, CW; garden weed, Hull and
abundant on Hull dock wastes (R. 1902); King George
Dock, Hull 12, 1932, AKW (W. 1938); High St, Hull 12,
1977, EHW.

Saponaria L.

S. officinalis L.
Soapwort.   1798.
Naturalised alien mainly. Roadsides, hedgebanks, waste
places, railway sidings; usually near houses. Meadows by
river sides (Baines, 1840). Formerly grown in cottage
gardens. Uncommon.
L.D. Shipton near Market Weighton 84 (Teesdale, 1800);
Brough Cockle Pits 82, 1887, YNU Excursion.
Wolds Burton Fleming 07, 1933, AEW (W. 1938);
Brantingham 92, 1955, IG; Rudston 06, 1970, EC; Ellerker
92, 1985, EHW.

Hold. King George Dock, Hull 12, 1932, AKW (W. 1938);
bombed site, Wincolmlee, Hull 12 and near tram sheds,
Hedon Rd 12, 1952, FEC; Easington 31, 1974 and Spring
Head railway sidings, Hull 02, 1979, FEC; Queen Elizabeth Dock, Hull 12, 1986, FEC.

Cerastium L.

C. arvense L.   Map 299.
Field Mouse-ear.   1840.
Native. Grassland on calcareous or sandy soils, including
roadsides; sand pits, chalk quarries, gravel pits; more
rarely on walls as at Welton 92 and North Newbald 93.
Locally frequent on the Wolds and in Lower Derwentland,
notably immediately adjacent to the Wolds in the North
Cave, Cliffe and Holme upon Spalding Moor areas 83, also
on the gravels of Holderness.

C. tomentosum L.
Snow-in-summer.
Established garden escape. Often thriving on roadsides
etc., near houses.

C. fontanum Baumg. subsp. **holosteoides** (Fr.) Salman
van Ommerang & de Voogd (*C. holosteoides* Fr.; *C.
vulgatum* auct., *C. triviale* Link.)
Common Mouse-ear.
Native. Fields, chalk grassland, waste places, cultivated
ground and wall tops.   Common.

C. glomeratum Thuill.   Map 300.
Sticky Mouse-ear.
Native. In open communities on chalk, gravel, sand and
cindery railway tracks; arable; waste places; path sides; on
walls. Locally frequent and widely distributed except on
heavy clay soils of Holderness.

C. diffusum Pers. (*C. atrovirens* Bab.; *C. tetrandrum*
Curt.)
Sea Mouse-ear.   OWEE.   1820.
Native. Near the sea, mainly on sand; rarely inland on
railway ballast.   Uncommon.
Wolds Near the lighthouse, Flamborough 27, 1820, WM,
herb. York Mus.; on the cliffs of Flamborough Head (R.
1902 & Flintoff, 1931); on disused railway, near Eppleworth 03, 1983, SMA.
Hold. Plentiful, Kilnsea Warren 41 (SYF), still there and
elsewhere on Spurn in short turf; Barmston 15, 1979, EC;
on disused railway, Fountain Rd, Hull 03, 1979, FEC.

C. semidecandrun L.   Map 34.
Little Mouse-ear.   1898.
Native. Open habitats on sandy soils. Infrequent and
mainly in Lower Derwentland.
Rare elsewhere:
U.D. Flixton 07, 1943, WAS; Firby 76, 1955, RG; Staxton
07 and Kennythorpe 76, 1958, FEC.
Hold. Easington shore 31, 1955, RG and Spurn Point 41,
1898 (R. 1902) and 1955, FEC, still present.

Myosoton Moench

M. aquaticum (L.) Moench [*Stellaria aquatica* (L.)
Scop.]   Map 157.
Water Chickweed.   1798.
Native. River banks, ditches, marshes, fens. Uncommon.
Mainly near the R. Ouse. Formerly near York and Hull,
frequent (Baines, 1840).
U.D. By Howsham Bridge 76, 1951, RG; Firby 76, 1981,
YNU Bot. Sect. Excursion.

L.D. Aughton 73, 1937, WAS (SYF); Naburn 53, 1964, FEC; near Barlby 63, 1964, FEC; near Melbourne 74, 1968, YNU Excursion; Hemingborough 62, 1981, YNU Bot. Sect. Excursion.
Hold. Near Beverley 03 (Teesdale, 1800); Dunswell Lane, Cottingham 03 (R. 1902); Burton Constable 13, 1988, YNU Excursion.

Stellaria L.

S. nemorum L.
Wood Stitchwort. 1850.
Native. Damp woods and by streams. Rare.
U.D. Howsham Woods 76, 1850, HI, herb. York Mus. (R. 1902); still at Howsham, 1958, YNU Excursion; near R. Derwent, Westow 76, GP (Flintoff, 1931); Firby 76, 1981, YNU Bot. Sect. Excursion.
L.D. Moreby Park 64, 1982, JP.

S. media (L.) Vill.
Common Chickweed.
Native. Cultivated land, disturbed ground, waste places. Abundant, in built-up areas as well as rural ones.

S. pallida (Dumort.) Piré (*S. media* var. *boraeana* Jord.)
Lesser Chickweed.
Native. On light sandy soils. Rare.
Hold. Near Brigham 05, 1987, EC.
Records for Sutton on Hull 13, CW (R. 1902) and for ten km square 93 (Perring and Walters, 1962) are doubtful being for non-sandy districts.

S. neglecta Weihe (*S. umbrosa* Opiz)
Greater Chickweed.
Native. Damp borders of copses, shady ditches, hedgebanks, stream sides. Uncommon.
U.D. Bank of R. Derwent, near Firby 76, 1985, EC, det. P. Benoit.
L.D. Allerthorpe Common 74, 1958, RG.
Hold. Burstwick 22, CW (R. 1902); as garden weed, Cottingham 03, 1954, RG.

S. holostea L. Map 301.
Greater Stitchwort.
Native. Woods, hedgebanks and sometimes on roadsides as in the Beverley area.
Locally common, but the map shows that it is missing from much of the Wolds north of Kilnwick 94 and also from Holderness north of Hornsea 14.

S. palustris Retz. Map 197.
Marsh Stitchwort. CNE. 1798.
Native. Marshy meadows, by ditches and in base-rich fens, very local.
It is a characteristic plant of the water-meadows and ditches by the R. Derwent, although often in small quantity. Other records:
U.D. Bank of the R. Derwent, Kirkham 76 (Baines, 1840).
L.D. Howden 72 and Skipwith Common 63 (R. 1902), still on Skipwith Common and by pond, Skipwith 63, 1958, RG; Skirpenbeck 75, 1956, CT; Thornton 74, 1958, RG; near Melbourne 74, 1968, YNU Excursion.
Hold. Beverley (Teesdale, 1800); edge of Hornsea Mere 14 (R. 1902), still there but as a form which is not glaucous; Kelleythorpe 05, 1968, FEC; near Wansford 05, 1969, MC; Withernwick 23, 1989, RJ.

S. graminea L. Map 302.
Lesser Stitchwort.
Native. Meadows and other grassy places, including roadsides.
Common in most areas, but missing from parts of the Wolds and apparently infrequent in Holderness.

S. uliginosa Murr. (*S. alsine* Grimm) Map 166.
Bog Stitchwort.
Native. Marshy places by streams and ponds, sometimes at the base of tall vegetation; on wet wood rides. Generally frequent, but apparently scarce in Holderness east of the R. Hull valley.

Sagina L.

S. apetala Ard.

Subsp. *apetala* (*S. ciliata* Fries)
Ciliate Pearlwort. 1901.
Native. Dry grassland, heaths, bare ground, on walls. Uncommon.
U.D. Firby Wood 76, 1958, RG.
L.D. Skipwith Common 63, 1906, WI; Houghton Woods 83, 1939, AKW (SYF); railway near Escrick 64 and Howden 73, 1977, railway land survey, ITE; Langwith 64, 1980, EB; disused railway near Harswell 83, 1987, FEC.
Hold. Salt End Common 12, 1901 (R. 1902): Landsdowne St, Hull 02, 1951, FEC.

Subsp. *erecta* F. Herm. (*S. apetala* auct.) Map 303.
Annual Pearlwort.
Native. Bare soils, paths, gravel pits, railway tracks, on walls. Widely distributed, but apparently only locally frequent.

S. maritima Don
Sea Pearlwort. OSE. 1965.
Native. Maritime plant. Uncommon.
On coping stones by R. Humber, King George Dock, Hull 12, 1965, EC and between coping stones, Queen Elizabeth Dock, Hull 12, 1983, FEC; on river bank, Paull 12, 1983, FEC. On coast path, Kilnsea 41, 1967, WAS and locally on stony ground on cliff-top path, Skipsea 15, 1983, FEC. In abundance on Spurn Point 41 on an area rarely inundated by salt-water.

S. procumbens L.
Procumbent Pearlwort.
Native. Paths, lawns, grass verges, stream-sides. Common, including built-up areas.

S. nodosa (L.) Fenzl
Knotted Pearlwort. CNE. 1840.
Native. Moist sandy, gravelly and peaty places. Always uncommon and usually in small quantity.
U.D. Sand pit, Flixton 07, 1957, FEC; Wintringham 87, 1968, FEC.
L.D. Tilmire 64 (Baines, 1840); Brough 92 and Everingham 84 (R. 1902); Broomfleet 92, 1952, AW; Allerthorpe Common 74, 1956, Miss Evans; Langwith 64, 1980, EB.
Wolds Gravel pit, near Rudston 06, 1965, EC; by spring, Great Givendale 85, 1969, FEC; Elloughton 92, 1970, JG; Speeton 17, 1973, MC.
Hold. Kelleythorpe 05, 1948, RL; Leven Canal 04, 1952, FEC; Easington saltings 41, 1970, TD.

Minuartia L.
M. hybrida (Vill.) Schischk. (*Arenaria tenuifolia* L.)
Fine-leaved Sandwort. CSE. 1840.
Native. Dry rocky or stony places; on walls. Rare.
U.D. 'In a field near Kirkham Abbey' 76 (Baines, 1840), still present 1928, HB.
L.D. On disused railway track, Kipling Cotes 94, 1985, DRG.

Honkenya Ehrh.
H. peploides (L.) Ehrh. (*Arenaria peploides* L.)
Sea Sandwort. ONE. 1978.
Native. Mobile sandy shingle. On the R. Humber shore of Spurn Point from Kilnsea to the site of the old lifeboat cottages 41, forming a wide pure zone until recently. Also recorded along the R. Humber at Easington 31, 1955, RG, still present. Rarely on disturbed sand on the R. Humber bank as at Welwick 31. Here and there on the sea coast: Hornsea 24, 1950, IG; Barmston Drain end 15, 1955, RG; Fraisthorpe 16, 1955, RG & 1970, MC. Formerly at Auburn 16, 1896, HBWS.

Moehringia L.
M. trinervia (L.) Clairv. (*Arenaria trinervia* L.) Map 83.
Three-nerved Sandwort.
Native. Woods and plantations on well-drained soils. Frequent and widely distributed.

Arenaria L.
A. serpyllifolia L. Map 304.
Thyme-leaved Sandwort.
Native. Bare soil and open grassland on chalk and sand; on cindery railway tracks; on arable; on walls.
On bombed sites and other waste places in the Hull area. Common on the Wolds; scattered elsewhere.

A. leptoclados (Reichb.) Guss. Map 305.
Slender Sandwort. c. 1895.
Native. Very dry places, railway tracks, on walls. Infrequent, but sometimes in great quantity. Records include:
L.D. Olympia Mills, Selby 63, 1956, DM; North Cave 83, 1971, JG; railway near Escrick 64, 1977, railway land survey, ITE.
Wolds On old wall Bishop Burton 93, 1959 and Knapton Settlement 87, 1959, FEC; Brantingham 92, 1971, JG; disused railway near Kipling Cotes station 94 and near Cherry Burton 94, 1981, FEC; Kirkburn Grange 95, 1985, EC.
Hold. Bombed site, Hull 02, 1951, FEC; Priory Yard Sidings, Hull 02, 1982; Whitedale railway station 14, 1983, FEC.

Spergula L.
S. arvensis Map 236.
Corn Spurrey.
Native. Weed of arable, also on waste ground and sandy tracksides; a calcifuge. Common on sandy soils of Derwentland; also frequent in Holderness where there is a calcium deficiency; uncommon on the Wolds.

Spergularia (Pers.) Presl
S. rubra (L.) J. & C. Presl (*Buda rubra* Dum.) Map 48.
Sand Spurrey.
Native. On sand, rarely on cindery railway tracks. Uncommon, mainly in Lower Derwentland.
L.D. Skipwith Common 63 (R. 1902); North Cave 83, 1950, FEC; Houghton Woods 83, 1953, RG: Allerthorpe Common 74, 1953, RG, still present; Langwith Common 64, 1965, FEC; Tollingham Warren 83 and Snake Hall 83, 1981, FEC.
Hold. Spring Head railway sidings, Hull 02, 1978, FEC; in quantity on disused railway, Hollym 32, 1983, FEC.

S. rupicola Lebel ex Le Jolis var. ***glabrescens*** Bréb
Rock Sea-spurrey. OWEE.
Native. Filey 18, E. Drabble (BEC 8, 1927, 529).

S. media (L.) C. Presl [*Buda media* (L.) Dum.] Map 220.
Greater Sea-spurrey. 1879.
Native. Salt-marshes and river-shore.
Frequent along the R. Humber, west to Broomfleet.

S. marina (L.) Griseb. [*Buda marina* (L.) Dum.
Map 219.
Lesser Sea-spurrey.
Native. Top of salt-marshes and in marshy places on the land-ward side of the R. Humber bank; sometimes in quantity.
Frequent along the R. Humber from Spurn 41 west to Yokefleet 82. By the R. Hull, near Sutton Bridge 03, 1957, ESt. In drier places on the riverside path at Paull 12 and on the cliff top at Skipsea 15, 1983, FEC. Also on the coast on Flamborough Head 27, 1953, FWA and at Barmston Drain end 15, 1955, RG. Plants with winged and wingless seed occur on Cherry Cob Sands 22 and near Yokefleet 82.

Corrigiola L.
C. litoralis L.
Strapwort. 1969.
Adventive. Disused railway tracks on bare cinders. Rare.
The species is known as a British native only at Slapton Ley, S. Devon, v.c. 3, where it occurs on sandy and gravelly banks of pools and in the Channel Islands. Pyrah (1959) recorded that the species was widespread on the ballast of railway tracks in the Castleford area, S.W. Yorks., v.c. 63 and it was recorded on railway tracks in Herts., v.c. 20 and Northumberland, v.c. 67 in 1958 and as early as 1928 in S. Lancs., v.c. 59 (Kent, 1959).
Four records for v.c. 61. North Cave 83, 1969, ATD; Spring Head Sidings, Hull 02, 1978 and near South Cave 93, 1985, HiP; all these localities being on the disused Hull and Barnsley line. Disused line, near Harswell 84, 1987, Mrs Whittaker. Persisting as long as conditions remain suitable.

Scleranthus L.
S. annuus L. Map 46.
Annual Knawel. 1836.
Native. Calcifuge.
Usually on dry sandy ground including arable; also recorded for wall tops, North Cave 83 and on boulder clay cliffs, North Ferriby 92 (R. 1902). Locally frequent in Lower Derwentland in the 1950s, becoming uncommon; post-1970 records: Barmby Moor 74 and Bunny Hill 83, 1981, FEC; disused railway, Harswell 83, 1987, EHW.
Other records:
U.D. Sand pits, Staxton 07, 1956, RG and Flixton 07, 1957, FEC; Wintringham 87, 1957, FEC.
Wolds Near Speeton 17, 1973, MC.
Hold. Gravel pit, Brandesburton 14, 1969, EC.

PORTULACACEAE

Montia L.
M. fontana L.
Blinks. 1899.
Native. Wet places on non-calcareous soils, including pond sides and wood rides. Uncommon, but widely scattered.

All records:
L.D. Tilmire, near Market Weighton 83, JJM (R. 1902); Allerthorpe Common 74, 1937, RG; rides, Skipwith Common 63, 1982, EB.
Wolds Near springs Wharram Dale 86 and near Settrington (R. 1902); near Burton Agnes 16, 1970, MC; Flamborough 27 and Bempton 17, 1970, MC; Speeton 17, 1973, MC.
Hold. Very common, Swine Moor, Beverley 03, 1899 and Salt End Common, 1900 (R. 1902); Pulfin Bog 04, 1935, RG.
Both subsp. *fontana* and subsp. *chondrosperma* (Fenzl) Walters occur and more work is required to determine their distribution. Subsp. *chondrosperma* is recorded for Figham Common 03, 1968, MC; also Speeton and Buckton 17, 1973, MC, det. S.M. Walters.

M. perfoliata (Willd.) Howell (*Claytonia perfoliata* Donn ex Willd.)
Springbeauty.
Naturalised alien. Waste places, usually on light sandy soils. Uncommon.
L.D. Near golf course, Brough 92, 1939, AKW; Wheldrake 64, 1977, JL; established at Naburn hospital 64, 1981, EB.
Hold. Spurn 41, TP (R. 1902), still abundant there in both light and shade, flourishing under Sea Buckthorn; R. Humber shore, Easington 31, 1955, RG & 1984, FEC; in quantity at Withernsea 32, 1956, CP; Hempholme 04, 1977, AM.

AMARANTHACEAE

Amaranthus L.
A. retroflexus L.
Amaranth.
Casual. Native of America. Waste places. Uncommon.
L.D. Olympia Oil Mill Sidings, Selby 63, WAS & JK (W. 1938).
Hold. Frequent, West Dock, Hull, CW (R. 1902); King George Dock, Hull 12, 1933, AKW (W. 1938); bombed site, Little High St, Hull 12, 1978, FEC.
Var. *delelei* (Richter & Loret) Thell. Garden weed, Sutton on Hull 13, 1952, FEC; det. J. P. M. Brenan.

CHENOPODIACEAE

Chenopodium L.
C. bonus-henricus L.
Good-King-Henry.
Naturalised alien. In nitrogen-rich habitats, farm yards, roadsides. Formerly much used as a vegetable. Infrequent now, but widely scattered.

C. polyspermum L.
Many-seeded Goosefoot.
Native? Waste places and cultivated ground. Rare.
L.D. In quantity on newly disturbed ground, Spaldington 73, 1970, DWS; garden weed, Heslington 64, 1980, EB.
Hold. West Dock, Hull 02 (R. 1902).

C. album L.
Fat-hen.
Native. Waste places and cultivated land. Very common. Several varieties have been recorded.

C. album x *C. ficifolium* = *C.* x *zahnii* J. Murr
Skipwith 63, 1929, G.C. Druce (Rep. BEC 9, 1929, 34).

C. ficifolium Sm.
Fig-leaved Goosefoot.   CSE.
Native? Waste ground, arable, manure heaps. Rare.
U.D. Woodhouse Farm, Flixton 08, 1982, CSVY.
L.D. Howden Dyke Island 72, 1972, RHu & JHu.
Hold. West Dock, Hull 02 (R. 1902).

C. murale L.
Nettle-leaved Goosefoot.
Native? Waste places, cultivated ground. Uncommon.
Hold. Hull docks (R. 1902); garden weed, Coltman St, Hull 02, 1951, FEC and Kilnsea Warren 41, 1978, FEC.

C. urbicum L.
Upright Goosefoot.
Native? Waste ground and arable. Uncommon.
L.D. Between Fulford and Heslington 64 (Baines, 1840).
Hold. Hull docks (R. 1902); Cottingham 03, 1957, RG.

C. rubrum L.   Map 306.
Red Goosefoot.
Native. Waste places, cultivated ground, rubbish tips, farm yards. Infrequent, but widely distributed.
Particularly common in the Old Town of Hull, when the ground was disturbed by bombing during the last war and by demolition and construction work since. An abundance of seed of this species was found in more than one stratum during an archaeological dig in Sewer Lane, in Old Hull (Armstrong, 1974).

Beta L.
B. vulgaris L. subsp. *maritima* (L.) Arcang.
(*B. maritima* L.)
Sea Beet.   OSE.
Native. On sea shores.
Both this and subsp. *vulgaris* have been recorded at the coast and more rarely along the R. Humber, but need more critical study. Both subsp. are recorded for King George Dock, Hull 12 (W. 1938).

Atriplex L.
A. littoralis L.   Map 206.
Grass-leaved Orache.   1798.
Native. Along the R. Humber above high-water, mainly on the river bank, sometimes at the edge of a salt-marsh.
Frequent from Spurn 41 to Salt End 12; also recorded for Hessle 02, 1947, RG. On bombed site near the R. Hull, Harcourt St, Hull 12, 1952, FEC. Here and there on the coast: Barmston Drain end 15, 1955, RG; Fraisthorpe and Auburn 16, 1970, MC; on cliff near Aldborough 23, 1983, FEC.

A. patula L.
Common Orache.
Native. Cultivated ground, waste places. Frequent and widely distributed.
Var. *erecta* Huds. On a wall, Welton 92, CW (R. 1902); bombed site, Witham, Hull 13, 1951, FEC.

A. prostrata Boucher ex DC. (*A. hastata* auct.) Map 307.
Spear-leaved Orache.   1840.
Native. Waste places, roadsides; on sand and shingle, above high water, at the coast and along the R. Humber. Only locally frequent.

83

A. longipes Drejer x *A. prostrata*
Barmston 15, 1978, EC, det. P. Taschereau (PT).

A. glabriuscula Edmondst. (*A. Babingtonii* Woods)
Babington's Orache.   ONE.
Native. On sandy and shingly shores at or somewhat above
high water mark. Uncommon and under-recorded.
Hessle 02 and near Hull on the R. Humber bank (R. 1902);
Barmston 15, 1980, EC, det. PT.
Var. *virescens* Lange Withernsea 32, CW (R. 1902).

A. glabriuscula x *A. prostrata*
Barmston 15, 1980, EC, det. PT.

A. glabriuscula x *A. longipes*
Barmston 15, 1980, EC, det. PT.

A. laciniata L. (*A. sabulosa* Rouy)
Frosted Orache.   ONE.   1798.
Native. On sand and gravelly shores at about high water
mark. Rare.
Hornsea 24 (Teesdale, 1800); on river shore, Spurn Point
41, 1986, EC; Barmston 16, 1986, comm. EC.

Halimione Aellen
H. portulacoides (L.) Aellen (*Atriplex portulacoides* L.)
               Map 211.
Sea-purslane.   OSE.   *c.* 1845.
Native. Salt-marshes, especially fringing channels and
pools; ordinarily flooded at high tide. May be locally
dominant as on the river side of the chalk bank on Spurn
Point. Locally plentiful along the R. Humber west from
Spurn 41 to Salt End 12. On the coast at Barmston Drain
end 15 and at Auburn 16.

Suaeda Forsk. ex Scop.
S. maritima (L.) Dumort.   Map 221.
Annual Sea-blite.
Native. Salt-marshes; an early coloniser of bare mud.
Frequent from Spurn 41 west to Cherry Cob Sands 12; also
near Brough 92.

Salsola L.
S. kali L.

Subsp. *kali*
Prickly Saltwort.
Native. Sandy shores. Very local.
In quantity on the river side of Spurn Point 41 and locally
on the sea-shore there; carried onto the Point during the
1978 flooding and still flourishing on sand by the road. On
the shore of the R. Humber at Easington 31, 1975, FEC and
on the coast at Barmston 15 and Fraisthorpe 16, 1970, MC;
on the south side of Bridlington 16, 1986, M. Simms; at
Hornsea 24, 1987, DRG.

Subsp. *ruthenica* (Iljin) Soó (*S. pestifer* A. Nels.; *S. kali*
var. *tragus* DC.)
Spineless Saltwort.
Alien. Waste places. Rare.
Hold. Hull docks (R. 1902); bombed sites, Wincolmlee
and Merrick St, Hull 12, 1952, FEC, det. J.P.M. Brenan.

Salicornia L. Glasswort.
A critical examination of *Salicornia* sp. at Spurn 41 was
made by K. Fenton (1977) at a time of establishment and
extension of salt-marsh vegetation, resulting from the build
up of extensive beds of *Spartina*. Specimens collected by

K. Fenton were determined by I.K. Ferguson at Kew;
nomenclature is as in *Flora Europaea*.
Further study of *Salicornia* sp. in the salt-marshes by the R.
Humber is required. Samphire is still gathered for pickling
and for use as a vegetable.

S. europaea L.
Glasswort, Marsh Samphire.
Native. On bare mud; a pioneer species.
Appears to be the common species in the upper levels of
salt-marshes at Spurn 41 and along the R. Humber west to
Paull.

S. ramosissima J. Woods   OWEE.
Native. Upper part of salt-marshes on bare, rather firm
mud.
The following records require confirmation: Welwick 31,
1927, CMR; Stone Creek 21, 1972, EC.

S. dolichostachya Moss   OWEE.
Native. On firm mud and muddy sand.
Present throughout the salt-marsh at Spurn 41 from upper
to lower levels, being more abundant in the latter (Fenton,
1977); first recorded 1974, KF.

S. fragilis P.W. Ball & Tutin (incorporating *S. lutescens*)
Native.
Mainly in the lower part of the salt-marsh at Spurn 41 and
in the marsh adjacent to the chalk bank (Fenton, 1977).

TILIACEAE

Tilia L.
T. platyphyllos Scop.
Large-leaved Lime.
Native?
Leavening 75, 1970, ATD.

T. cordata Mill.
Small-leaved Lime.
Introduced presumably.
Near Rise Park 14, CW (R. 1902).

T. cordata x *T. platyphyllos* = *T.* x *vulgaris* Hayne (? *T*
x *europaea* L.)
Common Lime.
Introduced. Frequently planted and grows well.

MALVACEAE

Malva L.
M. moschata L.   Map 308.
Musk Mallow.   *c.* 1845.
Native. Grassy places on sand, gravel and chalk; chalk
quarries, roadsides, drain and railway banks. Infrequent;
most records are for the Wolds.
Post-1970 records:
L.D. North Hill Plantation, near Bugthorpe 75, 1977, TC.
Wolds Weedley 93, 1977, TC, confirming an old record
(R. 1902); West Lutton 96, 1977, TC & FEC; Wharram 86,
1977, TC; Elloughton Dale 92, 1979, EHW; disused
railway station, Kipling Cotes 94, 1981, FEC.
Hold. Disused railway station, Skirlaugh 13, 1984, FEC.

M. sylvestris L.   Map 309.
Common Mallow.
Native. Roadsides, waste places and field edges. Widely distributed and locally frequent, often found in or near towns and villages.

M. neglecta Wallr. (*M. rotundifolia* auct.)   Map 310.
Dwarf Mallow.   1878.
Native. Waste places, fields, roadsides. Infrequent, but widely scattered.
Said to be formerly common on waste ground and rubbish heaps (R. 1902).
Post-1970 records:
U.D. East Heslerton 97, 1986, EC.
L.D. Stillingfleet 54, 1975, TFM; Fulford 64, 1981, EB; Dunnington 65, Bolton and Full Sutton 75, 1983, CSVY.
Wolds Thwing 07, 1970, EC; near Kilham 06, 1971, MC; Burton Fleming 07, 1977, EC; near Staxton 07, 1983, CSVY; near Foxholes 07, 1983, HP.
Hold. Near Driffield 05, 1970, MC; near Cherry Cob Sands 22, 1983, CSVY.

LINACEAE

Linum L.

L. usitatissimum L.
Flax.
Formerly widely cultivated in the East Riding for production of linen, particularly in Lower Derwentland; grown occasionally in Holderness recently. Occurs regularly as a casual, near seed warehouses and elsewhere in the Old Town, Hull, rarely elsewhere.
Has appeared in great quantity occasionally from dormant seed, as when a dyke was cleaned at Aughton 73.
Other records:
L.D. Skipwith Common 63, 1956, IG; in quantity as garden weed, Bubwith 73, 1982, FEC.
Hold. Near Keyingham railway station 22, 1953, FEC; disturbed ground near site of old flax mill, Hull Bridge, Beverley 03, 1978, comm. FEC.

L. perenne L. subsp. *anglicum* (Miller) Ockendon (*L. anglicum* Mill.)
Perennial Flax.
Native. Calcareous grassland. Uncommon.
Wolds Beverley 03, Dr Hull and Driffield Wold 06, MH (R. 1902); West Heslerton 97, *c.*1906, AGT & WGS; Sherburn 97, 1951, JW, still present; near Duggleby 86, 1961, FEC, still present; Burdale 86, 1968, MC, still present; near Hunmanby 17, 1973, MC, still there; near Millington 85, 1983, MW.

L. catharticum L.   Map 311.
Fairy Flax.
Native. Grassland and disturbed soil mainly on calcareous soils. Common on the Wolds; sparingly in Holderness, mainly on gravel or coastal sands; local in Lower Derwentland immediately adjacent to the southern wolds; occasionally off the wolds along railways.

Radiola Hill

R. linoides Roth
Allseed.   1840.
Native. Sandy or peaty depressions on heaths where water has stood in winter, including wood rides. Rare.
L.D. Langwith 64 (Baines, 1840); Houghton Moor 83, JJM and Skipwith Common 63, 1900, JFR (R. 1902);

Allerthorpe Common 74, 1908, JJM (Trans. HSFNC 1909, 4, 105), found on the southernmost ride, 1960, FEC but lost during afforestation, on new forest ride, 1985, CH; Stamford Bridge 75, 1913, WB.

GERANIACEAE

Geranium L.

G. pratense L.   Map 52.
Meadow Crane's-bill.   1877.
Native. Grassy places, mainly roadsides.
Locally common on the Wolds, particularly on the western belt and in Derwentland; infrequent in Holderness, still present in the Hornsea area as formerly (R. 1902).

G. sylvaticum L.
Wood Crane's-bill.
Established adventive. Roadsides. Rare.
L.D. Bubwith 73, 1973, EC; near Stamford Bridge 75, 1981, DEH.

G. endressii Gay
French Crane's-bill.
Garden escape. Uncommon.
Wolds Londesborough Park 84, 1972, TFM; Wauldby Green 93, 1980, EHW.

G. phaeum L.
Dusky Crane's-bill.   1840.
Alien. Grown in gardens and naturalised on hedgebanks. Uncommon.
L.D. Fulford 64 (Baker, 1854), extinct by 1902 (R. 1902); near Wheldrake 64, 1945, KGP; Fangfoss 75, 1956, MT.
Wolds Londesborough 84 (Baines, 1840); Boynton, Bessingby, Sewerby 16, RJF & Major Lawson (W. 1938), still at Boynton, 1970, MC; Birdsall 86, 1956, Lady Middleton.
Hold. Wansford and Elmswell 05 (R. 1902); still at Elmswell, 1965, MC.

G. sanguineum L.
Bloody Crane's-bill.   1877.
Native. Grassland on calcareous soils. Uncommon.
In great quantity on a roadside bank near Huggate 85 and near the mouth of Primrose Valley 17; first recorded for the cliffs between Filey and Flamborough, 1877, WWh (R. 1902).
Other records:
Wharram 86, 1959, FEC; near North Grimston 86, 1961, FEC; Londesborough 84, 1968, EHW; Boynton 16, 1970, MC; near Fordon 07, 1982, NCC.

G. pyrenaicum Burm. f.
Hedgerow Crane's-bill.   CSE.   1810.
Native. Hedgebanks, waysides, grassy places.
Said to be formerly frequent (R. 1902); uncommon throughout the last forty years.
Post-1950 records:
U.D. Kirkham 76, 1958, FEC, still present; first recorded near the Abbey, 1810, WM (herb. York Mus.); near Wintringham 87, 1964, YNU Excursion.
L.D. Near Yapham Common 75, 1954, RG; near North Cave 83, 1955, FEC; Hotham 83, 1970, FEC.
Wolds North Grimston Hill 86, 1961, FEC; North Ferriby 92, 1980, FEC.
Hold. Brandesburton 04, 1969, YNU Excursion.

G. columbinum L.
Long-stalked Crane's-bill.
Native. Usually on bare chalk, including arable. In chalk grassland only in Cottondale 07, 1964, FEC; habitat later destroyed. Uncommon and now only on the Wolds.
Wolds Side of railway, Weedley 93, 1947, FEC; Wauldby 93, 1948, FEC; Langton 86, 1956, FEC; Burdale 86, 1956, WAS; North Newbald 93, 1957, FEC; near Weaverthorpe 97, 1966, FEC; Fordon 07, 1967, FEC.
Hold. Near Cottingham 03, Driffield 05 (R. 1902).

G. dissectum L.   Map 312.
Cut-leaved Crane's-bill.
Native. Arable fields and gardens, grassland, roadsides and waste places. Frequent.

G. molle L.
Dove's-foot Crane's-bill.
Native. Dry grassland, cultivated ground, chalk quarries, gravel pits, roadsides. Very common.
Var. *aequale* Bab.
Bombed site, Great Passage St, Hull, 1952, FEC (herb. FEC), conf. Brit. Mus.; between Thixendale and Raisthorpe 86, 1956, GAN.

G. pusillum L.   Map 313.
Small-flowered Crane's-bill.
Native. Cultivated and waste ground, usually in open habitats; sand and gravel pits. Infrequent except locally.

G. lucidum L.
Shining Crane's-bill.   1840.
Probably always introduced. Usually on walls. Rare.
U.D. Kirkham Abbey 76 (Baines, 1840).
Wolds Walls at Londesborough 84 (Baines, 1840); stony waste, Hunmanby Hall School 07, 1972, EC.
Hold. Near Cottingham (R. 1902); Bentley 03, JJM (Trans. HSFNC, 1908, *4*, 105); East Park, Hull 13, 1950, IG; on waste place, Sunk Island 21, 1986, JD.

G. robertianum L.   Map 314.
Herb-Robert.
Native. Deciduous woodland, copses, hedgebanks, shady lanes. Common on the Wolds and locally elsewhere.

Erodium L'Hérit.
E. cicutarium (L.) L'Hérit.   Map 37.
Common Stork's-bill.
Native. On dunes, dry grassland, arable and waste places; mainly on sand.
Locally frequent in Lower Derwentland; scattered elsewhere, except on the Wolds where it is uncommon; chalk quarry, Willerby 03, 1946, FEC; near St Austin's Stone 93, 1954, FEC; Thixendale 86, 1965, FEC; Burton Fleming 07, 1971, EC; disused railway station, Fimber 96, 1981, FEC.
Subsp. *dunense* Andreas occurs at Spurn 41, together with the widespread subsp. *cicutarium*, 1984, JRC & MN.

E. moschatum (L.) L'Hérit.
Musk Stork's-bill.   2nd half 18th century.
Native. Waste places near the sea.
Atwick 14, 2nd half 18th century, WW; Spurn 41, YNU Excursion, Aldborough 23, 1901, TP (R. 1902). No recent record.

OXALIDACEAE

Oxalis L.
O. acetosella L.   Map 84.
Wood-sorrel.   1840.
Native. Woods, avoiding very heavy, wet soils; formerly also in hedgerows (R. 1902). Frequent.

O. corniculata L.
Procumbent Yellow-sorrel.
Introduced. Garden weed, Sewerby Park 16, 1970, FH; Fulford 64, 1980, EB.

BALSAMINACEAE

Impatiens L.
I. parviflora DC.
Small Balsam.
Alien. A native of moist shady places in Central Asia; introduced into Britain *c*.1850.
Common in or near Hull gardens as a weed of cultivation (R. 1902). Pearson's Park 03, CW (W. 1938). Very rare now: edge of cricket circle, Anlaby Rd, Hull 02, 1978, RCr.

I. glandulifera Royle   Map 256.
Indian Balsam, Policeman's Helmet.   1929.
Native of Himalaya; introduced to Britain as a garden plant in 1839. River bank, near Garrowby 75 (BEC. *9*, 1929, 109). Plentiful by R. Ouse above Selby 63, WAS (W. 1938); at Cawood 54, 1941, YNU Excursion. Now fully naturalised and plentiful along the R. Ouse and R. Derwent. Also occurring in scattered localities, but usually not persisting:
L.D. Near cottage garden, Ellerker 92, 1935, AKW (W. 1938).
Wolds Hunmanby Hall grounds 07, 1984, EC.
Hold. By drain on school playing field, east Hull 13, 1950, FEC; Pearson Park, Hull 03, 1978, RCr; garden weed, Beverley 03, 1978, Mr Gooding.

ACERACEAE

Acer L.
A. pseudoplatanus L.
Sycamore.
Naturalised alien. Common in woods and plantations; self-perpetuating.

A. campestre L.   Map 315.
Field Maple.   CSE.
Native. Woods, hedges. Widely distributed and locally frequent.
Fine trees in Burton Bushes, Beverley 03. In 17% of hedges examined in Lower Derwentland, in 35% of those on the Wolds and in more than 75% of hedges in Holderness (Boatman, 1980, 41-44).

HIPPOCASTANACEAE

Aesculus L.
A. hippocastanum L.
Horse-chestnut.
Introduced. Was commonly planted and often self sown; grows well in the area.

AQUIFOLIACEAE

Ilex L.
I. aquifolium L.
Holly. OSE.
Native. Woods, hedgerows.
Grows on all soils except very wet ones. Very tall trees in Burton Bushes, Beverley.
Locally common. Found as a hedgerow plant in Holderness, only in the south-west corner i.e. west of the R. Hull and south of GR northing 400 (Boatman, 1980, 41-44).

CELASTRACEAE

Euonymus L.
E. europaeus L.
Spindle. 1898.
Native. Hedges, usually on the chalk. Uncommon.
Sometimes planted on roadsides as between South Cave and Newport in the 1940s.
L.D. Holly Carrs Wood 64, 1987, JL.
Wolds Boynton 16, 1898; Sledmere 96, JTH (R. 1902) and 1960, YNU Excursion; Grimston Brow roadside 86, 1981, Wharram Research Project. Recorded for two Wolds hedges including one on York Grounds farm 93 (Boatman, 1980, 41-44).
Hold. Near Anlaby 02 and near Cottingham 03 (R. 1902).

RHAMNACEAE

Rhamnus L.
R. cartharticus L.
Buckthorn.
Native. Woods, hedges; usually on calcareous soils. Infrequent.
Boatman (1982) found the species in 50% of the hedges examined on the Wolds and half of those on Jurassic strata; he also records it as a feature of the scrub at the bottom of the chalk scarp as at Weedley Springs 93, Goodmanham 84 and Millington 85.
There are a number of other scattered records:
U.D. Scagglethorpe 87, 1956, RG.
L.D. Everingham 84 (R. 1902); Skipwith 63, 1906 (Trans. HSFNC, 1907, *3*, 300); Houghton Woods 83, 1908, (Trans. HSFNC, 1909, *4*, 105) and 1938, AKW; Allerthorpe Common 74, 1955, RG; near Fulford 64, 1981, EB; near Dunnington 65, 1984, JL.

Frangula Mill.
F. alnus Mill. (*Rhamnus frangula* L.)
Alder Buckthorn. 1866.
Native. Moist heaths, commons; on sandy soils. Infrequent and almost entirely in Lower Derwentland.
Records include:
L.D. Langwith Wood 64, 1866, WWh (R. 1902) and 1965, FEC; Skipwith 63, 1895, HJW (R. 1902) & 1970, MC; Houghton Woods lane 83, 1908 (Trans. HSFNC, 1909, *4*, 105); Allerthorpe Common 74, 1953, RG & 1982, FEC; North Cliffe 83, 1955, RG; Whittaker Wood 74, and Melbourne 74, 1957, RG; Kilpin 72, 1970, GMG; Fulford 64, 1980, EB; near Dunnington 65, 1983, CSVY.
Hold. Lanes near Cottingham 03 (R. 1902) and Gilly Woods 03, 1979, EHW.

LEGUMINOSAE

Lupinus L.
L. arboreus Sims
Tree Lupin.
Naturalised escape of cultivation. Native of California.
On sandy ground between Staxton and Flixton 07, 1982, spreading CSVY.

Genista L.
G. tinctoria L.
Dyer's Greenweed. CE. 2nd half 18th century.
Native. Old grassland.
Only one post-1950 record: Risby 03, 1957, CV; habitat later destroyed.
Other records:
L.D. Heslington 64 (Baines, 1840); North Cave 83, JFR (R. 1902); Barthorpe 75, GP (Flintoff, 1931).
Hold. Atwick 14, 2nd half 18th century, WW; Sunderlandwick 05, JTH and near Foredyke drain, Sutton on Hull 13 (R. 1902).

G. anglica L.
Petty Whin. OWEE.
Native. On dry heaths. Rare now; all records for Lower Derwentland.
Langwith 64, 1834, HPa; near Holme River Head 83, JJM and Allerthorpe Common 74 (R. 1902), last seen, 1986, EHW; near Snake Hall 83, 1905 (Trans. HSFNC *3*, 218); Cliffe 83, 1908 (Trans. HSFNC *4*, 105) and North Cliffe Wood, 1956, FEC; Breighton Common 73, 1948, JMT; Skipwith Common 63, 1982, EB.

Ulex L.
U. europaeus L. Map 316.
Gorse, Furze, Whin. OWEE.
Native. Heaths, hedgerows, rough grassy places. Common.
A characteristic plant of heaths and commons. It was once particularly common in Lower Derwentland; it is still frequent but in greatly reduced quantity there. It was once widely used as food for rabbits and other animals, for fuel, for hedging and in fox coverts. There has consequently been a complicated history of planting, conservation and destruction so that it is now widely distributed if not always in great quantity. Has long occurred on the high wolds (R. 1902); since the reduction of rabbits by myxomatosis it has become dominant on many chalk hillsides. Research has shown that whilst most roots are produced in a soil with a pH initially between 5 and 6, some healthy roots are produced in calcareous material at a pH above 7 and that plants can acidify the soil (Grubb, Green & Merrifield, 1969). Frequent in hedges in Holderness; may be destroyed by frost in a severe winter. Occurs in quantity on the Flamborough Headland, adopting a cushion-like habit on the coast.

Cytisus L.
C. scoparius (L.) Link [*Sarothamnus scoparius* (L.) Wimm. ex Koch] Map 317.
Broom.
Native. On heaths and waste ground and in woods, usually on sandy soils, strongly calcifuge. Locally frequent in Lower Derwentland and on gravels of Holderness; scattered elsewhere.

Ononis L.

O. repens L.   Map 318.
Common Restharrow.
Native. Mainly on chalk: on grassland, in chalk pits, by roadsides and on railway banks; gravel pits. Common on the Wolds and on calcareous sands at Spurn 41 and along the R. Humber at Kilnsea 41 and Easington 31. Scattered elsewhere.

O. spinosa L.
Spiny Restharrow.
Native. In rough grassy places. Infrequent.
Mainly on the R. Humber bank and on the coast.
Other records:
L.D. Skirpenbeck 75, 1956, MT.
Hold. By Hornsea Mere 14 (R. 1902), still present; by Kelk Beck, near Harpham 06, 1958, RG; Wansford 05 and Lowthorpe 06, 1969, MC; Nafferton 05, 1973, MC; Arnold roadside 13, 1979, FEC; gravel pit, Burshill 04, 1983, FEC.

O. repens x ***O. spinosa***
Hornsea Mere 14, 1971, FEC; Spurn Point 41, 1977, FEC; Tunstall 33, 1979, FEC; R. Humber bank, Easington 31, 1983, FEC.

Medicago L.

M. falcata L.
Sickle Medick.
Established alien. Waste places, refuse tips, railway track. Uncommon.
L.D. Near Brough 92, CW (R. 1902); Selby and Barlby 63, 1920, JBF.
Wolds Quarry, near North Newbald 93, 1957, RG; Fimber 86, 1964, MC.
Hold. King George Dock, Hull 12, 1934, AKW; near Pearson's Oil Mill, Clough Rd, Hull 03, 1937, AKW (W. 1938); Kelsey Hill 22, 1938, AKW; Witham 12, 1951 and Tower St, Hull 12, 1952, FEC; refuse tip, Leads Rd, Hull 13, 1960-1970, EC; disused railway, Chamberlain Rd, Hull 13, 1979, EC; Spurn 41, 1987, FEC.

M. falcata x ***M. sativa*** = ***M.*** x ***varia*** Martyn
Established alien.
U.D. Wintringham 87, 1964, FEC.
Wolds Woo Dale hillside 93, 1957, FEC; waste place North Ferriby 92, 1987, FEC.
Hold. Tower St, Hull 12, 1952, FEC; rubbish tip, Clough Rd, Hull 13, 1963, FEC; R. Humber bank, Skeffling 31, 1973, FEC; near North Bridge, Hull 12, 1976, FEC.

M. sativa L.
Lucerne.   1840.
Naturalised alien. Waste places, railway banks, field edges, roadsides. Infrequent.
Rarely on waste places in Hull, 1950-1953, FEC. Still grown in the Vale of Pickering and formerly on the Wolds (R. 1902); persisting as an escape of cultivation as at West Heslerton and Sherburn 97, 1982, FEC.

M. lupulina L.
Black Medick.
Native. Grassy places, including roadsides; sides of railway tracks. On a variety of soils. Common.

M. polymorpha L. (*M. denticulata* Willd.)
Toothed Medick.
Alien. Arable, gardens, waste places. Uncommon.

L.D. Olympia Oil Mills Sidings, Selby 63, WAS (W. 1938); on disturbed roadside verges, near Heslington 64, 1980, EB, not persisting; beet field, near Thornton 74, 1981, FEC.
Hold. Near Hull and cornfields, Wawne 03 (R. 1902); King George Dock, Hull 13, 1933-1935; allotments, Spring Head 02, 1937, AKW (W. 1938).

M. arabica (L.) Huds.
Spotted Medick.
Alien. Arable, roadsides, waste places, mainly on light soils. Uncommon.
L.D. Skipwith Common 63, 1923, RG; roadside, Elvington 74, 1937, WAS; Aughton 74, 1937, AKW (W. 1938); railway station, Bubwith 73, 1972, TFM; well established and spreading at Fulford 64, 1980, EB.
Hold. Hull docks (R. 1902); King George Dock, Hull 12, 1933-1935 (W. 1938).

Melilotus Mill.

M. altissima Thuill. (*M. officinalis* auct.)   Map 258.
Tall Melilot.   1898.
Alien. Naturalised in waste places, railway banks, chalk quarries, sand pits, gravel pits. Infrequent, but widely scattered; uncommon in and near to Hull.
Early records: 'waste places and cliffs', Auburn 16, *c*.1898, HBWS; Hessle 02 and Kelsey Hill 22 (R. 1902), still at Kelsey Hill, 1955, RG.
Post-1970 records include:
Hold. Spurn 41, 1980, FEC; Alexandra Dock, Hull 12, 1982, FEC; gravel pit, Gransmoor 15, 1982, FEC; near Little Kelk 16, 1984, EC.

M. officinalis (L.) Pall. (*M. arvensis* Wallr.)   Map 259.
Ribbed Melilot.   1908.
Established alien. Waste places. Uncommon, except in the Hull area where it sometimes occurs in quantity.
King George Dock, Hull 12, 1933-1937, AKW (W. 1938). Established on 8% of Hull bombed sites by 1953, when it was on 14% of Old Town sites, still locally common in the Old Town, Hull, 1976. Near Cottingham 03, 1960, FEC; disused railway Spring Head, Hull 02, 1981, FEC; Alexandra Dock, Hull 12, 1983, FEC.
Other records:
U.D. Sand pit, Staxton 07, 1957, FEC; near Wintringham 87, 1964, YNU Excursion.
L.D. Market Weighton 84, 1908, JJM (Trans. HSFNC, *4*, 105); Elvington 74, 1973, JLu.
Wolds Chalk pit, Kipling Cotes 94, 1968, TFM; roadside between Sledmere and Bridlington, 1970, FH.
Hold. Kilnsea Warren 41, 1978, FEC.

M. alba Medic.   Map 257.
White Melilot.   1902.
Alien. Naturalised in fields, waste places, sand pits, gravel pits.
First records: cultivated fields near Hull and on the docks (R. 1902). Still mainly in the Hull area; infrequent elsewhere. Established on 5% of Hull bombed sites, 1953; and particularly common on sites of the Old Town, Hull and still there to 1976. Has now been recorded in several widely scattered localities, mainly since 1970.

M. indica (L.) All.
Small Melilot.
Casual. Waste ground, towpaths. Uncommon.
L.D. Allerthorpe 74, CW (R. 1902); Pocklington Canal 74, 1980, RGu.

Wolds Welton 92 (R. 1902); Skidby chalk pit 03, 1953, AKW.
Hold. Sutton on Hull 13, CW and near docks, Hull (R. 1902); King George Dock, Hull 12, 1935-1937, AKW (W. 1938); refuse tip, Hessle 02, 1946, AKW; Witham, Hull 12, 1950 and bombed site, High St, Hull 12, 1951, FEC; garden weed Cottingham 03, 1951, RG; Victoria Dock site, Hull 12, 1972, FEC; Spurn 41, 1978, FEC and filled-in dyke, New Cleveland St, Hull 12, 1980, FEC.

Trifolium L.

T. pratense L.
Red Clover.
Native. In grassy and waste places. Common.
Var. *sativum* Cultivated for hay and frequently naturalised. Some fine forms on waste places in the Old Town, Hull 12.

T. medium L.   Map 58.
Zigzag Clover.   CE.
Native. Grassy places including Wolds grassland, railway banks, road verges, wood rides. Locally frequent in Holderness and on the Wolds; scarce elsewhere.

T. incarnatum L.
Crimson Clover.
Casual. Arable, waste places. Rare.
L.D. In cornfields, near Howden 72, JBe; Market Weighton 84, JJM (R. 1902); Riccall 63, 1920, JBF (W. 1938).
Wolds High Fordon 07, 1915 (N.H. Scarb.); arable field near Thixendale 86, 1956, YNU Excursion.
Hold. Refuse tip, Hessle 02, 1944, AKW; bank of disused railway, east Hull 13, where it may have been introduced with grass seed, 1979, MG.

T. arvense L.   Map 50.
Hare's-foot Clover.   1840.
Native. Sandy fields, sand dunes, sand and gravel pits.
Locally frequent in Lower Derwentland and the Vale of Pickering; uncommon in Holderness including: Spurn 41 (R. 1902), still present; on Alexandra Dock, Hull 12 in quantity, 1979, FEC, still there.

T. striatum L.
Knotted Clover.   1798.
Native. Short turf and open habitats on sand, more rarely on gravel or chalk. Uncommon.
U.D. Sand pit, Flixton 07, 1938, WAS (SYF) and 1957, FEC; Wintringham 87, 1964, FEC; near Staxton 07, 1983, CSVY; near Folkton 08, 1984, DRG.
L.D. Market Weighton 83, 1898, JJM (R. 1902); field and sand pit, North Cave 83, 1953, FEC.
Wolds Ganton 97, 1955, WHS; cliff top, Flamborough 27, 1955, RG.
Hold. Sandy fields, Leven 14 (Teesdale 1800); Spurn 41, 1926, YNU Excursion, still present; near Welwick 31, 1946, RG; sand dunes Easington 31, 1955, RG; Brandesburton gravel pits 14, 1955, RG.

T. scabrum L.
Rough Clover.   CSE.   1888.
Native. On sand or gravel. Uncommon.
U.D. Wintringham 87, 1964, YNU Excursion.
Hold. Spurn 41, 1888 (R. 1902), still present; gravel pit, near Welwick 31, 1946, WAS; sand dunes, near Easington 31, 1955, RG & 1986, NCC.

T. subterraneum L.
Subterraneum Clover.   OSE.
Native. On sand.
One record only: near Barmby Moor 74, 1977, PA.

T. suffocatum L.
Suffocated Clover.   OSE.   1946.
Native. In grassy places or open situations on sand. Very rare.
Hold. Kilnsea Warren 41, 1946, R. Good, still there; also at the southern end of Spurn 41, 1971, TD, still present.

T. hybridum L. subsp. *hybridum*
Alsike Clover.
Escape of cultivation. Naturalised by roadsides and on waste places. Frequent.
Subsp. *elegans* (Savi) Asch. & Graebner also occurs.

T. repens L.
White Clover.
Native. Lawns, pastures, roadsides, waste places. Common.

T. fragiferum L.   Map 319.
Strawberry Clover.
Native. Grassy places, mainly on heavy clay and often saline soils. Infrequent.
Mainly on the bank of the R. Humber as at North Ferriby 92, 1944, FEC; Easington 31, 1954, RG; Kilnsea 41, 1957, FEC, still present; Brough Haven 92, 1971, JG; Skeffling 31, 1973, FEC. Also on the coast at Speeton 17 (Flintoff, 1931).
Rarely inland:
L.D. Near canal, Market Weighton 83 (R. 1902); Sancton 83, 1908 (Trans. HSFNC, *4*, 125); Scrayingham 76, 1975, EB.
Hold. Hedgebank, Foston 15, 1957, RG; Driffield 05, 1964, JR & MC; near Copper Hall, Skerne 05, 1969, FEC; by Hornsea Mere 14, 1976, FEC.

T. resupinatum L.
Reversed Clover.
Casual. Waste places.
High St, Hull 12, 1978 & 1980, FEC; Pulman St, Hull 02, 1983, HFo.

T. campestre Schreb. (*T. procumbens* auct.)   Map 320.
Hop Trefoil.
Native. Dry grassland, mainly on chalk and sand; gravel pits; railway lines and sidings; dock reserves. Widely distributed and locally frequent, chiefly on the Wolds.

T. dubium Sibth.
Lesser Trefoil.
Native. Dry grassland on a variety of soils, disused railways, waste places; a persistent lawn weed. Common.

T. micranthum Viv. (*T. filiforme* L. nom. ambig.)
Slender Trefoil.   OSE.
Native. Short turf or open communities, usually on sand or gravel. Uncommon.
L.D. Skipwith Common 63, 1954, RG: Allerthorpe

Common 74, 1958, RG.
Wolds Near Brantingham 93, 1986, EHW.
Hold. On tumuli, near Cottingham 03 (R. 1902) and 1942, RG, habitat later destroyed; Kilnsea Warren 41, 1946, RG; Rise Park 14, 1982, FEC; near Tophill Low 04, 1985, EHW.

Anthyllis L.
A. vulneraria L.   Map 242.
Kidney Vetch.
Native. Chalk grassland, chalk pits, roadsides, railway verges. Frequent on the Wolds. In Holderness, it is mainly on railway tracks and sidings and on gravel.
Rarely on sand as at Wintringham 87, 1957, FEC.

Lotus L.
L. corniculatus L.
Common Bird's-foot-trefoil.
Native. Grassy places, waste places, chalk quarries, gravel pits. Common, but less frequent on road verges than formerly.

L. tenuis Waldst. & Kit. ex Willd.
Narrow-leaved Bird's-foot-trefoil.   CSE.   1874.
Native. Grassy places, usually on clay. Uncommon.
At the northern edge of its climatic range, it has been recorded for several localities on the R. Humber bank, but has been lost from some as a result of management changes; still on the foreshore near Hessle where it has long been known (R. 1902). On bombed site, High St, Hull 12, 1951, FEC and in quantity on waste land by Hedon Haven 12, 1984, FEC.
In other scattered localities, usually not persisting,
U.D. Near Muston 08, 1984, DRG.
L.D. Plentiful in clay pit, Broomfleet 82, 1969, MC.
Wolds Kipling Cotes 94, 1874, H.B. Mosier (R. 1902).
Hold. Barfhill covert 04, 1956, RG: disused aerodrome, Lissett 15, 1963, FEC; near runway Thornholme 16, 1970, MC; on disused railway, Preston 12, 1971, FEC; near Harpham 06, 1971, MC.

L. uliginosus Schkuhr   Map 321.
Greater Bird's-foot-trefoil.   CSE.
Native. Damp grassy places, marshes, dykes, roadside verges on clay soils. Frequent except on the Wolds.
A feature of Holderness roadsides, less commonly on railway banks as near Sigglesthorne station 14, 1980, FEC.

Galega L.
G. officinalis L.
Goat's-rue.
Alien. Naturalised on waste places and roadsides. Rare.
Wolds Roadside, North Ferriby 92, 1967, EC.
Hold. Fertile plants, Green Lane, Hull 02, 1975-1977, FEC, site now destroyed.

Robinia L.
R. pseudoacacia L.
False-acacia.
Alien. Planted in one or two places.
L.D. Tree in hedgerow, near Fulford 64, 1977, EB.
Wolds South Cave 93, 1945, FEC.

Astragalus L.
A. danicus Retz.   Map 4.
Purple Milk-vetch.   CNE.   1727.
Native. Chalk and limestone grassland, usually on south-facing slopes; chalk quarries; rarely on gravel. Very infrequent, sixteen post-1950 records.
Records include:
Wolds Near Easthorpe 84, 1727, TK; by the road from Malton to Settrington (Teesdale, 1794); Langton Wold 86 (Baines, 1840), still there; Garton Wold 96, 1905 (Trans. HSFNC, *3*, 218); chalk quarry, Worsendale 85, 1957, FEC, still present; Birdsall Brow 86, 1972, FEC; on Fordon bank 07, 1968, FEC, still present; near Hunmanby 17, 1973, MC; East Heslerton 97, 1982, NCC; Muston 07, 1983, PW.
Hold. Coneygarth, Brandesburton 14, 1899, RHP (R. 1902) and 1956, RG; banks of canal, Driffield 05, 1906 (Trans. HSFNC, *3*, 301).

A. glycyphyllos L.
Wild Liquorice.   CE.
Native. Rough grassy places. Rare.
L.D. On gravelly roadsides, near Elloughton 92 (R. 1902); in grassy lane and on railway, North Cave 83, 1980-1985, EHW.

Ornithopus L.
O. perpusillus L.   Map 43.
Bird's-foot.   1899.
Native. Heaths and other dry sandy places. Locally frequent in Lower Derwentland; infrequent in the Vale of Pickering. Decreasing.

Coronilla L.
C. varia L.
Crown Vetch.
Established alien. Waste places. Rare.
Wolds Chalk quarry, Kipling Cotes 94, 1958, FEC & PG, still there.
Hold. Tower St, Hull 12, 1952, FEC; railway line, Driffield 05, 1967, MC & JR and 1972, EHW.

Hippocrepis L.
H. comosa L.
Horseshoe Vetch.   CSE.   1925.
Native. Chalk and limestone grassland. Uncommon.
Wolds Langton Wold 86, 1925, GP, still present; near Staxton 07, 1956, TFM; Waterdale 86, 1956, KGP; near Duggleby 86, 1967, DJB, still present.

Onobrychis Mill.
O. viciifolia Scop.
Sainfoin.   *c.*1740.
Probably always a relic of cultivation. Fields, roadsides; more rarely on chalk grassland. Uncommon.
First cultivated in the Hunmanby area 07, *c.*1740 (Strickland, 1812) and apparently a popular Wolds crop for a time.
U.D. Cornfield Staxton 07, 1957 and Rillington 87, 1958, FEC; Sherburn 97, 1982, RJ.
L.D. Market Weighton 84, 1908, JJM (Trans. HSFNC, *4*, 105).
Wolds Garton 95, Foxholes 07 (Baines, 1840); near Nafferton 05 (R. 1902); Skidby 03, 1950, WHS; Sledmere

96, 1954, RG; Fridaythorpe 86, 1956, YNU Excursion; Langton Wold 86, 1956, FEC; Huggate 85, 1958, FEC; Fordon 07, 1969, FEC, still present.

Vicia L.

V. hirsuta (L.) Gray　　　　　　　　Map 322.
Hairy Tare.
Native. Grassy places, roadsides, railway banks; sometimes in arable; waste places. Widely distributed, but rarely in quantity. Uncommon in Holderness, east of the R. Hull valley and mainly on disused railway lines.

V. tetrasperma (L.) Schreb. (*V. gemella* Crantz)
Smooth Tare.
Native. Grassy places, drain banks, waste places, open woodland. Uncommon.
It occurs at Spurn 41 where it has long been known (R. 1902) and at a few places on or near the R. Humber bank from Welwick 31 eastwards.
Other records:
L.D. Heslington Fields 64, 1800, WM (herb. York Mus.); near Seaton Ross 74, 1958, FEC; disused railway, Foggathorpe 73, 1987, FEC; near Owsthorpe 83, 1987, EHW.
Wolds Tibthorpe 95, 1956, FEC; Garrowby 75, 1957, FEC; Lowthorpe 06, 1969, FEC; near Foxholes 07, 1977, EC.
Hold. Marfleet 12 and near Hull (R. 1902); Hull docks, CW (W. 1938); bombed site, High St, Hull 12, 1951, FEC; Paull Rd, Hull 12, 1953, FEC; Burstwick 22, 1955, FEC; Kelsey Hill gravel pits 22, 1957, Mrs Elliott.

V. cracca L.
Tufted Vetch.
Native. Grassy places, hedgebanks, roadsides. Common.

V. sylvatica L.
Wood Vetch.　　　CNE.　　　1888.
Native. Woods, hedges. Rare.
Wolds Raywell Woods 93, 1888; bushy banks of Speeton Beck 17, 1901 (R. 1902); Pocklington Wood 85, 1949, RL & 1961, FEC.

V. sepium L.
Bush Vetch.
Native. Grassy places, wood borders, roadsides. Common.

V. sativa L.
Common Vetch.
Subsp. *sativa*
Escape from cultivation. Field borders, waste ground. Infrequent.

Subsp. *nigra* (L.) Ehrh. (*V. angustifolia* L.)
Narrow-leaved Vetch.
Native. Grassy places, roadsides, arable fields; on a variety of soils. Common.

V. lathyroides L.
Spring Vetch.　　　　　　　　1798.
Native. Short turf, mainly on sandy soils. Rare.

U.D. Flixton 07, 1916 (N.H. Scarb.).
L.D. Market Weighton 84, JJM (Nat. 1898, 299); Barmby Moor 75, 1977, PA.
Hold. Near Beverley (Teesdale, 1800); Kilnsea Warren 41, 1898, AEL (R. 1902), still on Spurn Point.

Lathyrus L.

L. aphaca L.
Yellow Vetchling.
Alien. A Mediterranean species, probably introduced with grain; not persisting. Rare.
L.D. Near Elvington 74, 1973, JLu; near Barmby on the Marsh 72, 1970, MFW.
Hold. Hull docks (R. 1902); King George Dock, Hull 12, 1933, TS (W. 1938); site of Queen's Dock, Hull 12, 1950, FEC.

L. nissolia L.
Grass Vetchling.
Native.
Near Sigglesthorne 14, Mrs Wharton (Teesdale, 1800). Extinct.

L. hirsutus L.
Hairy Vetchling.
Alien; usually a casual. Rare.
L.D. Railway bank, Selby 63, JK & WAS (W. 1938).
Hold. Hull docks (R. 1902); waste ground, Bridlington 16, Major Lawson (W. 1938); Queen Elizabeth Dock, Hull 12, 1980, FEC, conf. E.J. Clement.

L. pratensis L.
Meadow Vetchling.
Native. Grassy places, including roadsides and railway banks. Common.

L. tuberosus L.
Tuberous Pea.
Alien. Rare.
Wolds High Fordon 07, 1947, ERC (N.H. Scarb.); Staxton 07, 1968, Miss Robson.
Hold. King George Dock, Hull 12, 1935, AKW (W. 1938).

L. palustris L.
Marsh Pea.　　　CNE.　　　1798.
Native. Fenland marshes. Rare.
L.D. Heslington Fields 64, c.1820 (Baines, 1840), still present (Baker, 1854); near Thornton 74, 1969, FEC.
Hold. 'Abundantly near Beverley' (Teesdale, 1800); still known by the R. Hull, north of Beverley 04, where it has long been known. Near Hull, 1805 (O.B.G.), extinct by 1902 (R. 1902).

L. montanus Bernh.　　　　　　Map 323.
Bitter-vetch.
Native. Permanent grassland, waysides, wood rides. Infrequent.
Several localities in the Birdsall, Kirkham area 76 & 86, on the cliffs near Reighton 17 and by the R. Derwent near Elvington 74.
Uncommon elsewhere:
L.D. Near Bielby 74, 1957, RG; Pocklington 84, 1980,

RGu.
Wolds Little Wood, North Newbald 93, 1962, FEC; near Muston 08, 1985, DRG.
Hold. Burton Bushes, Beverley 03, 1969, MC; near Arnold 13, 1979, FEC.

ROSACEAE

Spiraea L.
S. salicifolia L.
Bridewort.
Introduced.　　Uncommon.
L.D. Selby 63, JK (W. 1938); bank of R. Derwent, Wheldrake 64, 1980, JL.
Hold. Development site, Bridlington Ave, Hull 03, 1978, FEC.

S. douglasii Hook.
Introduced.　　Rare.
L.D. Houghton Woods 83, 1930, WAS (W. 1938) and 1953, RG.

Filipendula Mill.
F. vulgaris Moench (*Spiraea filipendula* L.)　　Map 13.
Dropwort.　　　　　　　　　　　　　　　　*c.*1845.
Native.　　Calcareous grassland.
Frequent in the grazed chalk grassland area of the Wolds. Rare in Holderness on glacial gravel: in fields and meadows at Burton Constable 13 and in 'the Leys', Hornsea 24, late 18th century, WW; on gravelly morainic mounds of Holderness as at Brandesburton (R. 1902), still in gravel pit, Brandesburton 14, 1956, RG; on morainic deposits, Arnold 13, 1973, FEC, still there.

F. ulmaria (L.) Maxim. (*Spiraea ulmaria* L.)　　Map 324.
Meadowsweet.
Native.　　Marshes, stream and drain sides, wet woods; in hedgerows and on roadsides on the clay soils of Holderness.　　Common.

Rubus L.
R. idaeus L.
Raspberry.
Native.　　Woods, copses.　　Fairly frequent.

R. saxatilis L.
Stone Bramble.
Native.
Driffield Canal area 05, 1929, YNU Excursion.

R. spectabilis Pursh.
Garden escape.　　Rare.
Wolds Hunmanby 07, 1965, EC; Risby Park 03, 1967, FEC.

R. caesius L.
Dewberry.
Native.　　Hedges, wood margins, lane sides.　　Frequent.

R. caesius x *R. idaeus*
Howsham 76, 1979, A. Newton (AN); Hunmanby Hall

school grounds 07, 1984, EC, conf. AN.

R. fruticosus L. *sensu lato*
Bramble.
Native.　Commons, woods, lanes, waste places; bird-sown in city gardens.　Very common.

The microspecies of *R. fruticosus*
The following account is based on the field records of A. Newton and herbarium specimens determined by him or E.S. Edees; many of the records of A. Newton are available as a ten km reference only. Records from specimens in the herbarium of the Yorkshire Philosophical Society determined by Revd W.M. Rogers (Catalogue of British Plants in the Herbarium by H.J. Wilkinson) are also included; other old records (see Robinson, 1902) are not included.

Sect. *Suberecti* P.J. Muell.

　R. bertramii G. Braun 63

　R. plicatus Weihe & Nees
　L.D. Allerthorpe Common 74, 1979, A. Newton (AN).

Sect. *Corylifolii* Lindley

　R. conjungens (Bab.) Rogers
　U.D. Sherburn 97, 1985, EC, det. AN.

　R. eboracensis Wats.
　L.D. Full Sutton 75, 1979, AN; North Cliffe 83, 1980, EC, det. AN.
　Wolds Ganton 97, 1985, EC, det. AN; Kilham　06, EC, det. AN.
　Hold. Kilnsea 41, 1979, AN; Cranswick 05, 1985, EC, det. AN.
　Also recorded for ten km squares: 64,73, 74, 96, 32.

　R. pruinosus Arrh. (*R. sublustris* Lees)
　L.D. Allerthorpe Common 74, 1959, RC, det. E.S. Edees; Dunnington 64, 1985, EC, det. AN;
　Holme upon Spalding Moor 83, 1985, EC, det. AN.
　Wolds Kilham 06, 1985, EC, det. AN.

　R. warrenii Sudre 76.

　Another as yet unnamed species has been found mainly in Holderness in 06, 13, 14 16; also in 93 & 16.

Sect. *Sylvatici* P.J. Muell.

　R. gratus Focke
　L.D. Houghton Woods 83, EC, det. AN.

　R. carpinifolius Weihe & Nees
　L.D. Skipwith 63, 1885, HJW, det. Revd W.M. Rogers (WMR).

　R. platyacanthus Muell. & Lef.
　L.D. Full Sutton 75, 1979, AN.

R. nemoralis P.J. Muell. (*R. selmeri* Lindeb.)
L.D. Langwith 64 and Skipwith 63, 1883, HJW, det. WMR; Skipwith 63 and Full Sutton 75, 1979, AN; Holme upon Spalding Moor 83, EC, det. AN.
Also recorded for ten km squares: 64, 65, 74.

R. laciniatus Willd.
Bird-sown garden alien.
Wolds Low Wood, Tibthorpe 95, 1958, FEC.
Hold. Garden weed, east Hull 13, 1979, FEC; Sutton on Hull 13, 1985, EC.

R. lindleianus Lees
L.D. Skipwith Common 63, 1979, AN; Dunnington 65, 1985, EC, det. AN.
Hold. Burton Bushes 03, 1979, AN.

R. robii (W. Wats.) A. Newton
L.D. Skipwith Common 63, 1979, AN; Allerthorpe Common 74, 1979, AN; Langwith 64, 1985, EC, det. AN.
Also recorded for ten km square 73.

R. amplificatus Lees
L.D. North Cliffe 83, 1985, EC & AN; Dunnington 64, 1985, EC & AN.
Hold. Cottingham 03, 1985, EC & AN.
Also recorded for ten km square 76.

R. pyramidalis Kalt.
L.D. Skipwith 63, 1985, EC & AN.

R. calvatus Lees ex Bloxam
L.D. Langwith 64, 1883, HJW, det. WMR.

R. polyanthemus Lindeb. (*R. pulcherrimus* Neum.)
L.D. Skipwith Common 63, 1979, AN; Full Sutton 75, 1979, AN; Tollingham 83, 1982, EC, det. AN; Holme upon Spalding Moor 83, 1985, EC, det. AN.
Hold. Beverley 03, 1979, AN.
Also recorded for ten km squares: 73, 74, 15.

R. cardiophyllus Muell. & Lefèv.
L.D. Skipwith Common 63, 1969, AN.

R. elegantispinosus (A. Schumach.) H.E. Weber
Established horticultural taxon.
U.D. Ganton 97, 1985, EC, det. AN.
Also recorded for ten km square 04.

Sect. *Discolores* P.J. Muell.

R. ulmifolius Schott
L.D. North Duffield 63, 1975, EC, det, E.S. Edees (ESE).
Hold. Burton Constable 13, 1969, AN and Burstwick 22, 1969, AN; Cranswick 05, 1985, EC, det. AN.
Also recorded for ten km squares 64, 73, 96, 14, 31.

R. procerus P.J. Muell.
Himalayan Giant.
Established horticultural taxon.

Hold. Brandesburton 14, 1975, EC, det. AN.
Also recorded for ten km square 74.

R. anglocandicans A. Newton (*R. falcatus* Kalt.)
Hold. Brandesburton 14, 1975, EC, det. ESE; Burstwick 22, 1979, AN.
Also recorded for ten km square 04.

Sect. *Sprengeliani* (Focke) Watson

R. sprengelii Weihe
L.D. Skipwith 63, 1985, EC, det. AN.

Sect. *Appendiculati* (Genev.) Sudre

R. vestitus Weihe & Nees
U.D. Howsham 76, 1979, AN.

R. leucostachys Schleich.
Skipwith 63, 1885, HJW, det. WMR.

R. mucronulatus Bor. (*R. mucronifer* Sudre)
L.D. Sutton Wood 64, 1961, RC, det. ESE; Allerthorpe 74, 1979, AN; small form, Houghton Wood 83, EC, det. AN; Langwith 64, 1985, EC, det. AN; North Cliffe 83, 1985, EC, det. AN.

R. leyanus Rogers
Hold. Between Sewerby and Bridlington 16, 1897, H.J. Fisher, herb. HJW, det. WMR.

R. radula Weihe ex Boenn.
U.D. Burythorpe 76, 1979, EC, det. AN.
L.D. Full Sutton 75, 1979, AN.
Wolds Between Kilham and Rudston 06, 1985, EC, det. AN.
Also recorded for ten km squares: 74, 96, 14.

R. echinatoides (Rogers) Sudre
L.D. North Duffield 63, 1975, EC, det. ESE; Dunnington 64, 1985, EC, det. AN.
Hold. Burton Bushes 03, 1979, AN; Burton Constable 13, 1979, AN.
Also recorded for ten km squares: 96, 14.

R. rosaceus Weihe & Nees
L.D. Langwith 64, 1885, HJW, det. WMR.

Sect. *Glandulosi* P.J. Muell.

R. hylocharis W.C.R. Wats.
L.D. Melbourne 74, 1975, EC, det. ESE; Full Sutton 75, 1979, AN; Tollingham 83, 1982, EC, det. AN; Langwith 64, 1985, EC, det. AN.; Elvington 64, 1985, EC, det. AN.

R. dasyphyllus (Rogers) Rogers
U.D. Kennythorpe 76, 1985, EC, det. AN.
Wolds Sledmere 96, 1982, EC, det. AN; Boynton 16, 1985, EC, det. AN.

Potentilla L.

P. palustris (L.) Scop.   Map 194.
Marsh Cinquefoil.   CNE.   1820.
Native. Fens and bogs; may be locally dominant. Uncommon; some habitat loss.
U.D. Low Moor, near Rillington 87, 1970, RMH; Kennythorpe Moor 76, 1970, ATD; Leavening 76, 1975, EC.
L.D. Heslington 64, 1820, WM (R. 1902) and 1957, FEC; Skipwith Common 63, WNC (R. 1902) and 1970, FEC; near Howden 72, JBe (R. 1902); near Snake Hall 83, 1953, FEC; Duck Nest 83, 1955, RG, still there; Allerthorpe Common 74, 1958, ABM & 1984, YNU Excursion.
Hold. Lowthorpe 06 and Pulfin Bog 04 (R. 1902), still at Pulfin, 1954, FEC; near R. Hull, Driffield 05 (R. 1902) and 1970, MC; near Wansford 05, 1960, FEC, still present; Hornsea Mere 14 (R. 1902) and 1982, FEC; Roos Bog 22, 1949, RL; Kelleythorpe 05, 1955, RG; near Fraisthorpe 16, 1970, MC.

P. sterilis (L.) Garcke (*P. fragariastrum* Pers.) Map 325.
Barren Strawberry.
Native. Scrub, open woods, wood margins, hedgebanks. Locally frequent; mainly on the Wolds.

P. anserina L.
Silverweed.
Native. Roadsides, waste places, sand dunes, field sides. Common. Thrives on bare ground, where it can extend its runners to form a carpet.

P. recta L.
Suphur Cinquefoil.
Established alien.   Rare.
L.D. Grassy field, Bielby 74, 1958, FEC, persisting for some years; disused airfield, Pocklington 74, 1984, JD.

P. norvegica L.
Ternate-leaved Cinquefoil.
Alien.   Casual.   Rare now.
L.D. Old mill site, Brough 92, 1939, AKW.
Hold. Frequent on the dock wastes, Hull (R. 1902); Ings Road, Hull 13, 1933, AEW; King George Dock, Hull 12, 1931, FS & 1936, AKW (W. 1938) and 1959, FEC; Victoria Dock site, Hull 12, 1972, EC.

P. tabernaemontani Aschers.
Spring Cinquefoil.
Native.   Calcareous grassland.   Very rare.
Knapton Wold 87, 1974, G. Simpson.

P. erecta (L.) Räusch. (*P. silvestris* Neck.)   Map 326.
Tormentil.
Native. Commons, heaths, edges of fens, particularly common on light acid soils. Common on the sandy soils of Derwentland; locally frequent on Wolds grasslands and in the R. Hull valley; uncommon in Holderness east of the R. Hull valley.

P. anglica Laichard. (*P. procumbens* Sibth.)
Trailing Tormentil.   CNE.
Native. Wood edges, grassland on slightly acid soil. Rare.
L.D. Houghton Woods 83, Allerthorpe 74 and Skipwith

Common 63 (R. 1902), still on Skipwith Common, 1984, EB; wood ride, Langwith 64, 1965, FEC; near North Cliffe 83, 1972, EC, det. F.Perring; Duck Nest 83, 1981, EC.

P. anglica x **P. erecta** = **P.** x **suberecta** Zimmet.
Sometimes replacing *P. anglica* in grassland in Lower Derwentland: Everingham Carrs 74, 1960, FEC, det. D.E. Allen; Hasholme Carr 83, 1980, FEC.

P. reptans L.
Creeping Cinquefoil.   1840.
Native. Grassland, roadsides, grassy lanes on basic and neutral soils; chalk and gravel pits, fixed dunes. Common.

Fragaria L.

F. vesca L.   Map 327.
Wild Strawberry.
Native. Woods and scrub on base-rich soils; basic grassland; chalk pits. Frequent on the Wolds, scarce elsewhere.

F. moschata Duchesne (*F. elatior* Ehrh.)
Hautbois Strawberry.
Introduced.
In young plantations, Brantingham 93, CW (R. 1902).

F. ananassa Duchesne
Garden Strawberry.
Introduced; the commonly cultivated Strawberry.
Naturalised occasionally on railway banks and beside tracks.
L.D. Oxmardyke 82, 1957, RG.
Hold. Hessle 02, 1931, AKW; near Wassand Low Crossing 14, 1980, FEC; near Withernsea 32, 1984, KS.

Geum L.

G. urbanum L.   Map 328.
Wood Avens.
Native. Woods, hedgebanks and shady places. Common.

G. rivale L.   Map 329.
Water Avens.
Native. By springs, in marshes and in damp woods on base-rich soils. Usually in shade. Locally frequent in a belt at the western side of the Wolds; uncommon elsewhere.
Along railway lines: Weedley 93, 1970, FEC; near Driffield 05, 1970, MC; near Burdale 86, 1981, FEC; Bubwith 73, 1982, FEC.
Absent from marshes and woods of the R. Hull valley and the rest of Holderness except in the Cottingham area.

G. rivale x **G. urbanum** = **G.** x **intermedium** Ehrh.
                                                    Map 330.
Occurring with one or both parents. Not uncommon in woods on the Wolds in the main distribution zone of *Geum rivale*.

Agrimonia L.

A. eupatoria L.   Map 331.
Agrimony.
Native. Grassy banks, roadsides, wood clearings, sides of railway tracks. Frequent and widely distributed, but rarely in quantity.

A. procera Wallr. [*A. odorata* auct., non (Gouan) Mill.]
Fragrant Agrimony.   1946.
Native.   Wood borders, hedges, roadsides, cliffs.   Rare.
Hunmanby cliffs 17, 1946, SMW;   Fish Ponds Wood,
Risby 03, 1948, GD & JE & 1957, RG, herb. HLU.

Alchemilla L.
A. vulgaris L. *sensu lato*
Lady's-mantle.
Native.   Somewhat infrequent.   The distribution of the
following species may not be fully known.

A. filicaulis Buser subsp.*vestita* (Buser) M.E. Bradshaw
Hairy Lady's-mantle.   CNE.
Grassland.   Uncommon.
U.D.   Field below Howsham Wood 76, 1956, FEC.
Wolds Raywell 93, 1952, GD;   Weedley 93, 1952, DAW;
Millington Pastures 85, 1953, FHP;   North Grimston 86,
1954, RG;   North Newbald 93, 1955, FEC;   Bishop Wilton
85, 1957, FEC;   green lane, near Croomdale Plantation 96,
1957, RG.
Hold. Cottingham 03, 1956, RG;   near Wansford 05, 1956,
RG;   Risby 03, 1958, FEC.

A. xanthochlora Rothm.
Intermediate Lady's-mantle.
Native.   Grassland, open woods.   Uncommon.
U.D.   Kennythorpe 76, 1958, FEC;   Kirkham Abbey
Woods 76, 1958, RG;   near Firby 76, 1980, NCC.
Wolds Oxpasture Wood 86, 1956, RG;   Low Wood,
Tibthorpe 95, 1958, FEC;   Spring Wood, Tibthorpe 95,
1961, MEB;   Settrington Wood 87, 1969, TFM.

A. glabra Neygenf.
Smooth Lady's-mantle.   CNE.
Native.   Grassland, open woods.   Uncommon.
L.D.   Black Plantation, Holme upon Spalding Moor 73,
1957, RG, herb. HLU.
Hold.   Cottingham 03, 1952, GD, herb. HLU;   waste
ground, east Hull 13, 1953, FEC, det. M.E. Bradshaw.

Aphanes L.
A. arvensis L. [*Alchemilla arvensis* (L.) Scop.] Map 332.
Parsley-piert.
Native.   Arable fields and other open habitats on both basic
and acid soils; in sand and gravel pits.   Common on the
Wolds, infrequent elsewhere.

A. mexspectata Lippert [*A. microcarpa* auct., non (Boiss.
& Reut.) Rothm.]
Slender Parsley-piert.   1953.
Native.   Arable fields and other open habitats on sandy acid
soils, more rarely on gravel.   Uncommon.
U.D.   Sands Wood, Wintringham 87, 1956, RG, herb.
HLU;   near Potter Brompton 97, EC.
L.D.   Houghton Woods 83, 1953, RG;   Skipwith Common
63, 1954, CMR;   Langwith Common 64, 1965, YNU
Excursion;   Barmby Moor 74, 1973, FEC.
Hold. Rise Park 14, 1982, FEC;   near Brigham 05, 1987,
EC.

Sanguisorba L.
S. officinalis L. [*Poterium officinale* (L.) A. Gray] Map 55.
Great Burnet.   1803.
Native.   Damp grassland mainly, but sometimes in apparently dry grassy places, in lanes and on railway banks.   A
characteristic plant of the flood meadows by the R. Derwent.   Locally frequent in Lower Derwentland and on clay
over chalk in the Birdsall area;   uncommon elsewhere.

S. minor Scop.
Subsp. *minor* (*Poterium sanguisorba* L.)
Salad Burnet.   Map 24.
Native.   Calcareous grassland, chalk quarries, railway
embankments; sometimes on neutral soils.   Widely distributed and common on the Wolds, uncommon elsewhere as
on the gravels of Holderness.

Subsp. *muricata* Briq. (*Poterium polygamum* Waldst. &
Kit.)
Fodder Burnet.   1960.
An alien, native of the Mediterranean region.   Formerly
grown as a fodder crop and occurring as a relic of cultivation
on roadsides and waste places.   May also occur as a more
recent introduction.   Rare.
Wolds On roadside between Foxholes and Sherburn 97,
1960, WAS.
Hold. On railway sidings, Hessle Road, Hull 02, 1972,
FEC and by disused railway, Swine 13, 1981, FEC.

Acaena Mutis ex L.
A. novae-zelandiae Kirk (*A. anserinifolia* auct.)
Pirri-pirri-bur.
Alien.   Native of E. Australia and New Zealand.
Naturalised on disused runway of airfield, Skipwith Com-
mon 63, 1960, Hull Nats. Excursion, persisting.

Rosa L.
R. arvensis Huds.
Field-rose.
Native.   Hedges, woods and scrub.   Frequent.

R. arvensis x *R. canina* = *R.* x *wheldonii* W.-Dod
Cliff top, Hunmanby Gap 17, 1980, EC.

R. pimpinellifolia L.
Burnet Rose.   CE.   1901.
Native.   Cliff tops, hedges.   Uncommon and local.
On the coast of Filey Bay e.g. near Reighton and Hun-
manby 17.
Rare inland: Kilnwick 94, 1905, FHW (Nat. 1905, 217);
Sunderlandwick 05, 1971, FEC.

R. rugosa Thunb.
Japanese Rose.
Established alien.
Sand le mere 33, 1957, RG.

R. canina L.
Dog-rose.
Native. Hedges, woods, scrub. Common.
Various varieties occur:
Var. *hemitricha* (Rip.) W.-Dod Near Folkton 07, 1974,

EC.
Var. *sylvalorum* (Rip.) Rouy Near Cottam 96, 1980,
EC.
Var. *senticosa* (Ach.) Baker Cliff top, Hunmanby Gap
17, 1980, EC.
Var. *stenocarpa* (Déségl.) Rouy Between Kilham and
Rudston 86, 1980, EC.
Determinations by Dr R. Melville (RM).

R. canina x *R. coriifolia*
Near Kilham 06, 1980, EC.

R. dumetorum Thuill.
Native.
Distinguished from *R. canina* L. by Dr R. Melville.
Wolds Var. *hemitricha* (Rip.) W.-Dod Near Folkton 07,
1974, and at Kilham 06, 1980, EC, det. RM.
f. *urbica* (Lem.) W.-Dod Cliff top, Hunmanby Gap 17,
1980 EC, det. RM.

R. afzeliana Fr. (*R. dumalis* Bechst.)
Native. Woods, hedges, scrub.
L.D. Near Fulford 64, 1981, EB, det. Dr Melderis.
Wolds Var. *glaucophylla* (Winch) W.-Dod Near Kilham
06, 1980, EC, det. RM.

R. afzeliana x *R. sherardii*
Near Kilham 06, 1980, EC, det. RM.

R. coriifolia Fr. var. *subcollina* Chr.   CNE.
Native.
Near Folkton 07, 1974, EC, det. RM.

R. coriifolia x *R. canina*
Near Kilham 06, 1980, EC, det. RM.

R. obtusifolia Desv.
Round-leaved Dog-rose.
Native. Hedges, scrub, etc.
Leconfield 04, CW (R. 1902).

R. tomentosa Sm.
Harsh Downy-rose.
Native. Woods, hedges, scrub.
L.D. Banks of R. Derwent (Baines, 1840); Langwith 64,
1883, HJW (R. 1902).
Wolds Primrose Valley 17, 1956, RG.
Hold. Leconfield 04, CW (R. 1902).
Var. *globosa* Hilston 23 (R. 1902).

R. sherardii Davies
Sherard's Downy-rose.
Native. Woods, hedges, scrub.
Wolds Filey 18, 1922 (N.H. Scarb.).
Var. *suberecta* (Ley) W.-Dod Cliff top, Hunmanby 17,
1980, EC, det. RM.
Hold. Var. *omissa* (Déségl.) W.-Dod Withernsea 32,
1947, RL.

R. mollis Sm. (*R. villosa* auct., non L.)
Soft Downy-rose.
Native. Woods, hedges, scrub.

L.D. Langwith 64, 1883, HJW (R. 1902).
Wolds Var. *mollis* Sm. f. *glandulosa* W.-Dod Near
Folkton 07, 1974, EC, det. RM.

R. rubiginosa L.
Sweet-briar.   CE.
Native. Scrub and hedges, mainly on calcareous soils.
Wolds High Fordon 07, 1916, G.W. Temperley (N.H.
Scarb.).
Hold. Spurn 41 (R. 1902); by Driffield Canal 05, 1960,
YNU Excursion.

R. arvensis x *R. gallica* = *R.* x *alba* L.
Introduced.
Wolds Chalk quarry, Foxholes 07, 1974, EC.

Prunus L.
P. spinosa L.
Blackthorn.
Native. Hedges, woods, thickets; on all soils. Still com-
mon, but cleared from many waysides in recent years.

P. domestica L. subsp. *domestica*
Wild Plum.
Introduced and commonly grown.
Mainly hedges, often near villages; very variable.
Infrequent but widely distributed.

Subsp. *insititia* (L.) C.K. Schneid.
Bullace.
Naturalised alien. Still persisting in some hedges, less
common than formerly.

P. avium (L.) L.
Wild Cherry.
Native. Woods and hedges. Infrequent and mainly on the
Wolds.
Other records:
Hold. Cottingham 03, 1950, AKW; Burton Constable 13,
1954, RG; Burton Bushes, Beverley 03, 1975, FEC.

P. padus L.
Bird Cherry.
Probably always introduced. Woods. Uncommon.
L.D. Skirpenbeck 75, 1956, MT.
Wolds Hanging Fall Wood, Sledmere 96, 1960, YNU
Excursion.
Hold. 'Very uncommon in Holderness' (R. 1902); Park
Lane, Cottingham 03, 1951, AKW.

Cotoneaster Medicus
C. horizontalis Decne.
Wall Cotoneaster.
Cultivated; rarely bird-sown.
Wolds In chalk pit, Hessle 02, 1967, FEC.

Pyracantha M.J. Roem.
P. coccinea M.J. Roem.
Pyracantha.
Established garden escape.   Rare.
Chalk pit, Hessle 02, 1956, RG.

Crataegus L.

C. laevigata (Poir.) DC. (*C. oxyacanthoides* Thuill.)
Midland Hawthorn.
Native. Woods, less frequent in hedges.
Only rarely recorded, but there has been insufficient critical study of Hawthorns.
U.D. Leavening 76, 1975, YNU Excursion.
L.D. Dunnington 65, 1955, RG, herb. HLU; near Naburn 64, 1980, EB.
Hold. Sand dunes near Easington 31, 1955 and Gransmoor Wood 16, 1957, RG, herb. HLU.

C. monogyna Jacq.
Hawthorn.
Native. Scrub, woods and hedges. Common dominant in scrub on all soils. Widely planted at time of enclosure and still the commonest hedgerow shrub; also bird-sown. Many hedges have been destroyed in the last twenty years to create larger fields.

Sorbus L.

S. aucuparia L. [*Pyrus aucuparia* (L.) Ehrh.]
Rowan.
Native, also frequently planted and often bird-sown. Woods, scrub, hedges. Mainly on the sandy acid soils of Lower Derwentland. Found in 17% of hedges examined in Lower Derwentland and not found in hedges elsewhere (Boatman, 1980).

S. intermedia (Ehrh.) Pers. (*Pyrus intermedia* Ehrh.)
Swedish Whitebeam.
Planted and sometimes bird-sown.
Wolds North Ferriby 92 (R. 1902).
Hold. Near Aldborough and Roos 23, *c.*1972, EBM.

S. aria (L.) Crantz [*Pyrus aria* (L.) Ehrh.]
Common Whitebeam.
Introduced. In copses and hedges.
Wolds Hedge, N.W. of St Austin's Stone 93, 1955, RG; Bainton 95, 1978, EBM.
Hold. Cottingham and Willerby 03 (R. 1902).

Pyrus L.

P. pyraster Burgsd. (*P. communis* auct.)
Wild Pear.   1840.
Introduced. Hedges, wood borders, also as isolated trees.
L.D. North Cave 83 (R. 1902); large tree on road, north of Yokefleet 82, 1954, RG.
Wolds Roadside scrub, near Little Wood, Walkington 93 (Boatman, 1975).

Malus Mill.

M. sylvestris Mill. (*Pyrus malus* L.)
Crab Apple.
Native. Woods, hedges, scrub. Often descended from cultivated apples. Widely distributed and locally frequent. In 47% of hedges examined in Lower Derwentland, in 5% of those on the Wolds and in 18% of those in Holderness (Boatman, 1980).

CRASSULACEAE

Sedum L.

S. telephium L.
Orpine.   1840.
Native. Usually on sandy or gravelly soil; may be a garden escape. Uncommon.
L.D. Heslington Fields and Fulford 64 (Baines, 1840); near Skipwith 63, 1920, WI; railway bank, near Broomfleet 82, 1964, FEC & PMG; disused railway, near Asselby 72, 1983, YNU Bot. Sect. Excursion.
Hold. Pulfin Bog 04, 1951, RL & FEC, persisting for some years.

S. anglicum Huds.
English Stonecrop.
Alien.
L.D. Airfield, Pocklington 74, 1984, YNU Excursion.

S. album L.
White Stonecrop.
Established garden escape.
Hold. Kilnsea Warren 41, 1952, RG, still there.

S. acre L.   Map 246.
Biting Stonecrop.
Native. On well drained soils; walls, fixed dunes, chalk quarries, sand pits, railway tracks and platforms. Widely distributed, particularly frequent along disused railway lines and sometimes in great quantity. Reported as formerly frequent on gravelly chalk fields (R. 1902).

S. reflexum L.
Reflexed Stonecrop.
Introduced. Rare.
L.D. Disused railway station, Harswell 84, 1987, FEC.
Hold. Church wall, Skipsea 15, 1957, RG, still present; disused railway station, Ottringham 22, 1986, FEC.

Sempervivum L.

S. tectorum L.
House-leek.
Introduced. Formerly often on old wall tops and thatch in villages (R. 1902). Uncommon now.
Wolds Rudston (R. 1902); cottage roof, Thwing 07, 1983, EC; churchyard wall, Goodmanham 84, 1983, EC.
Hold. Thearne 13 and Hornsea Bridge 24, FS (W. 1938); Beeford 15, 1955, RG; Castle Hill, Cottingham 03, 1956, RG; Coniston 13, 1956, RG.

SAXIFRAGACEAE

Saxifraga L.

S. spathularis Brot. x **S. umbrosa** = **S.** x **urbium** D.A. Webb
Londonpride.
Introduced. Uncommon.
Wolds Londesborough 84 (Baines, 1840); near Hessle station 02, 1931, AKW; Hunmanby 07, 1971, EC; Beckhead Wood, Great Givendale 85, 1986, JL.

S. hirsuta L.
Kidney Saxifrage.
Introduced. Plentiful in a wood, Boynton 16 (Flintoff, 1931). Naturalised in Hunmanby Hall grounds 07, 1980, EC, det. Professor Webb.

S. hirsuta x *S. umbrosa* = *S.* x *geum* L.
Introduced at Boynton 16, Major Lawson (Flintoff, 1931); Hunmanby Hall grounds 07, 1980, EC.

S. spathularis x *S. hirsuta* = *S.* x *polita* (Haw.) Link
Plants in Hunmanby Hall plantation 07, 1980, EC are probably this hybrid, having arisen locally from the parents, naturalised there for over fifty years, the *S. hirsuta* present being an unusual form (det. Prof. Webb).

S. tridactylites L.
Rue-leaved Saxifrage.   1836.
Native. On walls and in open habitats on calcareous soils, more rarely in sand pits. Uncommon.
Sometimes in great quantity as in a first ley on chalk, Worsendale 85, 1957, FEC and on a disused railway line 94, Kipling Cotes, 1977, HiP.
U.D. Sand pit, Flixton 07, 1958, FEC.
L.D. Heslington 64, 1836, HPa, Hotham 93 (R. 1902); airfield, Holme upon Spalding Moor 83, 1978, AP; Hemingborough 63, 1981, DRG.
Wolds North Newbald 93 (R. 1902) and 1969, MC; St Austin's Stone, Drewton Dale 93 (R. 1902) and 1954, FEC; 'Fairy Stones', Burdale 86 (R. 1902) and 1968, MC; Staxton Wold 07, 1955, TFM; near Hunmanby 17, 1973, MC.
Hold. Old house tops, Hull, GN (R. 1902); old wall, Cottingham 03, 1955, IG.

S. granulata L.
Meadow Saxifrage.
Native. Basic and neutral grassland. Uncommon.
Described as 'locally abundant in Derwentland and in gravelly places in Holderness', but only five localities are specified (R. 1902).
L.D. Brough 92, CW, North Cave 83 (R. 1902); still at Brough, 1953, AKW; Hotham and Dryham 83, 1951, FEC.
Wolds Lowthorpe 06, Fimber 86, MBS (R. 1902); North Newbald 93, 1951, FEC; Staple Howe, Knapton 87, 1958, FEC; Millington Pastures 85, 1958, FEC; Birdsall 86, 1970, MC; Brantingham 93, 1976, JA; South Cave 93, 1980, JES.
Hold. Kelsey Hill 22 (R. 1902); still there, 1945, FEC.

Tellima R.Br.
T. grandiflora (Pursh) Dougl. ex Lindl.
Fringe-cups.
Established garden escape. Uncommon.
Wolds Hunmanby Hall grounds 07, 1971, EC; woodland, near Ellerker 92, 1976, JA.

Chrysosplenium L.
C. oppositifolium L.   Map 67.
Opposite-leaved Golden-saxifrage.   1810.
Native. Streamsides, spring-fed marshes, wet grounds in woods; usually in shade. Infrequent and local.

Most post-1950 records are for the ten km squares 76, 86 and 03.
Other records:
L.D. Langwith 64, 1810, WM.
Wolds By stream, Pocklington Wood 85, 1957, RG.

C. alternifolium L.
Alternate-leaved Golden-saxifrage.   CNE.
Native. Wet woods. Rare.
U.D. Settrington Wood 87, MBS (R. 1902), conf. 1969, MC.
L.D. Moreby Park 64, 1929, HB.

PARNASSIACEAE

Parnassia L.
P. palustris L.
Grass-of-Parnassus.   CNE.   1840.
Native. Marshes, including fens. Said to be formerly common in wet clayey places in all divisions (R. 1902), ten localities being specified. Uncommon now.
Most recent records are for the cliffs of Filey Bay 17, where it has long been known.
Other records:
U.D. Kirkham 76 (Baines, 1840); near Wintringham 87, 1964, FEC; Flixton Carrs 07, 1971, FEC & MC, the last two habitats now drained.
L.D. In spongy boggy places in Heslington Fields 64 (Baines, 1840); Brough 92, CW and Allerthorpe Common 74 (R. 1902).
Wolds Newbald Springs (R. 1902), still present, but in small quantity, 1968, FEC; Drewton Dale 93 (R. 1902).
Hold. Cottingham Common 03 (R. 1902), habitat destroyed. Near the R. Hull and its feeder streams: Bell Mills 05 (R. 1902) and 1970, MC; Kelleythorpe 05, 1949, RL; near Wansford 05, 1963, FEC. Carnaby airfield 16, 1969, MC; gravel pit, Brandesburton 14, 1969, EC & 1981, FEC.

GROSSULARIACEAE

Ribes L.
R. rubrum L. [*R. sylvestre* (Lam.) Mert. & Koch]
Red Currant.
May be native in a few localities, but also bird-sown from gardens. Infrequent.

R. nigrum L.
Black Currant.
Native, also bird-sown from gardens. Woods and hedges. Very infrequent; several scattered records.

R. alpinum L.
Mountain Currant.
Introduced; an escape of cultivation. Uncommon.
Wolds Welton 92 (R. 1902); Londesborough 84 (R. 1902) and 1958, RG; Raywell 93, 1955, RG; Boynton 16, 1969, MC.

R. uva-crispa L. (*R. grossularia* L.)
Gooseberry.
Probably always a garden escape. Woods and hedges.
Frequent.

DROSERACEAE

Drosera L.
D. rotundifolia L.
Round-leaved Sundew.   CNE.
Native. On wet acid soils, mainly on dyke sides. Rare.
L.D. Near Market Weighton 83, JJM and on Skipwith
Common 63, WNC & HJW (R. 1902); still at Skipwith,
1964, FEC and on Allerthorpe Common 74, 1957, FEC,
still present.

D. anglica Huds.
Great Sundew.   CNE.
Native. Usually amongst *Sphagnum* on the wetter parts of
bogs.
Only recorded for Scagglethorpe 87, MBS and long extinct
(R. 1902).

D. intermedia Hayne
Oblong-leaved Sundew.   CNE.   1883.
Native.   Damp places on heaths.   Rare.
L.D. Near Market Weighton 83, JJM and Skipwith 63,
1883, WNC & HJW, still at Skipwith in 1900 (R. 1902) and
later (Flintoff, 1931, 231); Ricall Common 63, WNC
(YNU Circ., 1912); Allerthorpe Common 74, 1985, CH.

LYTHRACEAE

Lythrum L.
L. salicaria L.   Map 153.
Purple-loosestrife.   *c.*1845.
Native. By rivers, ponds and drains; in reed swamps at lake
and canal margins, marshy-meadows. Frequent in the R.
Hull valley and locally frequent in Lower Derwentland;
scattered elsewhere.

L. portula (L.) D.A. Webb (*Peplis portula* L.)
Water-purslane.   1883.
Native. Damp places on sandy acid soils, including marshy
ground along woodland rides. Uncommon.
L.D. Houghton Woods 83, 1892, JJM (R. 1902) and 1958,
FEC; Skipwith Common 63, 1883, HJW (R. 1902) and
1933, WAS; North Cliffe Wood 83, 1955, RG; Langwith
Common 64, 1956, FEC; near Sandhill Lock 74, 1957,
FEC; Allerthorpe Common 74, 1958, FEC & 1985, DRG;
South Cliffe 83, 1981, DRG.

THYMELAEACEAE

Daphne L.
D. laureola L.   Map 71.
Spurge-laurel.   CNE.   1836.
Native.   Woods and hedges.   Very infrequent.
Records include:

L.D. Wheldrake 64, 1982, EB.
Wolds Londesborough 84 (Baines, 1840); near Branting-
ham 93 (R. 1902) and 1976, JA; Lowthorpe and Thwing 06,
1969, MC; Burton Agnes, Rudston and Boynton 16, 1970,
MC; North Grimston 86, 1973, EHW.
Hold. Easington 31 (R. 1902); near Burton Constable 13
(R. 1902) and 1978, FEC; woods by Hornsea Mere 14,
1955, FEC.

ELAEAGNACEAE

Hippophae L.
H. rhamnoides L.
Sea-buckthorn.   1884.
Native. 'Abundant on the sandy peninsula of Spurn, being
the principal shrub there' (R. 1902), first recorded in 1884,
P.F. Lee. Continued to be the dominant plant over considerable areas but its spread was checked by rabbits eating the
young shoots until the spread of myxomatosis in 1953 from
which time its dominance greatly increased. Also bird-
sown on the bank of the nearby Kilnsea canal and on the
Humber bank near Easington 31, 1975 and as far away as
the Kelsey Hill gravel pits 22, 1955-1962, FEC. Also
recorded for Filey Bay 17, 1886, N. Masterman, herb. BM
(Groves, 1958); near Filey 17, 1957, RG.

ONAGRACEAE

Epilobium L.
E. hirsutum L.   Map 333.
Great Willowherb.
Native. By rivers, canals, dykes, ponds; may be a local
dominant in marshes and reed swamps; sometimes in drier
areas particularly on clay soils as on Hull bombed sites and
on Holderness roadsides. Common.
On 15% of all bombed sites and on 41% of sites in the Old
Town, Hull, 1950-1953, FEC.

E. hirsutum x *E. parviflorum* = *E.* x *intermedium*
Ruhmer
Derwent banks at Ganton 97, 1948, HR (N.H. Scarb.).

E. hirsutum x *E. montanum* = *E.* x *erroneum* Hausskn.
Knapton, 87, 1957, F.E. Crackles, det. G.M. Ash, herb.
FEC.

E. hirsutum x *E. obscurum* = *E.* x *anglicum* E.S. Marshall
Derwent banks, near Ganton 97, 1948, HR (N.H. Scarb.).

E. parviflorum Schreb.   Map 334.
Hoary Willowherb.
Native. Stream banks, marshes, fens; more rarely on drier
ground. Frequent.

E. montanum L.
Broad-leaved Willowherb.
Native. Woods, plantations, mainly on base-rich soils,
hedgerows, waste places; a garden weed extending into
built-up areas. Common.

E. montanum x *E. roseum* = *E.* x *mutabile* Boiss. & Reut.
Bombed site, Blanket Row 02, Hull, 1950, F.E. Crackles, det. G.M. Ash; Escrick Park 64, 1982, FEC.

E. roseum Schreb.
Pale Willowherb.
Native. Damp places in woods, plantations; garden weed and on waste places. Uncommon.
L.D. Garden weed, Fulford 64, 1981, EB; Escrick Park 64, 1982, FEC.
Wolds Leman's Wood 94, 1956, RG; wood, Lowthorpe 06, 1972, FEC; near Burton Fleming 07, 1977, EC.
Hold. Dyke side, near Cottingham 03 (R. 1902); as a casual on Hull docks (W. 1938); on several bombed sites in Hull 02 & 12, 1950-1953, FEC, not seen in Hull since; garden weed, Driffield 05, 1977, EC.

E. ciliatum Rafin. (*E. adenocaulon* Hausskn.) Map 255.
American Willowherb.   1952.
Established alien; native of N. America.
First British record 1891. Waste places, gardens, hedges, railway tracks. Infrequent, but spreading rapidly.
First noted on a bombed site in central Hull 02, 1952 and on three other bombed sites, Hull 02 & 12 in 1953, FEC, det. G.M. Ash. Continued to spread in the Hull area, noted in east Hull 13, 1973, FEC. It has become widely distributed in v.c. 61 since 1970.
Pre-1975 records outside Hull:
L.D. Roadside, near Skipwith Common 63, 1969, TFM; Everingham 84, 1969, MC; Naburn Lane, near York 64, 1971, TFM; Market Weighton 84, 1972, FEC.
Wolds Wharram 86, 1969, MC; Londesborough Park 84, 1972, TFM; Lowthorpe 06, 1972, FEC.
Hold. Gas works, Bridlington 16, 1970; Beverley 03, 1971, FEC.

E. ciliatum x *E. parviflorum*
Foston on Wolds 05, 1978, EC, det., T.D. Pennington.

E. tetragonum L. (*E. adnatum* Griseb.)
Square-stalked Willowherb.   1938.
Native? Waste places, gravel pits, gardens. Uncommon.
All records for Holderness: casual on Hull docks 12 (W 1938); cinder road, Cottingham 03, 1949, RG, herb. HLU; frequent on site of Hedon Road tram sheds, Hull 12, 1953, FEC and on four east-central Hull bombed sites 13, 1950-1953, FEC, det. G.M. Ash; Kelsey and Burstwick gravel pits 22, 1955, FEC; gravel pit, Catwick 14, 1957, RG, herb. HLU; garden weed, Driffield 05, 1979, EC.

E. adnatum x *E. obscurum* = *E.* x *thuringiacum*
Hausskn.
King George Dock, Hull 12, 1937, AKW, det. G.M. Ash (Nat. 1938, 46).

E. lamyi F.W. Schultz   1937.
Alien. Waste places. Rare.
Hold. King George Dock, Hull 12, 1937, CMR (BEC *12*, 41); bombed sites, Emily St, Hull 12, 1952, FEC, det. G.M. Ash and Percy St, Hull 02, 1975, FEC.

E. obscurum Schreb.   Map 335.
Short-fruited Willowherb.   1798.
Native. Clearings in moist woods; damp ground by ponds, lakes and dykes. Infrequent.
Most records for Lower Derwentland including: Langwith Common 64, 1956, FEC; Sutton Wood 64, 1958, FEC and Houghton Woods 83, 1972, FEC.
Scattered elsewhere:
U.D. Muston Carr Farm 08, 1946, SMW.
Wolds Sewerby 26, 1970, MC; Londesborough Park 84, 1978, YNU Excursion.
Hold. Rise Park 14, 1971, FEC; near Hornsea Mere 14, 1980, RH; near Hollym 32, 1984, FEC.

E. palustre L.   Map 182.
Marsh Willowherb.
Native. Marshes, fens, by ponds.
Widely distributed, but somewhat infrequent. Said to be formerly 'common in dykes near Hull and Cottingham' (R. 1902); not so now.
Usually regarded as a calcifuge, but the East Riding distribution does not reflect this nor does it throw a great deal of light on its requirements.

E. palustre x *E. parviflorum* = **E.** x *rivulare* Wahlenb.
By lagoon, near Withernsea 32, 1986, FEC.

Chamerion Rafin.
C. angustifolium (L.) J. Holub [*Chamaenerion angusti-folium* (L.) Scop.; *Epilobium angustifolium* L.]
Rosebay Willowherb.
Native. Wood margins and clearings; waste places; railway banks; gardens.
Very common and often dominant over considerable areas. Until the middle of the last century, the species was a local British plant, occurring mainly in rocky places and on scree.
First vice-county records are in Robinson, 1902:
L.D. Houghton Woods 83, Skipwith Common 63.
Wolds Near South Cave, Yorkdale and Sledmere Woods 96, MBS, Elloughton Vale 92, CW.
It occurred on 65% of Hull bombed sites, 1950-1953, FEC.

Oenothera L.
O. biennis L.
Common Evening-primrose.
Established alien. Native of N. America. Casual. Waste places. Rare.
L.D. Olympia Oil Mill Sidings, Selby 63, 1937, AKW (W. 1938).
Hold. King George Dock, Hull 12, 1933, AKW, Anlaby Common 02, 1937, AKW (W. 1938); bombed site, Hull 12, 1950, FEC; Queen Elizabeth Dock, Hull 12, 1983, FEC; Alexandra Dock, Hull 12, 1986, FEC.

O. glazioviana Micheli ex C. Martius. (*O. erythrosepala* Borbás)
Large-flowered Evening-primrose.   1956.
Established alien. Waste places. Uncommon.
U.D. Rillington 86, 1958, FEC.
L.D. Skirpenbeck 75, 1956, MT; Poor Allotments, Barmby Moor 74, 1972, FEC.

Wolds Chalk pit, South Cave 93, 1959, FEC.
Hold. Disused refuse tip, Hull 13, 1963, EC; Priory Sidings, Hull 02, 1972, FEC.

Circaea L.

C. lutetiana L.   Map 68.
Enchanter's-nightshade.
Native. Woods and damp shady places. Frequent in woods on the Wolds; also in scattered localities in Holderness and in Lower Derwentland.
More rarely in other habitats: 'on roadside, between Beverley and Hull' 03 (R. 1902); as a garden weed e.g. at Beverley Westwood Hospital 03, 1977, FEC.

HALORAGACEAE

Myriophyllum L.

M. verticillatum L.
Whorled Water-milfoil.   1798.
Native. Ponds, drains, canals, especially in base-rich water. Always uncommon; now rare.
L.D. Staddlethorpe 82, CW (R. 1902); Aughton 73, 1932, WAS & JK; Oxmardyke delphs 82, 1958, RG; Fulford Ings 64, 1960, TFM; near Broomfleet 82, 1984, DRG.
Wolds Londesborough 84, 1908, JJM (Trans. HSFNC, *4*, 105).
Hold. Ditches about Beverley 03 (Teesdale, 1800); at Marton 13 and in Leconfield moat 04 (R. 1902); Leven Canal 04, 1950-1974, FEC; Kelsey Hill gravel pit 22, 1955, FEC.

M. spicatum L.   Map 104.
Spiked Water-milfoil.
Native. Ponds, canals, lakes, streams, dykes. Locally frequent.
Most records for the R. Hull valley; scattered localities in Lower Derwentland and the rest of Holderness, including Hornsea Mere 14.

M. alterniflorum DC.
Alternate Water-milfoil.
Native. Ponds, dykes. Rare now.
L.D. Sandholme 83, 1958, RG.
Hold. Kelsey Hill gravel pits 22 and dykes near Hull, 'very common', YNU Excursion (R. 1902).

HIPPURIDACEAE

Hippuris L.

H. vulgaris L.   Map 100.
Mare's-tail.   1840.
Native. Canals, old ponds, streams, drains, a lake.
Frequent in the R. Hull valley, north of Beverley; scattered elsewhere in Holderness and in Derwentland. Still by Hornsea Mere 14.

CALLITRICHACEAE

Callitriche L.
Most species are probably under-recorded.

C. stagnalis Scop.
Common Water-starwort.
Native. Temporary pools, ponds, dykes, streams. Frequent.

C. platycarpa Kütz. (*C. verna* auct.)
Various-leaved Water-starwort.
Native. Temporary pools, ditches, streams, canal.
Near Silburn Lock, Pocklington Canal 74, 1981, CN.

C. obtusangula Le Gall
Blunt-fruited Water-starwort.   OSE.
Native. Temporary pools, ponds, dykes, streams. Rare.
U.D. River Derwent, near Malton 77, 1958, WAS.

C. hamulata Kütz. ex Koch (*C. intermedia* Hoffm.)
Intermediate Water-starwort.
Native. Ponds, lakes, streams.
Said to be formerly common (R. 1902).
Hold. Drain, near Arram 04, 1953, FEC.

C. hermaphroditica L.
Autumnal Water-starwort.
Native. Ponds, lakes, canals, dykes.
L.D. Ditch, near Bubwith 73, 1984, DRG.

LORANTHACEAE

Viscum L.
V. album L.
Mistletoe.
Native. Parasitic, most commonly on apple trees.
Hold. Formerly in several gardens in the Hull area and on Hawthorn in Green Lane, Newland, Hull where it was extinct by 1902 (R. 1902). Frequent in old orchard, Thwaite Hall, Cottingham 03, 1936, FEC and at Haworth Hall, Hull 03, 1976, JA.

CORNACEAE

Cornus L.
C. sanguinea L. [*Thelycrania sanguinea* (L.) Fourr.]
       Map 69.
Dogwood.
Native. Scrub and hedgerows, especially on calcareous soils. Generally infrequent, but widely distributed. Found in 25% of Wolds hedges examined, including hedges on Jurassic strata; in 31% of Holderness hedges examined and 3% of those in Lower Derwentland (Boatman, 1980).

ARALIACEAE

Hedera L.

H. helix L.
Ivy.
Native. On trees in woods and in hedges; on walls.
Sometimes carpeting the floor of woods and plantations.
Common.

UMBELLIFERAE

Hydrocotyle L.

H. vulgaris L.   Map 186.
Marsh Pennywort.
Native.   Damp or wet places, usually on acid soils.
Locally frequent in Lower Derwentland, sometimes in
great quantity. Infrequent elsewhere, mainly in the Vale of
Pickering and in the R. Hull valley.

Sanicula L.

S. europaea L.   Map 88.
Sanicle.   1836.
Native. Woods, especially on the chalk.
Common on the Wolds; uncommon elsewhere.

Eryngium L.

E. maritimum L.
Sea-holly.   OSE.   1840.
Native. In open communities on coastal sand. Uncommon.
In quantity locally on Spurn Point 41 where it has been
known since 1898 (R. 1902). Shore of the R. Humber
between Patrington and Spurn 31 (Baines, 1840); still on
the R. Humber bank near Easington 31, but rare.
Formerly recorded for the coast, north of Spurn: sparingly
at Hornsea 24 and near Hollym 32 (Teesdale, 1800); south
of Bridlington 16 (R. 1902).
One plant, Barmston 15, 1955, RG.

Chaerophyllum L.

C. temulentum L.   Map 336.
Rough Chervil.
Native. Hedgebanks, wood borders, grassy lanes, road-
sides.
Locally common on the Wolds, infrequent elsewhere.

Anthriscus Pers.

A. caucalis Bieb. [*Chaerophyllum anthriscus* (L.)
Crantz; *Anthriscus vulgaris* Pers., non Bernh.]
Bur Chervil.   1877.
Native. Roadside banks, arable field margins, waste places,
mainly on loose sandy soils; sand and gravel pits. Uncommon and decreasing. Said to be formerly common in sandy
places locally (R. 1902).
U.D. Sand pits at Flixton 07, 1938, WAS and at Staxton 07,
1956, RG & 1971, MC; Wintringham 87, 1965, RK &
1986, EC; near Potter Bromptom and at East Heslerton 97,
1986, EC.
L.D. Market Weighton 84, JJM (R. 1902); near South
Cliffe 83, 1950, FEC; near North Cave 83, 1953, FEC &
1987, EHW.
Wolds On oolitic limestone, South Cave 93, HFP (Trans.

YNU, 1877, 17); chalk pit, Wharram 86, 1950, YNU
Excursion & 1987, EHW.
Hold. Coneygarth gravel pit 14 (R. 1902); Kilnsea Warren
41, 1946, RG and south of chalk bank, Spurn, 1954, FEC,
believed to have been lost as a result of myxomatosis and
the decline of the rabbit.

A. sylvestris (L.) Hoffm.
Cow Parsley.
Native. Roadsides, edges of woods, hedgebanks and waste
places. Very common; abundant along roadsides and
lanes, particularly in Holderness, rendering verges white
when flowering in the early summer. Lost from some roadsides due to use of herbicides.

Scandix L.

S. pecten-veneris L.
Shepherd's-needle.
Native. Weed of arable, especially cornfields. Formerly
said to be 'in all cornfields' (R. 1902). Apparently uncom-
mon, but in widely scattered localities by 1950; now very
rare due to changes in agricultural practice.
Post-1950 records include:
U.D. Near Rillington 87, *c.*1970, RMH.
L.D. Near River Head, Market Weighton 83, 1954, FEC.
Wolds Skidby 03, 1952, RG; Kipling Cotes 84, 1956,
FEC; Sledmere 96, 1960, FEC.
Hold. Winestead 22, 1950, FEC; near grain warehouse,
Leven Canal Head 14, 1953, FEC; Keyingham 22, 1953,
FEC; near Fitling 23, 1954, RG; near Preston 13, 1955,
FEC; on wall, Ryehill 22, 1955, FEC.
Also occurred as a casual on Hull docks (R. 1902), King
George Dock, Hull 12 (Wilson, 1938) and on rulley sweep-
ings, High St, Hull 12, 1952, FEC and by nearby seed
warehouse, 1953, FEC.

Myrrhis Mill.

M. odorata (L.) Scop.
Sweet Cicely.   1840.
Possibly always introduced. Hedges, roadsides. Un-
common.
U.D. Kirkham 76 (Baines, 1840).
L.D. Hedge outside cottage garden, South Cliffe 83, 1957,
RG & 1982, EC; Bubwith Ings 73, 1977, TFM.
Wolds Near Burton Fleming 07, 1967, EC; Great Givendale 85, 1969, TFM; Boynton 16, 1970, MC.
Hold. Near Victoria Dock, Hull 12, 1973, FEC.

Torilis Adans.

T. japonica (Houtt.) DC. [*Caucalis anthriscus* (L.) Huds.]
Upright Hedge-parsley.
Native. Mainly a hedgerow plant, also in wood borders and
grassy places. Common.

T. arvensis (Huds.) Link (*Caucalis arvensis* Huds.)
Spreading Hedge-parsley.   CSE.
Native? Arable fields.   Rare.
L.D. Between Cliffe and Holme upon Spalding Moor 83,
1937, AKW (Nat. 1938, 47).

102

T. nodosa (L.) Gaertn. [*Caucalis nodosa* (L.) Scop.]
                                  Map 337.
Knotted Hedge-parsley.   CSE.   1806.
Native. Dry, often somewhat bare banks, old chalk quarries; also on arable. Very infrequent in the 1950s; rare now.
Most records for the species as an arable weed are for the Wolds; there are also several post-1950 records for on or near the R. Humber bank.
Post-1960 records:
Wolds Cornfield, near Driffield 05, 1960, YNU Excursion; near Flamborough railway station 17, 1960, FEC; near Nafferton 06, 1971, MC.
Hold. Humber bank, Paull Holme 12, 1963, FEC.

Caucalis L.

C. platycarpos L. (*C. daucoides* L.)
Small Bur-parsley.   1820.
Alien. Formerly a cornfield weed and dock alien. No recent record.
L.D. Barmby Moor 74, 1820, SH, herb. York Mus.
Hold. Hull docks, 1899-1902 (R. 1902); King George Dock, Hull 12, 1933, AKW (W. 1938).

C. latifolia L.
Greater Bur-parsley.
Introduced. Casual. Waste places. Rare.
Hold. West Dock, Hull 02 and waste ground, east Hull 13 (R. 1902); King George Dock, Hull, 1934-1937, AKW (W. 1938).

Coriandrum L.

C. sativum L.
Coriander.
Alien, probably native of the eastern Mediterranean.
Seeds identified in a 13th century water course, Sewer Lane, Hull (Armstrong, 1977).
The seeds are used for flavouring and still imported. Occurs as a casual. Uncommon.
L.D. Water Fulford 64, 1928, HB; Howden 72, 1978, RTh.
Hold. Hull docks 02 (R. 1902); King George Dock, Hull 12, 1933, AKW (W. 1938) and 1953, FEC; Hessle refuse tip 02, 1947, AKW; bombed sites Clarence St, 1951 and Charlotte St, Hull 12, 1975, FEC; Spurn 41, 1958, MMN.

Smyrnium L.

S. olusatrum L.
Alexanders.   1798.
Introduced. Formerly cultivated as a pot-herb and sometimes naturalised.
Hedges, grassy places, waste places. Uncommon.
L.D. Near South Cliffe 83, 1972, DRG.
Hold. Near Beverley 03, rare (Teesdale, 1800); Bentley 03, 1908, JJM (Trans. HSFNC, 1909, *4*, 105); Wold Gate, Bridlington 16, introduced by Major Lawson (Flintoff, 1931); Haltemprice Lane, Hull 03, introduced *c.*1898, by W. Bromby (W. 1938), still there 1946, FEC; Catwick 14, 1939, TS (SYF); in park land surrounding St German's church, Winestead 22, 1949, RL & 1983, AB; in hedge, near Patrington 32, 1958, RG.

Conium L.

C. maculatum L.   Map 338.
Hemlock.
Native. Drain banks, canal banks, damp places in woods, waste places. Frequent, but absent from the drier parts of the Wolds.

Bupleurum L.

B. rotundifolium L.
Thorow-wax.
Introduced. Casual. Cornfields. Not seen now.
Wolds Several places (Baines, 1840).
Hold. Hedon 12, TP and Hull docks 02 (R. 1902).

B. lancifolium Hornem. (*B. subovatum* auct.)
False Thorow-wax.
Introduced. Casual. Waste places, gardens. Rare.
L.D. Fangfoss 75, 1963, MT.
Wolds Garden weed, Hunmanby 07, 1972, Mr Rowntree.
Hold. West Dock, Hull 02, CW (R. 1902).

B. tenuissimum L.
Slender Hare's-ear.   1900.
Native. On the salt-marsh side of the R. Humber bank, more rarely on the top or on the landward side of the bank. Very rare now.
First found at Paull Holme 12, 1900 and at Salt End Common 12, 1901, TP (R. 1902). Petch (1905, 230) states that it 'may be found all along from Salt End to Welwick 31, 2ft high when growing amongst long grass on the Hedon Haven bank or barely 6" in more exposed positions'. Persisted near the Hedon Haven 12, 1938, AKW, where it was said to be 'in its only native Yorkshire station' (Nat. 1939, 27). Refound at Paull Holme, 1963, FEC, but the habitat was destroyed by the building of the present high river bank. Near Hawkins Point 21, 1963, PMG. On the top of the bank at Skeffling 31 after disturbance, as a short erect form, 1966, FEC, disappearing as the community became closed. At the landward side of the bank near Kilnsea 41, 1974, FEC, still there 1978; by dyke, Easington 31, 1986, MU (Crackles, 1966, 49-51; Crackles & Garnett, 1967, 32).

Apium L.

A. graveolens L.   Map 202.
Wild Celery.   1798.
Native. By and in brackish dykes near the R. Humber bank; on saltings and on the R. Humber shore from Hessle 02 to Saltmarshe 72. Also on the banks of the R. Hull, north to Haworth Hall 03. Locally frequent.

A. nodiflorum (L.) Lag.   Map 135.
Fool's Water-cress.   CSE.
Native. By ponds and streams; in ditches and in very marshy ground. Frequent.

A. nodiflorum x *A. repens* = *A.* x *riddelsdellii* Druce Meadow by the side of Hornsea Mere 14, 1975, FEC, det. R.D. Meikle (Crackles, 1976). A dot in the *Atlas of the British Flora* for ten km square 63 (Perring & Walters, 1962) should be for *A. repens*.

A. repens (Jacq.) Lag. (*Sium repens* auct.; *Heloscadium repens* Koch)
Creeping Marshwort.
Native. Pond sides and wet meadows, flooded at times. Very rare in the British Isles, now only known from Ports Meadow, Oxford. Formerly at the line ponds, Skipwith Common 63; specimens collected on August 2nd, 1885 by F.A. Lees are in his herbarium in the City Art Gallery & Museum, Bradford; identification conf. 1975, R.D. Meikle. The Skipwith line ponds are lost, but the species may occur elsewhere in the vice-county. The species was recorded for several Yorkshire localities by Baines (1840), including marshy ground on Tilmire 64 and in ditches near Beverley 03, but Lees in *The Flora of the West Riding* (1888) suggested that these records probably applied to a procumbent form of *A. nodiflorum*. The Skipwith plants were described by F.A. Lees in the Botanical Record Club Report for 1875, 123; for differences between *A repens* and the hybrid with *A. nodiflorum* see Crackles, 1976.

A. inundatum (L.) Reichb. f.
Lesser Marshwort. 1840.
Native. Shallow pools, ponds, a canal. Uncommon and decreasing.
L.D. Tilmire 64 (Baines, 1840); Skipwith 63, WNC (R. 1902); church pond, Skipwith 63, 1937, GAN; pond west of Snake Hall Plantation 83, 1953, FEC, habitat destroyed; near Broomfleet House 82, 1955, RG; pond, Howden 73, 1987, BHG.
Wolds Ponds on cliff slopes, north of Hunmanby Gap 17, 1955, RG & 1971, FEC; shallow pond, Buckton 17 (Flintoff, 1931) and 1973, MC.
Hold. Arram Beck 04, 1898 (R. 1902); muddy pond between Roos and East End, Halsham 22, 1949, RL; Leven Canal 04, 1952, FEC; Kelsey Hill 22, 1955, FEC.

Petroselinum Hill
P. crispum (Mill.) Nyman [*Carum petroselinum* (L.) Benth.]
Garden Parsley. 1930.
Naturalised escape from cultivation. Uncommon.
Wolds Flamborough 27 (Flintoff, 1931); railway cutting, Flamborough 17, 1958, RG; railway north of Eppleworth Wood 03, 1958, RG.
Hold. In ditches, Kilnsea 41, 1930, RG; near Easington 31 (Flintoff, 1931); between Kilnsea and Spurn 41, 1933 (SYF).

P. segetum (L.) Koch [*Carum segetum* (L.) Benth. ex Hook. f.]
Corn Parsley. OWEE. 1800.
Native. Drain sides, cornfields. Rare now. Said to be common near Hull on the authority of Revd J. Dalton (Baines, 1840).
Wolds One plant, cornfield near Fridaythorpe 86, 1956, RK.
Hold. Specimens from cornfields near Hull, 1800, W. Brunton, herb. York Mus.; between Hull and Hedon 12, 1853, CCB (Baker, 1854); Skidby Drain, Hull 03 and Burstwick 22, 1897, CW (R. 1902); on drain side, Paull Holme 12, 1965, EC (Crackles, 1966, 49-50); Fosham 23, 1976, EBM.

Sison L.
S. amomum L.
Stone Parsley. OSE. 1840.
Native. Drain sides and other grassy places. Very rare. 'In moist situations, near Hull' (Baines, 1840), on authority of Revd J. Dalton (Baker, 1854); unknown near Hull by 1902 (R. 1902) and believed to have been recorded in mistake for *Petroselinum segetum.*
L.D. Near Howden 72, JBe (R. 1902).
Hold. Drain side by R. Humber bank, Paull Holme 12, 1963, PMG (Crackles, 1966); by R. Humber bank, near Patrington 31, 1966, YNU Excursion; near Outstray Farm, Patrington 31, 1980, FEC; by railway near Bridlington 16, 1977, railway land survey, ITE; drain side by R. Humber bank, Old Hall Farm, Sunk Island 21, 1986, YNU Excursion.

Cicuta L.
C. virosa L.
Cowbane.
Native. In shallow water and marshes.
L.D. Pond near Langwith 64 and marshy places between Kexby and Elvington 74, HI (Baker, 1854); last seen 1870, FAL (SYF). Extinct.

Carum L.
C. carvi L.
Caraway. 1661.
Possibly formerly native in the Hull area; later a rare casual.
Hold. In the close called Granswick in Myton, near the town of Hull, 1661, J. Ray. 'In low lying and fertile pastures near Hull ... in plenty and even in the fields' (Ray, in Camden, 1695). Teesdale (1800) says the Caraway was so plentiful in meadows adjoining the R. Humber, near Hull that the poor people gathered seed to sell to the druggists. Revd F. Brokesby recorded that the Caraway at Hessle was as good as the cultivated sort and Robinson (1902) records that J.R. Boyle, the Hull archivist, said that certain fields in West Hull are mentioned in deeds as 'carvi' fields. Cultivated on the Wolds in the 19th century (R. 1902). Found only as a dock alien by 1902 (R. 1902); also King George Dock, Hull 12, 1933, AKW (W. 1938) and on a bombed site, High St, Hull 12, 1950, FEC.

Conopodium Koch
C. majus (Gouan) Loret (*C. denudatum* Koch) Map 339.
Pignut. OWEE.
Native. Grassland, including Wolds grassland. Common. In small quantity in a few woods e.g. Leman's Wood 94, 1956, RG; Grimthorpe Wood 85, 1967 and Bratt Wood 84, 1972, FEC.

Pimpinella L.
P. saxifraga L. Map 21.
Burnet-saxifrage. 1798.
Native. Grassland on calcareous soils, chalk quarries, rarely on sand; also recorded on gravel in Holderness. Common on the Wolds; infrequent elsewhere.

P. major (L.) Huds. Map 340.
Greater Burnet-saxifrage. *c.*1845.
Native. Roadsides, hedgebanks, sides of railway tracks, railway sidings. Locally common on roadsides in the Selby

to York area; early records for this area are near Selby 63, WNC and on banks of the R. Ouse, near Barlby 63 (R. 1902).
Other localities are scattered, mainly by railway tracks.
Wolds East of South Cave railway station 93, 1958, RG; Hunmanby 17, 1973, MC; Wharram 86, 1983, FEC.
Hold. Spring Head 02 (R. 1902); Spring Head, sidings and railway, Hull 02, 1978, FEC; at Bridlington Priory 16, 1967, JR & MC; by railway line, near Bridlington 16, 1977, railway land survey ITE; by disused railway, Skirlaugh 13, 1982, FEC; Priory Yard Sidings, Hull 02, 1983, FEC.

Aegopodium L.

A. podagraria L.   Map 341.
Ground-elder, Goutweed.
An ancient introduction; formerly grown as a pot herb and medicinal plant. Waste places and roadsides, near houses; a very persistent garden weed. Frequent.

Sium L.

S. latifolium L.
Greater Water-parsnip.   1840.
Native. A fenland species, surviving in ponds, dykes and by a lake and a canal. Uncommon. Said to be formerly 'common in all the smaller dykes in Holderness especially, as well as in other divisions' (R. 1902).
Post-1950 records:
L.D. North Cave 83, 1952, AW & 1985, EHW; Broomfleet delphs 82, 1955, RG; Bubwith 73, 1957, RG; Aughton Ings 73, 1972, FEC.
Hold. Hallytreeholme 04, 1956, FEC; Barmston Drain, Aike 04, 1956, FEC; Watton Carrs 04, 1957, FEC; by Hornsea Mere 14, 1962, FEC, still present; Leven Canal 04, 1970, FEC; near Hollym 32, 1984, FEC.

Berula Koch

B. erecta (Huds.) Coville (*Sium erectum* Huds.) Map 95.
Lesser Water-parsnip.
Native. Feeder streams of the R. Hull, including stretches with a chalk bottom; by dykes, ponds and marl pits and on marshy ground. Locally frequent in the R. Hull valley and present in the R. Derwent valley.
Scattered elsewhere including:
U.D. Very fine plants on carrs near Muston 08, 1984, DRG.
L.D. In Pocklington Canal at Walbut and Sandhill Locks 74, 1981, NCC.

Oenanthe L.

O. fistulosa L.   Map 190.
Tubular Water-dropwort.
Native. Marshes, flood meadows, by ponds and a canal. Generally infrequent, most records being for Lower Derwentland.
Uncommon in Holderness including by Leven Canal and Hornsea Mere 14 and on Spurn Point 41, 1975, FEC. In three localities on the coast in the Speeton to Filey area 17. Said to be formerly very common in the dykes of Holderness (R. 1902).

O. silaifolia Bieb. (*O. peucedanifolia* auct.)   Map 191.
Narrow-leaved Water-dropwort.   OSE.
                              1840, rediscovered 1969.
Native. A characteristic plant of the flood meadows by the R. Derwent; locally frequent, unknown elsewhere.

'Near the R. Derwent, in the parish of Sutton on Derwent' (Baines, 1840); not accepted (Baker, 1854) or by Robinson, 1902. Bubwith 73, 1969, E. Chicken, previously recorded as *O. lachenalii*, 1937, WAS. Aughton Ings 63, 1972, YNU Bot. Sect. Excursion; Wheldrake Ings 74, 1973, FEC. Near Breighton 73, North Duffield Ings 63, East Cottingwith 74 and Sutton upon Derwent 74, 1979-1981, SP; near Kexby 75, 1983, CSVY.

O. lachenalii C.C. Gmel.
Parsley Water-dropwort.   CSE.   1900.
Native. In brackish and freshwater marshes and fens. Rare.
L.D. Near Market Weighton 83, JJM, Howden 72, JBe and Brough swamp 82, CW (R. 1902). Not known in the Derwent flood meadows and the record for Aughton Ings (SYF) should be for *S. silaifolia*. Near Broomfleet delphs 82, 1963, FEC & PMG and 1984, DRG.
Hold. Formerly occurred in dykes near the Humber bank (Petch, 1905, 221); near Patrington 31, 1900, TP (R. 1902). In brackish marshes behind the Humber bank: by canal, near Kilnsea 41, 1966, YNU Excursion; locally frequent between Easington and Skeffling 31, 1973, FEC; still near Skeffling, 1983, but very scarce, FEC.

O. crocata L.
Hemlock Water-dropwort.   OWEE.
Native. Wet places. Most often found in places subject to inundation by high tides. Uncommon.
L.D. Near Selby 63, WNC and Howden 72, JBe (R. 1902); west of Boothferry Bridge 72, 1956, RG, herb. HLU & 1983, YNU Bot. Sect. Excursion, in quantity; Howden Dyke Island 72, 1970, RHu & JHu per DWS; Laxton Clough 72, 1983, RHu & JHu; inlet east of Blacktoft 82, 1984, YNU Bot. Sect. Excursion.
Wolds On shore, R. Humber, North Ferriby 92, 1987, TB.

O. aquatica (L.) Poir. (*O. phellandrium* Lam.) Map 106.
Fine-leaved Water-dropwort.   CE.
Native. Ponds, dykes in water-meadows. Infrequent, most records for Lower Derwentland; decreasing. Said to be formerly 'common in muddy dykes of Holderness' (R. 1902). Post-1950 records outside Lower Derwentland:
U.D. At Welham 76, 1957, FEC.
Hold. Haltemprice Lane, Hull 03, 1953, AKW; Hallytreeholme 04, 1956, FEC; Swine 13, 1956, FEC; near Holmpton 32, 1956, RG; Meaux 03, 1958, FEC.

O. fluviatilis (Bab.) Colem.   Map 107.
River Water-dropwort.   OWEE.   1960.
Native. Only in the R. Hull, including the West Beck. A plant of southern England; almost endemic to England, very rare on the continent.
First recorded for Yorkshire in 1946 (Nat. 1946, 138). First noted in the East Riding, near Driffield 05, 1960, W.A. Sledge and then as the submerged form at Hempholme Lock, 1967, FEC (Crackles, 1968). It is now known to occur for some nine miles; it is uncommon in the upper reaches of the West Beck, but frequent from just north of Corps Landing to Hempholme Lock; it flowers freely in the beck. Found in the tidal part of the river to just south of Wilfholme 04, 1970, FEC, where it usually occurs as the submerged form.

Aethusa L.

A. cynapium L.   Map 342.
Fool's Parsley.
Native. A weed of cultivated ground, waste places, gravel pits. Frequent.

Foeniculum Mill.
F. vulgare Mill.
Fennel.
Alien.Waste places.May become naturalised. Uncommon.
L.D. Near Olympia Oil Mills, Selby 63, 1921, JBF; airfield, Pocklington 74, 1973, FH.
Wolds Chalk pit, Hessle 02, CW (R. 1902), still there, 1938 (W. 1938) and near the foreshore at Hessle, 1957, RG; Etton Wold 94 and disused railway, Gardham 94, 1985, EHW.
Hold. Hull docks (R. 1902); near Beverley barracks 03, 1943, AKW; site of Queen's Dock, Hull 12, 1950, FEC; Bridlington 16, 1956, JA1; refuse tip, Hull 13, 1963, EC; Spurn 41, 1974, FEC.

Silaum Mill.
S. silaus (L.) Schinz & Thell. (*Silaus flavescens* Bernh.)
                                             Map 57.
Pepper-saxifrage.   CE.   1840.
Native. Meadows, grassy banks, gravel pits. Generally somewhat infrequent; a characteristic plant of the water-meadows by the R. Derwent; widely scattered along the western edge of the Wolds, sometimes at the bottom of Wolds valleys as in Waterdale 86; also elsewhere on the Wolds as at Burton Fleming 07, 1971, MC. In meadows by the upper reaches of the R. Hull as near Copper Hall, Skerne 05, 1969, FEC.
Other Holderness records include: by Hornsea Mere 14, 1978, FEC and at the northern part of Spurn 41, 1978, FEC; by the Lambwath stream, Withernwick 23, 1984, FEC and in old pasture, Hollym 32, 1984, FEC.

Angelica Hoffm.
A. sylvestris L.   Map 343.
Wild Angelica.   CNE.
Native. Marshes, open damp woods and in damp clayey places. Common; locally abundant in the R. Hull valley. On chalk hillside, Scoardale 85, 1971, FEC.

Peucedanum L.
P. palustre (L.) Moench
Milk-parsley.   CNE.   1798.
Native. Fens. Very rare.
L.D. Between Howden and the Ouse Swing Bridge 72, *c.*1880, FAL (Trans. HSFNC *3*, 99).
Hold. Marshes near Beverley, abundantly (Teesdale, 1800); specimen collected Beverley, 1796, CM, herb. York Mus. (R. 1902). Reed beds, Hornsea Mere 14, 1912 (Bolam, 1913), confirmed 1979, R. Hawley, herb. FEC.

Pastinaca L.
P. sativa L. [*Peucedanum sativum* (L.) Benth. ex Hook. f.]
Wild Parsnip.
Native? Waste places. Uncommon.
L.D. Roadside, Skipwith 63, 1942, WAS.
Wolds East of South Cave station 93, 1958, RG; Nafferton 06, 1969, MC.
Hold. Kelsey Hill gravel pits 22, CW and Hull docks 02 (R. 1902); King George Dock, Hull 12, 1953 and bombed site by seed warehouse, High St, Hull 12, FEC; Spurn Point 41, 1974, FEC.

Heracleum L.
H. sphondylium L.
Hogweed.
Native. In grassy places, including roadsides, flowering just after *Anthriscus sylvestris*; hedgerows, woods and

plantations. Common.
Var. *angustifolia* Huds. noted here and there:
U.D. Near Howsham Bridge 76, 1955, RG.
L.D. Gypsey Wood Lane 64, 1955, Naburn 64 and Kelfield 53, 1955, RG.
Wolds Hunmanby Gap 17, 1955, RG.
Hold. Old railway line, Whitedale 14, 1984, FEC.

H. mantegazzianum Somm. & Levier
Giant Hogweed.   1931.
Alien. Naturalised in waste places and by rivers, streams and roadsides; in plantations. First record: near Springhead Waterworks 02,1931, AKW (W. 1938). Other records:
U.D. Farmyard, Muston 07, 1983, YNU Excursion.
L.D. By river, Breighton 73, 1982, FEC; near Low Catton 75, 1984, JL.
Wolds Near Elloughton 92, 1933, AKW (W. 1938); Sunderlandwick 05, 1969, MC; Walkington 03, 1972, DRG; near Middleton 94, 1972, FEC; Thwing 07, 1976, EC.
Hold. Plantation, Hollym 32, 1948, RL; Hymer's College, Hull 02, 1969, MC; Hedon Road, Hull 12, 1978, FEC; King George Dock, Hull 12, 1978, RTh; by Holderness Drain 04, 1987, DW.

Daucus L.
D. carota L. subsp. *carota*   Map 344.
Wild Carrot.
Native. Grassland; chalk pits; sand dunes; in arable; by railway tracks; mainly on calcareous soils. Locally frequent, but the patchy distribution is difficult to explain. Formerly said to be 'very common, especially in Holderness..' (R. 1902); very local in Holderness now and mainly near the R. Humber and along the coast.

CUCURBITACEAE

Bryonia L.
B. dioica Jacq.   Map 65.
White Bryony.   CSE.
Native. Hedges, wood borders and scrub, on well drained soils. Locally frequent in the South Cave 93, North Cave and Hotham 83 areas and at the western side of Lower Derwentland. Very infrequent in Holderness, including localities in the Beverley 03 and Brandesburton 14 areas.

EUPHORBIACEAE

Mercurialis L.
M. perennis L.   Map 81.
Dog's Mercury.
Native. Woods, plantations; mainly on the Wolds, infrequent elsewhere. Rarely in other habitats: on drain sides as along the Holderness Drain, Hull 13 and on Wolds grassland in Millington Pastures 85 and Thorndale 85, 1982, NCC.

Ricinus L.
R. communis L.
Castor Oil Plant.
Alien. Waste places. Uncommon.
Hold. Near Hull docks 02 and oil mills, Hull (R. 1902); King George Dock, Hull 12, 1931, AKW (W. 1938); warehouse site, High St, Hull 12, 1952, FEC. On the tideline on the sea-shore at Spurn 41, 1963, FEC.

Euphorbia L.

E. lathyrus L.
Caper Spurge.   1936.
Introduced. Waste places, roadsides. Formerly cultivated for its fruits, used as capers. Seeds can remain dormant in the soil for many years.
Casual in gardens, turning up in particular areas near Hull e.g. Willerby 03 and Wawne 13; it is suggested that the seeds may have been formerly introduced with night soil. Uncommon.
Other records:
U.D. Road bank, Kirkham 76, 1958, RG.
L.D. By roadside, Elvington 74, 1936, WAS (W. 1938); near Fangfoss 75, 1956, CT.
Wolds Garden weed, Thwing 07, 1970, EC.
Hold. Kilnsea 41, 1947, FEC; Cottingham 03, 1953, RG; Arnold 13, 1973, FEC; Driffield 05, 1978, EC.

E. helioscopia L.   Map 345.
Sun Spurge.
Native. Cultivated and waste ground. Frequent and widely distributed.

E. peplus L.   Map 346.
Petty Spurge.
Native. Cultivated and waste ground. Widely distributed and locally frequent.

E. exigua L.   Map 227.
Dwarf Spurge.
Native. In arable. Infrequent; most records for the Wolds. Rare in Lower Derwentland: near Snake Hall 83, 1954, FEC.

E. esula L. x **E. waldsteinii** (Sojak) A. R. Smith = **E.** x **pseudovirgata** (Schur) Soó (**E. virgata** auct., non Waldst. & Kit.; **E. uralensis** auct., non Fischer & Link)
Leafy Spurge.   1947.
Alien. Waste and grassy places. Rare.
Hold. Naturalised in fixed dunes, Spurn 41, 1947, Miss Fox, still present; railway, near Driffield 05, 1972, EHW.

E. cyparissias L.
Cypress Spurge.   1840.
Possibly native on chalk grassland, near Millington 85, 1954, JFH-S.
Otherwise introduced:
L.D. Skirpenbeck 75, 1956, MT.
Hold. Near Hornsea 14 (Baines, 1840); Salt End Common 12, 1933, AKW (W. 1938); roadside, Kirkella 02, 1961, FD.

POLYGONACEAE

Polygonum L.

P. aviculare L. *sensu lato*
Knotgrass.
Native. Abundant throughout the vice-county. On tracks, waste places, arable ground and on roadsides. The following three segregates occur:

P. aviculare L. *sensu stricto*
Common and widely distributed.

P. rurivagum Jord. ex Bor.
Cornfield Knotgrass.
Introduced.

U.D. Barley field, near Burythorpe 76, 1974, EC.
Hold. Waste ground, near West Dock, Hull 02 (R. 1902).

P. arenastrum Bor. (*P. aequale* Lindm.)
Equal-leaved Knotgrass.
Native. Mainly on sand and gravel.
U.D. Sand pits, Staxton 07, 1956, RG; near Folkton and Muston 08, 1983, CSVY.
L.D. Disused gravel pit, Thorpe le Street 84, 1952, RL; near North Duffield 63 and Bolton 75, 1983, CSVY.
Hold. Hull docks (R. 1902); King George Dock, Hull 12, 1933, TS (W. 1938); waste tip, Hessle 02, 1946, AKW & RL; R. Hull bank, Pulfin Bog 04, 1951, AKW; Haverfield pits 31, 1983, FEC; Wilmington, Hull 13, 1987, FEC.

P. bistorta L.
Common Bistort.   1840.
Native. Meadows and roadsides. Uncommon.
L.D. Fulford Ings 64, WWh (R. 1902) and 1979, EB; Ellerton 73, 1969, EHW; water-meadows, Aughton 63, 1972, FEC; East Cottingwith 74, 1980, NCC.
Wolds Londesborough (Baines, 1840); near Kilnwick 94, 1939, TS; Hesslewood 02, 1939, AKW.
Hold. Near Beverley 03, Dr Hull, Cottingham 03, Swine 13, Marfleet 13 (R. 1902); near Watton 04, 1970, MC; above moat, Leconfield Castle 04, 1974, EHW.

P. amphibium L.   Map 347.
Amphibious Bistort.
Native. Floating in ponds, lakes, canals and dykes; the terrestrial form on banks by water, in marshy meadows and on waste places on heavy soils. Frequent in the R. Hull valley and in much of Lower Derwentland; scattered elsewhere.

P. persicaria L.
Redshank.
Native. Cultivated land and waste places. Common and locally abundant.
Var. *elatum* Gren & Godr.
West Dock, Hull 02, CW (W. 1938).

P. lapathifolium L. (inc. *P. nodosum* Pers.)
Pale Persicaria.   1840.
Native. Cultivated land and waste places.
Early records: Heslington Fields 64 (Baines, 1840); near Hull and Hedon 12, abundant and luxuriant on the dock wastes (R. 1902). Widely distributed and frequent in most areas; scarce on the Wolds.

P. hydropiper L.   Map 193.
Water-pepper.
Native. Damp places, including wood rides; mainly on sandy acid soils. Mainly in Lower Derwentland where it is locally frequent.
Uncommon in Holderness including: Marton 13 (R. 1902); Birkhill Woods 03, 1956, RG; Wawne 03, 1957, RG; Bentley Moor Wood 03, 1967, FEC; Arram 04, 1969, MC; Burton Constable 13, 1988, YNU Excursion.

P. mite Schrank
Tasteless Water-pepper.   CE.   1956.
Native. A local British plant, mainly in the south and usually occurring in ditches and by ponds. Rare.
L.D. Stillingfleet 54, 1956, SMW; Fulford Ings 64, 1979, EB; in arable field by recently dredged ditch, near North Duffield 64, 1983, CSVY; near Barmby on the Marsh 62, 1985, TFM.

P. minus Huds.
Small Water-pepper.   CE.   1798.
Native.   In wet marshy places and beside ponds.   Rare.
L.D. In a swampy place in sandy lane near Dryham 83, 1903, JFR (Trans. HSFNC *3*, 99).
Hold. Woodmansey, near Beverley 03 'in a place where water stands in winter' (Teesdale, 1800);   Risby 03, 1838, herb. Motley (Nat. 1902, 344). Extinct.

P. polystachyum Wall. ex Meissner
Himalayan Knotweed.
Introduced.
Near Riccall 63, 1961, M. McC. Webster, still there.

Fallopia Adanson
F. convolvulus (L.)A. Löve (*Polygonum convolvulus* L.)
Black-bindweed.
Native.   Cornfields and other cultivated ground, waste places.   Frequent.

Reynoutria Houtt.
R. japonica Hout (*Polygonum cuspidatum* Sieb. & Zucc.)   Map 260.
Japanese Knotweed.   1935.
Alien.   Native of Japan;   naturalised and difficult to eradicate. Chalk pits, waste places. Locally frequent in the Hull area, scattered elsewhere.
Pre-1950 records:
Willerby 03 and Hessle chalk pits 02, 1935, AKW (W. 1938); Gilly Woods Lane 03, 1943, FEC; near Skidby 03, 1953, RG;   Clough Road, Hull 13, 1953, FEC.
Widely distributed in the Hull area by 1975; large bushes flowering freely in the Old Town and in the Citadel 12, FEC.
Other records:
L.D. Near Asselby and near Boothferry Bridge 72, 1983, YNU Excursion.
Wolds Londesborough 84, 1956, RG;   near Ellerker and Brantingham 92, 1971, JG; Walkington Grange 93, 1979, DRG.
Hold. Near Burshill 04, 1969, CMR; Beverley 03, 1973, JA;   Paull 12, 1984, FEC.

R. sachalinensis (Friedrich Schmidt Petrop.) Nakai (*Polygonum sachalinense* Friedrich Schmidt Petrop.)
Giant Knotweed.
Alien. Native of Sakhalin and Japan; naturalised. Rare. Hessle quarry 02, 1966, EC.

Fagopyrum Mill.
F. esculentum Moench
Buckwheat.
Alien. Native of central Asia. Waste places, usually as a casual. Uncommon. May be an escape of cultivation; cultivated as a crop near Langwith Common 64, 1956, FEC.
L.D. Escrick 64, an escape, WNC (R. 1902); Olympia Oil Mill Sidings, Selby 63, WAS & JK (SYF); Allerthorpe Common 74, 1952, AW.
Wolds Near Langtoft 06, 1971, MC.
Hold. Near Hull docks 02 (R. 1902); King George Dock, Hull 12, 1933, AKW (W. 1938);   Hessle tips 02, 1943, AKW; bombed site, Myton St, Hull 02, 1951, FEC; near seed warehouse, High St, Hull 12, 1975, FEC.

Rumex L.
R. acetosella L.   Map 348.
Sheep's Sorrel.
Native. Dry commons and heaths, cultivated land; usually on poor acid soils. Common except on the Wolds.
The aggregate species is now divided into three segregates: the common widely distributed plant is **R.** acetosella *sensu stricto*;
R. angiocarpus Murb. is not known to occur, but we have:

R. tenuifolius (Wallr.) Löve
Narrow-leaved Sorrel.   1958.
Native. Dry sandy places on commons and on sandy arable. Uncommon.
U.D. Near Ganton 97, 1982, FEC; Wintringham 87, and near West Heslerton 97, 1986, EC.
L.D. Sutton Wood 74, 1958, FEC; Allerthorpe Common 74, 1962, FEC; near Skipwith 63, 1965, FEC; Wheldrake 64, 1965, TFM; Poor Allotments, Barmby Moor 74, 1973, FEC; near Snake Hall 83, 1981, YNU Excursion; Houghton Woods 83, 1984, EC.
Hold. On Alexandra Dock reservation, Hull 12, 1979, FEC.

R. acetosa L.
Common Sorrel.
Native. Meadows, roadsides, waste places. Common.

R. hydrolapathum Huds.   Map 131.
Water Dock.   CE.
Native. By rivers, canals and a lake and in adjacent marshes and dykes. Said to be formerly frequent in Holderness, including dykes near Hull (R. 1902); now mainly along and near the R. Hull north of Beverley; still luxuriant in shallow water at Hornsea Mere 14, 1979. Uncommon in Lower Derwentland, mainly on the site of the former Walling Fen, 82 & 83.
Other records include:
U.D. Near Firby 76, 1981, YNU Bot. Sect. Excursion.
L.D. Near Selby 63 (R. 1902); by the R. Derwent, near Bubwith 73, 1956, RG; near Thornton 74, 1956, RG; near Skirpenbeck 75, 1956, MT.

R. longifolius DC.
Northern Dock.
Native. Damp grassy places. Rare.
L.D. Naburn Sewage Works 64, 1979, EB, det. D.J. Hodgson.

R. crispus L.
Curled Dock.
Native. Grassy places, waste and cultivated ground. Common.

R. crispus x **R. obtusifolius** = **R. x pratensis** Mert. & Koch (*R.* x *acutus* auct., non L.)
Near Broomfleet 82, 1984, EB.

R. obtusifolius L.
Broad-leaved Dock.
Native. Waste ground, roadsides, field borders. Common.

R. sanguineus L.   Map 349.
Wood Dock.   1840.
Var. *viridis* (Sibth.) Koch
Wood rides, roadsides and waste places; thriving best on clay. Widely distributed, but either somewhat infrequent in most areas or under-recorded.

108

Var. *sanguineus*
Blood-veined Dock.
Alien.   Rare.   On roadsides.
Near Sand le Mere 33, 1899, CW (R. 1902).

R. conglomeratus Murr.   Map 350.
Clustered Dock.   1898.
Native. In marshy meadows; pond, ditch and stream-sides; waste places on heavy soils as at Hull. Widely distributed and frequent.

R. conglomeratus x *R. obtusifolius* = *R.* x *abortivus*
Ruhmer
Fulford Ings 64, 1979, E. Bray, det. D.H. Kent.

R. conglomeratus x *R. maritimus* = *R.* x *knafii* Celak.
Skipwith 63, 1930, G.C. Druce (Nat. 1931, 22) and by drying pond, Skipwith, WAS (SYF); Little Skipwith, 1984, EC det. J. Akeroyd.

R. palustris Sm. (*R. limosus* auct.)
Marsh Dock.   1903.
Native. By pond sides, clay and gravel pits; marshes, dykes. Rare.
L.D. Skipwith 63, HJW & JFR (Trans. HSFNC, *3*, 1903, 99) and 1933, CMR.
Hold. Brick ponds, near Hawthorn Avenue, Hull 02, SM & CW (Trans. HSFNC, *3*, 1903, 99).

R. maritimus L.
Golden Dock.   1798.
Native. On the margins of pools, in clay pits and wet hollows in marshy fields, by dykes and ponds. Rare.
L.D. Riccall 63, WNC (R. 1902); Skipwith 63, HJW & JFR (Trans. HSFNC, 1903, *3*, 99) and WAS (SYF); Little Skipwith 63, 1984, EC.
Wolds Grindale 17, 1973, MC; Boynton 16, 1985, EC.
Hold. Woodmansey 03 (Teesdale, 1800); old brick-field ponds, with brackish water, Dairycoates, Hull 02, 1901, SM (R. 1902).

URTICACEAE

Parietaria L.
P. judaica L. (*P. diffusa* Mert. & Koch; *P. officinalis* auct.)   Map 250.
Pellitory-of-the-wall.
Native. Old walls, particularly church walls. Uncommon.
U.D. Kirkham Abbey 76, MBS (R. 1902) and 1958, FEC.
L.D. Bridge near Blacktoft 82, 1954, RG; Stillingfleet 54, 1957, RG.
Wolds Brantingham 92, 1952, IG.
Hold. Beverley 03, Dr Hull (R. 1902); Cottingham church 03 (R. 1902) and 1952, IG; Easington 31, 1955, RG; church wall, Barmston 15, 1956, FEC; church wall, Watton 04, 1957, FEC; Lowthorpe church 06, 1969, MC; Bridlington Priory 16, 1969, MC; Kilnsea 41, 1978, EP; railway brickwork, Patrington 32, 1983, FEC.

Urtica L.
U. urens L.   Map 351.
Small Nettle.
Native. Cultivated ground and waste places, particularly common on sandy soils. Widely distributed; common in Lower Derwentland and locally frequent as in the Hull area.

U. dioica L.
Common Nettle.
Native. Hedgebanks, woods, plantations, waste places. Very common.

CANNABIACEAE

Humulus L.
H. lupulus L.   Map 352.
Hop.
Escape of cultivation.   Hedges.   Infrequent.
Most records for Lower Derwentland, also occurs in the Cottingham, Beverley area.   Still in Snuff Mill Lane, Cottingham 03, where it has long been known.
Records include:
L.D. Near North Cave 83, 1980, EHW & JES; near Hemingborough 63, 1981, DRG; Breighton 73, 1982, FEC & JD.
Hold. Beverley 03, 1973, JA; near Hornsea Mere 14, 1979, RH.

Cannabis L.
C. sativa L.
Hemp.   1933.
Alien. Once widely grown as a crop in the East Riding. Now a rare casual; introduced as bird seed.
L.D. Olympia Sidings, Selby 63, WAS & JK (SYF).
Hold. King George Dock, Hull 12, 1933, AKW (W. 1938); near seed warehouse, High St, Hull 12, 1977, EHW; by Humber Dock, Hull 02, 1982, FEC; near docks, east Hull 12, 1982, FH.

ULMACEAE

Ulmus L.
U. glabra Huds. (*U. montana* Stokes)
Wych Elm.
Native.   Woods, plantations, hedges.   Frequent.

U. glabra x *U. plotii* = *U.* x *elegantissima* Horwood
In roadside hedgerow between Market Weighton and Sancton, 1947, R.L. (Nat. 1948, 26).

U. procera Salisb.
English Elm.
Native and often planted. In hedges and wood margins and by roads. Was frequent, but numerous trees have been felled in recent years because of Dutch Elm disease.
Var. *suberosa*
Burton Constable, Bilton 13, Wansford 05 and Thixendale 86 (R. 1902).

U. carpinifolia Gleditsch
Small-leaved Elm.
Introduced.
A large population, near Boynton 16, 1980, RGu.

MORACEAE

Ficus L.
F. carica L.
Fig.
Introduced, rarely self-sown and naturalised.
Seeds found in archaeological excavations at Hull: in 13th century quay infill High St, Hull 12 (Ayers, 1979); in 13th

century water course and in 16th and 17th century pits, Sewer Lane, Hull 02 (Armstrong, 1977) and in 14th century floor deposits and chalk-lined garderobe pit, Scale Lane, Hull 12 (Armstrong, 1980).

On spare ground, Pryme St, Hull 02, 1952, FEC; by dry dock, Little High St, Hull 12, 1977-1980, FEC.

MYRICACEAE

Myrica L.
M. gale L.
Bog-myrtle.   ONE.   1798.
Native.   Bogs, wet heaths and fens.   Extinct.
L.D. Langwith 64 (Baines, 1840); Houghton Moor 83 (Teesdale, 1800) and *c*.1850, GN (R. 1902); Sutton upon Derwent 74, 1887 (SYF).
Hold. Leven Carrs and Arram 04, 2nd half 18th century, WW.

PLATANACEAE

Platanus L.
P. x ***hispanica*** Miller ex Muenchh. (*P.* x *hybrida* Brot.)
London Plane.
Planted. Frequent in the Hull area; also occurs as specimen trees in parkland.

BETULACEAE

Betula L.
B. pendula Roth (*B. verrucosa* Ehrh.)   Map 353.
Silver Birch.
Native. Woods, heaths, commons, hedges; especially on sandy soils. Locally frequent in Lower Derwentland, where it was found to occur in 17% of hedges examined (Boatman, 1980).

B. pubescens Ehrh.
Downy Birch.   CNE.
Native. Hedges, woods, heaths, commons, hedges.
In wetter situations than *B. pendula* and at its best on damp peaty soil. Mainly in Lower Derwentland, where it was found in 30% of hedges examined (Boatman, 1980).

Alnus Mill.
A. glutinosa (L.) Gaertn.   Map 354.
Alder.
Native. Wet places in woods, by lakes and streams; in hedges. Locally frequent in Derwentland. In 40% of hedges examined in Lower Derwentland (Boatman, 1980). Uncommon in Holderness; by Hornsea Mere 14 where it has long been known (R. 1902).

CORYLACEAE

Carpinus L.
C. betulus L.
Hornbeam.   CE.
Native; also planted.
Some old trees near Little Weighton 93 in hedgerows; in shrubberies, Anlaby 03 (R. 1902).
More recent records include:
U.D. Kirkham 76, 1927, GP.
L.D. Ellerker and Cockle Pits, Brough 92, 1938, RG.

Wolds Hanging Fall Wood, Sledmere 96 YNU Excursion.
Hold. Burton Bushes, Beverley, 03, 1978, FEC.

Corylus L.
C. avellana L.   Map 355.
Hazel.
Native. Woods, copses, scrub, hedges, old lanes; on damp or dry basic and damp neutral soil. Widely distributed and locally frequent.

FAGACEAE

Fagus L.
F. sylvatica L.
Beech.
Native in S.E. England. Usually assumed to be introduced north of the R. Humber, but there are some fine trees on the Wolds and one wonders if it is native in the south of the vice-county. Woods, roadsides. Frequent.

Castanea Mill.
C. sativa Mill.
Sweet Chestnut.
Alien. 'Growing well into fine trees on the Wolds as at Mount Airey, S. Cave' (R. 1902).
Other records:
L.D. Houghton Woods, 83, TS (W. 1938).
Wolds Head's Lane, Hessle 02, 1925, FEC; Skidby chalk pits 03, TS (W. 1938).
Hold. Salthouse Rd, Hull 13, TS (W. 1938).

Quercus L.
Q. cerris L.
Turkey Oak.
Naturalised alien.   Frequently planted and naturalised.

Q. ilex L.
Evergreen Oak, Holm Oak.
Introduced; occasionally planted.

Q. robur L.
Pedunculate Oak.
Native.   Woods, hedgerows.   Frequent.

Q. petraea (Mattuschka) Liebl.
Sessile Oak.
Native.   Most frequent on acid soils.

Q. patraea x **Q. robur** = **Q.** x **rosacea** Bechst.
Trees with characters of both species do occur.

SALICACEAE

Populus L.
P. alba L.
White Poplar.
Alien. Naturalised in damp situations. Very infrequent. By the disused railway, near Whitedale 14, 1983, FEC.

P. canescens (Ait.) Sm.
Grey Poplar.
Planted.   Woods, hedges.
'Frequently found in hedges of old lanes' (R. 1902).
Wolds Eppleworth Wood 93, *c*.1960, FEC.
Hold. Formerly in Inglemire Lane, Hull and at Cottingham (R. 1902).

P. tremula L.
Aspen.
Native. Woods, plantations, roadsides; mainly on rather poor moist soils. Infrequent, most records for Lower Derwentland. In 15% of hedges examined in Lower Derwentland and in 2% of those examined in Holderness (Boatman, 1980).

P. nigra L.
Black Poplar.
Mainly introduced. Very infrequent. Likely to be native at Willow Garth, Boynton 16, 1982, NCC.
Var. *italica* Duroi
Lombardy Poplar.
Frequently planted.

P. x *canadensis* Moench
Italian Poplar.
Introduced.
Asselby Island 72, 1971, DWS.

Salix L.

S. pentandra L.
Bay Willow.   CNE.   1798.
Native. River sides, marshes, fens. Uncommon.
U.D. Staxton 07, 1971, MC.
L.D. Selby 63, WNC; Howden 72, JBe (R. 1902); near Snake Hall 83, 1955, AKW; Thornton 74, 1981, EC; west of Sancton 83, 1982, DRG; Houghton Hall lake 83, 1986, DRG.
Hold. Near Beverley (Teesdale, 1800); still by the R. Hull at Pulfin Bog 04 and formerly also at Arram 04 (R. 1902); Hull (Baines, 1840); King's Mill, Driffield 05 (R. 1902) and 1972, EC; Kelleythorpe 05, 1948, RL; near Wansford 05, 1970, MC.

S. alba L.   Map 356.
White Willow.
Native and planted. By rivers, drains and streams. Frequent in the R. Hull valley, infrequent elsewhere.
Var. *caerulea*
L.D. Dunnington 65, 1972, EC.
Hold. Dunswell 03, 1971, EC.

S. alba x *S. pentandra* = *S.* x *ehrhartiana* Sm.
Firby Wood 76, EB, conf. R.C.L. Howitt (RCLH).

S. alba x *S. fragilis* = *S.* x *rubens* Schrank
L.D. Newport 83, 1972, EC; male, Fulford Ings 64, 1980, EB, conf. B. Howitt (BH).
Hold. Keyingham 22, 1971, Spurn 41, 1971, Hatfield 14, 1972, all EC.

S. babylonica L. x *S. fragilis* = *S.* x *pendulina* Wenderoth
Female, Skipwith Common 63, EB (Bray, 1985).

S. alba var. *vitellina* (L.) Stokes x *S. babylonica* = *S.* x *sepulcralis* Simonk.
Planted.
L.D. Skipwith 63, 1979, EB, det. RCLH.
Hold. Near Beverley 03, 1971, EC.

S. fragilis L.   Map 357.
Crack Willow.
Native, but often planted. By streams, rivers, drains and ponds. Widely distributed and locally common, particularly in Holderness.

S. triandra L.
Almond Willow.
Native? Sides of rivers, ponds and a lake. Uncommon.
L.D. Near Selby 63, WNC (R. 1902); near Fulford 64, 1982, EB; bank of R. Ouse, Hemingbrough 62, 1985, TFM.
Hold. Hornsea Mere 14, CW (R. 1902); Brandesburton 04, 1972, EC; on the R. Humber bank, near Skeffling 31, 1973, FEC, det. G.A. Nelson.

S. triandra x *S. viminalis* = *S.* x *mollissima* Hoffm. ex Elwert
L.D. Fulford Ings 64, 1979, EB, det. RCLH; Hemingbrough 72, 1981, WB, det. R.D. Meikle (RDM).
Hold. Boynton 16, 1971, EC.

S. purpurea L.
Purple Willow.   CSE.   1798.
Native, may also have been planted. By streams, rivers and ponds. Uncommon.
L.D. Market Weighton, 1899 (R. 1902).
Wolds Harpham 06, 1970 and Nafferton 05, 1971, MC; Boynton 16, 1971, EC.
Hold. Near Beverley (Teesdale, 1800); Kelleythorpe 05, 1970, MC; near Dunswell 03, 1975, JA.

S. purpurea x *S. viminalis* = *S.* x *rubra* Huds.
L.D. Female, Fulford Ings 64, 1981, EB, det. RCLH.
Hold. Dunswell Lane 03, CW & JFR (R. 1902).

S. daphnoides Vill.
Planted. Near Naburn Ings and sewage works 64, 1980, EB, conf. RDM.

S. viminalis L.   Map 358.
Osier.
Native or escape of cultivation. By streams and ponds, also commonly planted. Widely distributed and locally frequent. Formerly frequently cultivated in Holderness (R. 1902).

S. caprea L.   Map 359.
Goat Willow.
Native. Woods, scrub and hedges. Frequent. In 17% of hedges examined in Lower Derwentland and 3% of those examined in Holderness (Boatman, 1980).

S. caprea x *S. cinerea* = *S.* x *reichardtii* A. Kerner
U.D. Staxton 07, 1972, EC.
L.D. North Cave 93, 1972, EC; Allerthorpe Common 74, 1984, YNU Excursion; disused railway, Harswell 84, EB.
Wolds Disused railway, Wharram 86, 1982, EB, conf. RDM.

S. caprea x *S. viminalis* = *S.* x *sericans* Tausch ex A. Kerner
L.D. Newport 83, 1972, EC; Fulford 64, 1982, EB, det. RDM.
Hold. Beverley 03, 1971, EC, det. RCLH.

S. cinerea L.   Map 360.
Native. Woods, hedges; by streams and becks, in marshes and fens; in gravel pits. Frequent. In 57% hedges examined in Lower Derwentland, in 5% of those examined on the Wolds and in 10% of those in Holderness (Boatman, 1980).
The distribution of the two subspecies is not fully known.

Subsp. *cinerea*
Grey Willow.
In base-rich fens and marshes.

Subsp. *oleifolia* Macreight [subsp. *atrocinerea* (Brot.) Silv. & Sob.]
Rusty Willow.
The frequent subsp. in Lower Derwentland, occurring for instance at Hayton 84, 1952, RL; Allerthorpe Common 74, 1962, FEC and Fulford Ings 64, 1982, EB.

S. cinerea x *S. viminalis* = *S.* x *smithiana* Willd.
L.D. Near Bubwith 73, 1972, TFM; Stillingfleet 54, 1979, EB; female, Naburn Ings 54 (Bray, 1985).
Hold. Dunswell 03, 1971, EC.

S. aurita L.
Eared Willow.   CNE.   1798.
Native. Damp woods, scrub, heaths; on acid or slightly basic soils. Infrequent, mainly in Lower Derwentland.

S. aurita x *S. cinerea* = *S.* x *multinervis* Doell
Male, Skipwith Common 63, 1982, EB.

S. aurita x *S. repens* = *S.* x *ambigua* Ehrh.
Female, Skipwith Common 63, HFP (SYF) and 1984, EB, det. BH.

S. repens L.   Map 45.
Creeping Willow.
Native. Damp heathland. Uncommon.
Post-1950 records:
L.D. Near Broomfleet House 82, 1955, RG; Duck Nest 83, 1955, RG; Houghton Woods lane 83, 1957, RG; Breighton Common 73, 1958, FEC; Allerthorpe Common 74, 1964, Langwith Common 64, 1965 and Skipwith Common 63, 1970, all FEC and all still present; California, Barmby Moor 74, 1973, FEC; roadside, near North Cliffe 83, 1980, FEC, still present.
Formerly in Holderness at Gransmoor 16 (Flintoff, 1931) and at Hall Ings, Cottingham 03, 1933, AKW.
Both var. *repens* and var. *argentea* occur.

ERICACEAE

Andromeda L.
A. polifolia L.
Bog-rosemary.   CNE.
Native.
Bogs near Howden 72, T. Knowlton (Teesdale, 1800). Extinct.

Calluna Salisb.
C. vulgaris (L.) Hull   Map 31.
Heather.   1835.
Native. Heaths, moors and open woods on acid soils; rarely on leached soils on the Wolds. Locally dominant on heaths and commons, particularly in Lower Derwentland; the number of localities decreasing as a result of afforestation and reclamation of land for agriculture.
Other records include:
U.D. Wintringham 87, 1957, FEC; Staxton 07, 1971, MC; Low Moor, Rillington 87, 1971, RMH.
Wolds On limestone, Langton 76, 1950, FHP; one plant, chalk hillside, near Duggleby 86, 1963, FEC; rare on hillside, Waterdale 86, 1982, NCC; pathside, cliff slope,

Speeton 17, 1984, SMA.
Hold. Birkhill Wood 03 (R. 1902) and 1945, FEC; Gransmoor 16 (Flintoff, 1931), still present. In quantity on sand on Alexandra Dock reserve, Hull 12, 1978, FEC, still present.

Erica L.
E. tetralix L.   Map 36.
Cross-leaved Heath.   OWEE.   1836.
Native. Damp heathland.
On heaths and commons in Lower Derwentland, sometimes in quantity as on Skipwith 63 and Allerthorpe 74 Commons and Houghton Moor 83.
Rare elsewhere:
U.D. Kennythorpe Moor 76, 1970, ATD and Staxton 07, 1971, MC.
Never as frequent as Heather (R. 1902). Decreasing through loss of habitat.

E. cinerea L.
Bell Heather.   OWEE.   1900.
Native. Dry heaths and commons. Rare.
Tilmire 64, 1900, WB; on spur of higher land and by dyke, Allerthorpe Common 74, 1961, and still surviving by wood rides; on Poor Allotments, Barmby Moor, 74, 1972, FEC, habitat now destroyed; near Wilberfoss 74, 1983, RJ.

Vaccinium L.
V. vitis-idaea L.
Cowberry.
Introduced.
Alexandra Dock reservation, Hull with *Calluna vulgaris* and other heathland plants, 1979, FEC; otherwise unknown in v.c. 61 or south of ten km square 78 (N. Yorks. moors, v.c. 62) on the east side of England.

V. myrtillus L.
Bilberry.   CNE.
Native. Heaths, moors and woods on acid soils. Rare.
U.D. Kennythorpe 76, 1970, ATD.
L.D. Cliff Wood and Skipwith Common 63, WNC (R. 1902).
Hold. On sand on Alexandra Dock reservation, Hull 12, 1979, FEC, still present.

PYROLACEAE

Pyrola L.
P. minor L.
Common Wintergreen.   *c.*1845.
Native. Woods, heaths. Rare.
L.D. Langwith 64, *c.*1845, A. Smith; Houghton Woods 83, JJM (R. 1902) and 1930, YNU Excursion; near Barlby Common 63, 1912, WNC; Everingham 84, 1946, JMT; Allerthorpe Common 74, 1958, ABM, still present.
Wolds Near Tibthorpe 95, 1906, Miss Piercy (Trans. HSFNC, *3*, 301); Lund Wood, North Grimston 86, 1950, PLG.

MONOTROPACEAE

Monotropa L.
M. hypopitys L. *sensu lato* (*Hypopitys monotropa* Crantz)
Yellow Bird's-nest.   1840.
Native. Woods, usually under Beech. Rare.
All records are for the Wolds:
Boynton 16 (Baines, 1840); Mount Airey, South Cave 93, 1891, GHH & RHP (Trans. HSFNC *4*, 1912, 220); Sledmere 96, 1930, EMM; Brantingham 93, 1950, WHS; near Elloughton 92, 1967, FEC; in quantity under conifers in Forestry Commission woodland, Wintringham 87, 1969, GS.
The Elloughton plants are subsp. *hypophegea* (Wallr.) Soó; other populations have not been critically examined.

PLUMBAGINACEAE

Limonium Mill.
L. vulgare Mill. (*Statice limonium* L.)
Common Sea-lavender.   OSE.   Mid 19th century.
Native. Salt-marshes. Uncommon.
Sparingly at Bridlington 16, mid 19th century, herb. M. Waller, extinct there by 1901 (Petch, 1901). First recorded for South Holderness on muddy shores near Hedon 12, 1901 and on Sunk Island 21 (R. 1902). Petch (1901) comments on the scarcity of the species along the R. Humber and attributes this to the lack of extensive areas about half-way between the highest and lowest tide-marks; two tufts occurred outside a newly built bank opposite Welwick 31. Abundant at Salt End and Hedon Haven 12, 1920. The Welwick salt-marsh is the only one where the species now occurs in abundance and where it has done so for at least forty years. It also now occurs on Sunk Island 21, near Skeffling and Easington 31 and on Spurn Point 41.

Armeria Willd.
A. maritima (Mill.) Willd.
Thrift, Sea Pink.   ONE.   Map 203.
Native. Salt-marshes and maritime cliffs. Uncommon.
In quantity locally on the cliffs of the Flamborough Headland.
Infrequent on salt-marshes along the R. Humber; all post-1950 records have been between Paull 12 and Spurn 41. Formerly common between Hessle 02 and Hull and all the way to Spurn (R. 1902).

PRIMULACEAE

Primula L.
P. veris L.   Map 361.
Cowslip.
Native. On chalk grassland and in meadows and pastures, on railway banks, in chalk quarries; rarely in woods. Still common on the Wolds and sometimes in abundance, locally frequent in Holderness, scarce in Lower Derwentland. Described as formerly 'exceedingly common in every meadow of Holderness, and also in the other divisions' great quantities being brought to the markets in the second week of May for making wine (R. 1902). A Cowslip meadow is now rare in Holderness.

P. veris x **P. vulgaris** = **P.** x **polyantha** Mill. (*P. variabilis* Goupil)
Several scattered records; occurring where the parental species grow together.

P. vulgaris Huds. [*P. acaulis* (L.) Hill]   Map 86.
Primrose.
Native. Woods, sites of woodland, dyke sides, on sea cliffs; more rarely under hedges. Widely distributed, but scarce near built-up areas. Locally frequent on the Wolds and in Holderness; infrequent in Lower Derwentland. Its distribution map matches in a general way the map of wood place-names (Smith, 1937), so that it may have mainly survived on old woodland sites.

Hottonia L.
H. palustris L.   Map 101.
Water-violet.   CNE.   1798.
Native. Ditches in water-meadows and elsewhere, canals, ponds and in a brackish canal below the Humber bank near Skeffling 31, 1966, FEC. Infrequent.
A dyke with the species plentiful and in flower as at Tophill Low 04, 1971 and near Hornsea Mere 14, 1978 is a rarer sight than formerly. In quantity in a pond in North Cliffe Wood 83, 1954, FEC; lost, then appeared on the side of freshly cut pits, 1984, & 1986, DJB.
Most post-1950 records are for the middle and lower stretches of the R. Hull valley and for Lower Derwentland. Said to be common in Holderness dykes formerly (R. 1902); rare now east of the R. Hull valley. Pond, near Hollym 32, 1948, RL.

Lysimachia L.
L. nemorum L.   Map 80.
Yellow Pimpernel.
Native. Damp places in woods, often by tracks where water stands in winter. Somewhat uncommon and local. Mainly in the Cottingham and Beverley areas as at Risby 03 (R. 1902) and 1963, FEC; Gilly Woods 03 (R. 1902) and 1950, FEC; Bentley Moor Wood 03, 1967, FEC; Bygot Wood 04, 1971, FEC; Little Wood, near North Newbald 93, 1972, FEC; Burton Bushes, Beverley 03, 1978, FEC.
Other records:
U.D. Firby Wood 76, 1958, FEC; Howsham Wood 76, 1958, RG.
L.D. Formerly at Selby 63, WNC and at Howden 72, JBe (R. 1902); North Cliffe Wood 83, 1954, FEC; Sutton Wood 74, 1961, FEC; Langwith woods 64, 1965, FEC.
Wolds Settrington 87, 1987, ND.
Hold. Rise Park woods 14, 1983, FEC.

L. nummularia L.   Map 362.
Creeping-jenny.
Native. Moist grassy places, marshes, ditch edges, canal sides. Locally frequent in the R. Hull and R. Derwent valleys, with a few other scattered records in Lower Derwentland and Holderness. Described as formerly 'very common by dykes and drains in Holderness' and it occurred near Selby 63, WNC (R. 1902). The tetrad map shows a similar distribution to that of many fenland marsh species.

L. vulgaris L.   Map 152.
Yellow Loosestrife.   1840.
Native. In fenland marshes; by rivers, canals and dykes in former fenland areas. Infrequent.
Occurs locally in the R. Hull valley as at Pulfin Bog 04, where it has long been known (R. 1902) and by Leven Canal 04. It occurs in the R. Derwent valley in the Kirkham area where it was first recorded by MBS (R. 1902) and near Breighton 73, 1979, NCC; in former fenland areas in Lower Derwentland, notably in ten km squares 82 and 83 and by the Pocklington Beck and Canal 74. Formerly in

Inglemire Lane, Hull 03 (R. 1902); still in Holderness at Roos Bog 22, 1970, FEC and in dykes, near Hollym 32, 1985, FEC.

L. punctata L.
Dotted Loosestrife.
Garden escape, sometimes naturalised.   Uncommon.
L.D. Skipwith Common 63, 1982, EB.
Wolds Near Walkington 93, 1973, EHW; roadside near Bempton 17, 1975, EC.

[*L. thyrsiflora* L.
Tufted Loosestrife.
Native.
Recorded for 'E. Yorks.' by J. Ray in Camden's *Britannia* ed. Gough, 1685, and believed to refer to an East Riding locality (R. 1902). In fact the record was for Leckby Carr in the North Riding, v.c. 62.]

Anagallis L.
A. tenella (L.) L.   Map 173.
Bog Pimpernel.   OSE.   1840.
Native. Damp peaty places and bogs. Uncommon and decreasing.
U.D. By springs, Wintringham 87, 1964, FEC; near Firby 76, 1981, DRG.
L.D. Barlby Moor 63 and Skipwith Common 63 (Baines, 1840), at Skipwith, 1970, GAS & ET; near Brough 92, CW and Market Weighton 83, JJM (R. 1902); near Snake Hall 83, 1953, FEC; Langwith Common 64, 1956, FEC; Heslington Fields 64, 1957, FEC; in dyke, Allerthorpe Common 74, 1959 and still on rides on the Common, 1985, FEC; Tollingham Warren 83, 1969, MC.
Wolds Thornwick Bay 17, 1967, MC; near springs, Leavening 76, 1972, FEC; near Buckton and Speeton 17, 1973, MC & FEC.
Hold. Cottingham 03 (Baines, 1840) and 1898, but gone by 1900 (R. 1902); King's Mill, Driffield 05, 1898 (R. 1902) and 1950, IG.

A. arvensis L.

Subsp. *arvensis*
Scarlet Pimpernel.
Native. On cultivated land, including gardens; in open situations on sand dunes and waste places. Frequent.
The blue-flowered form occurred at Spurn 41, 1984, BS.

Subsp. *foemina* (Mill.) Schinz & Thell. (*A. caerulea* Schreb.)
Introduced. Casual. Uncommon.
L.D. Near Newsholme, Howden 72, JBe (R. 1902).
Wolds Asylum grounds, Walkington 93, 1908, HC (W. 1938).
Hold. Very common amongst the dock aliens, Hull (R. 1902); King George Dock, Hull 12, 1934, AKW; Queen's Dock site 12, 1934, HJD; bombed site, High St, Hull 12, 1951, FEC.

A. minima (L.) E.H.L. Krause (*Centunculus minimus* L.)
Chaffweed.   CE.   1798.
Native. Damp sandy places in open situations on heaths. Rare.
L.D. Houghton Moor, the side next to Newbald 83 (Teesdale, 1800) and 1893, JJM (R. 1902). On a common between Holme upon Spalding Moor and Market Weighton 83 (Baines, 1840); Skipwith Common 63, WNC (R. 1902); Allerthorpe Common 74, 1908, JJM (Trans. HSFNC *4*,

105) and 1981, TFM.

Glaux L.
G. maritima L.   Map 210.
Sea-milkwort.   1798.
Native. Salt-marshes and brackish marshes behind the R. Humber bank; on the shore of the R. Humber west of Hessle. Frequent.
Here and there on the sea coast as at Barmston Drain end 15, 1955, RG, on cliffs of the Flamborough Headland 27, 1970, MC and near Filey 18, 1984, RGu.

Samolus L.
S. valerandi L.   Map 195.
Brookweed.   1840.
Native. In wet places, usually in open communities; not always persisting. Uncommon.
L.D. Heslington Fields 64 and between Holme upon Spalding Moor and Hotham 83 (Baines, 1840), still on Heslington Fields, 1957, FEC; Staddlethorpe 82, CW and Skipwith Common 63 (R. 1902); Houghton Woods 83, 1953, RG; Bunny Hill 83, 1955, RG; by delph, Broomfleet 82, 1958, FEC; Allerthorpe Common 74, 1969, FEC; Tollingham 83, 1969, MC.
Wolds Filey Brigg 17, 1956, RG; Flamborough cliffs 27, 1970, MC.
Hold. Formerly frequent near Hull (R. 1902); gravel pit, Kelsey Hill 22, 1953, FEC; by Lambwath Stream, Skirlaugh 13, 1957, FEC; Emmotland 05, 1964, MC; frequent by Leven Canal 04, 1968, FEC; gravel pit, Brandesburton 14, 1970, MC; Arram Carrs 04, 1979, FEC.

BUDDLEJACEAE

Buddleja L.
B. davidii Franch.
Butterfly-bush.   1938.
Alien. Native of China. Commonly grown in gardens and naturalised on waste places and on walls. Uncommon.
Wolds Chalk pits, Hessle 02, AKW (W. 1938), still present.
Hold. On a number of Hull bombed sites e.g. Albion St 02, 1950; Mytongate 02, High St 12 and Buckingham St 13, 1975, FEC. On Pease warehouse by High St wharfe, Hull 12, 1978, FEC; near Bridlington 16, 1977, railway land survey, ITE; on railway brickwork, Whitedale 14, 1981, FEC.

OLEACEAE

Fraxinus L.
F. excelsior L.
Ash.
Native. Woods, plantations, hedges. Common, especially on calcareous soils. Mature trees were a characteristic feature of hedges on the Wolds and in Holderness forty years ago, but most of these have been lost as hedges have been destroyed.

Ligustrum L.
L. vulgare L.   Map 77.
Wild Privet.
Native. Woods and hedges. Locally frequent on the Wolds in 10 km squares 92, 93, 94 and 95 and in hedges on neutral

soils in the R. Hull valley in 10 km squares 03 and 04. Boatman (1980) found the species in 10% of Wolds hedges examined and 2% of those in Holderness.

APOCYNACEAE

Vinca L.
V. minor L.
Lesser Periwinkle.   1798.
Garden escape. Woods, copses, hedgebanks; cultivated in old cottage gardens. Uncommon.
U.D. Kirkham Abbey 76 (Teesdale, 1800); near Kirkham (Flintoff, 1931); Scagglethorpe 86, 1956, RG.
Wolds Londesborough 84 (Baines, 1840); Raywell 93, 1956, FEC; Long Plantation, North Ferriby 92, 1958, FEC.
Hold. Abundant by the old sunken road, near Elmswell 95 (R. 1902); Fraisthorpe 16, 1955, RG; Hutton 05, 1957, RG; Sunderlandwick 05, 1969, MC; Kilnsea Warren 41, 1974, FEC.

V. major L.
Greater Periwinkle.   1840.
Established garden escape.   Uncommon.
U.D. Kirkham Abbey Hall 76, 1955, RG.
Wolds Londesborough 84 (Baines, 1840); Welton 92, CW (R. 1902); near South Cave railway station 93, 1953, IG; near Bainton 95, 1978, EBM.
Hold. Common in plantation, Cottingham 03, 1936, TS; Spurn 41, 1974, FEC.

GENTIANACEAE

Centaurium Hill
C. pulchellum (Sw.) Druce [*Erythraea pulchella* (Sw.) Fr.]
Lesser Centaury.   1840.
Native.   Rare; not known now.
L.D. Allerthorpe Common 74, 1953, RG, herb. HLU.
Hold. On the cliff at Bridlington Quay 16 (Baines, 1840); probably the plant gathered near Spurn, 1892, GHH (R. 1902).

C. erythraea Rafn (*Erythraea centaurium* auct.) Map 363.
Common Centaury.   *c.*1845.
Native. Dry grassland, wood clearings, sides of railway tracks, chalk quarries; rather rare on chalk grassland. Fairly frequent and very widely distributed.

C. littorale (D. Turner) Gilmour
Seaside Centaury.
Native.
Filey Brigg 17, 1945, ERC & HR (N.H. Scarb.).

Blackstonia Huds.
B. perfoliata (L.) Huds.
Yellow-wort.   CSE.   1798.
Native. Bare chalk, chalk grassland, fixed dunes; rarely on non-calcareous soils. Uncommon.
L.D. Skipwith Common 63, 1970, TFM.
Wolds Near Beverley 03 (Teesdale, 1800); near Willerby

03 (R. 1902), still there in quarry and by railway, 1946, FEC; Goodmanham 84 (Trans. HSFNC, 1909, *4*, 105) and 1970, MFN; near Flamborough 27 (Flintoff, 1931); near Brantingham 93, 1951, FEC; Cowlam valley 96, 1967, JR & MC; Eppleworth 03, 1968, DWS; Swindale 93, 1973, EHW; chalk quarry, Hessle 02, 1974, JKi; Elloughton Dale 92, 1979, EHW; Flamborough Head 26, 1984, SMA; chalk quarry, Sherburn 97, 1985, ND.
Hold. Frequent at Spurn 41, 1898 (R. 1902), still present; Alexandra Dock, Hull 12, 1979, FEC, still there; Victoria Dock, Hull 12, 1985, FEC; waste place, near Salt End 12, 1986, FEC.

Gentiana L.
G. pneumonanthe L.
Marsh Gentian.   CNE.   1661.
Native.   Damp heathland.   Rare.
Lost from several localities due to loss of habitat. 'On many heathy grounds', 1661, J. Ray as he journeyed from Hull to Selby (Lankester, 1840).
Almost all records for Lower Derwentland: Holme upon Spalding Moor 83 and Everingham 74, 1727, TK; Langwith 64, 1837, HPa; Tilmire 64, Ross Moor 74, Melbourne and other places near Pocklington (Baines, 1840); Allerthorpe Common 74 (R. 1902) and 1963, FEC, now lost due to land drainage; Skipwith Common 63, WNC (R. 1902), still present; Houghton Woods 83, GN (R. 1902); Heslington Common 64, 1957, FEC, still present.

Gentianella Moench
G. campestris (L.) Börner (*Gentiana campestris* L.)
Field Gentian.   CNE.
Native. Pastures, usually on acid or neutral soils. Some early records, but no confirmation.
L.D. Near Holme upon Spalding Moor 83, 1908, JJM (Trans. HSFNC, *4*, 105).
Wolds Driffield Wold 06, MH (R. 1902).
Hold. Atwick 15, 2nd half 18th century, WW; near Beverley, Dr Hull (R. 1902).

G. amarella (L.) Börner (*Gentiana amarella* L.) Map 15.
Autumn Gentian, Felwort.   CNE.   1727.
Native. Grassland on chalk and limestone, bare chalk; chalk pits. Distribution almost restricted to the grazed grassland belt of the Wolds; also in old sandstone quarry, near North Cave 93, 1986, DJL.
First record: near Londesborough 84, 1727, TK.

MENYANTHACEAE

Menyanthes L.
M. trifoliata L.   Map 189.
Bogbean.   CNE.   1898.
Native. Ponds, edges of lakes, bogs, fens; locally dominant. Very infrequent.
Recent records are mainly for localities along the spring line. Lost from some former sites.
Records include:
U.D. Near Leavening 76, 1972, FEC; near Firby 76, 1981, YNU Bot. Sect.
L.D. Near Melbourne 74, 1968, FEC.

Wolds Lowthorpe 06 (R. 1902), conf. 1971, MC; Goodmanham 84, 1956, FEC; rich flush, Acklam 76, 1970, ATD; on the coast near Filey 17, 1971, FEC; near Buckton 17, 1971, MC; North Newbald 93, 1979, FEC.
Hold. Pulfin Bog 04 (R. 1902), still there, 1954, FEC; extensive beds at Hornsea Mere (R. 1902) and 1912 (Bolam, 1913), not known at the Mere now, may have been lost with the cessation of reed cutting (Bolam, 1913); by the R. Hull near Driffield and Wansford 05, 1960, FEC, still present.

POLEMONIACEAE

Polemonium L.
P. caeruleum L.
Jacob's-ladder.
Introduced here. Garden escape or bird alien.
L.D. Houghton Woods 83, 1888, JFR and Naburn by the R. Ouse 54, HS (R. 1902); Water Fulford 64, 1928, HB.
Hold. Garden weed, Hornsea 24, 1978, FEC.

BORAGINACEAE

Cynoglossum L.
C. officinale L.
Hound's-tongue.   CE.   1840.
Native. Grassy places on sand, gravel and chalk. Rare.
U.D. Sand pit, Heslerton 97, 1956, RG.
L.D. Near Market Weighton (Baines, 1840); Naburn 54, WNC (R.1902); near Cottingwith 64, 1979, NCC.
Wolds Millington 85, 1928, HB; High Wood, Tibthorpe 95, 1957, RG; Staxton 07, 1978, PD.

Symphytum L.
This difficult genus has recently been revised (Perring, 1969).

S. officinale L.
Common Comfrey.   1840.
Native. By rivers, streams and ponds.
Distribution not known because of confusion with *S. x uplandicum*. Most of the early records may be correct.
L.D. On banks of the R. Derwent near Kexby Bridge 75 (Baines, 1840); Howden Dyke 72, WNC (R. 1902); Woodhall, near Wressle 63, 1970, EC, det. F.H. Perring.

S. asperum x *S. officinale* = *S.* x *uplandicum* Nyman
             Map 364.
Russian Comfrey.
Naturalised alien. Introduced into Britain as a fodder plant in the last century. This is the usual *Symphytum* of roadsides and hedgebanks. Frequent, but less so than thirty years ago.

S. orientale L.
White Comfrey.   1945.
Established alien. Rare.
L.D. By church walk, Great Givendale 85, 1945, EY, still present; by church wall, North Cave 83, 1980, FEC.
Wolds Welton 92, 1977, FBS.

S. tuberosum L.
Tuberous Comfrey.
Established alien.
Recorded for the vice-county in Wats.Top.Bot., 1883. Reported near Great Givendale church (Nat. 1945, 141); this would seem to be in error for *S. orientale*.

Borago L.
B. officinalis L.
Borage.   1840.
Garden escape. Waste ground, usually near houses. Uncommon.
L.D. Skirpenbeck 75, 1957, MT.
Hold. Near Bridlington Quay 16 (Baines, 1840); Hornsea 24 (R. 1902) and 1984, KS; roadside verge, Molescroft 04, 1975, EC.

Pentaglottis Tausch
P. sempervirens (L.) Tausch [*Anchusa sempervirens* L.]
Green Alkanet.   1840.
Alien. Formerly grown and naturalised in hedgerows, usually near buildings. Uncommon.
U.D. Near Yedingham 87, 1972, EHW & PG.
L.D. Skirpenbeck 75, 1955, MT; Fulford 64, 1965, TFM.
Wolds Londesborough 84 (Baines, 1840); chalk pit, Marton 27, 1970, MC; near Hunmanby Gap 17, 1971, YNU Excursion; Swanland 92, 1978, AU; Hunmanby Hall grounds 07, 1984, EC.
Hold. Near Keyingham 22, 1950, BT; Arram 04 and Cottingham 13, 1953, FEC; near Skirlaugh 13, 1956, FEC; Spurn 41, 1956, FEC.

Anchusa L.
A. arvensis (L.) Bieb. (*Lycopsis arvensis* L.) Map 225.
Bugloss.
Native. Weed of arable on sand and gravel. Frequent. Its distribution shows a remarkable correlation with the distribution of both pre-glacial and post-glacial sands and gravels.
Amongst dock aliens, Hull (R. 1902); no recent records for the Hull area.

Amsinckia Lehm.
A. intermedia Fisch. & Mey.   Map 224.
Amsinckia.   1964.
Established alien. Arable and waste places, mainly on sandy soils. Has spread extensively in Lower Derwentland. The earlier records are:
Heslington Common 64, T.F. Medd (YNU Circular, 1965); well established on Langwith Common and in adjacent fields 64, 1965, FEC; near Thornganby 64, 1970, FEC; near Barmby Moor 74, 1972, FEC; Bubwith 73, 1973, FW; Skipwith Common 63, 1975, RDC; Spaldington 73, 1975, AWa; Burnby 84, 1975, EHW; Bunny Hill 83, 1965, TM; Brough Cockle pits 92, 1971, JG; abundant near Ellerker 92 and near South Cave 93, 1975, JA.
On gravel on the Wolds near Bainton 95, 1979, EBM and at Rudston 06, 1982, FEC; also on the Wolds near Millington 85, 1982, RJ. Two records for Upper Derwentland: near Scampston 87, 1984, BP; East Heslerton 97, 1986, EC. In Holderness, at Burton Constable 13, 1988, YNU Excursion.

Myosotis L.

M. scorpioides L. [*M. palustris* (L.) Hill]   Map 156.
Water Forget-me-not.
Native. In wet places, by streams and dykes and in ponds.
Frequent.
Said to be formerly very common in Holderness dykes (R. 1902).

M. secunda A. Murr. (*M. repens* auct.)
Creeping Forget-me-not.
Native.   In wet often peaty places.
Skidby and Risby fish-ponds (R. 1902) seem to be unlikely habitats for this species.
Recent scattered records also require confirmation.

M. laxa Lehm. subsp. *caespitosa* (K.F. Schultz)
N. Hylander (*M. caespitosa* K.F. Schultz)   Map 155.
Tufted Forget-me-not.
Native. In marshes and beside streams and ponds.
Locally frequent in Lower Derwentland; infrequent elsewhere.

M. sylvatica Hoffm.
Wood Forget-me-not.
Native or introduced. Probably native in damp woods and copses. Uncommon.
L.D. Plantations near Brough 92, 1901 (R. 1902); Fulford 64, 1965, TFM.
Wolds   Old road, Brantingham 93, 1955, RG;   near Grindale 17, 1955, RG: near Lowthorpe church 06, 1956, RG.
Hold. Wood, Kelleythorpe 05, 1951, FEC; in wood, Bell Mills, Driffield 05, 1968, FEC; Rise Park 14, 1971, FEC; Skillings Wood 16, 1987, EC.

M. arvensis (L.) Hill
Field Forget-me-not.   1837.
Native. Cultivated ground, wood borders and clearings, hedgebanks. Common.

M. discolor Pers. (*M. versicolor* Sm.)
Changing Forget-me-not.
Native. Cornfields and other open communities, mainly on sand, more rarely on gravel and calcareous soils. Uncommon and decreasing; most records for Lower Derwentland.
Said to be formerly 'common in cornfields, chiefly in the sandy western divisions' (R. 1902).
Post-1950 records:
U.D. Wintringham 87, 1986, EC.
L.D.   Cornfield near Wheldrake 64, 1956, FEC;   near North Cliffe Wood 83, 1956, RG; near Holme upon Spalding Moor 73, 1957, FEC; Allerthorpe Common 74, 1962, FEC; Langwith Common 64, 1965, FEC; Skipwith Common 63, 1969, TFM; Broomfleet 82, 1978, YNU Excursion.
Wolds   North Grimston 86, 1959, CMR;   Settrington Wood 86, 1969, TFM;   near Uncleby 85, 1981, YNU Excursion.
Hold. Rise Park 14, 1982, YNU Excursion.

M. ramosissima Rochel (*M. collina* auct.)
Early Forget-me-not.
Native. On dry shallow soils. Uncommon and decreasing.
Most records for Lower Derwentland. Frequent in short turf on Spurn Point 41 where it has long been known. Other post-1950 records:
U.D. Staxton 07, 1971, MC.
L.D. Edge of Low Wood, Holme upon Spalding Moor 83, 1954, FEC;   near North Cliffe Wood 83, 1955, FEC; disused railway station, Eastrington 83, 1976, FEC;   near Escrick 64, 1977, railway land survey, ITE;   Barmby Moor 75, 1977, PA.
Wolds   On cliffs, Reighton 17, 1968, FEC;   Ravensdale, Fordon 07, 1969 MC & JR;   Swindale 93, 1973, EHW; Southburn 95, 1979, EBM.

Lithospermum L.

L. officinale L.
Common Gromwell.   1840.
Native. In hedges, bushy places, wood borders; mainly on basic soils. Rare.
U.D. Oxclose Wood, near Kirkham 76 (Baines, 1840), still near Kirkham, 1958, FEC.
L.D. Frequent at Dunnington 65 and near Selby 63 (Baines, 1840);   Snake Hall Farm 83, 1955, RG.
Wolds Bratt Wood 84, 1956, RG; Lowthorpe 06, 1964, JR, still present.
Hold. On the dock wastes, Hull 02 (R. 1902); King George Dock, Hull 12, 1932, FS & 1935, AKW (W. 1938).

L. arvense L.
Field Gromwell.   1840.
Native. In cornfields and in other arable fields; also on dock waste land. No record since 1957.
L.D. Heslington Fields 64 (Baines, 1840); Selby 63, WNC (R. 1902);   Market Weighton, 1908, JJM (Trans. HSFNC *4*, 106);   Skirpenbeck 75, 1957, MT.
Hold. Near R. Hull in cornfields (R. 1902); at Arram 04, 1908, JJM (Trans. HSFNC *4*, 106) and 1953, FEC; Burstwick 22, 1955, FEC. Amongst dock waste plants, Hull 02, CW (R. 1902);   King George Dock, Hull 12, 1935, AKW (W. 1938).

Echium L.

E. vulgare L.   Map 365.
Viper's-bugloss.   1840.
Native. Chalk quarries, sandy fields and lanes. Infrequent.
Formerly frequent on the Wolds (Baines, 1840) and on dock wastes, Hull (R. 1902).
Post-1950 records include:
U.D. Sandy field, Wintringham 87, 1957, FEC.
L.D. Dominant in a sandy field, near North Cave 83, 1951, FEC;   Skirpenbeck 75, 1957, MT;   near Barmby on the Marsh 62, 1980, JES.
Wolds Chalk pit, Willerby 03, 1951, RG; Lowthorpe 06, 1951, RG;   in quantity in a chalk quarry, Worsendale 85, 1957, FEC, still present;   south of Flamborough 26, 1970, MC; Duggleby Dale 86, 1985, ND.
Hold.   Alexandra Dock, Hull 12, 1979, FEC;   Queen Elizabeth Dock, Hull 12, 1986, ABu.

CONVOLVULACEAE

Convolvulus L.

C. arvensis L.
Field Bindweed.
Native. Cultivated ground, waste ground, roadsides, railway banks. Common.

Calystegia R.Br.

C. sepium (L.) R.Br. [*Volvulus sepium* (L.) Junger]
                                                    Map 366.
Hedge Bindweed.
Native.   Hedges, drain banks, waste places.   Frequent.

C. pulchra Brummit & Heywood
Hairy Bindweed.   1961.
Introduced, naturalised near gardens.   Uncommon.
L.D. Burnby 84, 1961, SS; Asselby Island 72, 1971, DWS; Brough 92, 1979, AP.
Wolds Nafferton 05, 1969, MC; Towthorpe 86, 1970, RTh.
Hold. Garden weed, Beverley Westwood Hospital 03, 1977, FEC.

C. silvatica (Kit.) Griseb.   Map 251.
Large Bindweed.
Naturalised garden alien. Hedges, fences, drain banks, waste places. Common.
This S. European taxon is known to have been in Britain by 1835. Appears not to have been noted as a wild plant in the East Riding until after the Second World War. Widespread in the Hull and Withernsea areas by 1951, RL; on several bombed sites and rubbish tips, Hull, 1950-1953, FEC.

C. sepium x **C. silvatica** = **C. x lucana** (Ten.) G. Don.
Near Skirpenbeck 75, 1983, CVSY. May be overlooked.

C. soldanella (L.) R.Br.[*Volvulus soldanella* (L.) Junger]
Sea Bindweed.   1798.
Native.   Sand dunes.   Uncommon.
Owthorne 32 (Teesdale, 1800); abundant near Withernsea 32 and at Spurn 41 (R. 1902), still at Spurn. On the R. Humber bank near Easington 31. In one or two places on the sea coast, as at Sand le Mere 33 and Fraisthorpe 16, 1955, RG.

Cuscuta L.

C. europaea L.
Greater Dodder.
Native.
Parasitic on *Humulus* and *Urtica dioica* mainly.
Hemingborough 63, WNC (R. 1902). Extinct.

C. epithymum (L.) L. (incl. *C. trifolii* Bab.)
Dodder.   1852.
Native.
Parasitic on *Ulex*, *Calluna* and *Trifolium* sp. and various other plants.
L.D. Heslington Fields 64, 1852, JBa.
Wolds Londesborough 84, 1899, JJM; frequent as a garden weed in Welton nurseries 92 (R. 1902); quarry,

Hunmanby 17, 1916 (N.H. Scarb.).
Hold. Sand le Mere 33, 1894 and Spurn 41, 1897, Canon Maddock; clover field near Hull and in Hull nurseries (R. 1902). Extinct.

C. campestris Yunk.
Alien.
In seed garden, Cottingham 03, 1976, EC.

SOLANACEAE

Lycium L.
It seems there may have been confusion between the two *Lycium* sp., both having been called *L. barbarum* at some time. *L.barbarum* L. has greyish-white stems and grey-green lanceolate leaves, whilst *L. chinense* Mill. has broader, bright green leaves.

L. barbarum L. (*L.halimifolium* Mill.)
Duke of Argyll's Teaplant.
Long cultivated, naturalised in hedges.   Rare.
Hold. Sand dunes, Fraisthorpe 16, 1970, MC; Spurn 41, 1974, FEC; near Oustwick and Elstronwick 23, 1977, EBM.

L. chinense Miller (*L. barbarum* auct.)
China Teaplant.
Naturalised alien.   Uncommon.
L.D. Market Weighton 84, North Cliffe 83 (W. 1938).
Wolds Staxton 07, 1957, FEC; near Rowley 93, 1970, DWS.
Hold. Hornsea 24 (R. 1902); Patrington Haven 31, TS and near gas house, Hessle 02, AKW (W. 1938).

Atropa L.
A. belladonna L.   Map 63.
Deadly Nightshade. CSE.   2nd half 18th century.
Native. In woods, particularly of Ash, also in thickets on calcareous soils; sometimes in the open. Very local.
Locally frequent in the southern part of the Wolds in ten km square 93. It also occurs near Garrowby 75 & 85. On Beverley Westwood 03 in the 2nd half 18th century, WW. Frequent along the disused railway line, North Cave 83, 1978, EHW. Introduced into gardens in Hull and subsequently bird-sown as on a bombed site in central Hull 02, 1952, FEC and in Southcoates Lane, Hull 13, 1978, RCr. Bird-sown also near Newport 83, 1976, YNU Excursion.

Hyoscyamus L.
H. niger L.
Henbane.   1840.
Native. Sandy places, chalk grassland, on waste places and as a garden weed. Uncommon and often erratic in appearance.
L.D. Near Pocklington 84 (Baines, 1840); near Houghton Woods 83, TS (W. 1938); North Cave 83, 1969, MC.
Wolds Near St Austin's Stone 93, 1898, JFR (R. 1902); Flamborough cliffs (Flintoff, 1931); Wood Dale 96, 1960, YNU Excursion; Sewerby cliffs 26, 1970, MC; Thorpe Hall 16, 1971, Hull Nats. Excursion.
Hold. Near Beverley 03, Dr Hull and very common

118

amongst the dock aliens, Hull (R. 1902); King George Dock, Hull 12, 1934-1937 (W. 1938); on bombed sites and other waste places in Hull: High St 12, 1951, FEC, Clifton St 02, 1978, FEC and Hessle Road 02, 1984, FEC; Paull 12 (R. 1902) and 1968, RTh; Skirlaugh 13, 1957, RG; Kilnsea lane 41, 1958, FEC; Skeffling 31, 1961, CMR; sand pit, Brigham 05, 1974, EHW; garden weed, Spurn 41, 1978, BP & BS.

Solanum L.
S. dulcamara L.
Bittersweet, Woody Nightshade.   Map 367.
Native. Hedges, woods; also in marshy places and reed swamps as by the R. Hull. Frequent in Holderness and Lower Derwentland; scarce elsewhere.

S. nigrum L.   Map 368.
Black Nightshade.   1840.
Native. Cultivated ground, waste places. Infrequent as a weed of arable, mainly in Lower Derwentland. Locally frequent on waste places in the Hull area.
Formerly near South Cave (Baines, 1840) and abundant among the dock aliens (R. 1902).

Datura L.
D. stramonium L. (inc. *D. tatula* L.)
Thorn-apple.
Alien. Uncommon, but comes up apparently from dormant seed, particularly in hot summers. Gardens, arable, waste places.
Records include:
U.D. Ganton 97, 1984, MR.
L.D. Riccall 63, WNC (R. 1902); Elvington 74, 1935, GAN, Olympia Oil Mill Sidings, Selby 63, WAS & JK (W. 1938); Crabley Creek 92, 1979, BP; Skipwith 63, 1984, EC.
Wolds High Fordon 07, 1946 (N.H. Scarb.).
Hold. Beverley 03, 1957, RG; Kilnsea 41, 1958, FEC; Risby Park 03, 1972, FEC; Leads Road, Hull 13, 1976, EC; Willerby 03, 1978, FEC; near Hull docks 12, 1982, FH.

SCROPHULARIACEAE

Verbascum L.
V. thapsus L.   Map 369.
Great Mullein.   1892.
Native. Usually on a dry soil; chalk banks, chalk quarries, gravel pits, sand pits, waste places. Widely distributed, but infrequent; erratic, often appearing suddenly after site disturbance.

V. nigrum L.
Dark Mullein.
Native. On calcareous soils, usually in open habitats. Rare.
Wolds One plant, Risby 03, 1949, PLG; by rail track and in open woodland, Lowthorpe 06, 1968, EC and later.
Hold. On West Dock, Hull 02 (R. 1902).

V. blattaria L.
Moth Mullein.
Alien. Waste places. Uncommon.

Hold. West Dock, Hull 02 (R. 1902); King George Dock, Hull 12, 1931, TS (W. 1938); Tower St, Hull 12, 1951, FEC.

V. virgatum Stokes
Twiggy Mullein.
Alien. Waste places. Uncommon.
U.D. Frequent on wood rides and adjacent grassland, near Rillington 87, 1957, persisting at least to 1964, FEC, det. J.E. Lousley.
L.D. Olympia Oil Mill Sidings, Selby 63, WAS (W. 1938).
Hold. West Dock, Hull 02 (R. 1902); site of filled-in Foredyke Stream, Witham, Hull 12, 1980, FEC.

Antirrhinum L.
A. majus L.
Snapdragon.
Introduced. Naturalised, usually on old walls. Uncommon.
Wolds Hessle chalk pits 02, an escape (R. 1902).
Hold. Hedon 12, AKW (W. 1938); near Patrington church 32, 1956, RG; Walkergate, Beverley 03, 1978, EH.

Linaria Mill.
L. purpurea (L.) Mill.
Purple Toadflax.   1932.
Introduced. Much cultivated in gardens; only rarely established on waste places.
L.D. Parking place, Allerthorpe Common 74, 1981, FEC.
Hold. King George Dock, Hull 12, 1932, AKW (W. 1938); refuse tip, Hessle 02, 1947, AKW; bombed site, Hull 12, 1970, FEC; Victoria Dock, Hull 12, 1985, FEC.

L. repens (L.) Mill.
Pale Toadflax.   1960.
Established alien. Mainly on railway sidings and lines and dock reserves. Uncommon; mainly in the Hull area.
U.D. Sand pit, Staxton 07, 1962, MMN.
L.D. Old railway station, Eastrington 83, 1969, MC.
Wolds Near Thwing 06, 1971, EC.
Hold. Well established on Victoria Dock, Hull 12, 1960, FEC; locally frequent on Alexandra Dock, Hull 12, 1979, FEC; on Priory Yard railway sidings 02, 1972 and Spring Head Sidings, Hull 02, 1977, FEC; railway embankment, Fountain Rd, Hull 03, 1978, FEC; by railway lines still in use, between Cottingham and Beverley 03 and near Driffield 05, 1977, railway land survey, ITE.

L. repens x **L. vulgaris** = **L. x sepium** Allman
Alexandra Dock, Hull 12, JFR (W. 1938); Spring Head railway sidings, Hull 02, 1977, FEC and Priory Yard Sidings, Hull 02, 1982, FEC.

L. vulgaris Mill.   Map 370.
Common Toadflax.
Native. Cultivated fields, particularly on the chalk; railway banks, chalk quarries, waste places. Widely distributed, particularly frequent on the Wolds.

Chaenorhinum (DC.) Reichb.
C. minus (L.) Lange (*Linaria viscida* Moench) Map 243.
Small Toadflax.   1840.

Native. Chalk arable and quarries, cindery railway tracks. Locally frequent on the Wolds, and frequent along disused railway tracks in all areas providing the surface is still loose. Appears to have decreased as a weed of arable. Post-1950 records for arable include:
cornfields, near Thixendale 86, 1956, near West Lutton 86, 1957, Londesborough 84, 1957 and turnip field, Huggate 85, 1958, all FEC.

Kickxia Dumort.
K. elatine (L.) Dumort. [*Linaria elatine* (L.) Mill.]
Sharp-leaved Fluellen.
Native. Usually in cornfields on light soils. Rare.
L.D. Westholme, near Howden 72, JBe (R. 1902).
Wolds East of Brantingham 92, 1956, RG; Swindale, North Newbald 93, 1977, EHW.

Cymbalaria Hill
C. muralis Gaertn., Mey. and Scherb. [*Linaria cymbalaria* (L.) Mill.]   Map 249.
Ivy-leaved Toadflax.
Introduced into Britain as a garden plant in 1617. Naturalised on old walls, including railway brickwork. Widely distributed, but infrequent; most records for the eastern half of the vice-county.

Scrophularia L.
S. nodosa L.   Map 89.
Common Figwort.
Native. Mainly in woods and plantations. Infrequent; most records for Lower Derwentland and the southern wolds.

S. auriculata L. (*S. aquatica* auct.)   Map 371.
Water Figwort.   OSE.
Native. By streams, dykes and ponds; in wet woods. Sometimes on waste places on clay soils. Frequent.

Mimulus L.
M. guttatus DC. (*M. luteus* auct.)
Monkeyflower.
Naturalised garden plant. By streams, canal and ponds. Uncommon.
U.D. Wintringham Mill 97, 1955, TFM; Place Newton 87, 1970, MC.
L.D. South of Naburn 64, 1955, RG; Fulford Ings 64, 1970, TFM.
Wolds Gypsey Race as at Boynton 16, 1959, FEC; near Rudston 16 and at Caythorpe 16, 1970, MC.
Hold. By Driffield Canal 05, CW (R. 1902) and 1951, MHi.

M. moschatus Dougl. ex Lindl.
Musk.
Garden alien. Rare.
L.D. Heslington Fields 64, 1938, EJP; rides and wood edge, Houghton Woods 83, 1943, YNU Excursion; Wheldrake woods 64, 1965, YNU Excursion.

Limosella L.
L. aquatica L.
Mudwort.   CNE.   1883.

Native. On wet mud at the edges of ponds. Rare. Skipwith Common 63, 1883, HJW and later (R. 1902), still there, 1937, EJP.

Digitalis L.
D. purpurea L.   Map 372.
Foxglove.
Native. Open places in woods, mainly on acid soils. Locally frequent in Lower Derwentland; infrequent elsewhere.
Rare on the Wolds: Aldro 86 (R. 1902); Brantingham Dale 93, 1953, RG; Garrowby 75, 1958, GAN; North Dalton 95, 1985, DRG.

Veronica L.
V. beccabunga L.   Map 170.
Brooklime.
Native. Streams, ponds, ditches, marshy places. Frequent.

V. anagallis-aquatica agg.
The Water Speedwells are widely distributed, but require further critical study. In 1981, it was discovered that plants of several populations have a combination of characters of the two species, some having lilac flowers.

V. anagallis-aquatica L. *sensu stricto*   Map 169.
Blue Water-speedwell.
Native. Recorded for streams, dykes and marshy places in 67 tetrads: it is however probably greatly over-recorded. Since discovering that hybridization has apparently been widespread in the area, no true *V. anagallis-aquatica* has been seen by the author. *V. anagallis-aquatica s.s.* is likely to be or to have been the characteristic Speedwell of streams and to have occurred in the river valleys.

V. catenata Pennell   Map 171.
Pink Water-speedwell.
Native. Recorded as occurring in streams and becks as well as gravel pits, ponds and dykes. It is the characteristic species of stagnant water and is particularly frequent in Holderness.

V. anagallis-aquatica x **V. catenata** = **V. lackschewitzii** Keller
Sterile F_1 hybrids have been found in a gravel pit at Brandesburton 14 and by dyke near Howsham Bridge 76, 1981, FEC. Plants with a combination of characters of the two species and having a degree of fertility have been recorded as follows:
L.D. In a dyke near Harswell 84, 1982, FEC; near East Cottingwith 74, 1982, FEC & JD.
Wolds In stream, near Newbald Springs 93, 1982, FEC.
Hold. Foston Beck 05, 1982, FEC.

V. scutellata L.   Map 172.
Marsh Speedwell.
Native. Marshes and dykes, often on acid soils. Infrequent. Most records for Lower Derwentland.
Uuncommon elsewhere, including:
U.D. Near Howsham 76, 1958, YNU Excursion; Settrington 87, 1968, FEC.
Wolds Hunmanby Gap 17, 1955, RG; near Burton Agnes

16, 1970, MC; near Reighton 17, 1973, MC.
Hold. Driffield 05, CW (R. 1902); Figham Common 03, 1956, FEC.

V. officinalis L.　　　　　　　　　　　Map 373.
Heath Speedwell.
Native. Dry places on heaths, commons and other grass-land; open places in woods. Locally frequent, particularly in Lower Derwentland; somewhat infrequent elsewhere, including Wolds grassland.

V. montana L.　　　　　　　　　　　Map 92.
Wood Speedwell.　　　　　CE.　　　　1840.
Native. Woods. Infrequent, but widely distributed on the Wolds.
Other records:
U.D. Firby Wood 76 (Baines, 1840); Kirkham Hall woods 76, 1958, FEC.
L.D. Moreby Wood 54, 1955, RG.
Hold. Bentley Wood and Birkhill Wood 04, 1900 (R. 1902); Burton Bushes, Beverley 03, 1953, RG; Eleven Acre Plantation, near Bentley 03, 1967, FEC.

V. chamaedrys L.
Germander Speedwell.
Native. Grassy places, including pastures, lanes, road-sides, wood borders; garden weed, but not persisting in well cut lawns. Very common.

V. serpyllifolia L.　　　　　　　　　　Map 374.
Thyme-leaved Speedwell.　　　　　　　1836.
Native. Pastures, wood rides, lawns. Generally frequent, but few records for Holderness east of the R. Hull valley.

V. arvensis L.　　　　　　　　　　　Map 375.
Wall Speedwell.
Native. Usually on well-drained soils; on cultivated ground, old walls, railway tracks and in gravel pits. Widely distributed and frequent in most areas; scarce in Holder-ness.

V. hederifolia L.　　　　　　　　　　Map 376.
Ivy-leaved Speedwell.
Native. Cultivated ground, including gardens; also in other open habitats e.g. sand pits. Widely distributed and locally frequent on the Wolds and in the Hull and Beverley areas.

V. persica Poir. (*V. tournefortii* auct.)
Common Field-speedwell.
Naturalised alien. First recorded in Britain in 1825. Cul-tivated ground, including gardens; waste ground. Very common.
First v.c. 61 records: Heslington Fields 64 and Towthorpe Moor, near York, 1841, OAM (Baker, 1854). Frequent by the turn of this century (R. 1902).

V. polita Fr.
Grey Field-speedwell.　　　　　　　*c.*1845.
Native. Cultivated ground. Uncommon.
L.D. Heslington Fields 64, *c.*1845, OAM; near Scraying-ham 76, 1967, CMR; Holme upon Spalding Moor 83,

1987, EHW.
Wolds Near North Grimston 86, 1950, CMR; near Thix-endale 86, 1956, FEC; near Little Weighton 93, 1970, DWS; near Leavening 76, 1972, FEC; near Foxholes 07, 1977, EC.
Hold. Kelleythorpe 05, 1950, YNU Excursion; bombed site, High St, Hull 12, 1951, FEC; Sunk Island 21, 1986, FEC.

V. agrestis L.　　　　　　　　　　　Map 239.
Green Field-speedwell.
Native. Cultivated ground, waste places. Said to be formerly everywhere in cornfields and on cultivated ground (R. 1902). Infrequent now and decreasing. Most records for the Wolds and Holderness.

V. filiformis Sm.　　　　　　　　　　Map 264.
Slender Speedwell.　　　　　　　　　1956.
Established garden escape. Native of the mountains of Caucasus and Asia Minor. Grown in this country as a rock-garden plant by 1808, began its escape in the British Isles in 1927 (Bangerter & Kent, 1957). Thrives in well cut grassland: lawns, golf courses, cemeteries, roadsides; not known to produce seed in the area.
First v.c. 61 record outside gardens: roadside, Riplingham Rd, near Hull 03, 1956, IG.
Early records outside gardens:
U.D. Staxton sand quarry and roadside 07, 1969, GAN.
L.D. Roadside near Newton upon Derwent 74, 1972, TFM; near Wheldrake Ings 64, 1972, TFM.
Wolds Lowthorpe 06, 1969, EC.
Hold. Roadside, Bewholme 14, 1957, JAl; verge and ditch bank near Hornsea 14, 1959, JAl (Bangerter & Kent, 1962); Sunk Island 22, 1967, RTh; golf course, Sewerby Park, carpeted with the plant 16, 1971, FH.
First recorded as a lawn weed at Hornsea 14, 1959, JAl and east Hull 13, 1967, FEC. It spread rapidly as a lawn weed and on urban verges in Hull and adjacent villages during the 1970s; common lawn weed, near York 64, 1980, EB.

Pedicularis L.
P. palustris L.　　　　　　　　　　　Map 192.
Marsh Lousewort.
Native. Marshes. Uncommon and decreasing.
U.D. Wintringham 87, 1964, FEC; Flixton Carrs 07, 1971, MC.
L.D. Skipwith Common 63 (R. 1902); Snake Hall Com-mon 83, 1955, RG; Allerthorpe Common 74, 1958, ABM, still present; near Skirpenbeck 75, 1979, NCC; flood meadow, East Cottingwith 74, 1980, NCC.
Wolds Marshy areas by calcareous springs: Newbald springs 93, 1936, AKW; Great Givendale 85, 1969, FEC; Thornwick Bay 17, 1970, MC; Speeton 17, 1973, MC.
Hold. Near Hornsea Mere 14 (R. 1902), still there; Pulfin Bog 04 (R. 1902); Kelleythorpe 05, 1955, RG; near Wansford 05, 1960, YNU Excursion; King's Mill 05, 1971, MC.

P. sylvatica L.　　　　　　　　　　　Map 377.
Lousewort.
Native. Damp grassland, old pastures, commons. Very infrequent and decreasing. Said to be formerly frequent in

peaty and damp grassy places (R. 1902).
Early records:
Hall Ings, Cottingham 03; Bell Mills, Driffield 05, Risby Park 03 (R. 1902); still at Risby,1950, FEC.
Post-1970 records include:
L.D. Skipwith Common 63, 1970, MC; Allerthorpe Common 74, 1984, YNU Excursion; South Cliffe Common 83, 1986, DJL.
Wolds Fraisthorpe 16, 1970 and Flamborough Headland 27, 1970, MC.
Hold. Grass verge of minor road, Lockington 94, 1980, FEC.

Rhinanthus L.
R. serotinus (Schönh.) Oborny (*R. major* Ehrh.)
Greater Yellow-rattle.   1840.
Native.   Cornfields and grassy places.   Extinct.
L.D. Cornfields, Holme upon Spalding Moor 83 (Baines, 1840); potato fields, on recently reclaimed land, Skipwith Common 63, 1879, FAL; on roadside between Barlby and Riccall 63, 1912 (YNU Circular).
Wolds South Cave 93 (Baines, 1840).

R. minor L. (*R. crista-galli* auct.)   Map 378.
Yellow-rattle.
Native. Semi-parasitic on grass species. Old grassland, meadows, edges of marshy areas. Widely distributed and locally frequent, less common than formerly.

Melampyrum L.
M. pratense L.
Common Cow-wheat.   1798.
Native.   Woods usually.   Rare.
L.D. Near Howden 72, JBe (R. 1902); near Kexby 75, 1956, RG.
Hold. Near Beverley 03 (Teesdale, 1800); Birkhill Wood 03, GN, still there in abundance 1901 (R. 1902).

M. sylvaticum L.
Small Cow-wheat.   CNE.
Native.   Woods, usually in mountainous country.
Kirkham woods (Baines, 1840); identification questioned (R. 1902).

Euphrasia L.
E. officinalis L. *sensu lato*   Map 379.
Eyebright.
Native. Chalk grassland, pastures, heaths. Semi-parasitic on grass species. Locally frequent on the Wolds, rare elsewhere; decreasing through loss of habitat.
A number of species and numerous varieties and hybrids occur; these are difficult to identify. Little critical work has been carried out in the vice-county.

E. occidentalis Wettst.
Native. Grassy sea cliffs.
Flamborough Head, Edees (SYF).

E. nemorosa (Pers.) Wallr.
Native. The usual species.

E. stricta J.P.Wolff ex J.F.Lehm. (*E. brevipila* Burn. & Grem.)
Native. Pastures.
Bempton 17, Edwards (SYF).

Odontites Ludw.
O. vernus (Bellardi) Dumort. [*Bartsia odontites* (L.) Huds.]   Map 380.
Red Bartsia.
Native. Cultivated land, on paths, woodland rides, grassy lanes, waste places. Semi-parasitic on grass species. Seed foot-dispersed. Common, particularly on the Wolds and in Holderness.
Both subsp. *vernus* and subsp. *serotinus* (Syme) Corb. occur, but there has been no study of the distribution of the two subspecies.

OROBANCHACEAE

Lathraea L.
L. squamaria L.
Toothwort.   1792.
Native. In moist woods and copses; parasitic on roots of various trees. Uncommon.
U.D. Wood near Kirkham 76 (Teesdale, 1794) and 1968, FEC; Firby Wood 76, MBS (R. 1902); near Leavening 76, 1970, ATD.
Wolds Raywell woods 93, 1936, TS (SYF), and 1956, FEC; Eppleworth Wood 93, 1956, FEC, still present; Millington Wood 85, 1985, ND.

Orobanche L.
O. rapum-genistae Thuill. (*O. major* auct.)
Greater Broomrape.
Native.   Parasitic on roots of Gorse.   Rare.
Kelsey Hill gravel pit 22, CW & JWB (R. 1902); reappeared 1936, HJD (SYF).

O. elatior Sutton
Knapweed Broomrape.   CE.
Native. Chalk quarries, roadsides, banks and railway cutting; parasitic on roots of *Centaurea scabiosa*. Uncommon; mainly on the Wolds.
Seven post-1950 records for the South Cave, North Newbald area 93; in quantity in one locality.
Other records:
U.D. Welham 76, MBS (R. 1902).
Wolds Near Langton 76 (R. 1902); Ruston Parva 06 (Nat. 1930, 19); near Staxton 07, 1960, FEC; near Sherburn 97, 1964, FEC; near Grindale 16, 1970, MC; on Ganton Wold 97, 1983, RJ.

O. reticulata Wallr.
Thistle Broomrape.   CE.   1953.
Native. Parasitic on roots of *Cirsium arvense* and *C. eriophorum*. Rare.
Birdsall Estate 86, 1953, WAS, still present.

O. minor Sm.
Common Broomrape.   CSE.   1842.
Native. Parasitic on Clover and other herbaceous *Legumi-*

nosae. Rare.
L.D. Heslington Fields 64, 1842, JBa; Wressle 73, WNC (R. 1902); Fangfoss 75, 1959, CT.
Wolds High Fordon 07, 1946 and Staxton 07, 1947, ERC (N.H. Scarb.); on disused railway, Everthorpe 93, 1975, PLG.

O. ramosa L.
Hemp Broomrape.
Alien.
In great quantity on tomato plants under glass at Thorngumbald 22, 1909, H. Knight (W. 1938). Extinct.

LENTIBULARIACEAE

Pinguicula L.
P. vulgaris L.
Common Butterwort.   CNE.
Native. Bogs and spring-fed marshes. Uncommon and decreasing.
U.D. Near Wintringham and Settrington 87, 1968, FEC.
L.D. Brough 92, CW, Skipwith Common 63, WNC (R. 1902).
Wolds Flamborough Head (R. 1902) and 1955, RG; edge of drainage channels, North Newbald marsh 93, 1950, FEC, now lost; Buckton 17, 1954, DAu; near Acklam 76, 1970, ATD; Speeton 17, 1973, MC.
Hold. Hall Ings, Cottingham 03, HS (R. 1902); near Wansford 05, 1960, YNU Excursion, still present.

Utricularia L.
U. vulgaris L.
Greater Bladderwort.   1840.
Native. Ponds, dykes and a canal. Rare now.
Some of the following records may be referable to *U. australis* R.Br.
L.D. Abundant in the 'delphs', Staddlethorpe 82, Riccall 63, WNC (R. 1902); Skipwith Common 63 (Nat. 1921, 348); delph, Oxmardyke 82, 1958, RG.
Hold. Near Beverley 03 and Hull (Baines, 1840); Skidby drain, Hull 03, 1890-1893 (R. 1902); Hornsea Mere 14, 1912 (Bolam, 1913); old pond, Inglemire Lane, Hull 03, 1920, JWB, herb. FEC; Cross Drain, Leven Carrs 04, 1970, MC; Leven Canal 04, 1970, FEC.

U. minor L.
Lesser Bladderwort.   CNE.   1840.
Native. Peaty pools in acid bogs.
L.D. Several places near Selby 63 (Baines, 1840).
Hold. Near Beverley 03, Dr Hull (R. 1902).

VERBENACEAE

Verbena L.
V. officinalis L.
Vervain.   2nd half 18th century.
Native. Waysides and waste places. Rare.
L.D. Kexby 75, 1973, TFM.
Wolds Wold Newton 07 and Weaverthorpe 97, Driffield Wold 06, 1886, herb. M. Harman (SYF).

Hold. By Hornsea Mere 14, 2nd half 18th century, WW; Dunswell Lane, Cottingham 03 (R. 1902); bombed site, High St, Hull 12, 1952, FEC.

LABIATAE

Mentha L.
M. pulegium L.
Pennyroyal.   CSE.
Native. Wet places on sandy soil. Rare.
L.D. Ponds near Skipwith church 63, HJW (R. 1902); Skipwith Common 63, 1937, EJP.
Hold. By Hornsea Mere and at Hatfield 14, 2nd half 18th century, WW.

M. arvensis L.   Map 381.
Corn Mint.
Native. Arable fields, waste places; rarely on wood rides as at Rise Park 14, 1984, FEC. Formerly 'common in cornfields, chiefly in Derwentland' (R. 1902). Somewhat infrequent now and decreasing; most post-1950 records for Lower Derwentland; otherwise widely scattered, but rare in Holderness.

M. aquatica L.   Map 154.
Water Mint.
Native. Marshes, by dykes, streams, rivers and ponds. Common.

M. arvensis x *M. spicata* = *M.* x *gentilis* L.
Bushy Mint.
Alien and established garden escape.
Olympia Mills, Selby 63, DM; Kelk Beck, near Lowthorpe 06, 1972, EC, det. Dr R.M. Harley (RMH).

M. aquatica x *M. arvensis* = *M.* x *verticillata* L. (*M. sativa* L.)
Whorled Mint.
In damp places, Skipwith Common 63, 1900 (R. 1902); wet meadow, South Cliffe 83, 1972, EC, det. RMH; near Dunnington 65, 1983, CSVY; Tilmire 64 and near Broomfleet 82, 1984, EB.

M. aquatica x *M. spicata* = *M.* x *piperita* L.
Peppermint.   1840.
Introduced. Formerly cultivated as a source of peppermint. Naturalised by the sides of ditches, streams and damp roadsides. Rare now. 'Several places on the Wolds' (Baines, 1840).
U.D. Kirkham Abbey 76, 1958, RG; Settrington 87, 1959, CMR & FEC.
L.D. Newsholme 73, JBe (R. 1902); bank of R. Derwent, Barmby on the Marsh 62, 1985, TFM.
Wolds Ditch side, near Elloughton 92, CW, Newbald Springs 93 (R. 1902), still at North Newbald, 1965, EC.
Hold. Victoria Dock, Hull 12, 1975, EC.

M. spicata L. (*M. viridis* auct.)
Spear Mint.
Established garden escape. Waste places. Uncommon.
U.D. By the R. Derwent, Welham Springs 76, MBS (R.

1902); sand pit, Staxton 07, 1956, RG.
L.D. Skipwith Common 63, 1982, EB.
Wolds Bishop Burton 94, 1952, DAW; South Cave 93, 1953, RG.
Hold. Between Long Riston and Catwick 14, 1935, AMS (SYF); disused tip, Leads Rd, Hull 13, 1963, EC.

M. longifolia (L.) Huds. x *M. rotundifolia* = *M.* x *niliaca* Juss. ex Jacq.
High St, Hull 12, 1959, FEC, det. J.E. Lousley.

M. longifolia x *M. suaveolens* = *M.* x *rotundifolia* (L.) Huds.
Near Skipwith 63, 1982, EB, det. RMH.

Lycopus L.

L. europaeus L.   Map 151.
Gipsywort.
Native. By a river and canal, by lakes, ponds and dykes; in fen marshes. Locally frequent in the R. Hull valley and in Lower Derwentland.
Other records:
U.D. Flood meadow, Welham 76, 1979, NCC; near Firby 76, 1981, YNU Excursion.
Hold. On lock walls in Hull docks, as at Victoria Dock 12, 1973, FEC; by Hornsea Mere 14, 1979 and by Rise Park lake 14, 1982, FEC.

Origanum L.

O. vulgare L.   Map 19.
Marjoram.
Native. Chalk and limestone grassland, chalk pits, railway banks. Somewhat infrequent and almost confined to a belt at the west of the Wolds.
In quantity along the disused railway west of Cherry Burton 94, 1980, FEC.
Other records:
U.D. Rillington Low Moor 87, 1970, RMH.
L.D. Near Broomfleet 82, 1958, FEC; disused railway, North Cave 83, 1980, FEC.

Thymus L.

T. pulegioides L.   Map 27.
Large Thyme.   1952.
Native. Calcareous grassland, bare chalk, chalk quarries, disused railways. Widely distributed, but infrequent, almost confined to a belt at the west and north of the Wolds.
First records: on newly disturbed roadside verge, near Fimber 96 and near Boynton 16, 1952, Dr M.E. Bradshaw.
In quantity on disused railway line, near Weedley Springs 93, near South Cave quarry 93 and near Burdale 86. In Wharram Quarry Nature Reserve 86 and in quarry, near North Grimston 86.
For other records, see YNU Botanical Reports, *The Naturalist*, 1966-1972.

T. praecox Opiz subsp. *arcticus* (Durand) Jalas (*T. drucei* Ronn.; *T. serpyllum* auct.)   Map 26.
Wild Thyme.   ONE.
Native. Grassland on chalk and limestone, chalk quarries. Common in areas of grazed grassland on the Wolds; on slopes of all aspects.

Calamintha Mill.

C. ascendens Jord. (*C. officinalis* auct.)
Common Calamint.
Native.   Dry, usually calcareous banks.
Bishop Burton 93 (Baines, 1840); near Hessle 02, CW (R. 1902). Extinct.

Acinos Mill.

A. arvensis (Lam.) Dandy (*Calamintha arvensis* Lam.)
       Map 1.
Basil Thyme.
Native. Open habitats on calcareous soils, including arable; on walls; rarely on sand. Infrequent and mainly in a belt at the west of the Wolds.
On sand:
U.D. Wintringham 87, 1957, FEC; in sandpit, Staxton 07, 1957, FEC.
L.D. Allerthorpe Common 74, 1931, GAN.
In gravel pit in Holderness, at Brandesburton 14, 1955, RG.

Clinopodium L.

C. vulgare L. (*Calamintha clinopodium* Benth.)
       Map 382.
Wild Basil.   1840.
Native. Wood clearings and borders, scrub, grassland on calcareous soils, chalk quarries, railway banks. Mainly on the Wolds and particularly frequent in ten km squares 93 and 94.
Other records include:
L.D. Near Broomfleet 82, 1955, RG.
Hold. Drain side, near Wilfholme 04, 1957, FEC; edge of cornfield, near Angram Farm 04, 1957, FEC; near Dunswell 03, 1975, EHW.

Melissa L.

M. officinalis L.
Balm.
Introduced. By cycle path, Wilmington, Hull 13, 1987, FEC.

Salvia L.

S. verbenaca L. (*S. horminoides* Pourr.)
Wild Clary.   ME.   1840.
Native.
U.D. Kirkham Abbey walls 76 (Baines 1840).
L.D. Allerthorpe 74, CW (R. 1902); Pocklington 84, 1931, GAN.
Wolds Weaverthorpe 97, 1965, EC.
Hold. Amongst aliens at the Hull docks 02 (R. 1902); Skipsea Brough 15, 1986, GH.

Prunella L.

P. vulgaris L.
Selfheal.
Native. Grassland, waste places, clearings in woods; mainly on basic and neutral soils. Common.

Stachys L.

S. officinalis (L.) Trev. (*Betonica officinalis* L.; *Stachys betonica* Benth.)   Map 383.
Betony.   c.1845.
Native.

Wolds grassland, pastures, lanes, roadsides, railway banks, wood rides. Locally frequent on the Wolds, otherwise infrequent.

S. arvensis (L.) L.   Map 237.
Field Woundwort.   1840.
Native. Arable fields. Locally frequent on the chalk wolds, often in cornfields. Infrequent elsewhere, sometimes on sand.

S. palustris L.   Map 165.
Marsh Woundwort.
Native.   By streams, canal and ditches; in marshes. Sometimes in dry places, but such plants should be critically examined as the hybrid with *S. sylvatica* occurs in the area and is usually closer to *S. palustris* than to the other parent. Locally frequent in the R. Hull valley, scattered in Lower Derwentland, uncommon elsewhere.

S. palustris x **S. sylvatica** = **S.** x **ambigua** Sm.
Crushed leaves have the smell of *S. sylvatica*.
Cornfield edge, Tollingham 83, 1982, FEC; field edge, Boothferry Bridge 72 and on a bridge, by a hedgerow and as a garden weed at Barmby on the Marsh 64, 1983, FEC; near Staxton 07, 1983, CSVY.

S. sylvatica L.
Hedge Woundwort.
Native. Wood borders, hedgebanks, roadsides. Common.

Ballota L.
B. nigra L. subsp. *foetida* Hayek   Map 384.
Black Horehound.
Native. Roadsides, hedgebanks, often in villages; less commonly in sand and gravel pits and in waste places. Widely distributed and locally frequent in the South Cave area.
Records include: sand pit, Staxton 07, 1957, FEC and gravel pit, Brandesburton 04, 1959, FEC.

Lamiastrum Heister ex Fabr.
L. galeobdolon (L.) Ehrend. & Polatschek [*Galeobdolon luteum* Huds.; *Lamium galeobdolon* (L.) L.]
Yellow Archangel.   CE.   1840.
Native. Woods. Rare.
L.D. Howden 72, JB & Selby 63, WNC (R. 1902).
Wolds Woods, Londesborough (Baines, 1840); near Thorpe Hall 16, 1969, MC; High Mowthorpe 86,1985, ND.
Hold. Near Kilnwick 94, 1986, AJ.

Lamium L.
L. amplexicaule L.   Map 230.
Henbit Dead-nettle.   1831.
Native.   Cultivated ground, usually on light dry soils. Mainly on chalk;   also occurs in sand and gravel pits. Frequent on the Wolds; uncommon in Holderness and in Lower Derwentland.

L. hybridum Vill.   Map 231.
Cut-leaved Dead-nettle.   1840.
Native. Cultivated ground, including gardens. Infrequent, but widely scattered; most records for Lower Derwentland.

L. purpureum L.
Red Dead-nettle.
Native. Cultivated fields, gardens, waste place. Common.

L. album L.
White Dead-nettle.
Native. Hedgebanks, roadsides and waste places. Very common.

L. maculatum L.
Spotted Dead-nettle.
Garden escape, sometimes naturalised. Roadsides, waste places usually near houses, not usually persisting.
U.D. Shire Oaks 76, GP (W. 1938).
Hold. Near Cottingham 03 (R. 1902); sand pit, Keyingham 22, 1955, FEC; Hull General Cemetery 02, 1975, FEC.

Galeopsis L.
G. angustifolia Ehrh. ex Hoffm. (*G. ladanum* auct.)
                                          Map 14.
Red Hemp-nettle.
Native.   Almost confined to open communities on the chalk: chalk scree, railway cuttings, chalk quarries, more rarely on arable. Locally frequent on the Wolds; mainly in the grazed grassland belt; spread along the chalk bank of the Little Weighton to South Cave railway.
Rare away from the Wolds:
L.D. Howden 72, JBe (R. 1902); railway bank, near Broomfleet 82, 1963, FEC & PMG; fields, near Oxmardyke 82, 1978, JRo.

G. tetrahit L. *sensu lato*   Map 385.
Common Hemp-nettle.   1798.
Native. Cultivated land and waste places, often near farm buildings. Widely distributed, but infrequent in some areas. Now treated as two species:

G. tetrahit L. *sensu stricto* The usual species.

G. bifida Boenn.
Lesser Hemp-nettle.
May be under-recorded.
U.D. Near Fordon 07, 1913 (N.H. Scarb.); near Staxton 07, 1983, CSVY.
L.D. Near Bielby 74, 1958, FEC; Allerthorpe Common 74, 1961, FEC; Skipwith Common 63, 1964, FEC.
Hold. Leven 04, 1950, FEC; near Little Kelk 16, 1984, EC.

G. speciosa Mill. (*G. versicolor* Curt.)   Map 229.
Large-flowered Hemp-nettle.   CE.   *c.*1845.
Native. Arable, often on black peaty soil. Locally frequent in the R. Hull valley and in Lower Derwentland. Said to be formerly frequent in cornfields, near Hull (R. 1902).
First record: Heslington Fields 64, *c.*1845, OAM.

Glechoma L.
G. hederacea L. (*Nepeta glechoma* Benth.) Map 386.
Ground-ivy.
Native. Woods, plantations, hedgebanks; grassland and waste places, especially on the heavier soils. Common except in the driest and most exposed situations.

Nepeta L.

N. cataria L.
Cat-mint.   1900.
Native. Hedgebanks and roadsides, usually on calcareous soils.
L.D. By roadside hedges, near Selby 63, 1900 (R. 1902).
Wolds Goodmanham 84, 1908, JJM (Trans. HSFNC *4*, 106).
Hold. Beverley Park 03, 1908, JJM (Trans. HSFNC *4*, 106); King George Dock, Hull 12, 1933, TS (W. 1938). Probably extinct.

Marrubium L.

M. vulgare L.
White Horehound.   2nd half 18th century.
Native. Waste places, roadsides. Rare now.
Formerly valued for its medicinal properties. Once locally frequent: 'at North Cave (83), on the sand, almost as common as the dead nettles ...' (R. 1902). 'The chief plant on Coneygarth Hill, Brandesburton' (R. 1902); still in Coneygarth gravel pit 14, 1955, RG.
Other records:
Wolds South Cave 93 (R. 1902); Great Givendale 85, 1966, EC.
Hold. By Hornsea Mere 14, 2nd half 18th century, WW; Spurn 41, CW (R. 1902).
The decrease of this species in this and other areas of England is remarkable and the reason unknown.

Scutellaria L.

S. galericulata L.   Map 164.
Skullcap.
Native. By streams, ditches and lakes; in fens and open wet woodland. Rarely in apparently dry places as on the disused railway at Spurn 41, 1956, FEC. Frequent in the R. Hull valley; scattered in Lower Derwentland.
Uncommon elsewhere:
U.D. By the R. Derwent, near Welham 77 and at Firby 76, MBS (R. 1902), still at Firby, 1970, TFM; Kirkham 76, 1958, RG; Willerby Carr 08, 1980, JBo.
Hold. By Hornsea Mere 14 and by lake in Rise Park 14 (R. 1902), still in both places; Roos Bog 22, 1959, FEC; near Great Cowden 24, 1985, GH.

S. minor Huds.
Lesser Skullcap.   OWEE.
Native. Bogs and by ponds on acid soils. A western species in Britain, rare in v.c. 61.
Broughton Common, HFP (R. 1902) should be Breighton Common 73, still there 1957, WAS, herb. HLU, habitat destroyed by 1963; Skipwith Common 63, 1950, KGP, still there in 1959, JDL & WAS.

Teucrium L.

T. scorodonia L.   Map 387.
Wood Sage.
Native. Woods, heaths; usually on sand, less commonly on chalk. Locally frequent in Lower Derwentland, also occurs in the Kirkham area 76.
Other records:
U.D. Low Moor, Rillington 87, 1970, RMH.
Wolds Low Caythorpe 16, 1955, RMH; Risby 03, 1970,

DWS; cliff top, Speeton to Bempton 17 and at the bottom of cliffs at Speeton 17, 1971, FEC; near Birdsall 86, 1969, MC; along disused railway, Wharram 86, 1971, FEC.

Ajuga L.

A. reptans L.   Map 388.
Bugle.
Native. Woods mainly; less commonly in damp grassland, as on the roadside at Rise 14, 1954, FEC and on the bank of Pocklington Canal 74, 1955, FEC. Locally frequent. Possibly formerly more common in grassland in Holderness as Robinson (1902) said 'common in clayey places'.

PLANTAGINACEAE

Plantago L.

P. major L.
Greater Plantain.
Native. In open habitats, on paths, by roadsides, in cultivated ground, particularly at field entrances, waste places, disused railway tracks. Very common.

P. media L.   Map 22.
Hoary Plantain.
Native. Grassland, including roadsides and lawns, mainly on calcareous soils; sometimes on neutral soils. Common on the Wolds, infrequent elsewhere.

P. lanceolata L.
Ribwort Plantain.
Native. In grassy places on neutral and basic soils; roadsides, waste ground. Very common.

P. maritima L.   Map 215.
Sea Plantain.   1840.
Native. Salt-marshes and the foreshore of the R. Humber from Hessle 02 west to Saltmarshe 72. Frequent.
On mud of the Hedon Haven 12 and on the river wall at Paull 12. Locally frequent on coastal cliffs of Filey Bay 17 and Flamborough Head 26 & 27; also at Barmston 15.

P. coronopus L.   Map 214.
Buck's-horn Plantain.   CSE.   1840.
Native. Dry, more or less open situations, mainly on sandy and gravelly soils; rare away from the Holderness coast and the R. Humber bank. Locally common as at Spurn 41 and here and there on coastal cliffs. Uncommon along the R. Humber west of Patrington Haven, including the river wall at Paull 12, 1983, FEC.
By the R. Hull, Tower St, Hull 12, 1973, FEC.
Occurring inland on sand:
U.D. Staxton 07, 1957, FEC; roadside Ganton 97, 1969, EC. & 1982, FEC.
L.D. Allerthorpe Common 74 (Nat. 1927, 304); sand pit, North Cave 83, 1948, FEC.
Recorded as formerly occurring on the Wolds, the roadside from South Cave to New Village being specified (Baines, 1840).

Littorella Berg.
L. uniflora (L.) Aschers. (*L. juncea* Berg.)
Shoreweed.
Native. In shallow water or exposed on shores of non-calcareous ponds.
Skipwith Common 63, HJW (R. 1902), the only record.
Extinct.

CAMPANULACEAE

Campanula L.
C. latifolia L.   Map 389.
Giant Bellflower.   1626.
Native. Woods, hedgebanks, river and drain banks. Infrequent. 'In great plenty growing wilde upon the bankes of the River Ouse in Yorkshire as I went from Yorke to visite Selby ...', 1626, T. Johnson; the first British record. Most records for the Wolds where it is locally frequent, notably in ten km squares 84 and 16.
Other records include:
L.D. On dyke side, Newton upon Derwent 74, 1958, FEC.
Hold. Dyke by roadside, Leconfield 04, 1958, FEC & PG; Wassand 14, 1969, FEC; Beverley 03, 1970, AH; Haworth Hall 03, 1978, JA.

C. trachelium L.
Nettle-leaved Bellflower.   1792.
Native. Woods. Rare. Only on the Wolds.
In Heslerton Woods 97 (Teesdale, 1794). Occurrence in Yorkshire questioned (Baker, 1854). Recently found in Millington Wood 85, 1974, EC, det. D.W. Shimwell, still present.

C. rapunculoides L.
Creeping Bellflower.   1882.
Established garden alien. Uncommon.
L.D. North Cave station 83, 1934, AKW and lane to Allerthorpe Common 74, 1937, TS (W. 1938); Skirpenbeck 75, 1957, MT.
Wolds Near Brantingham 93, 1882, EAP (R. 1902); Warter 85, 1966, MC; Garton 95, 1969, MC.
Hold. Spurn Point 41, 1953, FEC.

C. glomerata L.   Map 8.
Clustered Bellflower.   1840.
Native. Grassland on calcareous soils, chalk quarries, railway banks. Frequent on the Wolds.
Rare elsewhere:
L.D. Near York (Baines, 1840); plentiful on the banks of the R. Ouse, near Selby 63, WNC (R. 1902) and 1912 (YNU Circular); Cockle Pits, Brough 92, 1955, RG.
Hold. Roadside, between Wansford and Skerne 05, 1951, RG.

C. rotundifolia L.   Map 390.
Harebell.
Native. Dry grassy places on both calcareous and sandy soils; hedges, lanes, railway banks, chalk scree and quarries; sand and gravel pits. Common on the Wolds, infrequent and somewhat local in Lower Derwentland.
Mainly confined to disused railway tracks in Holderness,

but occasionally in profusion on gravel. On clay cliffs at North Ferriby 92, 1950, FEC.

Legousia Durande
L. hybrida (L.) Delarb. [*Specularia hybrida* (L.) A. DC.]
                                                        Map 232.
Venus's-looking-glass.   CSE.   1800.
Native. Corn and turnip fields, now restricted to calcareous soils. Uncommon at any one time, yet recorded for many widely scattered localities since 1950, all on the Wolds. Most consistently recorded for the Langton area 86.
Recorded away from the Wolds:
L.D. Heslington Fields 64, 1800, WM, herb. York Mus.
Hold. Hull docks 02, 1900, JWB (R. 1902).

Jasione L.
J. montana L.
Sheep's-bit.   1798.
Native. In grassy places on light sandy soils.
All records for Lower Derwentland, most for ten km square 74. Very rare now. Sandy fields between Market Weighton and Sancton 83 (Teesdale, 1800); Allerthorpe Common 74, 1930, WAS; roadside drain near Sandhill Lock 74, 1957, FEC; Poor Allotments, Barmby Moor in quantity 74, 1973, FEC, habitat now destroyed; still near Barmby Moor 74, 1983, RJ.

RUBIACEAE

Sherardia L.
S. arvensis L.   Map 391.
Field Madder.
Native. Arable fields and waste places. Frequent on the Wolds, infrequent in Holderness, uncommon and local in Lower Derwentland.

Asperula L.
A. cynanchica L.
Squinancywort.   CSE.   1792.
Native. Dry calcareous grassland. Rare.
Wolds Hedgebanks, Langton Wold 86 (Teesdale, 1794), still on Langton Wold; near Settrington 87, 1983, RJ.

A. arvensis L.
Blue Woodruff.
Introduction. Waste places, gardens. An uncommon casual.
Hold. Waste ground and near docks, Hull (R. 1902); King George Dock, Hull 12, 1933, AKW (W. 1938). Bird seed alien, High St, Hull 12, 1977, EHW and in garden, Hornsea 24, 1978, FEC.

Galium L.
G. cruciata (L.) Scop. [*Cruciata chersonensis* (Willd.) Ehrend.]   Map 392.
Crosswort.
Native. Roadsides, grassy lanes, chalk quarries, gravel pits, open woodland, especially on calcareous soils. Very common on the Wolds, less frequent in Lower Derwentland and in Holderness, particularly east of the R. Hull valley; absent from urban Hull and apparently from most coastal areas.

G. odoratum (L.) Scop. (*Asperula odorata* L.)
Woodruff.
Native. Woods and hedges on calcareous soils. Uncommon.
U.D. Kirkham 76, 1923, GP.
L.D. Near Howden 72, JB (R. 1902); Broomfleet 82, 1953, AW; Skirpenbeck 75, 1957, MT.
Wolds West Ella 02 (R. 1902); Millington Wood 85, 1964, FEC, still present; Elloughton 92, 1970, JG; Settrington 87, 1987, ND.
Hold. Beverley Westwood 03 and Hall Ings, Cottingham 03 (R. 1902); Hyde Wood, Cottingham 03, 1953, AKW; Carnaby 16, 1970, MC; near Roos 23, 1975, EBM.

G. mollugo L.   Map 393.
Hedge-bedstraw.
Native. Hedgebanks, scrub, grassy slopes, particularly on base-rich soils; chalk quarries. Fairly frequent on grazed Wolds grassland; infrequent elsewhere. Sometimes on railway banks.

G. album Mill. (*G. erectum* Huds.)
Upright Hedge-bedstraw.
Native. Chalk grassland. Uncommon.
Wolds Staxton Wold 07, 1955, TFM; near Thixendale 86, 1956, FEC; Knapton Wold 87, 1957, FEC; near Duggleby 86, 1963, FEC.

G. mollugo x *G. verum* = *G.* x *pomeranicum* Retz.
L.D. Bubwith Ings 73, 1976, TFM.
Wolds Waterdale 86, 1956, WAS; Londesborough 84, 1958, RG; between Huggate and Thixendale 86, 1966, FEC; near Wintringham 87, 1968, EC; Brantingham 93, 1969, FEC.

G. verum L.   Map 394.
Lady's Bedstraw.
Native. Grassland mainly on calcareous soils, including Wolds hillsides, roadsides, railway banks, fixed dunes at Spurn 41. Common on the Wolds, locally frequent in Holderness; scarce and local in Lower Derwentland.
On sand as at Flixton Carr Farm 07, 1957 and Sands Wood Lane, Wintringham 87, 1957, FEC.

G. saxatile L.   Map 39.
Heath Bedstraw.
Native. Heaths, commons and woods on acid soils; a strict calcifuge. Locally frequent and often in great quantity in Lower Derwentland.
Occurs in quantity very locally elsewhere:
Wolds On the cliff top of Filey Bay, as near Speeton 17, 1971, FEC; Birdsall Brow 86, 1972, FEC.
Hold. Gransmoor Wood 16, 1955, RG; Bentley Moor Wood 03, 1967, FEC.

G. palustre L.   Map 143.
Common Marsh-bedstraw.   1798.
Native. Marshes, in and by dykes and by streams. Widely distributed and fairly frequent.

G. uliginosum L.   Map 185.
Fen Bedstraw.   CNE.   1845.
Native. Fens. Infrequent.
Mainly in the R. Hull valley and in Lower Derwentland; may be in quantity as at Pulfin Bend 04, where it has long been known (R. 1902).
Other records include:
U.D. Marshy ground, near mill pool, Sherburn 97, 1957,

FEC; Flotmanby Carrs 07, 1957, FEC; in spring-fed marsh, near Wintringham 87, 1964, FEC; near Leavening 76, 1972, FEC; near Firby 76, 1981, FEC.
Hold. Hornsea Mere 14, 1978, FEC; Roos Bog 22, 1987, FEC.

G. tricornutum Dandy (*G. tricorne* Stokes)
Corn Cleavers.
Introduced. Casual.
One post-1950 record. Said to be formerly 'frequent in cornfields', three localities being specified: Marfleet 12, near Sutton 13 and Benningholme 13 (R. 1902).
Other records:
Hold. On dock wastes, Hull (R. 1902); King George Dock, Hull 12, 1937, TS & AKW (W. 1938); bombed site, Jenning St, Hull 12, 1954, FEC, herb. FEC.

G. aparine L.
Cleavers.
Native. Hedges, woods, edges of cultivated fields, waste places. Very common.

G. parisiense L. (*G. anglicum* Huds.)
Wall Bedstraw.
Native in S.E. England.
Old wall, near Boynton 16, 1798, R. Teesdale.
Extinct.

CAPRIFOLIACEAE

Sambucus L.
S. nigra L.
Elder.
Native. Woods, scrub, hedges and waste places. Seeds distributed by birds to waste ground and gardens in towns as well as in rural areas. Common.

S. ebulus L.
Dwarf Elder.   1798.
Native? By roadsides and in waste places. Extinct.
Wolds Lund 94 (Teesdale, 1800).
Hold. Near Hornsea 14 and 'plentifully in the rector's garden at Sigglesthorne' 14, 2nd half 18th century, WW.

Viburnum L.
V. lantana L.
Wayfaring-tree.   CSE.
Native. Woods, scrub and hedges on calcareous soils. Near the edge of its climatic range. Uncommon.
Wolds Welton Dale woods 92 (R. 1902); Great Givendale 85, 1937, GAN & WAS (SYF); Melton Plantation 92, 1955 and near Brantingham 93, 1956, RG; near Fimber 95 & 96, 1971, DWS; Wauldby 93, 1978, FEC; chalk pit, Hessle 02, 1986, AJ.
Hold. Copses near Cottingham 03 (R. 1902).

V. opulus L.   Map 93.
Guelder-rose.
Native. Woods, scrub and hedges, preferring moist situations. Widely distributed and locally frequent.

Symphoricarpos Duham.
S. rivularis Suksd.
Snowberry.
Introduced. Commonly planted and probably bird-sown and more or less naturalised. It produces suckers and may form large thickets. Infrequent.

Widely distributed; most records for the Wolds and for Holderness.

Lonicera L.
L. xylosteum L.
Fly Honeysuckle.   1840.
Introduced.   Hedges, plantations.   Uncommon.
Wolds Londesborough 84 (Baines, 1840); York Dale, Sledmere 96, 1897, JTH (R. 1902) and 1965, MC; Filey 17, 1913 (N.H. Scarb.); Beckhead Wood Plantation, Great Givendale 85, 1968, DA.
Hold. Fairholme Wood, Swine 13, TS (W. 1938).

L. periclymenum L.   Map 78.
Honeysuckle.
Native. Hedges, woods. Frequent in Lower Derwentland, where it is a characteristic plant of woods and locally in Holderness where it mainly occurs in hedges; infrequent elsewhere.

L. caprifolium L.
Perfoliate Honeysuckle.   1840.
Introduced.   Hedges and scrub.   Uncommon.
L.D. Skirpenbeck 75, 1957, MT.
Wolds Londesborough 84 (Baines, 1840); West Ella 92 (R. 1902).
Hold. Spurn Point 31, 1981, BS.

ADOXACEAE

Adoxa L.
A. moschatellina L.
Moschatel.
Native.   Woods, hedgebanks.   Rare.
U.D. Kirkham Abbey 76, MBS (R. 1902) and 1925, GP; Firby and Howsham 76, GP (Flintoff, 1931); Kirkham Hall woods 76, 1968, FH.
L.D. Hedgerow near Heslington 64, 1882, WWh (SYF) and 1959, JP.
Wolds Boynton 16, 1910 (SYF); Sewerby 16, but believed to have been introduced (Flintoff, 1931).

VALERIANACEAE

Valerianella Mill.
V. locusta (L.) Betcke [*V. olitoria* (L.) Poll.] Map 395.
Common Cornsalad, Lamb's Lettuce.   1840.
Native. On arable and waste places, usually on dry soils; chalk pits, gravel pits, sand dunes. Widely distributed and locally frequent on the Wolds; uncommon elsewhere.
In quantity on Spurn Point 41 where it has long been known (R. 1902).
Early records include:
L.D. Heslington Fields 64 (Baines, 1840).
Hold. Kelsey Hill 22 (R. 1902), still present in 1943, FEC.

V. rimosa Bast.
Broad-fruited Cornsalad.   CSE.
Native.   Cornfields.
L.D. Holme upon Spalding Moor 83, 1890, CW (R. 1902); Market Weighton, 1908, JJM (Trans. HSFNC, *4*, 105). No later record.

V. dentata (L.) Poll.   Map 238.
Narrow-fruited Cornsalad.   1840.
Native. Cornfields, mainly on calcareous soils.

Infrequent, most records for the Wolds.
Other records include:
L.D. Langwith 64 (Baines, 1840); North Cave 83, 1953, FEC; near Melbourne 74, 1958, FEC; Tollingham 83, 1972, FEC.
Hold. Wawne 03 (R. 1902); Kelleythorpe 05, 1950, RL; Cattleholmes 05, 1968, FEC; near Ings Cottages, Arnold 13, 1973, FEC.
Var. *eriosperma* (Wallr.) Janch.
Hairy-fruited Cornsalad.
L.D. North Cave 83, 1953, FEC, det. Kew.

Valeriana L.
V. officinalis L. (*V. sambucifolia* Mikan f.)   Map 168.
Common Valerian.
Native. River and dyke sides, marshy ground; more rarely on dry soil as at Spurn 41. Common in the R. Hull valley; locally frequent in Lower Derwentland. In addition there are several records for ten km squares 76 & 86, otherwise it is uncommon.

V. dioica L.   Map 199.
Marsh Valerian.
Native. Fens and spring-fed marshes, by ponds. Most localities along the spring line at the western side of the Wolds; scattered localities elsewhere, mainly in the upper part of the R. Hull valley, by Hornsea Mere and locally in Lower Derwentland.

Centranthus DC.
C. ruber (L.) DC.
Red Valerian.
Naturalised garden escape; on old walls, in chalk pits, on railway banks and brickwork. Infrequent.
Very abundant in the chalk pits at Hessle 02 (R. 1902), still present. On railway banks and in cuttings, sometimes in quantity as near Broomfleet 82, 1964, FEC, near Enthorpe station 94, 1977, FEC and near Withernsea 32, 1984, KS; also on railway brickwork at Hedon 12, 1983, FEC and at Hornsea 24, 1980, FEC. On old walls: at Kirkham Abbey 76, 1955, RG; at Barmston 15, 1958, FEC.

DIPSACACEAE

Dipsacus L.
D. fullonum L.
Subsp. *sylvestris* (Huds.) P.Fourn. (*D. sylvestris* Huds.)
                                            Map 396.
Teasel.   CSE.   1840.
Native. Stream and drain banks; rough pastures, especially on clay; sometimes occurs as a garden weed. Locally frequent by the R. Humber and in the R. Hull valley; scattered elsewhere.

D. pilosus L.
Small Teasel.   CE.   1798.
Native.   Woods on chalk.   Rare.
Woods near Beverley 03 (Teesdale, 1800); this record is believed to have been for Risby 03, where it was collected, 1839, herb. Motley (Nat., 1902, 344), not reported in the last thirty years of the 19th century (R. 1902). Old chalk quarry, Hessle 02, 1966, EC.

Knautia L.
K. arvensis (L.) Coult. (*Scabiosa arvensis* L.)
Field Scabious.   CE.   1840.
Native. Grassland on calcareous soils, chalk pits; other

well-drained grassland, including roadsides. Common over the whole of the Wolds; infrequent elsewhere.

Scabiosa L.

S. columbaria L.　　　　　　　　　　　　Map 25.
Small Scabious.　　　　　　　　　　　　　1840.
Native. Chalk and limestone grassland; chalk pits. Common in the belt of grazed grassland at the west of the Wolds, thinning out in the northern belt of chalk grassland, but present along the dry ridge between Driffield and Bridlington. A good indicator of a shallow soil over chalk or limestone.
Rare off the chalk: west of Hotham 93, 1955, RG.

Succisa Haller

S. pratensis Moench (*Scabiosa succisa* L.)　Map 398.
Devil's-bit Scabious.　　　　　　　　　　1840.
Native. Grassland on both basic and somewhat acid soils. On Wolds hillsides, mainly on north-westerly and north-facing slopes. On fen-marshes as at Wansford 05. More rarely at wood borders. Fairly frequent in the chalk grassland belt of the Wolds; infrequent in Lower Derwentland and in scattered localities in Holderness.

COMPOSITAE

Bidens L.

B. cernua L.
Nodding Bur-marigold.　　　　　　　　　1839.
Native. By lakes, ponds, ditches and streams. Rare.
L.D. Near Holme upon Spalding Moor 83, JJM (R. 1902); on Skipwith Common 63, 1896, WNC, YNU Circ.; Bubwith 73, WJF (YNU Circ., 1937); Fulford Ings 64, 1980, EB.
Hold. Risby 03, 1839, herb. Motley (Nat., 1902, 344); near Hornsea Mere 14, 1899, JS (R. 1902).

B. tripartita L.
Trifid Bur-marigold.　　　　　　　　　　1840.
Native. In ditches, by ponds and lakes, streams and riversides. Uncommon.
L.D. Ponds at Fulford 64 (Baines, 1840); near Holme upon Spalding Moor 83 and Skipwith Common 63 (R. 1902); by pond at Skipwith 63, FEC, still there, 1984, EC; near Newport 83, 1969, FEC; Howden Dyke Island 72, 1970, RHu & JHu; by R. Ouse, near Boothferry Bridge 72, 1983, DRG; near Bubwith 73, 1983, CSVY. In cucumber houses, Elloughton 92, 1971, JG.
Hold. Beck-side, Beverley 03, 1970, MHu; dyke near Dunswell 03, 1975, JA; by Hornsea Mere 14, 1979, FEC.

Galinsoga Ruiz & Pav.

G. parviflora Cav.
Gallant Soldier.　　　　　　　　　　　　1952.
Established alien, native of S. America. Weed of arable and gardens, waste places. Uncommon, but sometimes in quantity.
L.D. Sutton upon Derwent 74, 1956, MT.; Riccall 63, 1967, MC & JR; cucumber houses, Elloughton 92, 1971, JG; Fulford 64, 1976, DU; Wholsea Grange 83, 1980, FEC; Skipwith Common 63, 1982, EB.
Hold. Garden weed, Leven 14, introduced with manure, 1952, FEC.

G. ciliata (Raf.) Blake
Shaggy Soldier.
Introduced. Casual. Native of America. Waste places. Rare.

Hold. Bombed site, Myton St, Hull 02, 1951, FEC; near docks, Hull 12, 1982, FH.

Xanthium L.

X. strumarium L.
Rough Cocklebur.
Introduced. Casual. Uncommon.
L.D. Olympia Oil Mill Sidings, Selby 63, 1934, WAS & JK.
Hold. Hull docks 02 (R. 1902); King George Dock, Hull 12, 1932, TS (W. 1938).

X. spinosum L.
Spiny Cocklebur.
Introduced. Casual. Uncommon.
L.D. Railway station, Skipwith 63, 1934, CMR (W. 1938).
Hold. Hull docks (R. 1902); King George Dock, Hull 12, 1933-1937, AKW (W. 1938) and 1960, FEC.

Senecio L.

S. jacobaea L.
Common Ragwort.　　　　　　　　　　　*c*.1845.
Native. Waste places, waysides, neglected pastures on all but the poorest soils; chalk quarries, gravel pits, sand dunes. Common.

S. aquaticus Hill　　　　　　　　　　　　Map 196.
Marsh Ragwort.
Native. Water-meadows, marshes. Widely distributed, but somewhat infrequent except locally in the water-meadows by the R. Derwent and in marshes in the R. Hull valley.

S. aquaticus x **S. jacobaea** = **S.** x **ostenfeldii** Druce
Wharram Percy 86 and Hornsea Mere 14, 1979, FEC; canal bank, Wansford 05, 1985, EC.

S. erucifolius L.　　　　　　　　　　　　Map 56.
Hoary Ragwort.　　　　　　　　　　　　1840.
Native. Roadsides, grassy lanes, field borders, open woods and wood borders, clay cliffs, railway banks, drain banks; mainly on calcareous and heavy soils. Locally frequent near the R. Humber bank in Holderness and in Lower Derwentland and on deposits on chalk as on the Birdsall Estate 86 and on clay cliffs near Filey 17; scattered elsewhere.

S. squalidus L.　　　　　　　　　　　　Map 261.
Oxford Ragwort.　　　　　　　　　　　　1926.
Established alien.
Native of Sicily and southern Italy; it flourishes on the slopes of Mount Etna and on soils derived from the volcanic ash of Mount Vesuvius. Its spread from the Oxford Botanic Gardens, where it had been cultivated since at least 1690, to London and elsewhere in England is well documented (Kent, 1956 & 1960).
The early spread was mainly along railways.
The first Yorkshire record is for the Hull docks, 1926, JFR (W. 1938); it was on King George Dock, Hull 12, 1934-1936 (W. 1938). By the end of the war it was commonly established on bombed sites in Hull and was spreading onto waste ground in adjacent villages (Kent, 1964). By 1950, it was on 48% of bombed sites and other waste places in Hull and on 62% of central and eastern Hull sites, FEC. It was frequent in the city on walls and by pavements and at the edges of bombed sites until 'Operation Clean Up', 1979, FEC.
Early records away from Hull:
U.D. One plant on a wall, Folkton 07, 1947 and a small

colony there by 1948, HR, also at Staxton 07, 1948, ERC (Kent, 1964).
L.D. Oxmardyke 82, 1958, RG.
Hold. One plant Spurn 41, 1946, AKW (Kent, 1964).
The species is now in small quantity in most villages; this spread having taken place from *c*.1966 and is in the main not associated with the presence of railways.

S. squalidus x *S. viscosus* = *S.* x *pseudonebrodensis* Simk. (*S.* x *londinensis* Lousley)
Described as new to science when found in London in 1944.
On bombed sites in Hull: two sites in High St 12, 1950, FEC; George St 12, 1950, FEC; two sites in Wincolmlee 12, 1953. In the Citadel, Hull 12, 1953, FEC; on rubbish tip, Clough Rd, Hull 03, 1952, FEC; on clearance site, Bridlington Ave, Hull 02, 1978, FEC. Found where the two species occur together, but probably only on recently disturbed soil.

S. squalidus x *S. vulgaris*
Owing to variation in the parents and confusion with rayed variants of *S. vulgaris*, this is a difficult hybrid to identify from morphological characters alone.
Believed to have occurred on Hull bombed sites: High St 12, 1950, FEC, conf. J.E. Lousley & 1978, FEC; Sewer Lane 02, 1952, FEC. Also on rubbish tip, Clough Rd, Hull 03, 1952, FEC.

S. sylvaticus L.   Map 47.
Heath Groundsel.   1840.
Native. In open communities on sand and gravel, particularly on heaths and commons. Somewhat infrequent; most records for Lower Derwentland. It also occurs on sand in Pickering Vale and on Spurn Point 41. Records away from the sandy tracts:
Wolds Hunmanby cliffs 17, 1955, RG; Birdsall 86, 1956, RG; chalk pit, Hessle 02, 1956, RG.
Hold. Skipsea Brough (R. 1902) and 1986, AJ; in beet field on calcareous clay, Bessingby 16, 1952, RG; bank of Leven Canal 14, 1953, AKW; gravel pit, Brandesburton 14, 1955, RG; Barfhill 04, 1956, RG; near Little Kelk 16, 1984, EC.

S. viscosus L.   Map 399.
Sticky Groundsel.   1902.
Alien. Railway tracks and sidings, waste places, sand and gravel pits. Most records for Lower Derwentland, but widely spread along railway tracks. Much less frequent than the map suggests, as it often does not persist.
First recorded for a railway track at Market Weighton 84, JJM (R. 1902). Formerly common amongst the dock waste plants, Hull (R. 1902) and later recorded for King George Dock, Hull 12, 1934, AKW & 1960, FEC. On 40% of Hull bombed sites, 1950, FEC, rarely seen in the city now.

S. vulgaris L.
Groundsel.
Native. Cultivated ground, including gardens; waste places. Very common.
Var. *radiatus* Koch Rayed form of Groundsel. Seems to have resulted from introgression from *S. squalidus* x *S. vulgaris* to *S. vulgaris*.
All records for the Hull area:
bombed sites, Hedon Road, Hull 12, 1950, FEC and High St, Hull 12, 1950, FEC; King George Dock, Hull 12, 1960, FEC; Bentley 03, 1958, RG. Introduced into the Hull University Botanic Gardens, *c*.1969, now an abundant

weed there and frequent elsewhere in Cottingham 03. Hybrids between var. *radiatus* and var. *vulgaris* occur in mixed populations as in the Botanic Gardens.

Doronicum L.
D. pardalianches L.
Leopard's-bane.   1840.
Naturalised garden alien. Woods, plantations. Infrequent, but sometimes in quantity.
U.D. West Flotmanby 07 (N.H. Scarb.).
L.D. Wheldrake 64, 1965, TFM.
Wolds Londesborough 84, Welton Woods 92 (R. 1902); edge of golf course, Kirkella 02, 1950, FEC; Cherry Burton 94, 1953, IG, still there; Filey 17, 1953, IG; dell near Raywell Sanatorium 93, 1957, FEC; Hunmanby 07, 1971, EC; Birdsall 86, 1980, FEC.

Tussilago L.
T. farfara L.   Map 400.
Colt's-foot.
Native. In open communities. Widely distributed on a variety of soils, but especially abundant on stiff clay soils; arable fields, waste places, roadsides; chalk quarries, gravel pits, sand pits. Common.
An abundance of this species is a feature of the boulder clay cliffs of Holderness, but it is also locally abundant on sands of Spurn 41.

Petasites Mill.
P. hybridus (L.) Gaertn., Mey. & Scherb. (*P. officinalis* Moench)   Map 401.
Butterbur.
Native. River and stream sides and wet meadows.
The East Riding plants are entirely male and the method of reproduction entirely vegetative. Frequent in the R. Hull valley and along the spring line at the west of the Wolds and adjacent areas; uncommon elsewhere.

P. albus (L.) Gaertn.
White Butterbur.   1886.
Established garden alien. Waste places, roadsides. Rare.
Hold. Garden escape, near Snuff Mill pond 03, 1886 (R. 1902); Boynton 16, 1969, MC.

P. fragrans (Vill.) C. Presl
Winter Heliotrope.
Naturalised garden escape.   Uncommon.
L.D. Sutton upon Derwent 74, 1949-1959, JP & KGP & 1961, YNU Excursion.
Wolds Near Hessle chalk pits 02, CW (R. 1902), still abundant on the railway bank near the chalk pits; Sewerby and Boynton 16, Major Lawson (Flintoff, 1931); Cherry Burton 94 and Walkington 93, TS (W. 1938); behind beach, Fraisthorpe 16, 1955, RG.

Calendula L.
C. officinalis L.
Pot Marigold.
Garden escape.   Uncommon.
Wolds Roadside, near Huggate 85, 1971, FH.
Hold. Refuse tip, Hessle 02, 1942, AKW; bombed sites, Hull 12, 1950-1953, FEC; gravel pit, Brandesburton 14, 1955, RG.

Inula L.
I. helenium L.
Elecampane.   1898.
Introduced.   Uncommon.

L.D. Near airfield, Elvington 64, 1945, GAN.
Wolds Wood, Weedley 93, 1958, RG; pit, near Great Givendale 85, 1964, Dr P.A. Briscoe.
Hold. Near Willerby 03, probably a garden outcast, 1898 and known some years before (R. 1902).

I. conyza DC.   Map 402.
Ploughman's-spikenard.   CE.   1928.
Native. On calcareous soil, in scrub and woods; sometimes in chalk grassland, fixed dunes, chalk quarries. Infrequent. Most records for the South Cave and Brantingham area, ten km squares 92 & 93.
Other records:
Wolds Millington 85, 1928, HB; chalk quarry, Willerby 03, 1947, FEC; Fordon 07, HR (N.H. Scarb.); Knapton Settlement 87, 1957, FEC; Wintringham 97, 1964, FEC; chalk pit, Hessle 02, 1966, FEC & PMG; Scoardale 85, 1971, FEC; Etton Wold 94, 1985, EHW.
Hold. Spurn Point 41, 1950, FEC, still present.

Pulicaria Gaertn.
P. dysenterica (L.) Bernh.   Map 403.
Common Fleabane.   1840.
Native. Marshes, wet meadows; by dykes, canal and becks. On clay, on roadsides in Holderness; on Filey 17 and Flamborough cliffs 27. Locally frequent, mainly in the R. Hull valley and elsewhere in Holderness and along the spring line at the west of the Wolds.

Filago L.
F. vulgaris Lam. [*F. germanica* (L.) L.]   Map 404.
Common Cudweed.
Native. Cultivated fields, on sand and gravel, but also on chalk; heaths, chalk quarries. Infrequent but widely distributed; decreasing.

F. apiculata G.E. Sm.
Red-tipped Cudweed.
Native. On sand.
Spurn Point 41, 1978, FEC, det. C. Jeffrey.

F. minima (Sm.) Pers.   Map 38.
Small Cudweed.
Native. In sandy places, sand pits. Very infrequent, most records for Lower Derwentland.
Other records:
U.D. Rillington 87, CW (R. 1902); near Sands Wood, Wintringham 87, 1957, FEC; sand pits, near Flixton 07, 1957, FEC; Kennythorpe 76, 1958, FEC.
Hold. Priory railway sidings, Hull 02, 1983, FEC.

Gnaphalium L.
G. sylvaticum L.   Map 405.
Heath Cudweed.
Native. Open woods and heaths on sandy soils. Uncommon.
L.D. Skipwith Common 63, WNC, Howden 72, JBe, Houghton Woods 83 (R. 1902); Bunny Hill 83, 1955, RG; Langwith Common 64, 1956, FEC & 1964, YNU Excursion; between Allerthorpe and Bielby 74, 1958, FEC; Allerthorpe Common 74, 1961, FEC.

G. uliginosum L.   Map 406.
Marsh Cudweed.
Native. In damp places in sandy fields, heaths, damp gravel. Frequent in Lower Derwentland and locally frequent in the R. Hull valley. On Holderness gravels as in gravel pits near Brandesburton 04 & 14, 1981, FEC.

Sometimes on railway tracks in Holderness.

Antennaria Gaertn.
A. dioica (L.) Gaertn.
Mountain Everlasting.   NME.
Native. Dry places. Rare; no recent record.
Wolds Between Cowlam and West Lutton 96, 2nd half 18th century, WW; Langton Wold 86, MBS (R. 1902), confirmed GP (Flintoff, 1931); High Fordon 07, 1911-1912 (N.H. Scarb.).
Hold. Near Beverley, 1829, Dr Hull (R. 1902).

Solidago L.
S. virgaurea L.
Goldenrod.
Native. Dry woods and grassland on acid soils.
All records for Lower Derwentland. Market Weighton 83, Skipwith Common 63, WNC and Newsholme 72, JB (R. 1902). There are recent records for Skipwith and Allerthorpe Commons, 63 & 74 respectively, and for Houghton Woods 83; these all require confirmation as there may have been confusion with *S. canadensis*.

S. canadensis L.
Canadian Goldenrod.   1936.
Naturalised alien. Native of N. America. Waste ground, roadsides, railway banks. Uncommon.
U.D. Flixton pits 07, 1957, TFM.
L.D. Skipwith 63, 1952, DAW; Houghton Woods 83, 1953, RG; Stamford Bridge 75, 1956, RG; East Cottingwith 74, 1957, RG; Allerthorpe Common 74, 1957, RG.
Wolds Bishop Burton 93, 1936, AKW (W. 1938).

S. gigantea Ait. subsp. *serotina* (O.Kuntze) McNeill
Early Goldenrod.
Naturalised alien. Native of N. America. Waste places. Uncommon.
Bombed sites, Hull 12, 1953, FEC, det. Kew; rubbish tip, Clough Rd, Hull 03, 1953, FEC.

S. graminifolia (L.) Salisb.
Alien. Native of N. America.
Established on Alexandra Dock, Hull 12, where it has been known since 1978, FEC.

Aster L.
A. tripolium L.   Map 205.
Sea Aster.
Native. Salt-marshes and on the R. Humber shore west of Hull, as far as Goole. Common.
Also occurs on the banks of the R. Hull north to Dunswell; also sometimes in brackish marshes behind the R. Humber bank. In quantity along the Fisherman's channel, Sunk Island 21, c.1960, FEC, still present. Has occurred on waste places in Hull: bombed site, Mark St, Hull 12, 1950 and on Hull refuse tips 13, 1953, FEC. Rare on the sea-coast; recorded for Barmston Drain end 15, 1955, RG.
Var. *discoideus* occurs and often replaces the normal form; recorded for Spurn 41, Stone Creek 21, Hessle 02, Blacktoft 82; also for rubbish tip, Clough Rd, Hull, near R. Hull 13 and refuse tip, Hessle 02. Petch (1905b) made a detailed study of the distribution of the rayed and discoid varieties.

The Michaelmas-daisies naturalised in Britain belong to a critical group of which the nomenclature and synonymy add to the difficulties. Our naturalised plants cannot be matched with those native in America and are likely to have arisen in Europe (Lousley, 1976).The more aggressive naturalised species are relatively unattractive as garden plants. We have records for one of them:

A. novi-belgii L.
Hairy Michaelmas-daisy.
The most commonly naturalised plant in the British Isles; it has wishy-washy blue rays in rather small heads. Waste places. Uncommon.
Hold. Bombed sites, Hull 02, 1951, FEC; disused rubbish tip, Leads Rd, Hull 13, 1963, EC.

Erigeron L.

E. acer L.   Map 407.
Blue Fleabane.   1840.
Native. Grassland on sandy and calcareous soils; sand pits, chalk quarries, chalk scree. Infrequent, but widely distributed and sometimes in quantity.
In abundance on sand and cindery ground on the dock reservation of Alexandra Dock, Hull 12, 1979, FEC; it also occurs on Queen Elizabeth Dock, Hull 12, 1980, FEC and on Priory Yard railway sidings, Hull 02, 1983, FEC.

E. canadensis L. [*Conyza canadensis* (L.) Cronq.]
Canadian Fleabane.   1949.
Alien. Waste ground, usually in open communities.
At the northern edge of its climatic range and usually not persisting.
L.D. Skipwith Common 63, 1982, EB; Full Sutton 75, 1983, CSVY; North Cave 83, 1987, RM.
Hold. Bricknell Ave, Hull 03, 1949, RG; Spurn Point 41, 1949, FEC; bombed sites, Hull: George St 02, 1950, FEC, Clarence St 12, 1950, FEC, Westcott St 13, 1950, FEC, High St 12, 1952, FEC; King George Dock, Hull 12, 1953, FEC; Victoria Dock, Hull 12, 1969-1976, FEC.

Bellis L.

B. perennis L.
Daisy.
Native. Short grassland, including lawns. Thrives on ground compacted by trampling. Very common.

Eupatorium L.

E. cannabinum L.   Map 142.
Hemp-agrimony.
Native. Stream and ditch banks. Locally frequent in the R. Hull valley; scattered elsewhere.
Lost from some early recorded localities:
L.D. Howden 72, JBe, Selby 63, WNC (R. 1902).
Wolds Weedley Springs 93 (R. 1902).

Anthemis L.

A. tinctoria L.
Yellow Chamomile.
Alien. Sometimes persists. Waste places, sand pits, chalk quarry, arable. Uncommon.
U.D. Sand pit, Staxton 07, 1956, RG.
Wolds Potter Brompton 97, 1956, RG; on arable, near Cowlam 96, 1960, YNU Excursion; Burton Fleming 07, 1970, EC.
Hold. Common amongst the aliens, West Dock, Hull 02 (R. 1902); King George Dock, Hull 12, 1939, AKW.

A. cotula L.
Stinking Chamomile.   1840.
Native. Arable, including cornfields; waste places. Uncommon now.
L.D. Heslington Fields 64 (Baines, 1840); near Skipwith Common 63, CW; Howden 72, JBe (R. 1902).

Hold. Rarely on Hull bombed sites 02 & 12, 1950-1953, FEC; Brandesburton 14, 1955, RG; near Etton 94, 1956, FEC; Kelsey Hill 22, 1955, YNU Excursion; Elstronwick 23, 1958, FEC; Rise 14, 1971, FEC.

A. arvensis L.
Corn Chamomile.   1840.
Native. Arable and waste places. Uncommon.
Locally frequent on sand in the Barmby Moor area 74 & 75, 1981, FEC.
L.D. Disturbed ground, near canal head, Market Weighton Canal, 83, 1954, FEC.
Wolds Near Kirby Grindalythe 96, 1960, YNU Excursion; edge of chalk quarry, near Thwing 07, 1970, EC.
Hold. Cornfields 'not infrequent' (R. 1902); King George Dock, Hull 12 (W. 1938); Bentley 03, 1952, DAW; cornfield, near Driffield Canal 05, 1960, FEC.

Chamaemelum Mill.

C. nobile (L.) All. (*Anthemis nobilis* L.)
Chamomile.
Native? Pastures, sandy commons, roadsides. Rare.
U.D. Between Scampston and Wintringham 87, 1956, TFM.
L.D. Skirpenbeck 75, 1956, MT.
Hold. Driffield 05, 1899, YNU Excursion (R. 1902).

Achillea L.

A. millefolium L.
Yarrow.
Native. Pastures, roadsides, railway banks, gravel pits; on all but the poorest soils. Very common.

A. ptarmica L.   Map 408.
Sneezewort.
Native. Damp grassland, water-meadows.
Locally frequent in Lower Derwentland, a characteristic plant of the water-meadows by the river. Infrequent elsewhere.
Occurred on a bombed site, High St, Hull 12, 1952, FEC.

Tripleurospermum Schultz Bip.

T. maritimum (L.) Koch (*Matricaria maritima* L.)
Native.

Subsp. **maritimum.**
Sea Mayweed.
Maritime plant of the drift line. Rare.
Flamborough Head 17 (Baines, 1840); Hunmanby Wyke 17, 1901 (R. 1902). Extinct.

Subsp. **inodorum** (L.) N. Hyland. ex Vaarama (*Matricaria inodora* L.)
Scentless Mayweed.
Arable, waste places; on a variety of soils. Common.
Var. **salinum** (Wallr.) Clapham
On sand and shingle and in other habitats by the sea.
Recorded by the R. Humber at Hessle 02, CW (R.1902); may be elsewhere.

Matricaria L.

M. recutita L. (*M. chamomilla* auct.)   Map 409.
Scented Mayweed.   1840.
Native. Cultivated and waste ground, on a variety of soils. Common and sometimes in great abundance in arable fields. Appears to have been favoured by the use of weed killers.
Given for only three localities by Robinson, 1902:

133

L.D. Heslington Fields 64 (Baines, 1840).
Hold. Near Rise 14; banks of R. Hull, near Driffield 05, JTH.

M. matricarioides (Less.) Porter [*M. suaveolens* (Pursh) Buchen.]
Pineappleweed.
Naturalised alien. Waysides, waste places, tracks, paths, field gateways. Very common.
A native of N.E. Asia, but established in many parts of the world. First recorded in Britain in 1871; date of introduction into the East Riding not known. Not given by Robinson, 1902. Described as locally abundant in the Allerthorpe area 74 in 1927 and to have made remarkable headway 'in late years' (Nat. 1927, 304). Spread has been mainly through transport of seeds in mud on foot-wear and on the wheels of vehicles.

Chrysanthemum L.

C. segetum L.   Map 226.
Corn Marigold.   1840.
Introduced? Corn fields and other arable on sand and lighter loams. Calcifuge. Locally frequent in Lower Derwentland and sometimes in quantity on peaty soil in the R. Hull valley as near Leven 04. Infrequent elsewhere.

Leucanthemum Mill.

L. vulgare Lam. (*Chrysanthemum leucanthemum* L.)
                                                    Map 410.
Oxeye Daisy.
Native. Grassland, chalk hillsides, chalk quarries, railway embankments. Widely distributed; frequent on the Wolds, particularly in the belt of grazed grassland; infrequent on the sands of Lower Derwentland and in Holderness.

L. maximum (Ramond) DC.
Shasta Daisy.
Garden escape. Occasionally established on roadsides and waste places.

Tanacetum L.

T. parthenium (L.) Schultz Bip. [*Chrysanthemum parthenium* (L.) Bernh.]   Map 411.
Feverfew.
Introduced. Formerly grown as a medicinal herb.
Waste places, railway stations; usually near buildings, often an obvious garden escape. Generally infrequent, but widely distributed; most records for Hull and adjacent towns and villages. Formerly on Hull docks (R. 1902).

T. vulgare L. [*Chrysanthemum vulgare* (L.) Bernh.]
                                                    Map 412.
Tansy.   1840.
Native. Roadsides, waste places, river and stream banks. Formerly much cultivated as a medicinal and pot herb. Banks of R. Ouse below York, abundant (Baines, 1840). Now locally frequent on or near the banks of the R. Derwent; otherwise infrequent, but widely scattered.

Artemisia L.

A. vulgaris L.   Map 413.
Mugwort. One of the aromatic plants known locally as **Green Ginger** (R. 1902).
Native. Waste places, roadsides, railway banks and stations. Still most frequent near houses and places of human activity. Widely distributed; particularly common in the Hull area and near towns and villages, also in much of Lower Derwentland. Infrequent over much of the Wolds,
except in the south.

A. absinthium L.
Wormwood.   1840.
Established alien. Formerly grown for its medicinal properties. Waste places. Uncommon.
Several records for the Hull area, particularly for the Old Town where there are some large old plants; on drain bank, east Hull 13, 1978, FEC. Formerly common amongst dock aliens (R. 1902).
Other records:
L.D. Heslington 65, 1970, TFM; Skipwith Common 63, 1982, EB.
Wolds Disused railway station, Wharram 86, 1959, FEC.
Hold. Aldborough 23 (Baines, 1840) and 1972, EBM; Coneygarth gravel pit, Brandesburton 14, 1969, MC; near Bail Wood 23, 1972, EBM; near Winestead 32, introduced with soil from Hull, 1981, FEC.

A. maritima L.   Map 204.
Sea Wormwood.   ONE.   1798.
Native. On the drier parts of salt-marshes e.g. at the edges of drainage channels. On the salt-marsh side of the R. Humber bank and by the sides of nearby drains.
Frequent from Paull 12 eastwards to Spurn 41. Otherwise apparently rare: riverside, Saltmarshe estate 72, 1950, FEC; foreshore, North Ferriby 92, 1960, FEC.

Carlina L.

C. vulgaris L.   Map 10.
Carline Thistle.   1798.
Native. Calcareous grassland, chalk quarries. Frequent in the grazed Wolds grassland belt and confined to it.

Arctium L.

A. lappa L. (*A. majus* Bernh.)
Greater Burdock.
Native. Apparently uncommon.
U.D. Howsham Bridge 76, 1957, RG.
L.D. Lowthorpe 06, 1951, RG; Welton Dale 92, 1957, RG; High Hunsley 93, 1957, RG; near Bishop Wilton 85, 1985, DEH.
Hold. Risby Park 03, 1955, RG; Barfhill Covert 04, 1956, RG.

A. minus Bernh. *sensu lato*
Lesser Burdock.
Native. Roadsides, waste places, field and wood borders. Very common.
The distribution of the three subspecies: subsp. ***minus***, subsp. ***pubens*** (Bab.) J. Arènes and subsp. ***nemorosum*** (Lej.) Syme require study.

Carduus L.

C. tenuiflorus Curt. (*C. pycnocephalus* auct.)
Slender Thistle.
Native. Waysides and waste places, especially near the sea.
Spurn 41, J. Farrah (R. 1902). The record for Market Weighton (R. 1902) was a misnaming, JFR (SYF).

C. nutans L.   Map 414.
Musk Thistle.
Native. Pastures, waysides, arable fields and waste places on calcareous soils, chalk quarries; more rarely on sandy soils and on gravel. Common on the Wolds and locally frequent on sand as in ten km square 83; infrequent elsewhere.

C. acanthoides L. (*C. crispus* auct.)   Map 415.
Welted Thistle.
Native. Damp grass verges, hedgerows, open woodland, waste places. Widely distributed, but only locally frequent.

C. acanthoides x *C. nutans* = *C.* x *orthocephalus* Wallr.
L.D. By river, Naburn 54, 1955, RG; east of Hotham 93, 1955, RG.
Wolds Everthorpe quarry 83, 1955, RG; near North Grimston 86, 1967, FEC; Sylvandale 85, 1972, YNU Excursion.
Hold. Near Pulfin Bog 04, 1937, WAS (SYF); Baswick Landing 04, 1957, RG.

Cirsium Mill.
C. eriophorum (L.) Scop. [*Cnicus eriophorus* (L.) Roth]   Map 12.
Woolly Thistle.   1626.
Native. Calcareous grassland, open scrub, chalk and limestone quarries. 'By Pocklington and in other places of the wolds', 1626, T. Johnson; the second British record. Almost confined to the grazed Wolds grassland belt and locally frequent from Pocklington northwards. Formerly near Flamborough, CW (R. 1902).

C. eriophorum x *C. vulgare* = *C.* x *gerhardtii* Schultz Bip.
Near North Grimston 86, 1955, WAS; Cowpasture Wood, Londesborough 84, 1958, RG.

C. vulgare (Savi) Ten. [*Cnicus lanceolatus* (L.) Willd.]
Spear Thistle.
Native. Fields, roadsides, waste ground. Very common.

C. palustre (L.) Scop. [*Cnicus palustris* (L.) Willd.]
                                                Map 416.
Marsh Thistle.
Native. Marshes, damp woods, stream sides; more rarely on well-drained Wolds hillsides, particularly in the Millington area 85. Frequent.

C. arvense (L.) Scop. [*Cnicus arvensis* (L.) Roth]
Creeping Thistle.
Native. Pastures, arable, roadsides, waste places. Very common.
Var. *setosum* C.A. Mey., with flat leaves and almost without prickles, occurs and is regarded as an alien: 'abundant on the dock wastes, Hull' (R. 1902), on bombed sites and other waste places in Hull, 1951 and subsequently, FEC.
Var. *incanum* (Fisch.) Ledeb. is a S. European form which occurred on Spurn Point 41 at least from 1957 to 1978, FEC.

C. acaule Scop.
Dwarf Thistle.   CE.   1906.
Native. Typically in closely grazed chalk grassland. Uncommon.
Beverley Westwood 03, 1904, HC (Nat. 1906, 437); in quantity there, 1967, FEC and subsequently. In a number of places in the Cowlam valley, including the sides of the Old Wold Gate 96, 1957, FEC; some sites now ploughed out. In quantity on a south-facing hillside, Drewton Dale 93, 1967, FEC; also on Welton Ings and near Ellerker 92, 1970, JG. Survived for some years in a plantation, near Wintringham 87, 1956, RG & 1964, FEC. There are other

records for the northern part of the Wolds, usually referring to single non-flowering rosettes; these records require confirmation. After the introduction of myxomatosis and subsequent lack of grazing, plants in some localities developed stems up to five inches high on which the flowering heads were held (f. *caulescens* Rchb.); this form also occurred in shade at Wintringham.

C. dissectum (L.) Hill [*Cnicus pratensis* (Huds.) Willd.]
Meadow Thistle.   OWEE.   1798.
Native.   Fens, bogs.   Uncommon.
L.D. Houghton Moor 83 (Teesdale, 1800); Staddlethorpe 82, CW (R. 1902); Breighton Common 73, 1945, JMT; Skipwith Common 63, 1954, RG; Allerthorpe Common 74 (SYF) and 1961, FEC, still present; near Broomfleet House 82, 1963, FEC.
Hold. Near Hull (Baines, 1840); Kelleythorpe 05 (SYF) and 1963, FEC.

C. dissectum x *C. palustre* = *C.* x *forsteri* (Sm.) Loud.
Skipwith Common 63, with both parents, 1942, WAS.

Silybum Adans.
S. marianum (L.) Gaertn. (*Mariana lactea* Hill)
Milk Thistle.   1840.
Established alien. Waste places and roadsides, usually near villages. Uncommon.
U.D. Near Rillington 87 (Baines, 1840).
Wolds Little Weighton 93 (R. 1902).
Hold. Outskirts of Bridlington 16, *c*.1920, GAN; King George Dock, Hull 12, 1933-1935, AKW (W. 1938); garden weed, Bilton 13, 1954, FEC.

Onopordum L.
O. acanthium L.
Cotton Thistle.   1901.
Established alien; usually a garden escape. Uncommon.
U.D. Sands Wood, Wintringham 87, 1967, EC.
L.D. Duck Nest 83, 1956, RG; roadside near cottage, near Holme upon Spalding Moor 83, 1970, FEC & DWS; near Hotham 83, 1973, DRG; Yapham 75, 1977, EB.
Wolds Rubbish tip, Wharram le Street 86, 1957, RG.
Hold. Hull docks (R. 1902); roadside, Hollym 32, 1984, FEC; foreshore Hessle 02, comm. FEC.

Centaurea L.
C. scabiosa L.   Map 11.
Greater Knapweed.   1840.
Native. Dry grassland, roadsides, especially on calcareous soils; chalk quarries. On railway banks and elsewhere on imported chalk; more rarely on sand and gravel. Common on the Wolds. Infrequent elsewhere.

C. montana L.
Perennial Cornflower.
Naturalised garden alien.   Roadsides.   Rare.
Wolds Near Eppleworth 03, 1980, FEC; Little Weighton 93, 1981, AJH.

C. cyanus L.
Cornflower.
Native. Cornfields and waste places. Formerly frequent in cornfields and occurring on dock waste, Hull (R. 1902). Now very uncommon owing to use of cleaner grain; an expanse of the blue flowers of this species, as noted at the side of a bean field at Bursea 83, 1981, FEC, is now a rare sight.
Other post-1950 records:

L.D. Near railway, Gilberdyke 82 and at Sandholme 83, 1956, RG.
Wolds Burton Raikes 93, 1967, JR and re-surfaced quarry, Burton Fleming 07, 1970, EC.
Hold. Conspicuous in cornfields near Swine 13, 1952, FEC; on disused tip, Hull 13, 1963, EC; Carnaby 16, 1970, MC.

C. nigra L.   *c*.1845.

Subsp. *nigra*
Common Knapweed, Hardheads.
Frequent.

Subsp. *nemoralis* (Jord.) Gugl.
Slender Knapweed.
Also occurs, but its distribution is not known.
On the Wolds, 1946, JFH-S; roadside, Arnold 13, 1978, FEC.

C. solstitialis L.
Yellow Star-thistle.
Alien.
Hull docks (R. 1902); King George Dock, Hull 12, 1933, TS and near Sutton 13, 1934, AEW (W. 1938).

Serratula L.
S. tinctoria L.   Map 417.
Saw-wort.   CE.   1798.
Native. Grassland, roadsides, wood margins and clearings; mainly on basic soils. On clay cliffs near Filey 17. Somewhat infrequent; most records for the Wolds.
Other records;
U.D. Yedingham 87, 1958, CMR & FEC; Flixton Carrs 17, 1971, FEC & MC.
L.D. Skirpenbeck 75, 1955, MT; Allerthorpe Common 74, 1958, FEC, still present; near Burnby 84, 1977, TFM; near Youlthorpe 75, 1986, DJL.
Hold. West of Huddlecross Plantation, Sigglesthorne 14, 1957, JA; by roadside ditch, near Arnold 13, 1973, FEC.

Cichorium L.
C. intybus L.
Chicory.   1806.
Mainly introduced. In a variety of habitats, usually in small quantity. Uncommon.
Formerly on the clay cliffs of Holderness (R. 1902). Formerly cultivated in the East Riding as a coffee substitute and adulterant. In 1850, 40-45% of the total United Kingdom's home-grown chicory was grown in the vicinity of York (Dr A. Harris, pers. comm.), Dunnington being one of the villages often named.
U.D. Sand pit Staxton 07, 1957, FEC.
L.D. Heslington Fields 64, 1806, WM; by Market Weighton Canal 83, 1947, FEC; North Cliffe 83, 1952, DAW; field border, near Bielby 74, 1958, FEC.
Wolds Scardale Plantation, Wintringham 97, 1957, FEC; railway bank, near Eppleworth 03, 1979, FEC & JES.
Hold. Very common with dock aliens 02 (R. 1902), King George Dock, Hull 12 (W. 1938) and found on roadsides and waste places near and in Hull occasionally: Priory Rd 03, 1934, FEC; Pickering Rd 02, 1937, AKW and by Humber Dock 02, 1978, FEC. By the R. Hull, near Driffield 05 (R. 1902).

Lapsana L.
L. communis L.
Nipplewort.
Native. Grassy lanes, roadsides, wood margins, hedges, pits, waste places. Common.

Arnoseris Gaertn.
A. minima (L.) Schweigg. & Koerte
Lamb's Succory.   CE.   1927.
Native. On sandy soils. Always rare and very local; probably now extinct.
All records for Lower Derwentland. Allerthorpe Common 74, 1927, F.A. Mason (Nat. 1927, 300) and 1945, YNU Excursion. On farm track and at field edge between Allerthorpe and Bielby 74, 1958, FEC; on grassy path and in field corner, near Seaton Ross 74, 1958, FEC; near Bielby 74, 1960, MMS.

Hypochoeris L.
H. radicata L.   Map 418.
Cat's-ear.
Native. Grassland, waysides, waste places, sand and gravel pits, chalk quarries. Frequent and widely distributed, but often in small quantity.

H. glabra L.
Smooth Cat's-ear.   CE.   1890.
Native. In open communities on sand. Rare.
U.D. Rillington 97 (SYF); sandy lane and sand pit, near Wintringham 87, 1956, RG.
L.D. Skipwith 63, 1905, J. Foggitt; Allerthorpe 74 (SYF); field side, between Allerthorpe & Bielby 74, 1958, RG.
Hold. Spurn 41, 1910, CW (SYF).
The Allerthorpe and Rillington plants were var. *erostris* Coss. et Germ., whilst the Spurn plant was the beak-fruited var. *Balbisii* Loisel (SYF).

Leontodon L.
L. autumnalis L.
Autumn Hawkbit.
Native. Grassland including roadsides, waste places; chalk quarries, sand pits. Very common.

L. hispidus L.   Map 419.
Rough Hawkbit.
Native. Chalk and limestone grassland, chalk quarries and scree, railway banks; especially on calcareous soils. Common on the Wolds; infrequent elsewhere.

L. taraxacoides (Vill.) Mérat (*L. hirtus* auct.) Map 420.
Lesser Hawkbit.
Native. Dry grassland, especially on base-rich soils, chalk quarries; fixed dunes. Widely distributed in the Wolds grassland belt; also locally frequent on Spurn Point; otherwise infrequent.
Sometimes on gravel as at Kelsey Hill 22, 1955, YNU Excursion and at Brandesburton 14, 1981, FEC.

Picris L.
P. echioides L.   Map 54.
Bristly Oxtongue.   OSE.   1798.
Probably a very early introduction. Roadsides, sides of ditches, field edges, waste places; mainly on heavy soils. Near the northern edge of its climatic range in the vice-county and tending to become coastal.
Frequent on or near the Humber bank from Spurn 41 to Hull and locally westwards to Blacktoft 82 and along the coast between Spurn and Hornsea 24; otherwise

infrequent in Holderness, rare elsewhere.
Early records: sides of ditches, near Beverley (Teesdale, 1800) and frequent by the sides of Skidby drain 03 (R. 1902).

P. hieracioides L.   Map 20.
Hawkweed Oxtongue.
Native. Grassland on chalk hillsides and banks; chalk quarries. Almost restricted to the belt of grazed chalk grassland on the Wolds and locally frequent, mainly in ten km squares 85 and 86.
In quantity on the railway bank of the Hull to Doncaster railway line, near Broomfleet 82, 1964, FEC. Said to be formerly 'not infrequent' on the dock wastes, Hull (R. 1902).

Tragopogon L.
T. pratensis L.
Goat's-beard.
Native. Meadows, roadsides, drain banks, waste places.

Subsp. *pratensis*
Rare.
Wolds Near Rudston 06, 1954, RG.
Hold. Cottingham Rd, Hull 03, 1952, DAW.

Subsp. *minor* (Mill.) Wahlenb.
Common.

T. porrifolius L.
Salsify.
Introduced. Cultivated for its tap roots and occasionally escaping. Rare.
Hold. Formerly frequent near the Hull docks 02 (R. 1902); cliffs, near Bridlington 16, 1930, WLW (W. 1938); garden weed, Hessle 02, 1984, Mrs Hardaker.

Lactuca L.
L. serriola L.
Prickly Lettuce.
Alien. Waste places. Uncommon.
Hold. King George Dock, Hull 12, 1935-1937, AKW (W. 1938); bombed sites, Hull: Jenning St 12, 1951, FEC, Francis St 02, 1985, FEC; refuse tip, Clough Rd, Hull 13, 1951, FEC; Leads Rd, Hull 13, 1962, EC; new verge, Hull 02, 1986, EC.

L. virosa L.
Great Lettuce.   1798.
Native? Grassy places, including roadsides; walls. Uncommon.
U.D. Walls of Kirkham Abbey 76 (R. 1902).
L.D. Between York and Skipton (R. 1902); North Duffield 63, 1937, YNU Circular; Laytham 73, 1956, RG; hedgebank, west of Bubwith 73, 1957, WAS & GAN; Skipwith Common 63, 1982, EB; near Holme upon Spalding Moor and North Cave 83, 1987, EHW.
Hold. On dry banks and in hedges, near Beverley 93 (Teesdale, 1800); Walkington 93 (Baines, 1840); King George Dock, Hull 12, 1932, FS (W. 1938).

Mycelis Cass.
M. muralis (L.) Dumort. [*Lactuca muralis* (L.) Gaertn.]
                    Map 421.
Wall Lettuce.
Native. Woods, on base-rich soils; walls. Somewhat infrequent on the Wolds; uncommon elsewhere.

Sonchus L.
S. arvensis L.
Perennial Sow-thistle.
Native. Weed of cultivated land, drain banks, waste places, gravel pits. Very common.

S. oleraceus L.
Smooth Sow-thistle.
Native. Cultivated ground, roadsides, waste places. Common.

S. asper (L.) Hill
Prickly Sow-thistle.
Native. Cultivated ground, waste places, chalk quarries, gravel and sand pits. Common.

Cicerbita Wallr.
C. macrophylla (Willd.) Wallr.
Common Blue-sow-thistle.   1951.
Naturalised garden alien. Roadsides and other grassy places. Uncommon.
U.D. Howsham 76, 1956, FEC.
L.D. North Cave 83, 1939, AKW, still there; canal, Newport 83, 1956, RG; near Fulford 64, 1980, EB.
Wolds South Cave 93, 1951, IG; Goodmanham 84, 1951, RG & 1971, FEC.
Hold. Roadside near Hornsea 14, 1979, RH; by the Willerby to Beverley Rd 03, 1982, EHW.

Hieracium L. Hawkweeds
Hawkweeds are a difficult critical group in which minor variations are perpetuated by apomixis, and a very large number of these varieties have been given names. The publication in 1948 of *A Prodromus of the British Hieracia* compiled by H.W.Pugsley provided a sound basis for the studies of P.D.Sell, Dr C.West and others. Some locally collected specimens have been determined by experts, but further critical work is required.

Sect.*Vulgata* Fr.

H. exotericum sensu lato
Native. Railway bank, chalk quarry, Willerby 03, 1955, FEC, det. P.D. Sell (PDS).

H. vulgatum Fr.
Common Hawkweed.
Native.
L.D. Langwith 64, CW (R. 1902); railway bank, Broomfleet 82, 1958, FEC, det. PDS.

H. lepidulum (Stenstr.) Omang
var. *haematophyllum* Dahlst.
Native. Railway bank, chalk quarry, Willerby 03, 1955, FEC, det. PDS.

H. diaphanoides Lindeb. [*H. praesigne* (Zahn) Roffey]
Native. Railway bank, Spring Head, Hull 02, 1937, AKW det. C. West, herb. HLU.

H. diaphanum Fr.
Native.
Wolds Coombe Wood, near Sledmere 96, 1973, EC, det. C.E. Andrews.
Hold. King George Dock, Hull 12, 1933, D.W. Toyne (W. 1938).

H. strumosum (W.R. Linton) A. Ley
Native.
L.D. Langwith Common 64, 1956, FEC, det.
PDS. Also recorded in the *Critical Atlas*
(Perring,1972) for ten km squares 65 and 84.
Wolds Chalk bank, Millington Pastures 85,1958,
FEC, det. PDS; Cowlam 96, 1957, FEC,det. PDS;
disused railway, North Grimston 86, 1981, DRG.

Sect. *Tridentata* Fr.

H. tridentatum Fr.
Native.
L.D. Langwith 64, herb. JBa (SYF).
Wolds Willerby 03, 1937, AKW, det. Kew.

H. calcaricola (F. J. Hanb.) Roffey
(*H. tridentatum sensu* Pugsl. *pro parte*)
Native.
Recorded in the *Critical Atlas* (Perring,1972) for ten
km square 84.

Sect. *Umbellata* Fr.

H. umbellatum L.   1887.
Native.
Several records; most for Lower Derwentland:
Heslington 64,1887, GW; near Pocklington 84
(R. 1902); near Skipwith 63 and Market Weighton
(SYF); west of Osgodby Common 63, 1956, RG;
Langwith Common 64, 1956, FEC, det. PDS; Black
Plantation, Holme upon Spalding Moor 73, 1957,
RG; near Bielby 74, 1957,RG; disused railway,
Asselby 72, 1983, DRG; Allerthorpe Common 74,
1984, DRG.
Wolds Tibthorpe 95, JTH (R. 1902).

H. perpropinquum (Zahn) Druce (*H. boreale* auct.)
Native.
L.D. Skipwith Common 63; Langwith Common
64, 1865, WWh (R. 1902); oil mills, Selby 63,
1956, DM.

H. vagum Jord.
Native.
Wolds Deep Dale, Bishop Wilton 85, 1948, JFH-S.
Hold. On several bombed sites, Hull 02 & 12,
1950-1953, FEC, det. PDS.

H. pilosella L.   Map 244.
Mouse-ear Hawkweed.
Native. Short dry grassland, chalk hillsides, chalk quarries,
chalk scree, sides of railway tracks. Common on the
Wolds; locally frequent elsewhere.

H. aurantiacum L.
Fox-and-cubs.   1931.
Established garden escape.   Uncommon.
L.D. Near Howden station 73, 1937, AKW (W. 1938).
Wolds Tennis courts, Garrowby 75, 1957, FEC; Settring-
ton Wood 87, 1969, TFM; near Enthorpe 94, 1973, EHW;
Cherry Burton 94, 1976, EHW; near Bainton 95, 1980,
EBM.
Hold. Near Hessle station 02, 1931, AKW; old shipyard,
Hessle, 1937, TS (W. 1938); University College site, Hull
03, 1952, RG; Hyde Wood, Cottingham 03, 1953, AKW;
Hornsea 24, 1970, GH.

H. brunneocroceum Pugsl.   1956.
Established garden escape.   Uncommon.
L.D. Near Escrick Park 64, 1956, Mrs Ball; as a garden
weed and on disused railway, Eastrington 72 & 73, 1976,
FEC.
Hold. Priory Sidings, Hull 02, 1977, FEC; Alexandra
Dock, Hull 12, 1979, FEC; Winestead 32, 1981, FEC.

Crepis L.
C. vesicaria L. subsp. **haenseleri** (DC.) P.D. Sell
(*C. taraxacifolia* Thuill.)   Map 253.
Beaked Hawk's-beard.   1933.
Established alien. Waysides, waste places. Several rec-
ords for the Hull area, otherwise uncommon.
Records include:
L.D. Dryham 83, 1953, AKW; Kelfield 53, 1955, RG; by
R. Derwent, Breighton 73, 1955, RG; Naburn Lane, York
64, 1971, TFM; Skipwith Common 63, 1982, EB.
Hold. King George Dock, Hull 12, 1933 and later, AKW
(W. 1938); bombed sites, Hull 12, 1952, FEC; roadside,
Hedon Rd, Hull 12, 1955 and later, FEC; railway line,
Keyingham 22, 1955, FEC; Winestead 32, 1981, FEC; by
Hedon Haven 12, 1985, FEC; railway station, Hedon 12,
1986, FEC.

C. biennis L.
Rough Hawk's-beard.   1798.
Probably native.   Pastures, waysides, waste places.
Uncommon.
L.D. Near Wressle 73 (Flintoff, 1934); by R. Ouse, below
Cawood 54, 1941, WAS; Barmby on the Marsh 62, 1956,
RG; Turnham Hall 63, 1956, RG; Bubwith 73, 1972, EC;
frequent on disused railway, Eastrington 73, 1976, YNU
Excursion; Faxfleet 82, 1978, FEC.
Wolds West of Bishop Burton 94 (Teesdale, 1798),
identification questioned (R. 1902); Burton Agnes 16,
1923, Major Lawson (Flintoff, 1934); near Fordon 07,
1973, EC.
Hold. Kilnsea Warren 41, 1934, RG; waste place, Queen
St, Hull 12, 1978, FEC.

C. capillaris (L.) Wallr. (*C. virens* L.)   Map 422.
Smooth Hawk's-beard.
Native. Grassland, including roadsides; waste places;
chalk quarries; sand pits. Widely distributed; common on
the Wolds.

C. nicaeensis Balb.
Alien.   Arable.   Rare.
Hold. Bridlington 16, Major Lawson (Nat. 1932, 90);
Hinderwell 16, 1975, EC, det. Mr Marshall.

C. paludosa (L.) Moench   Map 423.
Marsh Hawk's-beard.   CNE.   *c.*1845.
Native. Stream sides, wet meadows, fens, wet copses.
Locally frequent in the Kirkham area, otherwise in scat-
tered localities mainly in the R. Hull valley and in Lower
Derwentland.

Taraxacum Weber **Dandelions.**
133 species of Taraxacum were described by Dr A.J.
Richards in *The Taraxacum Flora of the British Isles* (in
Watsonia as a Supplement to vol. *9*, 1972). Further
considerable advance has been made in the study of the
genus since 1972. About 250 species are now recognised
in the British Isles and a list of these was published
privately by C.C. Haworth and A.J. Rundle in January,
1986. My thanks are due to C.C. Haworth for advice and

information concerning authorities for names, classification and taxonomic order. I am indebted to Eric Chicken for the following records, except in the very few cases indicated. Identification was confirmed or determined by Dr A.R. Richards except where otherwise stated. See also Chicken (1986).

Taraxacun officinale Weber *sensu lato*
Common Dandelion.

Sect. ***Erythrosperma*** (H. Lindb. f.) Dahlst.

> ***T. argutum*** Dahlst.
> On cinders.
> Hull docks 12, 1979.
>
> ***T. brachyglossum*** (Dahlst.) Raunk.
> Well-drained soils.
> **U.D.** Sandy roadside, Scampston 87, 1976; on gravel, Staxton 07, 1977.
> **Wolds** Roadside dust, Rudston 07, 1976; pasture, Speeton 17,1976; Kilham 06, 1977.
>
> ***T. fulviforme*** Dahlst.
> Well-drained grassland.
> **U.D.** Roadside. Wintringham 87, 1976.
> **Wolds** Calcareous grassland, Acklam 76, 1973, FH and near Langton 86, 1979.
>
> ***T. lacistophyllum*** (Dahlst.) Raunk.
> **Lesser Dandelion.**
> Calcareous grassland.
> **Wolds** Millington 85, 1976; Langton 86, 1980; Hunmanby 07, 1980.
>
> ***T. oxoniense*** Dahlst.
> Calcareous grassland, sand-dunes.
> **Wolds** Quarry, Westow 76, 1974; Acklam 76, 1975; quarry, North Grimston 86, 1976; Langton 86, 1979.
> **Hold.** Newton, Hull 12, 1901, CW, herb. BM; Spurn 41, 1976.
>
> ***T. proximum*** (Dahlst.) Raunk.
> Dry grassland.
> **L.D.** Stillingfleet Common 54, 1979.
> **Wolds** Great Givendale 85, 1979.
>
> ***T. rubicundum*** (Dahlst.) Dahlst.
> Calcareous grassland.
> **Wolds** Fordon 07, 1976; Langton 86, 1979.
>
> ***T. simile*** Raunk.
> Well-drained habitats, including walls and paths.
> **L.D.** Woodland ride, Wheldrake 64, 1979.
> **Wolds** Langton 86, 1980.
> **Hold.** On cinders at Kelleythorpe 05, 1978 and on Hull docks 02, 1979.

Sect. ***Spectabilia*** (Dahlst.) Dahlst. emend. A.J. Richards

> ***T. faeroense*** (Dahlst.) Dahlst.
> Hull House, Hull 03, 1894, Fraser, herb. Wales.
>
> ***T. spectabile*** Dahlst.
> **Red-veined Dandelion.**
> Wet grassland.
> **U.D.** Wintringham 87, 1980; Folkton Carrs 08,

1979, conf. C.C.Haworth (CCH).
L.D. South Cliffe 83, 1975.
Hold. Driffield and Wansford 05, 1975; Harpham 06, 1978.

Sect. ***Naevosa*** M.P. Christiansen

> ***T. euryphyllum*** (Dahlst.) M.P. Chr.
> Wet grassland, mainly.
> **U.D.** Wintringham 87, 1980.
> **L.D.** Catton 75, 1979, det. CCH.
> **Wolds** Roadside, Burton Fleming 07, 1975.
> **Hold.** Kelleythorpe 05, 1978.
>
> ***T. pseudolarssonii*** A.J. Richards
> Wet grassland.
> **U.D.** Roadside, Staxton 07, 1973, det. CHH; Folkton Carrs 08, 1974, det. CHH.
> **Hold.** Driffield 05, 1975, det. AJR & CHH; Withernwick 23, 1980.
>
> ***T. richardsianum*** C.C. Haworth *ined.*
> Wet grassland.
> **Wolds** Woodland ride, Millington 85, 1976, det. CHH; Thixendale 86, 1979, det. CCH.

Sect. ***Celtica*** A.J. Richards

> ***T. haematicum*** Hagl.
> Water meadows and other wet sites.
> **L.D.** Bubwith 73, 1974; Melbourne 74, 1977.
> **Wolds** Kilham 06, 1977, det. CHH.
> **Hold.** Withernwick 23, 1980.
>
> ***T. laetifrons*** Dahlst.
> Wet grassland.
> **Hold.** Driffield 05, 1974.
>
> ***T. nordstedtii*** Dahlst.
> Wet places usually.
> **Wolds** Thixendale 86, 1979.
> **Hold.** Hull House, Hull 03, 1879, Fraser, herb. Wales; Driffield 05, 1975; Kelleythorpe 05, 1978; on sand, Spurn 41, 1976.
>
> ***T. praestans*** H. Lindb. f.
> Wet places.
> **L.D.** Melbourne 74, 1976.
>
> ***T. raunkiaeri*** Wiinst.
> Grassy places, usually on well-drained, base-rich soil.
> **U.D.** Staxton 07, 1975; roadside, Folkton 07, 1975; on sand, Scampston 87, 1976.
> **L.D.** Melbourne 74, 1977.
> **Wolds** Roadside Ruston Parva 06, 1975; Leavening 76, 1975; on road dust, Rudston 07, 1976; Speeton 07, 1976; Flamborough 07,1976.
> **Hold.** Driffield 05, 1977; wall top, Foston 15, 1979.
>
> ***T. bracteatum*** Dahlst.
> Grassy places, roadsides.
> **L.D.** Hay meadow, Melbourne 74, 1977.
> **Hold.** Great Kelk 15, 1979.

Sect. *Hamata* H. Øllgaard

T. boekmanii Borgvall
U.D. Old gravel quarry, Staxton 07, 1977.
Wolds Wood ride, Boynton 16, 1975, det. CCH.
Hold. Ditch, Burton Agnes 16, 1975, det. CCH.

T. hamatiforme Dahlst.
Roadside.
Hold. North Frodingham 05, 1979.

T. hamatum Raunk.
Roadsides.
U.D. Westow 76, 1974.
Wolds Boynton 16, 1975; Bishop Wilton 85, 1975; Wetwang 95,1979; near Sherburn 97, 1978, det. CCH.
Hold. Tunstall 33, 1976.

T. marklundii Palmgr.
Grassy places, roadsides.
Wolds Garton on the Wolds 95, 1977; Ruston Parva 06, 1975.
Hold. Near Wansford 05, 1977.

T. pseudohamatum Dahlst.
Roadside.
Hold. Gransmoor 16, 1984, det. CCH.

T. quadrans H. Øllgaard
Woodland ride.
Wolds Sledmere 96, 1979.

T. subhamatum M.P. Chr.
Roadside.
Hold. Near Leconfield 04, 1977.

Sect. *Vulgaria* Dahlst.

T. aequilobum Dahlst.
Roadsides.
Wolds Wetwang 95, 1979.
Hold. Little Kelk 05, 1977.

T. alatum H. Lindb. f.
Roadsides.
U.D. Burythorpe 76, 1975.
Hold. Carnaby 16, 1977, det. CCH.

T. ancistrolobum Dahlst.
Pastures, meadows, roadsides.
U.D. Folkton Carrs 08, 1975; Menethorpe 76, 1979.
L.D. Hay meadow, Melbourne 74, 1976.
Hold. Driffield 05, 1977; Brigham 05, 1979.

T. aurosulum H. Lindb. f.
Roadsides, pastures.
U.D. Folkton Carrs 08, 1977.
Hold. Driffield 05, 1977.

T. cordatum Palmgr.
Water meadow.
L.D. Bubwith 73, 1975.

T. dahlstedtii H. Lindb. f.
Grassy places, roadsides, etc.
U.D. Wintringham 87, 1976.

Hold. Gravel quarry, Hempholme 05, 1979; on cinders, Hull docks 12, 1979.

T. dilatatum H. Lindb. f.
Roadside.
Wolds Sledmere 96, 1977.

T. expallidiforme Dahlst.
Roadsides, waste places.
Hold. Foot of wall, Driffield 05, 1978.

T. fasciatum Dahlst.
Roadside.
Bishop Wilton 75, 1975.

T. huelphersianum Dahlst.
Roadside.
Wolds Burton Fleming 07, 1979.

T. insigne Ekman ex M.P. Chr. & Wiinst.
Dry grassland, roadsides.
U.D. Ganton 97, 1977, conf. CCH; meadow near Muston 07, 1981.
Hold. Brigham 05, 1979.

T. interveniens Haglund
Grassland.
Wolds Tumulus, Burton Fleming 07, 1976.

T. lingulatum Marklund
Meadows, roadsides.
Hold. Driffield 05, 1977, det. CCH; on road dust, Hutton Cranswick 05, 1978; meadow, Withernwick 23, 1980.

T. ochrochlorum Hagl.
Roadside.
Hold. Little Kelk 05, 1979.

T. ostenfeldii Raunk.
Roadside.
U.D. Wintringham 87, 1980.

T. pachymerum Hagl.
Wood ride, gravel quarry.
Wolds Boynton 16, 1975.
Hold. Hempholme 05, 1979.

T. pannucium Dahlst.
Usually in herb-rich meadows.
L.D. Meadow, Melbourne 74, 1977.
Hold. Hedge base, Driffield 05, 1979.

T. planum Raunk.
Roadside.
U.D. Scampston 87, 1976, det. CCH.

T. polyodon Dahlst.
Grassy places, roadsides.
U.D. Scampston 87, 1976.
Wolds Wood ride, Boynton 16, 1975; pasture, Folkton 07, 1978, det. CCH; cliff top, Barmston 16, 1979.
Hold. Driffield 05, 1979.

T. sagittipotens Dahlst. & R.Ohlsén
Roadside.
Hold. Driffield 05, 1977.

Plate 1   Waterdale

Plate 2   Chalk quarry, Flamborough

Plate 3   *Thymus praecox* (Wild Thyme)

Plate 4   *Cirsium acaule* (Dwarf Thistle)

Plate 6   *Polygala vulgaris* (Common Milkwort)

Plate 5   *Orobanche reticulata* (Thistle Broomrape)

Plate 7   *Trifolium medium* (Zigzag Clover)

Plate 8   Heathland, Skipwith Common

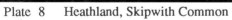

Plate 9   *Erica tetralix* (Cross-leaved Heath)

Plate 10   Wet area, Skipwith Common

Plate 11   *Myosurus minimus* (Mousetail)

Plate 12   Sand pit, Staxton

Plate 13   *Eriophorum angustifolium* (Common Cottongrass)

Plate 14   *Erica cinerea* (Bell Heather) and *Calluna vulgaris* (Heather)

Plate 15   Millington Wood

Plate 16   *Primula vulgaris* (Primrose) and *P. vulgaris* x *P. veris*

Plate 17   *Campanula latifolia* (Giant Bellflower)

Plate 18   Ash wood carpeted with Early Dog-violet, Tibthorpe

Plate 19   *Actaea spicata* (Baneberry)

Plate 20   *Ajuga reptans* (Bugle) and
Ophioglossum vulgatum (Adder's-tongue)

Plate 21   *Monotropa hypopitys* (Yellow Bird's-nest)

Plate 22   Upper reach of West Beck (R. Hull), near Driffield

Plate 23   *Oenanthe fluviatilis* (River Water-dropwort)
and *Ranunculus penicillatus* (Stream Water-crowfoot)

Plate 24   *Petasites hybridus* (Butterbur)

Plate 25   *Lathyrus palustris* (Marsh Pea)

Plate 26   Marsh, Bell Mills, near Driffield

Plate 27   *Menyanthes trifoliata* (Bogbean)

Plate 28   *Berula erecta* (Lesser Water-parsnip)

Plate 29   Leven Canal from Far Fox Aqueduct

Plate 30   *Myriophyllum verticillatum* (Whorled Water-milfoil) and *Nymphaea alba* (White Water-lily)

Plate 31   Bank of Leven Canal

Plate 32   Hornsea Mere

Plate 33   *Ranunculus lingua* (Greater Spearwort)

Plate 34   *Dactylorhiza incarnata* (Early Marsh-orchid)

Plate 35   Spurn Point

Plate 36   *Calystegia soldanella* (Sea Convolvulus)

Plate 37   *Artemisia maritima* (Sea Wormwood)
and *Catapodium marinum* (Sea Fern-grass)

Plate 38   *Eryngium maritimum* (Sea-holly)

Plate 39   *Limonium vulgare* (Common Sea-lavender), Welwick salt-marsh

Plate 40   *Trifolium fragiferum* (Strawberry Clover)

Plate 41   *Armeria maritima* (Thrift); cliff, Flamborough Head

T. sellandii Dahlst.
Grassland, roadside.
L.D. Cart-track, Melbourne 74, 1976.
Wolds Cliff top, Barmston 17, 1980.

T. stenacrum Dahlst.
Usually in open communities.
Hold. Roadside, Driffield 05, 1979.

T. subcyanolepis M.P. Chr. ex M.P. Chr. &
Wiinst.
Grassland.
L.D. Cart road, Melbourne 74, 1976.

T. subundulatum Dahlst.
Water meadows.
L.D. Melbourne 74, 1977.
Hold. Withernwick 23, 1980.

T. trilobatum Palmgr.
Water meadow.
Hold. Withernwick 14, 1981.

T. xanthostigma H. Lindb. f.
Grassy places.
Hold. Field path, Driffield 05, 1977.

MONOCOTYLEDONES

ALISMATACEAE

Baldellia Parl.
B. ranunculoides (L.) Parl. (*Alisma ranunculoides* L.)
Lesser Water-plantain.   1798.
Native. Damp places; beside streams, ponds and lakes and
in fen ditches. A decreasing species owing to loss of
habitat. Rare now, but apparently at least locally frequent
formerly (R. 1902).
L.D. Skipwith Common 63, WNC and near Howden 72,
JBe (R. 1902); by pond near Broomfleet House 82, 1952,
AW and still near Broomfleet, 1984, DRG; near Walbut
Lock 74, 1956, RG; frequent in marsh, Heslington Common 64, 1957, FEC; by Bielby Arm, Pocklington Canal 74,
1964, FEC.
Wolds Bempton cliff top 17, 1966, RD.
Hold. Ditches near Beverley (Teesdale, 1800); formerly
in the Hull area: Inglemire Lane 03, Dunswell Lane 03 and
in dykes in Salt Ings (R. 1902); Kelsey Hill 22, CW (R.
1902) and 1955, RG & FEC.

Luronium Raf.
[*L. natans* (L.) Raf. [*Elisma natans* (L.) Buchen.]
Floating Water-plantain.
Native. In the 'lake at Hornsea' (Teesdale, 1800); record
doubted (Baker, 1854). No confirmation.]

Alisma L.
A. plantago-aquatica L.   Map 119.
Water-plantain.
Native. Beside slow-flowing rivers, becks, ditches, drains
and canals; in ponds including gravel pits. Frequent in
Holderness, including the R. Hull valley and in Lower

Derwentland; scattered elsewhere.

A. lanceolatum With.
Narrow-leaved Water-plantain.   1798.
Native. By rivers, dykes, a canal and a pond. Uncommon.
L.D. Pond, near Broomfleet House 82, 1958, FEC, det. J.E.
Lousley; drain near Sutton Wood 74, 1958, FEC; Howden
Common 73, 1970, FEC; by R. Ouse, near Barmby on the
Marsh 72, 1983, DRG; Walbut Lock 74, 1984, DRG;
Skipwith Common 63, 1985, EC.
Hold. Marshes, near Beverley 04 (Teesdale, 1800); Sutton
drain, Hull 13, 1915, JWB, herb. FEC; drain side, Hull 02,
1961, BP; gravel pit, near Hempholme 05, 1969, YNU
Excursion; by R. Hull, near Baswick landing 04, 1970,
FEC; Tophill Low 04, 1979, DRG.

Damasonium Mill.
D. alisma Mill. (*D. stellatum* Thuill.)
Starfruit.   OSE.
Native. In a pond and dyke, near Stoneferry, Hull in the
1870s, EAP & Mr T. Dennis & FAL (BEC. 9, 1930, 373);
the only Yorkshire record for this southern species which is
now a rare British plant. Extinct.

Sagittaria L.
S. sagittifolia L.   Map 116.
Arrowhead.   1840.
Native. In dykes, drains, canals and slow-flowing rivers.
Mainly in the larger drains and other waters. Frequent in the
valleys of the R. Hull and R. Derwent and formerly in the
R. Foulness, but may now be lost as a result of pollution.
Not now known in Holderness away from the R. Hull
valley, except in the Holderness Drain; formerly recorded
for drains near Keyingham 22 (R. 1902).

BUTOMACEAE

Butomus L.
B. umbellatus L.   Map 137.
Flowering-rush.   1798.
Native. In drains, ponds, canals and at margins of rivers and
lakes. Infrequent; mainly in the R. Hull and R. Derwent
valleys; also by Pocklington and Leven Canals.
Other post-1950 records include:
L.D. Pond by R. Foulness, near Newport 83, 1969, FEC;
pond near Naburn 64, 1980, EB.
Wolds Near Hunmanby 17, 1973, MC.
Hold. By Holderness Drain, Hull 13, 1957, FEC; Rise Park
lake 14, 1971, FEC; Hornsea Mere 14, 1978, FEC.
There has been some loss of habitat, but there may also be
under-recording as the species does not always flower.

HYDROCHARITACEAE

Hydrocharis L.
H. morsus-ranae L.
Frogbit.   1840.
Native. Ponds and dykes. Last record: 1956.
U.D. R. Derwent, above Malton, 'not seen recently', 1953
(N.H. Scarb.).

141

L.D. Near Selby 63, WNC; Howden 72, JBe (R. 1902) and 1956, RG; in great quantity in ponds, Hemingborough 63, 1909, JFR & 1956, RG.

Hold. Formerly in the Hull area, in Inglemire Lane 03, GN and Salt Ings Lane, 1898 (R. 1902); old gravel pit, Kelsey Hill 22, 1955, FEC.

Stratiotes L.

***S. aloides* L.**
Water-soldier.   1626.
Native.   Ponds and ditches in fenland districts. Rare.
L.D. River Derwent (Baines, 1840).
Hold. Plentiful in ditches, about Rotsey 05, 1626, T. Johnson (Johnson 1633); the first British record. 'In slow rivers and ponds, Stork, near Beverley', presumably Storkhill 04 (Camden, 1789). On Leven Carrs 04 and near Hornsea Mere 14, latter half 18th century, WW. In ditches, near Beverley (Scaum's *Beverlac*, 1829). No further record until 1979 when it was found in a borrow pit, near Beverley 04, J. Higgins & S. Priest. The question arises as to whether the species could have survived on site, although it is not known to set viable seed in this country (Crackles, 1982).

Elodea Michx.

***E. canadensis* Michx.**   Map 98.
Canadian Waterweed.
Alien.   Native of North America.
Naturalised in slow-flowing rivers, becks, drains, canals, lakes and ponds, including gravel pits.
The first certain English record is for Foxton, Leics., v.c. 55, 1847. Said to be common in dykes and drains of the vice-county by 1902, but to be less conspicuous than twelve years earlier (R. 1902). Now common in the R. Hull valley from Leven Canal northwards; locally frequent in Lower Derwentland including Pocklington Canal; other localities scattered.

Lagarosiphon Harv.

***L. major* (Ridl.) Moss**
Curly Waterweed.
Alien. Ponds. Rare.
Skipwith Common 63, 1982, EB.

JUNCAGINACEAE

Triglochin L

***T. palustris* L.**   Map 198.
Marsh Arrowgrass.   1898.
Native. Marshes. Locally frequent along the spring line to the west of the Wolds and on the coast of Filey Bay 17. Infrequent in the R. Hull valley and in Lower Derwentland. By Hornsea Mere 14, 1978, FEC.

***T. maritima* L.**   Map 222.
Sea Arrowgrass.
Native. Salt-marshes, grassy places and open habitats. Frequent on salt-marshes from Spurn 41 west to Salt End 12; also on the R. Humber shore from Hessle 02 to Faxfleet 82 and on the cliffs of Filey Bay 17 and Flamborough Head 27. Also on the coast near Fraisthorpe 16.

ZOSTERACEAE

Zostera L.

***Z. marina* L.**
Eelgrass.
Native.   Cast up within Spurn Head, 1888 (R. 1902). Believed to be the species which continued to be washed up at Spurn until at least the late nineteen forties. Philip (1936) did not record this species and it decreased markedly in abundance in the British Isles from *c*.1933. Petch (1903) recorded the presence of *Zostera* pools from Skeffling to Spurn, but did not specify the species.

***Z. angustifolia* (Hornem.) Rchb. (*Z. marina* L. var. *angustifolia* Horn.)**
Narrow-leaved Eelgrass.   1932.
Native. On mud flats in estuaries and in shallow water mainly from low to mid-tide level. Rare.
Beds recorded in Spurn Bay, 1932 (Philip, 1936). Two patches were close together and *c*.55 metres from the shore of the narrow neck of Spurn 41, 1976, B. Pashby, det. Dr A.J. Richards. Also see Pashby, 1977.

***Z. noltii* Hornem. (*Z. nana* auct.)**
Dwarf Eelgrass.
Native. Above mid-tide level on the R. Humber shore. Pools, R. Humber flats, Spurn 41, 1974, KF & J. Borman, det. J.E. Dandy. Dr Ranwell, NCC, visited the area in May, 1975 and found the species in the Old Den region of Spurn Bight and opposite the narrow-neck where it formed extensive beds. By 1976 beds of the species had extended further north to almost opposite the Warren Cottage, BP & S.J. Weston (Pashby, 1977).

POTAMOGETONACEAE

Potamogeton L.

***P. natans* L.**   Map 110.
Broad-leaved Pondweed.
Native. Still or slow-moving basic or neutral water, usually less than one metre deep. Dykes, ponds including gravel and marl pits; also in canals. Common in the R. Hull valley, north of Beverley and locally in Lower Derwentland; scattered elsewhere.

***P. polygonifolius* Pourr.**   Map 112.
Bog Pondweed.   1895.
Native. Ponds and ditches with acid, usually shallow water. Uncommon.
Only known in Lower Derwentland: Skipwith Common 63, 1896, CW (R. 1902) and 1970, MC; Houghton Woods 83, 1953, RG; Allerthorpe Common 74, 1954, AW; Duck Nest 83, 1955, RG; Langwith Common 64, 1956, FEC. 'Common in Holderness drains' (R. 1902) must be the result of incorrect identification.

***P. coloratus* Hornem. (*P. plantagineus* Du Croz ex Roem. & Schult.)**
Fen Pondweed.   1841.
Native. Shallow ponds, pools and dykes, especially where the water is calcareous. Rare.

142

L.D. Heslington Fields 64, 1841, CCB (Baker, 1854); pools near railway, Market Weighton, JJM and pond on Barlby side of Skipwith Common 63, 1900, CW (R. 1902). **Wolds** Pond, Kelleythorpe 05, 1948, RL.

P. lucens L.　　　　　　　　　　　　Map 109.
Shining Pondweed.
Native. Canals, rivers, large drains, gravel pits. Frequent in the West Beck (R. Hull) from Wansford south and in other suitable waters in the R. Hull valley south to Beverley, including Frodingham Beck and the Old Howe; abundant in Leven Canal. Also frequent in the R. Derwent. Few other records:
L.D. Market Weighton Canal (1902) and 1940, GT; Pocklington Canal 74, 1902 (SYF) and 1956, RG.
Hold. Brandesburton gravel pits 14, 1957, RG, still there; Holderness Drain, Hull 13, 1970, FEC.

P. *gramineus* L. (*P. heterophyllus* Schreb.)
Various-leaved Pondweed.
Native. Ditches, ponds. Extinct.
Hold. Ditches in the marshes, near Beverley, 1794, R. Teesdale, herb. BM; ponds, Lowthorpe 06, 1890, YNU Excursion.

P. gramineus x *P. lucens* = *P.* x *zizii* Koch ex Roth
Holderness Drain, Routh Carrs 04, 1945, GT, herb. BM.

P. alpinus Balb.
Red Pondweed.　　　　　　　　　　　1798.
Native. Drains, a canal, becks and a river. Uncommon. All records for Holderness. Said to be formerly common in the R. Hull and in large drains (R. 1902). Rare now in the R. Hull; recorded just below the junction of the West Beck and Frodingham Beck 05, 1982, ECha.
Records include:
ditches, near Beverley (Teesdale, 1800); Barmston Drain at Newland 03, 1944, GT and at Watton 04, 1945, GT; Leven Canal 04, 1950, FEC; Watton Beck 04, 1970, FEC; drain, Tophill Low 04, 1971, FEC; Skerne Beck 05 and Frodingham Church Drain 05, 1982, ECha.

P. perfoliatus L.
Perfoliate Pondweed.　　　　　　　　1829.
Native. Rivers, a lake and a pond. Local.
Between Howsham and the R. Derwent 76, 1952, DAW. At least locally frequent in the R. Derwent as near Elvington 74, 1973, YNU Excursion, near Bubwith 73, 1981, DRG and at Firby 76, 1981, FEC. In the R. Foulness, near Newport 83, 1913, JWB, herb. FEC & 1969, FEC. Formerly near Beverley 03, 1829, Dr Hull and in Hornsea Mere 14 (R. 1902).

P. friesii Rupr.
Flat-stalked Pondweed.　　　　　　　1896.
Native. In drains, canals, streams, a river and a pond. Uncommon.
L.D. In Pocklington Canal by Hagg Bridge 74, 1945, GT, herb. BM & 1981, NCC, at Storwood 74, 1945, GT, herb. BM, at Walbut Lock 74, 1956 RG & 1981, NCC and in Bielby Arm 74, 1981, NCC. In pond, near Holme upon Spalding Moor 83, 1945, GT.

Hold. Dyke, west of Hull, 1896 (R. 1902); Queen's Rd, Hull 03, 1901, CW, herb. BM; Holderness Drain, Routh Carrs 04, 1945, GT, herb. BM: Leven Canal 04, 1952, FEC & 1981, NCC; Old Howe, North Frodingham 05, 1959, FEC & 1982, ECha; Frodingham Church Drain 05, 1982, ECha. In the R. Hull just below the junction between West and Frodingham Becks 05, 1982, ECha.

P. pusillus L.
Lesser Pondweed.
Native. Ponds, dykes, a canal and a lake. Uncommon.
L.D. Near Broomfleet 82 and at Selby 63, WNC (R. 1902); Market Weighton Canal 74, 1940, GT, herb. BM; near Loftsome Bridge 63 & 73, 1945, GT, herb. BM; dyke, Aughton Ings 63, 1972, FEC & CMR.
Hold. Pond near Beverley 03 (R. 1902); Kelsey Hill 22 (R. 1902) and 1947, RL, det. J.E. Dandy (JED) and GT; Hornsea Mere 14, 1938, A.H.G. Alston, herb. BM & 1957, FEC, det. JED & GT; Old Howe, near Lisset Bridge 15, 1945, GT, herb. BM.

P. obtusifolius Mert. & Koch
Blunt-leaved Pondweed.　　　CNE.
Native. Drains. Extinct?
Beverley 1798, RT, herb. BM; drains in Hull including one near Newland Avenue 03 (R. 1902).

P. berchtoldii Fieb.
Small Pondweed.　　　　　　　　　　1931.
Native. Lakes; ponds, including gravel pits; drains. Uncommon.
L.D. Ross Moor 74, 1945, GT, herb. BM; Gilberdyke 82, 1945, GT, herb. BM; pond Foggathorpe 73, 1987, DRG. **Wolds** Jenny Firkin Lake, near Pocklington 84, 1957, RG, herb. HLU; village pond, North Dalton 95, 1985, DRG.
Hold. Drain, Hull, 1931, RG, herb. HLU; drain, near Wilfholme landing 04, 1945, GT, herb. BM; Old Howe, near Frodingham 05, 1945, GT, herb. BM; gravel pits, near Foston 05, 1951, RG, herb. HLU; near Brandesburton 14, 1953, AKW, herb. HLU, near Burshill 04, 1957, RG, herb. HLU, Kelsey Hill 22, CW, herb. BM & 1955, FEC, det. GT; Hornsea Mere 14, 1987, DRG. All specimens in herb. HLU det. JED.

P. compressus L. (*P. zosteraefolius* Schumach.)
Grass-wrack Pondweed.
Native. Slow streams, ponds and ditches. Extinct.
Beverley 03, 1798, RT (Teesdale, 1800), conf. JED & GT.

P. acutifolius Link
Sharp-leaved Pondweed.
Native. Ponds, streams, ditches, chiefly in calcareous waters. Extinct.
Beverley 03, 1798 (Teesdale, 1800), det. JED & GT (SYF); herb. Sir J.E. Smith in herb. LINN (HSFNC *3*, 1903, 99).

P. crispus L.　　　　　　　　　　　　Map 108.
Curled Pondweed.　　　　　　　　　1840.
Native. Lakes, ponds, streams, canals, dykes, rivers. Locally frequent in Holderness, particularly in the R. Hull valley and in Lower Derwentland.
Rare elsewhere:

U.D. Folkton Carrs 08, 1984, DRG.
Wolds Speeton 17, 1971, YNU Excursion; pond, North Dalton 95, 1985, DRG.

P. pectinatus L. (including *P. interruptus* Kit.) Map 111.
Fennel Pondweed.   1798.
Native. Lakes, ponds, rivers, canals, dykes and drains; in base-rich and brackish waters. Locally frequent in the R. Hull valley; also in Hornsea Mere 14, 1957, FEC. Comparatively infrequent in Lower Derwentland apparently. In brackish water as in ditch, Salt End Common 12, 1910, TJF (SYF); dyke near Kilnsea 41, 1933, WAS and still in the Kilnsea area.

Groenlandia Gay

G. densa (L.) Fourr. (*Potamogeton densus* L.) Map 99.
Opposite-leaved Pondweed.   1840.
Native. Clear streams, canals, ponds, fen dykes, a gravel pit; where water is alkaline.
Frequent in the R. Hull valley from Arram 04 northwards. Other records include:
L.D. Formerly in the R. Derwent (Baines, 1840) and near Selby 63, WNC (R. 1902); dyke near Market Weighton Canal 83, 1954, FEC; below Silburn Lock, Pocklington Canal 74, 1981, NCC.
Hold. Dyke, Barmston 15, 1953, AKW; pond near Lelley 13, 1955, FEC; Kelsey Hill gravel pit 22, 1955, YNU Excursion; Lambwath Stream, Skirlaugh 13, 1957, FEC.

RUPPIACEAE

Ruppia L.

R. cirrhosa (Petagna) Grande (*R. spiralis* L. ex Dumort.; *R. maritima* auct.)
Spiral Tasselweed.   1907.
Native. Brackish dykes, pools and ponds. Rare.
Brackish pools on salt-marsh, Salt End 12, 1907, CW, herb. BM (Preston, 1985); brackish ditch, Kilnsea 41, 1933, WAS (SYF); Kilnsea Beacon Lane Pond 41, a borrow pit created 1978/9, 1981, P. Hayward (Crackles, 1983b).

R. maritima L. (*R. rostellata* Koch)
Beaked Tasselweed.   1900.
Native. Tidal pools, brackish dykes. Uncommon and rarely flowering or flowering late (Crackles, 1983a).
Tidal pools, Easington 41, 1900, TP and at Patrington Haven 31, 1901, TP (R. 1902) and 1932, G. Philip (GP). 'On drained ridges in Spurn Bay from Kilnsea to Spurn' 41 and at Easington 31, GP (Philip, 1936). Cherry Cob Sands 22, 1953, RG; brackish ditch behind the Humber bank, Skeffling 31, 1973, FEC and in two localities near Kilnsea 41, including a newly cut dyke, 1974, FEC; Kilnsea Beacon Lane Pond 41, 1981, FEC (Crackles, 1983a).

ZANNICHELLIACEAE

Zannichellia L.

Z. palustris L.   Map 118.
Horned Pondweed.   *c*.1845.
Native. Ponds, streams, drains. Locally frequent in the R.

Hull valley north of Leven. Uncommon elsewhere, including the following post-1950 records:
U.D. Stream, Settrington 87, 1958, FEC; Scampston Hall lake 87, 1964, FEC.
L.D. Near Broomfleet House 82, 1955, RG; pond, Wheldrake 64, 1956, RG; Pocklington Canal, near Silburn Lock 74, 1981, NCC; Duck Nest 83, 1981, DRG.
Hold. Drain, Cottingham Rd Hull 03, 1952, DAW; gravel pits at Kelsey Hill 22, 1955, FEC and near Brandesburton, 1969, YNU Excursion; Hornsea Mere 14, 1979, FEC.

Z. pedunculata Reichb.
Pedunculate Horned Pondweed.
Native. Brackish water.
In dyke by Long Bank, Kilnsea with *Ruppia* 41, 1933, WAS (SYF). In brackish canals behind the river bank near Easington and Skeffling 31, 1974, FEC.

Z. gibberosa Reichb.
Rough-fruited Horned Pondweed.
Native.
In the West Beck (R. Hull), 1969, FEC.

LILIACEAE

Narthecium Huds.

N. ossifragum (L.) Huds.
Bog Asphodel.   ONE.
Native. Wet acid places.
In a swampy place in Houghton Woods 83, 1888, JFR (R. 1902). Extinct.

Convallaria L.

C. majalis L.
Lily-of-the-valley.
Native. Woods on calcareous soils. Rare.
U.D. Firby 76, 1923, GP.
Wolds Hanging Fall Wood, Sledmere 96, 1960, YNU Excursion; Millington Wood 85, 1965, FEC & 1984, YNU Excursion.

Polygonatum Mill.

P. multiflorum (L.) All.
Solomon's-seal.
Native. Woods mainly. Uncommon.
U.D. Kennythorpe 76, 1958, FEC.
L.D. Water Fulford 64, 1928, HB.
Wolds Woods, near Welton 92 (R. 1902); quarry, Bishop Burton 93, 1952, RG; Deepdale, Bishop Burton 94, 1977, EHW.

Maianthemum Weber

M. bifolium (L.) Schmidt
May Lily.   CNE.
Native? Woods. Rare.
Allerthorpe Common 74, 1981, B. Jackson.

Ruscus L.

R. aculeatus L.
Butcher's-broom.
Alien. Shrubberies and copses. Uncommon.

144

L.D. Brough 92 (R. 1902).
Wolds North Ferriby 92, 1935, AKW; Hesslewood 02, 1945 & 1978, FEC; railway station, Nafferton 05, 1976, JR.
Hold. Bridle road, Bentley 03, 1938, TS (W 1938); Cottingham 03, 1960, FEC.

Lilium L.
L. martagon L.
Martagon Lily.
Introduced.   Grown in gardens, becoming naturalised in woods. Rare.
U.D. Howsham 76, 1974, EC.
Wolds Meaux 03, 1955, IG: Eppleworth Wood 03, 1957, FEC.

Fritillaria L.
F. meleagris L.
Fritillary.   1886.
Probably always introduced. Damp meadows and pastures. Not known now.
L.D. Riccall 63, a garden escape WNC (R. 1902).
Wolds Flamborough Head, 1886, YNU Excursion (N.H. Scarb.); spinney close to Sewerby House 16 (Flintoff, 1931); moist meadow, Bishop Burton 94, 1925, JWB, herb. FEC.

Gagea Salisb.
G. lutea (L.) Ker-Gawl. (*G. fascicularis* Salisb.)
Yellow Star-of-Bethlehem.   CE.
Native.   Damp woods and pastures, especially on basic soils.
U.D. Leavening 76, MBS (R. 1902).
L.D. St Leonard's Ings, Elvington 74 (Baines, 1840); Sutton upon Derwent 74, 1932, DH. No later record.

Ornithogalum L.
O. umbellatum L.
Star-of-Bethlehem.   1900.
Garden escape.   Uncommon.
U.D. Ganton 97, 1955, WHS.
L.D. Near cottage, Dryham 83, 1944, FEC; roadside, near Broomfleet 82, 1979, YNU Excursion.
Hold. Near the railway, Kelsey Hill 22, 1900, JWB (R. 1902), still there, 1945, FEC; Kilnsea Warren 41, 1926, YNU Excursion, still present; Foston 06, 1956, RG.

Hyacinthoides Medicus
(*Endymion* Dumort.)
H. non-scripta (L.) Chouard ex Rothm. [*Endymion non-scriptus* (L.) Garcke; *Scilla festalis* Salisb.]   Map 76.
Bluebell.   OWEE.
Native. Woods mainly; more rarely in hedgerows and on waysides. Frequent.

H. hispanica (Mill.) Rothm. [*Endymion hispanicus* (Mill.) Chouard]
Spanish Bluebell.
Introduced. Grown in gardens and sometimes naturalised. Several records for roadsides verges. Recorded for ten km squares: 72, 05, 06, 08, 15 and 16, 1964, EC.

Colchicum L.
C. autumnale L.
Meadow Saffron.   CSE.   2nd half 18th century.
Native.   Damp meadows.
Several old records; not known now.
L.D. Fulford Ings 64 (Baines, 1840); Woodhall 62, JBe and banks of R. Ouse, WNC (R. 1902); near Barlby 63, 1906 (Trans. HSFNC, *3*, 301).
Wolds Sledmere 96, 2nd half 18th century, WW; South Dalton 94 (Baines, 1840) where it still grew plentifully at the beginning of this century (R. 1902).

Paris L.
P. quadrifolia L.
Herb-Paris.   1835.
Native.   Woods.   Uncommon.
U.D. Burythorpe 76, 1963, BL; Kirkham Hall woods 76, 1968, FEC.
L.D. Langwith 64, 1835, HPa; North Cliffe Wood 83, 1953, E.Burstall.
Wolds Skidby chalk pit copses, *c*.1850, GN (R. 1902); Bratt Wood, Nunburnholme 84, 1947, Dr S.P.Rowlands; Raywell 93, 1952, GD; *c*.150 plants, Millington Wood 85, 1965, FEC; Enthorpe Wood 94, 1976, MC.
Hold. Bentley Wood 03, EAP (R. 1902); Birkhill Wood 03, 1942, FEC and persisting under shrubs, after oaks felled, at least to 1956, FEC.

JUNCACEAE

Juncus L.
J. squarrosus L.   Map 41.
Heath Rush.
Native.   Heaths, commons, wood rides; confined to acid soils. Locally frequent in Lower Derwentland.
Rare elsewhere, including:
U.D. Kennythorpe Moor 76, 1958, FEC.

J. tenuis Willd.
Slender Rush.   1968.
Naturalised alien. Native of North America. Uncommon.
L.D. Garden weed, Heslington 64, 1980, EB; Skipwith Common 63, 1982, EB.
Hold. Victoria Dock, Hull 12, 1968, EC; in local abundance on Alexandra Dock, Hull 12, 1979, FEC, still present.

J. compressus Jacq.
Round-fruited Rush.   1933.
Native.   Marshy places.   Uncommon.
U.D. Bank of R. Derwent, near Kirkham Priory 76, 1950, RL.
L.D. Bubwith 73, 1937, YNU Excursion; near Howden 72, 1945, JMT; East Cottingwith 74, 1958, FEC; Aughton Ings 73, 1972, YNU Bot. Sect. Excursion.
Wolds Millington Springs 85, 1958, FEC; Welton Ings 92, 1970, JG.
Hold. On gravelly shore, Hornsea Mere 14, 1933, RB & 1953, FEC, still there; Haworth Hall 03, 1973, JA.

J. gerardi Lois.   Map 212.
Saltmarsh Rush.
Native. Salt and brackish marshes. Frequent and some-
times in quantity on salt-marshes between Hull 12 and
Spurn 41. On the shore of the R. Humber between North
Ferriby 92 and Yokefleet 82. Here and there along the coast
as at Tunstall 33, 1951, AKW, Barmston Drain end 15,
1955, RG, Flamborough Head 27, 1984, SMA, north of
Filey 18, 1958, RG. Along the R. Hull near Haworth Hall
03, 1973, JA.
Rare inland:
L.D. Near Market Weighton Canal, north-west of
Broomfleet 82 1984, DRG.
Hold. In wet meadow by Hornsea Mere 14, 1980, FEC.

J. bufonius L. agg.   Map 424.
Toad Rush.
Three species are now recognised as occurring in the
British Isles (Cope & Stace, 1978 & 1983); two of these
occur in the vice-county:

J. bufonius L.
Native. Marshy ground, ditches, damp ground in sand and
gravel pits, where competition is slight or absent. Frequent.

J. ambiguus Guss. (*J. ranarius* Song. & Perr.)
Native. Halophyte; occurring on coastal sand and mud,
above high water mark. Rare.
On the northern part of Spurn Point 41 and in the Kilnsea
Beacon area 41, 1985, F.E. Crackles & M. Nicholls; Barm-
ston 15, 1985, EC (Crackles, 1986b). May occur elsewhere
on the coast and in open brackish situations behind the R.
Humber bank.

J. inflexus L. (*J. glaucus* Sibth.)   Map 425.
Hard Rush.
Native. Damp pastures, marshy ground; by streams, ponds
and lakes; preferring heavy basic and neutral soils. Common
in the R. Hull valley; frequent elsewhere.

J. effusus L.   Map 426.
Soft-rush.
Native. Widely distributed, but usually only dominant on
marshy ground and in wet woods on acid soils.
Var. *compactus* Hoppe occurs as well as the typical
form.

J. effusus x *J. inflexus* = *J.* x *diffusus* Hoppe
Diffuse Rush.
Near Driffield 05, 1972, EC; at edge of lake with both
parents, Rise Park 14, 1983, FEC.

J. conglomeratus L.
Compact Rush.
Native. Marshes; shows a marked preference for acid soils.
Apparently frequent, but distribution not accurately known
because of confusion with *J. effusus* var. *compactus*.

J. maritimus Lam.
Sea Rush.   1870s.
Native. On salt-marshes above high water mark of spring
tides. Rare.
On a shoaling bight south of Hilderthorpe 16 in the 1870s
& 1886, F.A. Lees (SYF). Along Kilnsea Canal at the
northern part of Spurn peninsula 41, 1964, FEC, still
present and locally dominant.

J. subnodulosus Schrank   Map 150.
Blunt-flowered Rush.   1938.
Native. Fens and marshes with base-rich water; by becks,
canals and water-filled gravel pits.
First record: Howden Dyke 72, 1938, AMS (SYF). Locally
frequent and often dominant in marshes in the R. Hull
valley; scattered in Lower Derwentland.
Uncommon elsewhere, including:
U.D. Flixton Carrs 07, 1957, FEC; near Kirkham Abbey
76, 1958, FEC; Wintringham 87, 1968, FEC; Jeffrey Bog
76, 1981, FEC.
Wolds Uncleby 85, 1957, RG; marsh, Woo Dale 93, 1958,
FEC; near Boynton 16 and on Flamborough Head 27,
1970, MC; Birdsall 86, 1983, DEH.
Hold. Kelsey Hill gravel pit 22, 1955, FEC; Brandesburton gravel pits 14, 1956, RG; Carnaby 16, 1970, MC.

J. acutiflorus Ehrh. ex Hoffm.   Map 148.
Sharp-flowered Rush.
Native. Marshy ground, by ponds and streams; in
ditches. Frequent.

J. acutiflorus x *J. articulatus* = *J.* x *surrejanus* Druce
Skipwith Common 63, 1984, EB.

J. articulatus L. (*J. lampocarpus* Ehrh.)   Map 149.
Jointed Rush.
Native. Marshy ground; by streams and ponds. Frequent.

J. bulbosus L. (*J. supinus* Moench)   Map 187.
Bulbous Rush.
Native. Marshy ground, wet rides in woods, in ditches;
chiefly on acid soils. Infrequent; almost entirely in Lower
Derwentland.
Other records:
U.D. By R. Hertford, near Staxton 08, 1955, TFM; Flixton
Carrs 07, 1960, FEC.
Hold. Gravel pit, Brandesburton 14, 1957, RG.

Luzula DC.
L. pilosa (L.) Willd. [*L. vernalis* (Reichard) DC.]
                                                      Map 79.
Hairy Wood-rush.   1901.
Native. Woods. Uncommon and usually in small quantity.
U.D. By river, near Kirkham Abbey 76, 1958, FEC; Firby
Wood 76, 1958, RG.
L.D. North Cliffe Wood 83, 1955, RG & FEC; Langwith
Common 64, 1956, RG; Ross Moor 74, 1956, FEC;
Whittaker Wood, Melbourne 74, 1956, RG; Allerthorpe
Common 74, 1956 GAN & 1984, YNU Excursion; Sutton
Wood 74, 1961, FEC.
Wolds Little Wood, near North Newbald 93, 1962, FEC.
Hold. Birkhill Wood 03, 1901 (R. 1902) and 1963, FEC;

146

Bentley Moor Wood 03, 1967, FEC; West Belt Plantation, Kilnwick 94, 1984, DMcCo.

L. sylvatica (Huds.) Gaudin [*L. maxima* (Reichard) DC.]
Great Wood-rush.   1900.
Native.   Woods.   Probably rare now.
U.D. Kirkham Hall woods 76, 1958, RG & FEC.
L.D. Houghton Woods 83, 1949, RL; Langwith Common 64, 1956, FEC; Allerthorpe Common 74, 1957, GAN; North Cliffe Wood 83, 1957, DJB.
Hold. Birkhill Wood 03, much more abundant than *L. pilosa* (R. 1902), one plant only seen in 1956, RG.

L. luzuloides (Lam.) Dandy & Wilmott [*L. albida* (Hoffm.) DC.]
White Wood-rush.
Alien.
Houghton Woods 83, 1953, RG.

L. campestris (L.) DC.   Map 427.
Field Wood-rush.
Native. Grassy places, including lawns. Widely distributed and particularly frequent on the Wolds and in the R. Hull valley.

L. multiflora (Retz.) Lejeune (*L. erecta* Desv.) Map 428.
Heath Wood-rush.
Native. Heaths, moorlands, woods; chiefly on acid soils. Both var. *congesta* and the typical form occur. Frequent in Lower Derwentland.
Infrequent elsewhere including:
U.D. Flixton Carrs 07, 1958, FEC.
Hold. Gilly Woods and Bentley Moor Wood 03, 1967, FEC; Alexandra Dock, Hull 12, 1979, FEC; on disused railway, near Great Hatfield 14, 1980, FEC.

AMARYLLIDACEAE

Allium L.
A. scorodoprasum L.
Sand Leek.   1840.
Native. Grassland and scrub on dry soils; by drains and rivers; open woodland. Uncommon.
Records include:
U.D. Near Firby 76, 1981, DRG.
L.D. Heslington Fields and at Fulford 64 (Baines, 1840); Barlby 63, WNC (R. 1902); Skipwith Common 63, 1952, IG; Brough Haven 92, 1955, RG; river bank, Turnham Hall near Hemingborough 63, 1956, RG; by drain near Sutton Wood 74, 1958, FEC; near Breighton 73, 1976, EC; Hemingborough 62, 1981, DRG.
Wolds Boynton 16 (Flintoff, 1931) and 1956, RG; south of Burdale station 86, 1956, RG; Eastdale 93, 1966, FEC; Grindale Wood 17, 1970, MC; Hessle 02, 1985, EHW.
Hold. Near Stoneferry, 1897, CW (R. 1902); Hampston Hall, near Thearne 03, 1957, RG; Haworth Hall 03, 1973, JA.

A. vineale L.
Wild Onion, Crow Garlic.   CE.   1840.
Native. Grassy places. Said to be frequent formerly (R.

1902); uncommon now.
L.D. Fulford and Heslington Ings 64 (Baines, 1840); Barlby 63, WNC (R. 1902); by R. Ouse, below Cawood 53, 1941, YNU Excursion; near Breighton 73, 1982, JD.
Wolds Hessle 02, 1966, RTh; Thwing 07, 1966, EC.
Hold. Banks of R. Hull, Weel 03, Stoneferry 13, CW (R. 1902); Salt End Common 12, 1905 (Trans. HSFNC, *3*, 218); Figham Common 03 (Nat. 1920, 391); Kilnsea 41, 1954, RG; Humber bank near Welwick 31, 1959, FEC, still present and in great quantity at the nearby Haverfield pits, 1983, FEC; near Carnaby 16, 1970, MC.

A. oleraceum L.
Field Garlic.   1840.
Native.   Dry grassy places.   Rare.
L.D. Fulford Ings 64 (Baines, 1840); Heslington Fields 64, *c.*1845, OAM; Barlby 63, WNC (R. 1902).
Wolds South Cave 93 (R. 1902); near West Lutton 96, 1960, YNU Excursion.
Hold. Banks of R. Hull, near Sutton Road Bridge, Hull 03, 1956, ESt.

A. ursinum L.   Map 59.
Ramsons.
Native. Damp woods and shady places, especially on basic soils. Frequent, mainly on the Wolds where it may be the dominant plant of a woodland ground-flora. Uncommon in Holderness, rare in Lower Derwentland.

Galanthus L.
G. nivalis L.
Snowdrop.   1840.
Naturalised alien. Woods, copses; more rarely in hedge banks. Infrequent, but in quantity in some woods and copses as at Great Givendale 85 and Winestead 22.

Narcissus L.
N. pseudonarcissus L.
Wild Daffodil.   1840.
Native and introduced. Damp woods and grass verges. Rare.
U.D. Near R. Derwent at Kirkham 76 (Baines, 1840).
L.D. Near R. Derwent at Elvington 74 (Baines, 1840); Wressle 73, WNC and Hotham Woods 83 (R. 1902). The native plant still occurs in Sutton Wood 74, FEC; in Sutton Rush Wood 74, 1984, DMcCo; also on roadsides in the Elvington area 74, 1962, FEC.
Wolds Boynton Woods and the valley of the Gypsey Race, near Bridlington 16, 1898 (R. 1902).

IRIDACEAE

Iris L.
I. foetidissima L.
Stinking Iris.   OSE.
Introduced.   Rare.
Wolds Plantation, Danes Dyke 26, 1955, RG; wood at foot of Ganton Brow 97, 1956, RG.
Hold. Beverley 03 (R. 1902); Spurn Point 41, 1978, BS.

I. pseudacorus L.   Map 128.
Yellow Iris.
Native. Marshes, swampy woods, at edges of rivers; by canals, lakes and ponds; by and in dykes. Widely distributed and locally common in the R. Hull valley, forming extensive beds by the river; also frequent along the western escarpment of the Wolds.

I. germanica L.
Flag Iris.
Escape of cultivation.
Wheldrake Wood 64, 1965, YNU Excursion; the only record.

Crocus L.
C. vernus (L.) Hill (*C. purpureus* Weston)
Spring Crocus.   1861.
Introduced.
Formerly naturalised in meadows near Beverley 03; specimens in herb. WAS, collected, 1861, 'H.H.' (SYF) and 1898 (R. 1902); reported as still there in the late 1930s, pers. comm. to FEC, 1979. J.J. Marshall recorded that, according to tradition, the species had formerly been cultivated near Beverley to produce saffron, the climate being unsuitable for the cultivation of *Crocus sativus* (Marshall, 1892). Extinct.

Tritonia Ker-Gawler
T. x *crocosmiflora* (Lemoine) Nicholson [*Crocosmia* x *crocosmiflora* (Lemoine) N.E. Br.]
Montbretia.
Established introduction.   Rare.
Wolds Near Filey 17, 1955, RG; Staxton 07, 1958, MMN.
Hold. Gravel pit, near Brandesburton 14, 1981, FEC.

DIOSCOREACEAE

Tamus L.
T. communis L.   Map 91.
Black Bryony.   CSE.
Native. Chiefly in hedges, also in wood margins. On moist well-drained fertile soils. Frequent in Holderness and on the southern part of the Wolds; scattered elsewhere.

ORCHIDACEAE

Cephalanthera Rich.
C. damasonium (Mill.) Druce (*C. grandiflora* Gray)
White Helleborine.   CSE.
Native. Under Beech on calcareous soils.   Rare.
Long Plantation, near Brough 92, 1920, Miss Burnett and Mrs Bisat (Nat. 1922, 22); Melton Wood 92, 1952, DAW, herb. HLU. These two records may refer to the same locality.

Epipactis Sw.
E. palustris (L.) Crantz
Marsh Helleborine.   CE.   1840.
Native.   Fens.   Rare now.
U.D. Wintringham 87, 1964, FEC; Flixton Carrs 07, 1971,

MC & FEC.   Both habitats destroyed.
L.D. Heslington Fields 64 (Baines, 1840).
Wolds Woo Dale bottom 93, 1892, MO (R. 1902); cliffs, Hunmanby 17, 1955, RG.
Hold. By the R. Hull, near Driffield 05, 1897, CW (R. 1902) and 1967, MC and still there; near King's Mill, Driffield 05, 1898, JTH and at Pulfin 04, 1900 (R. 1902); Kelleythorpe 05, 1950, RL & 1957, FEC.

E. helleborine (L.) Crantz [*E. latifolia* (L.) All., including *E. media*]
Broad-leaved Helleborine.   1882.
Native.   Woods and plantations.   Uncommon.
Said to be formerly common on the chalk as well as on the glacial drift of Holderness (R. 1902).
Post-1950 records:
L.D. Skipwith Common 63, 1953, IG & 1985, TFM; Allerthorpe Common 74, 1956, RG, still there; Kexby 75, 1967, JR & MC.
Hold. Burstwick 22, 1953, AW; Grimston 23, 1954, IG; Leman's Wood 94, 1956, FEC; Long Lane, Beverley 03, 1960, FEC; near Bentley 03, 1967, FEC; Risby 03, 1970, DWS; Weldon's Plantation 32, 1981, WH.

E. dunensis (T. & T.A. Stephenson) Godfery
Dune Helleborine.
Native.   Rare.
By a stream, Skipwith Common 63, 1985, TFM, det. Dr A.J. Richards.

E. phyllanthes G.E. Sm. var. *vectensis* Young
[*E. vectensis* (T. & T.A. Steph.) Brooke & Rose]
Green-flowered Helleborine.
Native.   Beech copses with Ivy-dominated ground flora. Rare.
Near South Cave 93, 1953, IG, det. Dr D.P. Young (Young, 1955). Found in a second locality near South Cave, 1977, JA.

Spiranthes Rich.
S. spiralis (L.) Chevall.
Autumn Lady's-tresses.   CSE.   2nd half 18th century.
Native.   Short grassland on calcareous soils.   Rare.
Wolds Some 150 plants on hillside, Cotton Dale 07, 1967, A. Newton & FEC, habitat destroyed, 1968. Two small colonies still occur in ten km square 07.
Hold. Formerly near cliff at Atwick 15, 2nd half 18th century, WW.

Listera R.Br.
L. ovata (L.) R.Br.   Map 429.
Common Twayblade.
Native. Moist woods and grassy places on base-rich soils. Frequent on the Wolds, but only rarely on grazed grassland and always on north or north-west facing slopes. Locally frequent in Lower and Middle Derwentland.
Uncommon elsewhere and particularly rare in Holderness east of the R. Hull valley: uncultivated bank, outer edge of 1850 enclosure on Sunk Island 21 (Petch, 1905); near Hornsea Mere 14, 1979, FEC; Weldon's Plantation 32, 1981, FEC; near Withernwick 23, 1984, FEC.

L. cordata (L.) R.Br.
Lesser Twayblade.   1834.
Native.   Peaty moors.
One locality only: 'in the greatest abundance, in a fir
plantation four miles east of York ..', 1834 (Baines, 1840);
in a fir-wood, near Langwith, S. Thompson and still there,
1875, H.R. Mosier (R. 1902). Extinct.

Neottia Ludw.
N. nidus-avis (L.) Rich.
Bird's-nest Orchid.
Native.   Woods especially of Beech, particularly on
humus-rich calcareous soils. Rare; no recent records.
U.D. Near Kirkham Abbey 76, MBS (R. 1902).
Wolds Undated records for Thorpe Hall grounds 16 and
Sledmere 96 (SYF).

Goodyera R.Br.
G. repens (L.) R.Br.
Creeping Lady's-tresses.   1841.
Native.   Pine woods.
One locality only: Houghton Woods 83, first collected,
1841, H.H. (? H. Hewetson), herb. WAS; still there 1888,
JJM (R. 1902) and herb. W. Reeves, Woodend Museum,
Scarborough. Extinct.

Coeloglossum Hartm.
C. viride (L.) Hartm. [*Habenaria viridis* (L.) R.Br.]
                                                    Map 430.
Frog Orchid.   CNE.   1727.
Native. Pasture and grassland, especially on calcareous
soils, rarely on woodland rides. Formerly said to be
'common especially on clay', although four localities only
were specified (R. 1902). First record: above Kilnwick
Percy Hall 84, 1727, TK. Several records for the first half
of this century. Uncommon now and probably only on the
Wolds.
Post-1950 records:
Wolds Primrose valley 17, 1955, RG; on rides, Low
Wood, Tibthorpe 95, 1956, FEC; near Cowlam 96, 1960,
FEC; Cotton Dale 07, 1964, FEC, habitat destroyed;
Thixendale 86, 1966, FEC; Lang Dale 07, 1969, MC;
Horse Dale 85, Goodmanham Dale 94 and Warren Dale 96,
1982, NCC; near Foxholes 97, 1985, YNU Excursion.
Hold. Between Bentley and Beverley 03, 1952, Miss
Sisley.

Gymnadenia R.Br.
G. conopsea (L.) R.Br. [*Habenaria conopsea* (L.) Benth.]
Fragrant Orchid.   1840.

Subsp. *conopsea*
Native. Chalk grassland, chalk pits, fens. Infrequent and
now mainly in the northern part of the Wolds as near West
Heslerton and Fordon, near Flamborough and on the coast
between Bempton and Filey. Lost from most localities
away from the Wolds.
L.D. Heslington Fields 64 (R. 1902) and Fulford Ings 64,
1877, WWh (R. 1902) and 1928, HB; Allerthorpe Common 74, 1927, YNU Excursion.
Wolds Arras 94 and North Newbald 93, JJM (Trans.
HSFNC, 1909, *4*, 105); Kipling Cotes 84, 1958, PG;

Ruston Parva 06, 1967, JR & MC.
Hold. Kelleythorpe 05, 1950, RL; gravel pit, Burstwick
22, 1955, FEC.

Subsp. *densiflora* (Wahlenb.) G. Camus, Bergon & A.
Camus
Fen marsh.
Jeffrey Bog 76, 1958, RG; Wintringham 87, 1967, TFM;
on cliffs, near Filey 18, 1984, DJT.

Platanthera Rich.
P. chlorantha (Custer) Reichb. (*Habenaria chloroleuca*
Ridl.)
Greater Butterfly-orchid.
Native.   Woods on calcareous soils.   Rare.
U.D. Damp places in Howsham Wood 76, MBS (R. 1902).
Wolds Near Tibthorpe 95, 1956, FEC and still there;
recorded in 1906 erroneously as *P. bifolia*; near Millington
85, 1974, EC; one plant near Butterwick 97, 1985, PG.

P. bifolia (L.) Rich. [*Habenaria bifolia* (L.) R.Br.]
Lesser Butterfly-orchid.   1836.
Native. It seems from the localities that the species mainly
occurred in bogs and marshes on acid soils, but it can occur
in woods on chalk. Rare.
L.D. Langwith 64, 1836, HPa; Skipwith Common 63,
WNC (R. 1902) and one plant, 1976, EB; Houghton Woods
83, 1909 (Trans. HSFNC *4*, 106).
Wolds Brantingham Dale 93 (R. 1902).
Hold. Birkhill Wood 03, GN & EAP (R. 1902).

Ophrys L.
O. apifera Huds.   Map 18.
Bee Orchid.   CSE.   1789.
Native. Chalk grassland, chalk quarries and cuttings; fixed
dunes and other calcareous soils. Infrequent.
On chalk grassland, particularly in the South Cave and
Brantingham 93 areas and formerly frequent there, but lost
from some localities by use of fertilisers and other changes
in agricultural practice. Also in grassland on roadside verge
between Bridlington and Grindale 16, 1970, MC and on
Flamborough Headland 26, 1984, SMA. Most records for
the northern part of the Wolds are for bare chalk, where
competition is at a minimum.
Other records:
Wolds On the cliffs, near Filey 18, 1984, DJT.
Hold. Kelsey Hill gravel pits 22, CW (R. 1902), still there
to 1950, FEC; on fixed dunes Kilnsea Warren (R. 1902),
one plant, 1950, FEC, not seen since; on Alexandra Dock,
Hull 12, 1983, FEC and Queen Elizabeth Dock, Hull 12,
1983, ABu.

O. insectifera L.
Fly Orchid.   CE.
Native.   Chalk grassland.   Extinct.
Wolds 'About Hessle' 02 (Baines, 1840), but identifica-
tion questioned (R. 1902); at Rudston 06, 1910, C.A.
Cheetham (SYF).

149

Orchis L.

O. simia Lam.
Monkey Orchid.   CSE.
Native.   Calcareous grassland.   One locality.
One plant was found in v.c. 61 by Mrs A. Fritchley in 1974, this being the first time the species had been recorded in the British Isles north of the R. Thames valley and was one of four British colonies known at the time (Crackles, 1975a). The plant was artificially pollinated in 1975 and other plants subsequently. 25 plants occurred in 1981 and nine flowering spikes; 14 plants having flowered at some time. No flowering spikes were produced in 1982 and no plants seen since. Details of the locality are withheld for conservation reasons.

O. ustulata L.
Burnt Orchid.   CE.   1836.
Native.   Chalk grassland.   Very rare now.
Said to be formerly frequent 'in meadows and pastures', seven localities being specified (R. 1902).
All records are given below:
U.D. Kennythorpe 76, MBS (R. 1902).
L.D. Fulford Ings 64, 1836, HPa; Brough 92, 1901 and Barlby 63, WNC (R. 1902); near Barmby Moor 74, 1931, GAN.
Wolds Brantingham Dale 93, 1850, GN and Arras 94, JJM (R. 1902); c.30 plants, Cotton Dale 07, BM & EC, 1964, habitat destroyed 1968; four plants, Fordon 07, 1965, FEC; four plants near Hunmanby 17, 1973, MC.
Hold. Hornsea Mere 14, 1898 (R. 1902).

O. morio L.   Map 431.
Green-winged Orchid.
Native. Meadows and pastures, especially on calcareous soils; chalk grassland, cliff tops, fixed dunes. Said to be formerly 'very common in Holderness and Derwentland' (R. 1902). Uncommon now and mainly on the northern part of the Wolds. Diminishing due to the ploughing of permanent grassland.
Post-1960 records include:
L.D. Newton Maske 74, 1979, SP.
Wolds Cowlam valley 96, 1960, FEC, habitats destroyed; Risby 03, 1964, FEC; Fordon 07, 1965, FEC; Cottondale 07, 1965, EC & FEC, habitat destroyed, 1968; near Nafferton 05, 1968, MC; Lang Dale 07, 1969, MC; cliff top, near Wandale 27, 1970, MC; Thorpe Hall 16, 1971, Hull Nats. Excursion; Warrendale 96, 1974, MC; Muston 07, 1983, PW.
Hold. Between Bentley and Beverley 03, 1952, DAW; Fitling 23, 1954, FEC; Spurn 41, 1964, FEC; between Beeford and Brandesburton 15, 1967, AWa.

O. mascula (L.) L.   Map 432.
Early-purple Orchid.
Native. Woods and plantations; grassland, including roadside verges, chiefly on base-rich soils. Said to be formerly 'very common in copses and woods' (R. 1902). Now somewhat infrequent.
Rarely in abundance as in woods near Welton 92, 1980 and Bishop Burton 04, 1985, EHW. On roadside verge, south of Burton Agnes 16, 1980, FEC and occasionally in the open on chalk hillsides e.g. at Fordon 07, 1965, FEC and on

an old earthwork on Fordon Bank 07, 1966, FEC.

Dactylorhiza Nevski

D. fuchsii (Druce) Soó   Map 433.
Common Spotted-orchid.
Native. Base-rich fens, marshes, damp meadows, grassy slopes on base-rich soils, chalk pits; also on wood rides and at wood borders; on railway banks. Frequent.

D. fuchsii x **D. maculata = D.** x **transiens** (Druce) Soó
Several records for scattered localities, sometimes in the absence of *D. maculata*.
Recent records include:
U.D. Sand pit, Staxton 07, 1969, FEC.
L.D. Tollingham 83, 1972, FEC.
Wolds Risby 03, 1963, FEC; near Birdsall 86, 1972, FEC; near Tibthorpe 95, 1981, EHW.
Hold. Near Wansford 05, 1985, EHW.

D. fuchsii x **D. incarnata = D.** x **kernerorum** (Soó) Soó
Often found where the parental species grow together.
Recent records include:
L.D. Allerthorpe Common 74, 1962, FEC.
Hold. Marsh by R. Hull, near Wansford 05, 1960, YNU Excursion and later; Kelleythorpe 05, 1968, FEC; Tophill Low 04, 1969, DRG; airfield, Carnaby 16, 1970, FEC; Hornsea Mere 14, 1972, FEC.

D. fuchsii x **D. praetermissa = D.** x **grandis** (Druce) P.F. Hunt
L.D. Broomfleet 82, 1948, RL; garden weed, Ellerker 92, 1973, FEC.
Wolds North Newbald 93, 1938, AKW & 1963, FEC, conf. V. Summerhayes (VS).
Hold. Near Scorborough 04, 1970, FEC.

D. fuchsii x **D. purpurella = D.** x **venusta** (T. & T.A. Steph.) Soó
Wolds Speeton 17, 1977, DJT.
Hold. Airfield, Carnaby 16, 1970, FEC, conf. VS; Alexandra Dock, Hull, 12, 1979, FEC, conf. P.F. Hunt (PFH). A large population of marsh orchids on Queen Elizabeth Dock, Hull, 12 is believed to be mainly this hybrid, 1982, FEC. The *D. purpurella* parent in the last two localities is form B (Steph.).

D. maculata (L.) Soó   Map 434.
Heath Spotted-orchid.
Native. On moist acid soils. Uncommon, but localities widely scattered.
On damp sandy heathland in Lower Derwentland as at Skipwith Common 63, Langwith Common 64 and Allerthorpe Common 74.
Other recent records are:
U.D. Sand pit, Staxton 07, 1969, FEC.
Wolds Near Birdsall 86, 1972, FEC; Buckton 17, 1972, FEC.
Hold. Risby 03, 1956, FEC; airfield, Carnaby 16, 1969, FEC.

D. maculata x *D. purpurella* = *D.* x *formosa* (T. & T.A. Steph.) Soó
Buckton 17, 1980, FEC.

D. incarnata (L.) Soó (*Orchis incarnata* L.)   Map 181.
Early Marsh-orchid.
Native.   Wet meadows and marshes, in fen peat.

Subsp. *incarnata*
Generally infrequent; most localities in the upper part of the R. Hull valley; also by Hornsea Mere.
Other recent records include:
L.D. Near Broomfleet House 82, 1958, FEC; Allerthorpe Common 74, 1962, FEC; near Thornton 74, 1969, FEC.
Wolds North Newbald 93, 1961, FEC, still present; Thwing Mere 07, 1966, EC; near Great Givendale 85, 1967, FEC; near Nunburnholme 84, 1975, EHW.
Hold. Risby 03, 1956, FEC; airfield Carnaby 16, 1970, MC.

Subsp. *pulchella* (Druce) H-Harrison f.
Fen-marshes.   Rare.
With subsp. *incarnata* near Wansford 05 and flowering two weeks later; also at Kelleythorpe 05, 1968, FEC; airfield, Carnaby 16, 1970, FEC.

D. incarnata x *D. maculata* = *D.* x *claudiopolitana* (Soó) Soó
Allerthorpe Common 74, 1962, FEC.

D. incarnata x *D. praetermissa* = *D.* x *wintoni* (A. Camus) P.F. Hunt
Tophill Low 04, 1978, FEC.

D. praetermissa (Druce) Soó   Map 435.
Southern Marsh-orchid.   OWEE.
Native. On marshes and in wet meadows, usually on base-rich soils. Only in the southern part of the vice-county; uncommon and decreasing.
Recent records include:
L.D. Broomfleet delphs 82, 1958, FEC; Ellerker 92, 1964, GDe; Aughton Ings 73, 1966, HOB; near East Cottingwith 64, 1980, NCC; North Cave 83, 1985, EHW.
Wolds North Newbald 93, 1935, AKW, still present; Brantingham 93, 1977, JA; Swindale 93, 1973, FEC.
Hold. Kelleythorpe 05, 1951, RG; Kelsey Hill gravel pits 22, 1962, FEC, habitat since destroyed; near Scorborough 04, 1970, MC & FEC; in brackish marshes, near Humber bank, near Easington 31, 1984, FEC.
Individuals with heavily ringed spotted leaves in populations of *D. praetermissa* were the basis of *Orchis pardalina* Pugsl. Such individuals occur at North Newbald, but have not been recorded elsewhere.

D. purpurella (T. & T.A. Steph.) Soó   Map 436.
Northern Marsh-orchid.
Native. Marshes, fens and damp pastures, especially on base-rich soils. At the southern edge of its range in v.c. 61. Uncommon.
The typical form (Steph. form A) is locally frequent on the Flamborough Headland.

It is rare elsewhere:
L.D. Skipwith Common 63, 1942, WAS; near Snake Hall 83, 1962, F. Bower, det. VS.
Wolds Newbald Springs 93, 1961, FEC.
Hold. Carnaby airfield 16, 1969, MC.
Form B, Steph. also occurs; it is a taller plant and the flowers have a wider, rounded, shallowly trilobed labellum.
Wolds Chalk quarry, near Flamborough 17, 1960, and subsequently, FEC, det. VS; Beacon Hill, Flamborough Head 26, 1970, MC.
Hold. Airfield, Carnaby 16, 1969, MC; Alexandra Dock, Hull 12, 1979, FEC, conf. PFH, still present; cliff top, Aldborough 24, 1979, FEC; in abundance, Victoria Dock, Hull 12, 1985, MG & FEC.

D. majalis (Reichb.) P.F. Hunt & Summerhayes subsp. *cambrensis* (R.H. Robert) R.H. Roberts.
Native.
Marsh by R. Hull near Driffield 05, 1963, F.E. Crackles, det. from photographs by R.H. Roberts, 1981; the first record for England (Crackles, 1986a).

Anacamptis Rich.
A. pyramidalis (L.) Rich. (*Orchis pyramidalis* L.)
                                          Map 2.
Pyramidal Orchid.   CSE.
Native. Grassland on chalk or limestone; railway banks, chalk quarries, fixed dunes. Fairly frequent in the chalk grassland belt of the Wolds and on high land between Driffield and Bridlington.
Cliff top between Speeton and Bempton 17. In quantity on Spurn Point 41, 1956, FEC, still persisting.

ARACEAE

Acorus L.
A. calamus L.
Sweet-flag.   1798.
Introduced. In shallow water at margins of ponds, in a stream. Uncommon.
U.D. Near Kirkham Abbey 76, MBS (R. 1902).
L.D. Skipwith Common 63, 1985, EC; near Howden 72, 1986, RHu.
Hold. By old ponds, Risby 03 (Teesdale, 1800); still at Risby where it flowers sparingly; Meaux 04, 1909 (Trans. HSFNC *4*, 171); old pits near railway, Kelsey Hill 22, 1955, FEC; Benningholme 13, 1987, RM.

Arum L.
A. maculatum L.   Map 61.
Lords-and-Ladies.   CSE.
Native. Woods and hedgerows; in some churchyards. Locally frequent on the Wolds, mainly south of Tibthorpe. Fairly frequent in Holderness; scattered in Lower Derwentland.

LEMNACEAE

Lemna L.

L. polyrhiza L.
Greater Duckweed. 1840.
Native. Still waters of ponds and ditches. Uncommon.
L.D. Near Selby 63, WNC (R. 1902); near Boothferry
Bridge 72, 1956, RG; Newsholme Park 72, 1956, RG;
Land of Nod 83, 1974, EC.
Hold. Near Beverley 03 (Baines, 1840); old fish ponds,
Swine 13, JWB; Hornsea, CW (R. 1902).

L. trisulca L. Map 103.
Ivy-leaved Duckweed. 1840.
Native. Ponds, a lake, a gravel pit, canals, rivers and drains.
Somewhat infrequent except locally in the R. Derwent
valley; surprisingly rare in some areas.

L. minor L. Map 102.
Common Duckweed.
Native. Ponds, lakes, water-filled gravel pits, dykes.
Frequent.

L. gibba L.
Fat Duckweed. 1798.
Native. Lakes, a canal, a river, dykes. Uncommon, but
sometimes in abundance.
L.D. Houghton Lake 83, 1952, DAW; Pocklington Canal
at lock near Thornton 74, 1955, RG and near Melbourne 74,
1968, FEC.
Wolds Buckton 17, 1973, MC; Bainton 95, 1980, EBM.
Hold. Formerly near Beverley 03 (Teesdale, 1800); near
Hull, Meaux Abbey 03, Hornsea Mere 14 and Preston 12
(R. 1902); Keyingham drain 22, 1954, FEC; R. Hull near
Hempholme Lock 04, 1967, FEC; Swine Moor 04, 1969,
MC; near R. Humber bank, Welwick 31, 1979, FEC.

SPARGANIACEAE

Sparganium L.

S. erectum L. subsp. **erectum** (*S. ramosum* Huds.)
Map 133.
Branched Bur-reed.
Native. On mud or in shallow water in ponds, lakes, ditches
and slow-flowing rivers. Locally common in the upper
reaches of the R. Hull valley and in the R. Derwent valley
and fairly frequent elsewhere.

S. emersum Rehm. (*S. simplex* Huds.) Map 117.
Unbranched Bur-reed.
Native. Rivers, lakes, ponds, dykes and a canal; absent
from acid waters. Locally frequent. Mainly in the R. Hull
valley.
Uncommon elsewhere:
L.D. Near Breighton 73, 1958, FEC; near Melbourne 74,
1958, FEC; Howden Common 73, 1970, FEC; Hasholme
Carr Farm 83, 1980, FEC; near Dunnington 65, 1983,
CSVY.
Hold. Near Ellerby 14, 1951, RG; Fraisthorpe 16, 1955,
RG.

S. minimum Wallr.
Least Bur-reed.
Native. Ditches, Swine Moor, Beverley 14 (Teesdale,
1800). Extinct.

TYPHACEAE

Typha L.

T. latifolia L. Map 134.
Bulrush.
Native. Reedswamps; often locally dominant in lakes,
ponds, canals and slow-flowing rivers. Frequent in Lower
Derwentland and locally in Holderness; also occurs here
and there in Upper Derwentland and on the Wolds in the
Settrington area.
Rare elsewhere: on the Wolds at Hunmanby 17, 1973,
FEC; Flamborough Head 27, 1984, SMA.

T. angustifolia L.
Lesser Bulrush. 1798.
Native. Reedswamps on more or less organic soils at the
edges of lakes, ponds, canals and slow-flowing rivers.
Uncommon.
L.D. Old marl pits between York and Market Weighton
(Teesdale, 1800); Houghton Moor 83 (R. 1902); Eastrington 72, 1956, RG; pit, Holme upon Spalding Moor 83,
1962, FEC; near Saltmarshe 72, 1968, FEC; near Fulford
64, 1980, EB.
Hold. Kelsey Hill gravel pits 22 (R. 1902) and 1955, YNU
Excursion; Hornsea Mere 14, 1897, CW (R. 1902), still
there; Paull Holme 12, 1948, RG; Roos Bog 22, 1949, RL;
gravel pit, Burstwick 22, 1953, FEC; gravel pit, Brandesburton 04, 1969, FEC; Thorpe Hall 16, 1969, FEC.

CYPERACEAE

Eriophorum L.

E. angustifolium Honck. Map 184.
Common Cottongrass. CNE.
Native. Wet bogs and acid fens. Infrequent.
Most records for Lower Derwentland; it also occurs in the
upper part of the R. Hull valley, on the Flamborough
Headland and near the coast of Filey Bay.
Uncommon elsewhere including:
U.D. Wintringham 87, 1968, FEC; near Ganton 97, 1971,
MC.
Wolds Near Acklam 76, 1972, FEC.
Hold. Kelsey Hill 22, 1950, FEC; gravel pit, near Bran-
desburton 14, 1981, FEC.

E. latifolium Hoppe
Broad-leaved Cottongrass. CNE.
Native. Wet places on base-rich soils.
Wolds Weedley Springs 93 (R. 1902); Filey undercliff,
JFR (N.H. Scarb.). Extinct.

E. vaginatum L.
Hare's-tail Cottongrass. CNE. 1840.
Native. Damp peaty places. Uncommon.
L.D. Skipwith Common 63, WNC and other places in
Derwentland (R. 1902), still at Skipwith, 1970, FEC;

Snake Hall 83, 1939, AKW, herb. HLU; Allerthorpe Common 74, 1958, ABM, herb. HLU; Houghton Woods 83, 1962, FEC; South Cliffe Common 83, 1986, DJL.
Hold. Near Beverley (Baines, 1840).

Trichophorum Pers.
T. cespitosum (L.) Hartman (*Scirpus cespitosus* L.)
Deergrass.   CNE.
Native.   Damp and peaty places, heaths.   Rare.
In quantity on Skipwith Common 63 and occurring on Allerthorpe Common 74; it has long been known in both localities (R. 1902).

Scirpus L.
S. maritimus L.   Map 218.
Sea Club-rush.   1798.
Native. In shallow water in dykes and ponds near the R. Humber. Frequent. Rarely on salt-marshes.
On the foreshore as at Hessle 02 and North Ferriby 92 and by the R. Hull, north to Haworth Hall 03. On the coast at Fraisthorpe and Auburn 16, 1970, MC.
Occasionally inland:
L.D. By Market Weighton Canal, near Broomfleet 82, 1984, YNU Excursion.
Hold. Kelsey Hill gravel pits 22, 1955, FEC; Hornsea Mere 14, 1798, RT & 1978, FEC; in dykes, Sunk Island 21, 1983, FEC.

S. sylvaticus L.
Wood Club-rush.   1792.
Native.   Marshes.   Uncommon.
Near Kirkham Abbey 76 (Teesdale, 1794) and 1958, YNU Excursion; Firby Wood 76, 1910, WI; Fulford Ings 64, 1979, EB; flood meadows, near Scrayingham 75 and south of Howsham Bridge 76, 1979, NCC.

Schoenoplectus (Reich.) Palla
S. lacustris (L.) Palla (*Scirpus lacustris* L.)
Common Club-rush, Dumbles.
Native.   Rivers, a canal, lakes and ponds.   Rare now.
In quantity by Leven Canal 04; also here and there by the R. Hull as at Hempholme Lock 04, 1967, FEC and at Tophill Low 04, 1979, DRG. More frequent formerly and used for making rush seats, mattresses and mats. Several references to Dumbles occur in local archives (Crackles, 1974 & 1983c).

S. tabernaemontani (C.C. Gmel.) Palla (*Scirpus tabernaemontani* C.C. Gmel.)   Map 132.
Grey Club-rush.   1878.
Native.   Streams, ditches, ponds, lakes.   Uncommon.
L.D. Occurs locally in the Broomfleet area, ten km square 82. First records: near Brough 92, CW and near Staddlethorpe 82, 1878, WWh (R. 1902).
Wolds Pond at Hunmanby 17, 1973, MC & FEC; North Ferriby 92, 1987, FEC.
Hold. Kelsey Hill gravel pit 22, 1955, FEC; Birkhill Wood 03, 1958, AKW; by stream, Kelleythorpe 05, 1968, FEC; Brandesburton gravel pits 14, 1981, FEC; by new borrow pits by the R. Hull at Pulfin Bend 04, 1983, FEC; by Hornsea Mere 14, where it has long been known and at Rise Park 14, FEC.

Isolepis R.Br.
I. setacea (L.) R.Br. (*Scirpus setaceus* L.)   Map 437.
Bristle Club-rush.
Native. Damp places. Sometimes among taller herbage in marshy meadows, more often on bare sandy or gravelly soil; wood rides. Infrequent.
Most records for Lower Derwentland; first record: Houghton Woods 83, 1930, YNU Excursion.
Other records:
U.D. Jeffrey Bog 76, 1981, YNU Bot. Sect. Excursion.
Wolds Filey Brigg 18, 1956, RG; Megdale 85, 1957, RG; Speeton 17, 1973, FEC; Buckton 17, 1980, FEC & JES.
Hold. Near Leven Canal 04, 1952, FEC; Wansford 05, 1970, MC; disused railway track, near Sigglesthorne station 14, 1980, FEC; near Pulfin Bog 04, 1983, FEC; Boynton 16, 1986, DB.

Eleogiton Link
E. fluitans (L.) Link (*Scirpus fluitans* L.)
Floating Club-rush.   1840.
Native. Ditches and ponds, particularly those with peaty water. Said to be formerly frequent in marshy places, although Cottingham 03 and Hull were the only localities cited (R. 1902). Rare now.
U.D. Flixton Carrs 07, 1945, YNU Excursion (N.H. Scarb.).
L.D. Edge of pond, Snake Hall 83, 1953, FEC; pool, Breighton Common 73, 1958, FEC.
Hold. Dyke, near Leven Canal 04, 1969, FEC & DWS; abundant, Cross drain, Leven 04, 1970, FEC.

Eleocharis R.Br.
E. acicularis (L.) Roem. & Schult.
Needle Spike-rush.   1840.
Native. Wet muddy places, usually at margins of ponds and pools. Rare.
L.D. Near Pocklington and on Dunnington Common 65 (Baines, 1840); Skipwith Common 63, 1878, FAL, herb. A. Bennett in herb. K (Trans. HSFNC, 1907, *3*, 99); Heslington Fields 64, 1984, EB.
Wolds Near Filey 17, 1947, HR (N.H. Scarb.).
Hold. Hall Ings, Cottingham 03, 1898, CW; Coneygarth gravel pit 04, 1955, RG; gravel pit, near North Frodingham 05, 1976, MC.

E. quinqueflora (F.X. Hartmann) Schwarz (*Scirpus pauciflorus* Lightf.).
Few-flowered Spike-rush.   CNE.   1798.
Native. Damp peaty places on moors and fens. Uncommon.
L.D. Houghton Moor 83 (Teesdale, 1800); Heslington Fields c.1845, OAM.
Wolds Newbald Springs 83, 1899 (R. 1902) and 1939, AKW; Deep Dale 85, 1970, MC; Flamborough and Thornwick Bay 27, 1970, MC; Buckton and Speeton 17, 1973, MC.
Hold. Marshes near Beverley (Teesdale, 1800); Hall Ings, Cottingham 03, 1900 and Driffield 05 (R. 1902); near Wansford 05, 1961, FEC; King's Mill 05, 1969, MC.

E. multicaulis (Sm.) Sm. (*Scirpus multicaulis* Sm.)
Many-stalked Spike-rush.   CNE.   1840.
Native. In wet places, usually in acid bogs and on wet sandy heaths. All records for Lower Derwentland.
Very few records:
Houghton Moor 83 (Baines, 1840); Skipwith Common 63 (R. 1902) and 1956, FEC; Hemingborough 72, 1956, RG; near Bielby 74, 1956, RG.

E. palustris (L.) Roem. & Schult.   Map 125.
Common Spike-rush.
Native. Marshy ground; margins of ponds, lakes and water-filled gravel pits. Fairly frequent.

E. uniglumis (Link) Schult.
Slender Spike-rush.   1967.
Native. In marshes with an open vegetation. Uncommon.
L.D. Thornton 74, 1969, FEC; clay pit, Broomfleet 82, 1969, MC; Aughton Ings 73, 1972, YNU Bot. Sect. Excursion.
Hold. Near Wansford 05, 1967, FEC, conf. S.M. Walters; Elmswell 95, 1968, FEC; gravel pits, Brandesburton 14, 1969, FEC; Hornsea Mere 14, 1969, FEC, still present.

Blysmus Panz.
B. compressus (L.) Panz. ex Link (*Scirpus caricis* Retz.)
                    Map 174.
Flat-sedge.   1898.
Native. Marshy places. Infrequent.
On spring-fed marshes at the western side of the Wolds; also locally in the upper reaches of the R. Hull valley. Also:
L.D. Houghton Woods 83, 1930, WAS; near Sancton 83, 1955, RG.
Wolds Newbald Springs 93 (R. 1902) and 1968, FEC.
Hold. By Hornsea Mere 14 (R. 1902), still present.

B. rufus (Huds.) Link
Saltmarsh Flat-sedge.
Native. Seeds found in 13th century quay infill by R. Hull, Hull in archaeological excavation (Ayers, 1979).

Cyperus L.
C. longus L.
Galingale.
Established alien. By ponds and in ditches. Rare.
L.D. Fulford Ings 64, 1979, EB.
Wolds Hessle 02, 1966, EC; Hunmanby 17, 1973, MC.

Schoenus L.
S. nigricans L.
Black Bog-rush.   1901.
Native. In peaty base-rich marshy places. Rare.
U.D. Wintringham 87, 1964, YNU Excursion; plentiful Flixton Carrs 07, 1971, MC & FEC, habitat destroyed.
Wolds Woo Dale 93, Trans. YNU, 1878, 18;
Kelleythorpe 05, 1899, YNU Circular, last recorded, 1951, FEC.
Hold. Hall Ings, Cottingham 03, 1901 (R. 1902).

Cladium Browne
C. mariscus (L.) Pohl
Great Fen-sedge.
Native. In reed swamps and fens. Very rare.
Has survived in a dyke in a fox covert near Wifholme 04, 1956, RG.

Carex L.
C. distans L.
Distant Sedge.   1895.
Native. Coastal plant within the spray zone; brackish marshes. Uncommon.
Formerly at Salt End Common 12 (R. 1902) and between Kilnsea Warren and the sea 41, 1955, FEC; still present behind the R. Humber bank: by canal, Kilnsea 41 and near Easington 31 and Skeffling 31.
On the coast: edge of pond, Sand le Mere 33, 1895, CW and near Bempton 17 (R. 1902); still at Sand le Mere, 1951,

AKW & RL; near Filey 18, 1957, FEC; Thornwick Bay 17, 1958, ABM; Flamborough Head 27, 1984, SMA.

C. hostiana DC. (*C. fulva* auct.)
Tawny Sedge.   1798.
Native. Base-rich flushes and marshes. Uncommon.
U.D. Wintringham 87, 1968, FEC; Leavening 76, 1972, FEC; near Firby 76, 1981, DRG.
L.D. Heslington Fields 64, *c.*1845, OAM & 1957, FEC; Houghton Woods 83, 1930, YNU Excursion.
Wolds Newbald Springs 93, 1938, AKW & 1968, FEC; Flamborough 27, 1958, RG; near Wharram 86, 1959, FEC.
Hold. Wet pastures, Beverley (Teesdale, 1800); between R. Hull and Driffield Canal 05, 1900 (R. 1902); Kelleythorpe 05, 1950, WAS; marsh by R. Hull, near Wansford 05, 1968, still present; King's Mill 05, 1968, MC.

C. hostiana x *C. viridula* subsp. *brachyrrhyncha* = *C.* x *fulva* Gooden.
U.D. Near Leavening 76, 1972, FEC.
Hold. King's Mill 05, 1968, FEC.

C. binervis Sm.   Map 32.
Green-ribbed Sedge.   OWEE.   1945.
Native. Heaths and rough pastures; on acid sandy soils. Uncommon.
U.D. Kennythorpe 76, 1970, ATD.
L.D. Allerthorpe Common 74, 1945, JMT, still there 1963, FEC; Breighton Common 73, 1945, JMT & 1958, FEC; North Cliffe Wood 83, 1955, FEC; Langwith Common 64, 1956, FEC; Thorpe Whin 84, 1956, RG; near Bielby 74, 1957, FEC; Sutton Wood 74, 1961, FEC; between Skipwith and Thorganby 64, 1981, FEC; near High Catton 75, 1981, DEH.
Hold. Bentley Moor Wood 03, 1967, FEC.

C. viridula Michx.

Subsp. *viridula* (*C. serotina* Mérat; *C.* flava var. *oederi* Retz.)
Small-fruited Yellow-sedge.
Native. Marshy ground on sand and gravel. Rare.
Skipwith Common 63, HFP (R. 1902) and 1974, H. Proctor; Kelsey Hill gravel pits 22, 1953, FEC; Burstwick gravel pits 22, 1955, YNU Excursion; Brandesburton gravel pit 14, 1969, EC. Lost from the gravel pit sites by tipping and further excavation for gravel.

Subsp. *brachyrrhyncha* (Celak.) B. Schmid (*C. lepidocarpa* Tausch)   Map 179.
Long-stalked Yellow-sedge.
Native. Base-rich fens, subject to seasonal flooding or flushing. Infrequent, but widely scattered along the spring lines.

Subsp. *oedocarpa* (N.J. Andersson) B. Schmid (*C. demissa* Hornem.)   Map 180.
Common Yellow-sedge.
Native. Damp grassy places and marshes, usually on acid soils. Infrequent.
Mainly in Lower Derwentland and locally in the R. Hull valley as by Aike Beck 04, 1953, AKW and in marshy field, near Leven Canal 04, 1952, FEC.
Other records:
U.D. Flixton Carrs 08, 1957, FEC; near Firby 76, 1981, DRG.
Hold. Coneygarth gravel pits 14, 1955, RG; near Carnaby 16, 1970, MC.

C. viridula subsp. *oedocarpa* x *C. hostiana*
Heslington Fields 64, 1957, FEC, conf. E. Nelmes & 1984, EB.

C. extensa Good.
Long-bracted Sedge.   OSE.   1957.
Native. Coastal plant within reach of salt spray. Rare and local.
In brackish marshes near the mouth of the R. Humber. First recorded near Kilnsea Beacon 41, 1957, FEC. Turned up in quantity along the then recently cut Kilnsea Canal 41, 1963, FEC. Also behind the R. Humber bank near to Skeffling 31, 1972, FEC and Easington 31, 1973, FEC, still present.
Localities given in Robinson (1902) suggest confusion with another sedge. Teesdale (1800) questioned the identity of plants he found near Beverley, one of the records given in Robinson's Flora.

C. sylvatica Huds.   Map 66.
Wood-sedge.
Native. Woods, copses. Locally frequent, mainly on the Wolds.

C. pseudocyperus L.
Cyperus Sedge.   1798.
Native. Ponds and stagnant water, often in woods. Uncommon.
L.D. Eastrington 72 and near Howden 72, 1956, RG; brick ponds, Melbourne 74, 1959, FEC; Escrick Park 64, 1982, EC.
Wolds Near Hunmanby 17, 1972, MC.
Hold. Dumble Pit, near Beverley 04 (Teesdale, 1800); fish ponds and ditches, Meaux 14, 1914, JJM (SYF) and 1957, RG; Figham Common 03, 1920, YNU Excursion; Risby Woods 03, 1957, FEC; Rise Park 14, 1971, DWS.

C. rostrata Stokes   Map 124.
Bottle Sedge.   c.1845.
Native. Wet peaty areas with a high water level; by a canal, a river, streams and drains. Locally frequent, mainly in the R. Hull valley. Other records include:
U.D. By mill pool, Sherburn 97, 1957, FEC; Wintringham 87, 1968, FEC; Flixton Carrs 08, 1971, MC; ditches, Kennythorpe 76, 1976, LM.
L.D. Heslington Fields 64, c.1845, OAM; Bealsbeck 83, 1955, RG; near Broomfleet House 82, 1955, RG.
Wolds Flamborough Head 27, 1955, RG; by Gypsey Race, Boynton 16, 1959, FEC.
Hold. By Hornsea Mere 14, (R. 1902) and 1953, FEC, field later drained; Roos Bog 22, 1950, RL.

C. vesicaria L.   Map 141.
Bladder-sedge.   1798.
Native. Edges of streams and dykes, by ponds and a canal, in ditches, marshy ground. Locally frequent in meadows by R. Derwent; otherwise uncommon, diminishing.
L.D. Staddlethorpe 82, YNU Trans., 1878; pond, Skipwith 63, 1956, FEC; Melbourne 74, 1968, FEC.
Wolds Weedley Springs 93 (R. 1902); Filey cliff 17, 1971, FEC.
Hold. Beverley, Hull and Cottingham 03 (Teesdale, 1800); near Sand le Mere 33, CW (R. 1902); Pulfin Bog 04, 1935, RG; near Roos 22, 1947, RL; Kelleythorpe 05, 1947, RL; Leven Canal 04, 1950, FEC & 1981, NCC; Arram Carrs 04, 1953, FEC; near Hornsea Mere 14, 1953, FEC, habitat later drained; Withernwick 14, 1956, FEC; near Beverley 03, 1981, EC; near Hollym 32, 1984, FEC.

C. riparia Curt.   Map 123.
Greater Pond-sedge.
Native. Forming large stands by slow-flowing rivers and canals, in ditches and around ponds. In wet fen woods as in Low Wood, Wassand 14. Formerly much more common in Holderness dykes than now. Frequent in the R. Hull valley; infrequent in other parts of Holderness and in Derwentland.

C. acutiformis Ehrh.   Map 121.
Lesser Pond-sedge.   1840.
Native. Beside slow-flowing rivers, streams, canals, ponds, lakes and dykes and in marshes. Tolerates shade.
Locally common, particularly in the R. Hull valley and in Derwentland, sometimes forming large beds; scattered elsewhere.

C. pendula Huds.
Pendulous Sedge.   CSE.
Native and introduced. Damp shady places. Uncommon and probably usually planted.
U.D. Ganton church 97, 1971, MC.
L.D. Tilmire 64, 1980, EB; Hotham 83, 1983, EHW.
Wolds Thorpe Hall 16, 1969, FEC; South Cave Castle 93, 1977, FEC.
Hold. Formerly at Birkhill Wood 03, 1901 (R. 1902); Jenny Brough Lane 92, 1972, JG; plantation near Driffield 05, 1984, EC.

C. pallescens L.
Pale Sedge.   1910.
Native. Wood rides and clearings, more rarely in marshy meadows. Uncommon.
U.D. Kirkham 76, 1958, FEC; Howsham Wood 76, 1970, TFM; Jeffrey Bog 76, 1981, FEC.
L.D. Bubwith 73, 1937, YNU Excursion; Holme upon Spalding Moor 73, 1957, FEC; Naburn and Fulford 64, 1980, EB; flood meadows, near Ellerton 64 and East Cottingwith 64, 1980, NCC. On drift line left by winter flooding, Newton Maske 74, 1981, FEC.
Wolds Thorpe 16, 1910, FAL (SYF).
Hold. Beverley 03, JJM (SYF); Birkhill Wood 03, 1956, FEC; Lakes Wood, Leconfield 04, 1961, FEC; Bentley Moor Wood 03, 1967, FEC.

C. panicea L.   Map 178.
Carnation Sedge.   1840.
Native. Marshes on basic soils: fens, calcareous flushes; locally frequent. Also occurs on marshy places on acid soils on the commons of Lower Derwentland.

C. flacca Schreb.   Map 438.
Glaucous Sedge.
Native. Calcareous grassland, fixed dunes, fens, railway verges, rough pastures, gravel pits. Common on the Wolds, otherwise widespread and locally frequent.

C. hirta L.   Map 439.
Hairy Sedge.
Native. Damp grassland on various soils. Frequent.

C. lasiocarpa Ehrh. (*C. filiformis* auct.)
Slender Sedge.   CNE.   1798.
Native. Marshes, particularly fens. Probably extinct.
L.D. East fringe of Skipwith Common 63, BEC, 1879, 74.
Hold. In marshes, about Beverley 03, very common (Teesdale, 1800); Kelleythorpe marsh 05, 1949, AKW & RL, where it rarely fruited.

C. pilulifera L.　　　　　　　　　　　Map 33.
Pill Sedge.
Native. Grassy or heathy places on sandy or peaty soils.
Very infrequent; mainly in Lower Derwentland including:
Allerthorpe Common 74, 1958, FEC, still present; Langwith
Common 64, 1964, FEC; Skipwith Common 63, 1970,
YNU Excursion; Sutton Wood 74, 1973, YNU Excursion;
Houghton Wood 83, 1986, FEC.
Other records:
U.D. Kirkham 76, 1968, YNU Excursion; Kennythorpe
76, 1958, FEC & 1970, ATD.
Hold. Bygot Wood 04, 1971, FEC; Alexandra Dock, Hull
12, 1979, FEC.

C. caryophyllea Latourr. (*C. verna* Chaix)　　Map 9.
Spring-sedge.　　　　　　　　　　　　　　1901.
Native. Dry calcareous grassland, fixed sand dunes. Locally
frequent on the Wolds.
Uncommon elsewhere:
L.D. Cockle Pits, Brough 92, 1951, FEC.
Hold. Gravelly fields, near Cottingham 03 (R. 1902);
Spurn Point 41, 1975, FEC; near Thearne 03, 1975, JA.

C. elata All. (*C. stricta* Good.)　　　　Map 122.
Tufted-sedge.　　　　　　　　　　　　　*c.*1845.
Native. By fen ditches, streams, rivers and a lake, where
there is at least seasonal flooding. Uncommon.
Locally frequent in the R. Hull valley, as by the trout stream
at Sunderlandwick. Formerly common by Leven Canal 04,
1950; became rare after the canal was dredged and the edge
cut away in 1965. Some very old plants at Pulfin Bog 04
and in Boat House Wood, Hornsea Mere 14, 1978, FEC.
Other scattered localities:
L.D. Heslington Fields 64, *c.*1845, OAM; Market Weighton
Canal, near Land of Nod 83, 1954, FEC; North Cliffe
Wood 83, 1954, FEC; near Thornton 74, 1965, FEC;
Ellerton Common 73, 1970, DWS.
Wolds Kipling Cotes 84, 1953, FEC.

C. acuta L.　　　　　　　　　　　　Map 120.
Slender Tufted-sedge.　　　　　　　　　1798.
Native. Sides of rivers, streams, lakes, ponds and dykes and
in marshy places; where there is a more or less constantly
high water level. First record: Beverley 1798, RT. Locally
frequent in the R. Hull valley as by the river at Pulfin Bend
04 and in the R. Derwent valley.
Uncommon elsewhere:
U.D. Wintringham 87, 1968, FEC.
L.D. By Pocklington Canal, near Sandhill Lock 74, 1964,
FEC; near Thornton 74, 1968, FEC.
Hold. Gravel pit, Kelsey Hill 22, 1955, FEC; Lambwath
stream, Withernwick 14, 1956, FEC; beds by Hornsea
Mere 14, 1978, FEC.

C. acuta x *C. acutiformis* = *C.* x *subgracilis* Druce
Bank of R. Hull, near Hallytreeholme 04, 1955, FEC, conf.
A.O. Chater (AOC), A.C. Jermy (ACJ) and R.W. David
(RWD), 1982, herb. FEC & herb. K (Crackles, 1984).

C. nigra (L.) Reichard (*C. goodenowii* Gay)　Map 177.
Common Sedge.
Native. Marshy ground, on both acid and basic soils.
Locally frequent in Derwentland; also occurring along the
spring lines, particularly at the west of the Wolds; infre-
quent in Holderness.

C. paniculata L.　　　　　　　　　　Map 140.
Greater Tussock-sedge.　　　　　　　　1840.
Native. In peaty places on base-rich soils, where water
levels are at least seasonally high; in fens. Tolerant of some
shade. First record: near Beverley 03 (Baines, 1840).
Locally frequent in the R. Hull valley, particularly by the
West Beck and its feeder streams.
Uncommon elsewhere:
U.D. Two plants at Burythorpe 76, 1958, FEC and one at
Firby 76, 1981, FEC.
L.D. Two large tufts by the Market Weighton Canal 82,
1984, DRG; Thornton Ings 74, 1988, NCC.
Hold. Hunmanby 17, 1973, MC.

C. appropinquata Schumach. (*C. paradoxa* Willd.)
Fibrous Tussock-sedge.　　　　CNE.　　　1843.
Native. Fens. Rare.
L.D. Heslington Fields 64, 1843, RS & 1856, OAM;
Langwith Common 64 (R. 1902).
Wolds Flamborough Headland 27, 1912 (Nat. 1914, 33).
Hold. Pulfin Bog 04, 1896 (R. 1902), still there 1968,
RWD; Leven Canal 04, 1904 (Trans. HSFNC *3*, 184) and
14, 1953, FEC. The record for boggy ground, near Drif-
field, 1898, CW (1902) is an error; specimens of this
gathering in herb. BM are *C. diandra*, RWD, pers. comm.

C. diandra Schrank (*C. teretiuscula* Gooden.)
Lesser Tussock-sedge.　　　　CNE.　　　1798.
Native. Wet peaty places. Rare.
Hold. Arram Carr, abundantly 04 (Teesdale, 1800);
Kelleythorpe 05, 1939, YNU Excursion, still there in
quantity, 1969, FEC; by R. Hull near Wansford 05, 1960,
YNU Excursion, still present.

C. diandra x *C. paniculata* = *C.* x *beckmannii* Keck ex
F. Schultz
Near Wansford 05 with both parents, 1960, FEC, still
present; identification confirmed AOC & RWD, 1981, the
first record for Great Britain (Crackles, 1983c).

C. otrubae Podp. (*C. vulpina* auct.)　　Map 440.
False Fox-sedge.　　　　　　　　　　　1840.
Native. Usually in damp situations on heavy soils; roadside ditches, beside dykes, by ponds, in gravel pits. Locally
common in Holderness and Derwentland.

C. otrubae x *C. remota* = *C.* x *pseudoaxillaris* K. Richt.
U.D. Howsham Wood 76, 1958, YNU Excursion.
Hold. Sides of ditches, near Beverley 03 (Teesdale, 1800);
bank of Skidby drain, Beverley Rd, near Hull, JFR (Nat.
1914, 214); by drain, Arram Carrs 04, 1979, J. Higgins.

C. disticha Huds.　　　　　　　　　Map 175.
Brown Sedge.　　　　　　　CNE.
Native. Fens, water-meadows and spring-fed marshes.
Frequent in the R. Hull and R. Derwent valleys; scattered
elsewhere in Lower Derwentland and in Holderness; very
local on the Wolds.

C. arenaria L.
Sand Sedge.　　　　　　　　　　　　　1798.
Native. Fixed sand dunes and wind blown sand. Local.
Frequent on Spurn Point 41. On or near the R. Humber bank
near Easington 31, 1955, RG, still there; near Welwick 31,
1963, FEC and near Skeffling 31, 1966, FEC. On the coast
at Sand le Mere 33, CW (R. 1902) and 1947, RL.

C. divisa Huds.
Divided Sedge.   CSE.   1798.
Native. Brackish marshes and damp grassland. Near the R. Humber bank and the sea-coast. Uncommon.
'In a meadow, called Derricots, near Hull' 02 (Teesdale, 1800), site built upon (R. 1902); Marfleet 12, 1894, near Hedon Haven 12, 1898 (R. 1902); on Salt End Common 12, 1901 (R. 1902) and 1955, FEC; near Easington 31, 1938, AKW; near Paull 12, 1954, FEC. Behind the R. Humber bank near Skeffling 31, 1975 and in quantity there on disturbed ground, 1981, FEC and near Easington 31, 1978, FEC. Near ponds, North Ferriby 92, 1955, RG and on Hessle foreshore 02, 1970, TD; in quantity Ferriby Ings 92, 1987, FEC. On the sea-coast, near Easington 41, 1970, ATD.

C. divulsa subsp. *leersii* (Kneuker) Walo Koch
Leers' Sedge.
Native. Roadsides, wood ride, waste places; strongly calcicole.
U.D. Roadside Kirkham 76, det. RWD, known since 1955, RG, but then believed to be *C. divulsa* subsp. *divulsa*; atypical due to frequent cutting.
Wolds Millington Wood 75, 1966, EC det. RWD; by spring, Wharram Percy 86, 1979, FEC.

C. spicata Huds.   Map 441.
Spiked Sedge.
Native. Damp grassland, more rarely in chalk grassland. Locally frequent at the western side of the Wolds; otherwise localities scattered.

C. muricata subsp. *lamprocarpa* Celak
Small-fruited Prickly-sedge.
Native. On sandy acid soils. Rare.
L.D. Sand pit, Deighton 64, 1956, R. Good, herb. HLU, det. RWD, 1982.

C. elongata L.
Elongated Sedge.   CNE.   1840.
Native. Boggy woods. Very rare.
Langwith 64, 1840, J.S. Rowntree, herb. MANCH & 1874, J. Carroll, herb. BM. Extinct.

C. echinata Murr.   Map 176.
Star Sedge.   CNE.   1896.
Native. Marshes on acid soils; also in mires with a high base status. Infrequent, but widely distributed.
Post-1950 records include:
U.D. Flixton Carr 08, 1957, FEC; Kirkham 76, 1958, YNU Excursion; Wintringham 87, 1968, FEC; Sherburn Ings 97, 1971, MC.
L.D. North Cliffe Wood 83, 1955, RG; Skipwith Common 63, 1956, FEC; Heslington Fields 64, 1957, FEC; Allerthorpe Common 74, 1957, FEC.
Wolds Near Great Givendale 85, 1970, FEC; near Lowthorpe 06, 1972, MC & FEC; Speeton and Buckton 17, 1973, MC & FEC; near Uncleby 85, 1980, FEC.
Hold. Marshy field by Leven Canal 04, 1952, FEC; near Wansford 05, 1968, FEC.

C. remota L.   Map 442.
Remote Sedge.   1840.
Native. Usually in shady situations on peaty soil with a high water-table for at least part of the year; wood rides; sometimes by dykes. Locally frequent in the R. Hull valley and in Derwentland.
Rare elsewhere:

Wolds Settrington Wood 86, 1970, FEC.
Hold. Burton Constable 13, 1956, RG; near Brandesburton 14, 1969, FEC; Rise Park 14, 1982, FEC.

C. curta Good.
White Sedge.   CNE.
Native. Wet places.
Between Stamford Bridge and Escrick, 1909 (SYF). Extinct.

C. ovalis Good.   Map 443.
Oval Sedge.
Native. Moderately acid soils with impeded drainage; wet meadows, woodland rides. Locally frequent in Derwentland and in the R. Hull valley.
Also recorded for several scattered localities, including the following post-1970 records:
Wolds Near Hunmanby, Reighton, Speeton and Bempton 17, 1973, MC.
Hold. Rise Park 14, 1971, FEC; Alexandra Dock, Hull 12, 1979, FEC; on disused railway, near Great Hatfield 14, 1980, FEC; near Goxhill 14, 1980, FEC.

C. pulicaris L.
Flea Sedge.   CNE.   1840.
Native. Damp calcareous grassland, fens, base-rich flushes. Uncommon.
U.D. Flixton Carrs 08, 1960, FEC; Wintringham 87, 1964, FEC; near Firby 76, 1981, DRG.
L.D. Heslington Fields 64, c.1845, OAM & 1957, FEC; Houghton Moor 83 (R. 1902).
Wolds Newbald Springs 93 (R. 1902) and 1972, FEC; near Birdsall 86, 1972, FEC; Buckton 17, 1980, SP.
Hold. Near Beverley 03, Dr Hull, Cottingham Common 03, GN, near Driffield and Wansford 05 (R. 1902); Kelleythorpe 05, 1950, FEC; conf. Wansford 05, 1969, MC.

C. dioica L.
Dioecious Sedge.   CNE.   c.1845.
Native. Near chalk springs and in fens. Uncommon.
U.D. Wintringham 87, 1969, FEC; near Leavening 76, 1975, YNU Excursion.
L.D. Heslington Fields 64, c.1845, OAM; at springs, Cockle Pits, Brough 92, 1901 (R. 1902).
Wolds Newbald Springs 93, 1972, FEC; Speeton 17, 1973, MC & FEC; Buckton 17, 1973, MC & FEC.
Hold. Pulfin Bog 04, 1920, YNU Excursion; near Wansford 05, 1960, FEC, still there, possibly the locality between Driffield Canal and the river where it was found in 1899 (R. 1902).

GRAMINEAE

Phragmites Adans.
P. australis (Cav.) Trin. ex Steudel (*P. communis* Trin.)
                                        Map 130.
Common Reed.
Native. In reedswamps and shallow water; by rivers, lakes and ponds and in dykes, including brackish places. Common in Lower Derwentland and Holderness and locally frequent in Upper Derwentland.
Occurs on the Flamborough Headland and near the coast of Filey Bay; otherwise rare on the Wolds: near Birdsall 86, 1971, MC.

Molinia Schrank
M. caerulea (L.) Moench (*M. varia* Schrank)   Map 444.
Purple Moor-grass.   1888.
Native. Damp and wet places, mainly on acid heaths; more rarely on fens. Infrequent, but locally plentiful. Most records are for Lower Derwentland.
Other records:
U.D. Flixton and Flotmanby Carrs 07 & 08, 1957, FEC; on moorland, Kennythorpe 76, 1958, FEC; abundant near spring, Wintringham 87, 1968, FEC; rich flush, near Acklam 76, 1970, ATD; fen near Staxton 07, 1971, FEC; near Firby 76, 1981, DRG.
Hold. On fen marsh: Hall Ings, Cottingham 03, 1897 (R. 1902), near Barfhill Wood 04, 1957, FEC and near Harpham 06, 1971, FEC. As a casual, bombed site, High St, Hull 12, 1952, FEC.

Danthonia DC.
D. decumbens (L.) DC. [*Sieglingia decumbens* (L.) Bernh.]
                                                                  Map 445.
Heath-grass.   1903.
Native. On somewhat acid grassland, but also on damp base-rich soils. Infrequent in Derwentland as on Skipwith Common 63, 1903, JFR (Trans. HSFNC *3*, 100) and 1954, DAW and near Newton upon Derwent 74, 1981, FEC; also infrequent on Wolds grassland.
Other scattered localities, including:
U.D. Wintringham 87, 1968, FEC.
Hold. West of Scorborough 04, 1956, RG; edge of fen, King's Mill 05, 1968, FEC; near Wansford 05, 1969, MC; Beverley Westwood 03, 1969, FEC; Fraisthorpe 16, 1970, MC.

Glyceria R.Br.
G. fluitans (L.) R.Br.   Map 145.
Floating Sweet-grass.
Native. Stagnant and slow-flowing shallow water; by ponds, canals and rivers; in ditches and marshes. Sometimes the dominant plant. Common.

G. fluitans x *G. plicata* = *G.* x *pedicellata* Townsend
U.D. Flotmanby Carrs 08, 1957, FEC, det. Dr C.E. Hubbard (CEH); Jeffrey Bog 76, 1981, FEC.
Wolds Waterdale 86, 1956, RK, det. CEH; Boynton 16, 1987, EC det. T.A. Cope.
Hold. Marshy ground by Hornsea Mere 14, 1951, FEC, det. CEH; Pulfin Bog 04, 1954, FEC, det. CEH; High Farm, Routh 04, 1971, FEC.

G. plicata Fr.   Map 146.
Plicate Sweet-grass.
Native. In ponds, streams, ditches and marshy places. Less common than *G. fluitans* and apparently with a more restricted distribution, mainly along the spring lines.

G. declinata Bréb.   Map 144.
Glaucous Sweet-grass.   1959.
Native. Muddy or dried up margins and shallow water of old ponds, by streams; in dykes and in marshes.
Very infrequent, including:
U.D. Near Wintringham 87, 1968, TFM.
L.D. On ride, where water stood, Allerthorpe Common 74, 1959, FEC.
Wolds Great Givendale 85, 1971, FEC; Octon 06, 1971, MC; Swaythorpe 06, 1971, MC; near Buckton and Speeton 17, 1973, FEC & MC.
Hold. Wood rides, Burton Bushes 03, 1969, MC; near Burton Agnes 16, 1970, MC; Routh 04, 1971, FEC; Lelley

23, 1972, FEC.
G. maxima (Hartm.) Holmberg [*G. aquatica* (L.) Wahlb.]
                                                                  Map 127.
Reed Sweet-grass.   1895.
Native. By rivers, canals, large ponds and lakes and in marshy areas subject to flooding in winter; growing in deeper water than other species of *Glyceria*. Frequent. Less commonly in drains and dykes.

Festuca L.
F. pratensis Huds. (*F. elatior* auct.)   Map 446.
Meadow Fescue.
Native. Meadows, pastures, roadsides, waste places. Frequent.

F. elatior L. (*F. arundinacea* Schreb.)   Map 447.
Tall Fescue.   1898.
Native. Grassy places, gravel and chalk pits, cliff tops. Widely distributed, but somewhat infrequent in many areas.

F. elatior x *F. gigantea* = *F.* x *gigas* Holmberg
By canal, Brigham 05, 1957, FEC, det. CEH, 1971, herb. FEC.

F. gigantea (L.) Vill. [*Bromus giganteus* L.]   Map 75.
Giant Fescue.   1897.
Native. Woods, plantations, shady places. Locally frequent, mainly in woods.

F. rubra L. subsp. *rubra*   Map 448.
Red Fescue.   1798.
Var. *rubra*
Chalk grassland, meadows, heaths, roadsides, waste ground. Common.
Var. *arenaria* Fries
A dominant grass on Spurn Point 41; it also occurs in sand dunes on the R. Humber bank, near Easington 31.
Var. *barbata* (Schrank) Richt.
Bombed site, George Yard, Hull 12, 1952, FEC, det. CEH; drain bank, near High Baswick 04, 1956, FEC, det. CEH.

F. nigrescens Lam. (*F. rubra* L. subsp. *commutata* Gaudin)
Chewings Fescue.
Alien.
On ballast of railway sidings, East Ella, Hull 02, 1980, JES, det. C.A. Stace.

F. ovina L.   Map 449.
Sheep's-fescue.
Native. On well-drained shallow soils on both acid and basic soils; calcareous grassland, heathy commons. Common on the Wolds, occasional elsewhere.

F. filiformis Pourr. (*F. tenuifolia* Sibth.)
Fine-leaved Sheep's-fescue.   1937.
Native. On sandy soils, heaths. Apparently uncommon.
L.D. Skipwith Common 63, 1954, RG, det. P.L. Thomas; Allerthorpe Common 74, 1955, AKW, det. CEH.
Hold. On sand on Alexandra Dock, Hull 12, 1979, FEC.

F. brevipila Tracey. [*F. trachyphylla* (Hackel) Krajina (1930), non Hackel ex Druce (1915)]
Hard Fescue.
Alien.
Chalk bank near Wintringham 97, 1986, EC, det. P.J.O. Trist (PJOT).

Festuca x *Lolium* = x *Festulolium*
Aschers. & Graebn.
F. pratensis x *L. perenne* = x *Festulolium loliaceum*
(Huds.) P. Fourn.
L.D. Tollingham 83, 1972, FEC; flood meadows, Wheldrake 74, 1980, NCC; bank of R. Derwent, Bubwith 73, 1983, FEC; Barmby on the Marsh 62, 1983, JL.
Wolds Millington 85, 1973, TFM; Uncleby 85, 1980, FEC; near Burdale 86, 1987, DEH.
Hold. Water-meadow, Withernwick 13, 1982, FEC.

F. elatior x *L. perenne* = x *Festulolium holmbergii* (Dörfl.)
P. Fourn.
L.D. River bank, Bubwith 73, 1983, FEC.
Hold. Tophill Low 04, 1978, FEC.

F. elatior x *L. multiflorum*
River bank, Bubwith 73, 1983, YNU Bot. Sect. Excursion, det. FEC.

Festuca x *Vulpia* = x *Festulpia*
Melderis ex Stace & Cotton
F. rubra agg. x *V. bromoides*
On ballast of disused railway siding, East Ella, Hull 02, 1980, J.E. Spencer, herb. JES, det. C.A. Stace. One of three British records. The *Festuca* parent is probably *F. nigrescens* (Ainscough, Barker & Stace, 1986).

Lolium L.

L. perenne L.
Perennial Rye-grass.
Native. Old pastures, meadows, roadsides and waste places. Extensively sown. Very common.

L. multiflorum Lam.
Italian Rye-grass.
Alien. Widely cultivated and naturalised. On roadsides, field margins and waste ground. Frequent.

L. multiflorum x *L. perenne* = *L.* x *hybridum* Hausskn.
Welham 76, 1957, FEC, det. CEH, herb. FEC.

L. temulentum L.
Darnel.   1840.
Alien. Casual in cultivated fields and rubbish tips. Rare by the beginning of this century (R. 1902). Extinct.
L.D. Cornfields, Langwith 64 (Baines, 1840); near Selby 63, WNC (R. 1902).
Var. *arvense* With.
L.D. Near North Cave 83, 1899 (R. 1902).
Hold. Walkington 93 and near Beverley 03 (Teesdale, 1800).

Vulpia C.C. Gmel.
V. fasciculata (Forssk.) Fritsch [*V. membranacea* (L.) auct., non Dumort.; *Festuca uniglumis* Ait.]
Dune Fescue.
Native.   Sand dunes.
Atwick, S. Gibson (R. 1902). No confirmation.

V. bromoides (L.) Gray   Map 450.
Squirreltail Fescue.   1798.
Native? On disused railway tracks, in gravel pits, on walls and waste ground; rarely in open woodland. Infrequent.
Post-1950 records include:
U.D. Near Kirkham Abbey 76, 1955, RG; Firby Wood 76, 1958, RG.
L.D. Plantation, Everingham 84, 1955, RG; Deighton 64,

1956, RG; Barmby on the Marsh 62, 1980, JES.
Hold. Railway sidings, Willerby 03, 1955, FEC; on wall, Ryehill 22, 1955, FEC; Easington 31, 1955, RG; on wall between Bentley and Walkington 03, 1967, FEC; gravel pit, Burshill 04, 1972, MC; Alexandra Dock, Hull 12, 1979, FEC.

V. myuros (L.) C.C. Gmel.
Rat's-tail Fescue.   1798.
Established alien. Mainly on railway tracks and sidings; also on waste places. Very infrequent.
First record: on walls, Beverley (Teesdale, 1800).
Post-1970 records:
L.D. Railway, Eastrington 73, 1976, FEC; Barmby on the Marsh 62, 1980, JES; near Fulford 64, 1980, EB. On drift line at edge of winter flooding, Newton Maske 74, 1981, FEC.
Wolds Disused railway, Epplewprth 03, 1979, JES & FEC and at Everthorpe 03, 1979, JES & FEC.
Hold. Priory Sidings, Hull 02, 1971, FEC; Carnaby airfield 16, 1972, EC; South Orbital Road, Hull 12, 1976, EC; Spring Head Sidings, Hull 02, 1981, JES & FEC; gravel pit, Brandesburton 14, 1981, JES; Hollym 33, 1983, FEC; railway station, Patrington 32, 1985, FEC; railway, Ottringham 22, 1986, FEC.

Puccinellia Parl.
P. maritima (Huds.) Parl. [*Glyceria maritima* (Huds.) Wahlb.]   Map 217.
Common Saltmarsh-grass.   OWEE.   1798.
Native. Salt-marshes and saltings. Dominates areas of salt-marshes along the R. Humber; also occurs on the shore from Hull west to Blacktoft 82. Rare along the sea coast: Hornsea sands 24 (BEC. *9*. 1931, 845); Barmston Drain end 15, 1955, RG; Flamborough Headland 27, 1984, SMA.

P. distans (L.) Parl. [*Glyceria distans* (L.) Wahlenb.]
Map 216.
Reflexed Saltmarsh-grass.
Native. On higher part of salt-marshes; more often on and behind the R. Humber bank. Frequent. Persisting for some time on reclaimed land.
On the shore of the R. Humber from Hessle west to Saltmarshe 72. Rare on the sea coast: Hornsea sands 24, RB (BEC, *9*. 1931, 845); Barmston Drain end 15, 1955, RG. As a casual on waste places in Hull: on bombed sites, Hull 12, 1951-1952 & 1975, FEC; near R. Hull, Sutton Rd, Hull 03, 1957, ESt. On roadside verge at M1 junction roundabout 72, 1980, N.E. Scott and at North Cave 83, 1987, FEC.

P. rupestris (With.) Fernald & Weatherby [*Glyceria procumbens* (Curt.) Dumort.]
Stiff Saltmarsh-grass.
Native. North landing, Flamborough 27, 1935, AMS (Nat. 1936, 48).

Catapodium Link.
C. rigidum (L.) C.E. Hubbard [*Dezmazeria rigida* (L.) Tutin; *Festuca rigida* (L.) Rasp.]   Map 451.
Fern-grass.   CSE.   1840.
Native. Dry, well-drained soils; on walls and disused railway tracks; edges of bare paths on chalk hillsides; chalk arable; chalk, sand and gravel pits. On sand at Spurn 41, 1975, FEC and on the R. Humber bank, near Easington 31, 1983, JES & FEC. Frequent on the Wolds and locally elsewhere; rare in Lower Derwentland.

C. marinum (L.) C.E. Hubbard [*Desmazeria marina* (L.) Druce]
Sea Fern-grass.   ME.
Native.   On coastal sands.   Rare.
On Spurn Point 41, 1952, DAW, still present and more frequent since the 1978 flooding.
Introduced. King George Dock, Hull 12, 1957, FEC, det. CEH.

Poa L.

P. annua L.
Annual Meadow-grass.
Native. Waste places, gardens and other cultivated land, waste places, roadsides. Very common.

P. nemoralis L.   Map 85.
Wood Meadow-grass.
Native. Woods. Infrequent, but widely distributed; sometimes in quantity.

P. compressa L.   Map 452.
Flattened Meadow-grass.   1898.
Native.   Dry places; mainly on walls.   Infrequent.
On coping stones on the river wall at Paull 12 and on the coast at Skipsea 15, 1983, FEC.

P. pratensis L.
Smooth Meadow-grass.
Native.   Meadows, roadsides, waste places.   Common.

P. angustifolia L.
Narrow-leaved Meadow-grass.   1946.
Naturalised adventive. Road and railway verges, on well-drained soils.
First Lane, Hessle 02, 1946, AKW, det. CEH. Recorded for railway verges in ten km squares 64, 73, 92, 03, 05 and 16, British Rail land survey, 1977 (Sargent *et al*, 1986).

P. trivialis L.
Rough Meadow-grass.
Native. Water meadows, pastures, waste and cultivated land, roadsides. Sometimes in quantity in woods. Very common.

Catabrosa Beauv.

C. aquatica (L.) Beauv.   Map 96.
Whorl-grass.
Native. Margins of ponds; in shallow ditches and slow-flowing streams, more rarely on marshy ground; often near springs. Very infrequent.
Most records for the R. Hull valley, including by canal, Brigham 05, 1957, FEC; near Wansford 05, 1960, YNU Excursion.
Other records include:
U.D. Flotmanby Carrs 07, 1957, FEC; Folkton Carrs 08, 1984, DRG.
Wolds Near Wharram 86, 1950, YNU Excursion; by springs, Millington 85, 1958, FEC; by the Gypsey Race near Boynton 16, 1969, EC and near Rudston 16, 1970, MC; Danes Dyke 27, 1970, MC; near Buckton and Speeton 17, 1973, MC, still present.

Dactylis L.

D. glomerata L.
Cock's-foot.
Native. Meadows, pastures, rough grassland, roadsides, waste places. Very common.

Cynosurus L.

C. cristatus L.   Map 453.
Crested Dog's-tail.
Native. Old grassland on a variety of soils, including chalk grassland. Widely distributed; common on the Wolds.

Briza L.

B. media L.   Map 454.
Quaking-grass.
Native. Grassland, especially on calcareous soils; on drier parts of fens; rarely on sand. Common on the Wolds, infrequent elsewhere; generally less widely distributed than formerly.

Melica L.

M. uniflora Retz.
Wood Melick.
Native. Mainly in woods, also on shady banks.Uncommon.
U.D. Near Kirkham Abbey 76, 1955, RG; Leavening Brow 76, 1970, ATD.
L.D. Sutton Rush Wood 74, 1984, DMcCo.
Wolds Near chalk pit, Skidby 03, 1951, RG; Raywell 93, 1955, RG; Thorpe Hall 16, 1969, FEC; Millington Wood 85, 1985, J. Hooley.
Hold. Hall Ings 03, Haltemprice Lane 03 and plantation, Swine 13 (R. 1902); Etton 94, 1945, AKW; near Haltemprice Priory 03, 1970, DWS; Colt Wood, Meaux 04, 1984, DMcCo; Leconfield Castle 04, 1986, AJ.

Bromus L.

B. erectus Huds.   Map 7.
Upright Brome.   1798.
Native. Calcareous grassland, sometimes dominant; also on Wolds roadsides. Locally frequent, but unevenly distributed on the Wolds.

B. ramosus Huds.   Map 64.
Hairy-brome.
Native. Open woodland, wood margins; sometimes in hedgerows. Frequent.

B. benekenii (Lange) Trimen
Lesser Hairy-brome.
Native. Characteristic of woodland on calcareous soils and should be searched for.
Only record: Wheldrake Ings 64, 1984, EB, det. PJOT.

B. inermis Leyss.
Hungarian Brome.
Alien.
Naburn Ings 64, 1971, TFM; near Fulford 64, 1980, EB.

B. sterilis L.
Barren Brome.
Native. Waste and cultivated land, waysides, hedgerows. Very common.

B. hordeaceus L. (*B. mollis* L.)
Soft-brome.
Native. Meadows, cultivated land, roadsides, waste ground. Very common.

B. hordeaceus x *B. lepidus* = *B.* x *pseudothominii* P.M. Smith, (as *B. hordeaceus* var. *leiostachys* Huds.)
U.D. Howsham 76, 1956, FEC, det. Dr C.E. Hubbard (CEH).
Wolds Deepdale, North Newbald 93, 1957, FEC, det. CEH.

160

B. thominei Hard.
Lesser Soft-brome.   1953.
Introduced. Cultivated land and roadsides. Uncommon.
U.D. Welham 76, 1957, FEC.
L.D. Near North Cliffe 83, 1953, FEC, det. CEH; North Cave 83, 1956, FEC; Langwith Common 64, 1957, FEC, det. CEH.
Wolds Worsendale 85, 1957, FEC; Langton 86, 1957, FEC, det. CEH.
Hold. Roadside between Halsham East End and Roos 22, 1949, RL, det. CEH; near Kelleythorpe 05, 1959, RL; bombed site, Blackfriargate, Hull 12, 1953, FEC, det. CEH; drain bank Arram Carrs 04, 1953, FEC, det. CEH; Spurn Point 41, 1956, FEC, det. CEH.
Var. *hirsutus* (Holmb.)
Langton 86, 1957, FEC, det. CEH.

B. lepidus Holmberg
Slender Soft-brome.   1937.
Native? Cultivated grassland, roadsides and waste land. Uncommon.
Post-1950 records:
U.D. Firby Wood 76, 1958, RG; sand pit, Staxton 07, 1956, RG.
L.D. Disused gravel pit, Thorpe le Street 84, 1952, RL; North Cave 83, 1953, FEC; near Market Weighton 83, 1956, FEC, det. CEH.
Wolds Flamborough Head 27, 1955, RG; near Thixendale 86, 1956, FEC, det. CEH.
Hold. Near Halsham 22, 1950, RL; near Driffield 05, 1951, RL; bombed site, High St, Hull 12, 1952, FEC, det. CEH; Railway Dock, Hull 02, 1978, FEC.
Var. *lasiolepis* Holmb.
Spring Head and Pickering Rd, Hull 02, 1937, AKW (SYF).

B. racemosus L.
Smooth Brome.   1798.
Native. Meadows, particularly water-meadows of Lower Derwentland; also in the carr land of Holderness. Uncommon.
L.D. Heslington Fields 64, c.1845, OAM; near Bubwith 73, 1956, FEC, det. CEH; near Wheldrake 64 & 74, 1957, FEC, det. CEH; near Thornton 74, 1969, FEC.
Hold. Marshes, near Beverley (Teesdale, 1800); Withernwick 14, 1956, FEC, det. CEH; Hollym 32, 1984, FEC.

B. commutatus Schrad.
Meadow Brome.
Native. Cultivated land, water meadows. Uncommon.
L.D. Bubwith 73, 1937, WAS & 1956, FEC; near Kelfield 53, 1941, WAS; Wheldrake Ings 74, 1957, FEC, det. CEH; Aughton Ings 73, 1972, YNU Bot. Sect. Excursion; near Elvington 73, 1973, YNU Excursion; near Barmby on the Marsh 62, 1985, TFM.
Hold. Waste ground, near Hull docks (R. 1902); between Burstwick and Kelsey Hill 22, 1956, FEC, det. CEH.

B. secalinus L.
Rye Brome.   1798.
Alien. Formerly grown as a cereal, also introduced as an impurity in the seeds of cereals; waste places. Rare.
L.D. Market Weighton 84 (Teesdale, 1800).
Wolds North Grimston 86, 1807, WM, herb. WM, York Mus.
Hold. Humber bank, Hessle 02, 1879, GW (R. 1902); bombed site, Sewer Lane, Hull 02, 1952, FEC.

***Brachypodium* Beauv.**
B. sylvaticum (Huds.) Beauv. (*B. gracile* Beauv.)
                                              Map 455.
False Brome.   1897.
Native. Woods, copses, persisting along roadsides in areas formerly wooded; railway banks. Usually on calcareous or base-rich soils. Locally common on the Wolds; infrequent elsewhere.

B. pinnatum (L.) Beauv.   Map 6.
Tor-grass.   1891.
Native. On chalk and limestone grassland; fixed dunes. Became dominant on much calcareous pasture after the introduction of myxomatosis. Comparatively scarce on southern and northern wolds, but spreading.
Spurn Point 41, 1975, FEC, lost by erosion.

***Elymus* L.**
E. caninus (L.) L. [*Agropyron caninum* (L.) Beauv.]
                                              Map 74.
Bearded Couch.
Native. Woods and hedgerows. Infrequent, but widely distributed.

E. repens (L.) Gould [*Agropyron repens* (L.) Beauv.]
Common Couch.
Native. Cultivated land, including gardens, meadows, waste places. Very common.
Var. *aristatum* Baumg.
Hold. Hessle foreshore 02, 1955, AKW, det. CEH; sand dunes Hornsea 24, AKW, det. CEH; Pulfin Bend 04, 1957, FEC, det. CEH.

E. pycnanthus (Godron) Melderis [*Agropyron pungens* auct. non Roem. & Schult.]   Map 209.
Sea Couch.   CSE.
Native. Dominant for stretches of the R. Humber bank on the salt-marsh side; upper part of salt-marshes; also on sand dunes on Spurn Point 41. Forms a pure belt along the Fisherman's Channel, Sunk Island 21. Also here and there on the Holderness coast.
Var. *setigerum* Dumort.
Hold. Barmston 15, 1955, RG; Easington 31, 1955, RG; Spurn Point 41, 1957, FEC, det. CEH; Sewerby 16, 1970, MC.

E. farctus (Viv.) Runemark ex Melderis [*Agropyron junceiforme* (A. & D. Löve) A.D. Löve; *A. junceum* auct.]
                                              Map 208.
Sand Couch.   1789.
Native. On sandy beaches. Very local.
On the coast: near Hornsea (Camden, 1789) and 1936, RB; Withernsea 32 and Spurn 41 (R. 1902); Sand le Mere 33, 1952, RG; still at Spurn; Barmston Drain end 15, 1955, RG; Fraisthorpe 16, 1970, MC; Sewerby 16, 1970, MC.
On the R. Humber bank, south of Easington 31, 1953, RG, still present.

E. farctus x *E. pycnanthus*
Spurn Point 41, 1947, RL, det CEH, still present; Hornsea 24, 1955, AKW, det. CEH; Barmston 15, 1958, FEC; on Humber bank, near Easington 31, 1983, FEC.

161

Leymus Hochst.

L. arenarius (L.) Hochst. (*Elymus arenarius* L.)
Lyme-grass.   ONE.   1798.
Native.   Sand dunes.   Very local.
A significant binder of sand on Spurn Point 31 & 41, mainly
on the river side.
Other coastal records: Hornsea 24 and Bridlington Quay 16
(Teesdale, 1800); Sand le Mere 33, 1954, RG; Barmston
Drain end 15, 1955, RG; Fraisthorpe 16, 1955, RG.
On the Humber bank, near Easington 31, 1953, AKW, still
present.

Hordeum L.

H. secalinum Schreb.   Map 53.
Meadow Barley.
Native. Old meadows and pastures; roadsides. Infrequent,
and somewhat local, mainly on moist soils; uncommon on
the Wolds.

H. murinum L.   Map 456.
Wall Barley.
Native. Waste ground and waysides, often near buildings.
Widely distributed; locally common near Hull and often
frequent at or near the coast.

H. marinum Huds.
Sea Barley.   OSE.
Native. Margins of salt-marshes, grassy sea-banks, sea
walls. Said to be formerly fairly frequent (R. 1902). Near
Hedon 12, 1901, TP. Extinct.

H. jubatum L.
Foxtail Barley.   1922.
Alien.   Waste ground, roadsides.   Uncommon.
L.D. Germany Lane, Fulford 64, 1967, TFM; verge of
York road, Shiptonthorpe 84, 1974, EC.
Hold. King George Dock, Hull 12, 1922, JFR & 1934,
AKW (W. 1938); bombed site, High St, Hull 12, 1953,
FEC; refuse tip, Hull 13, 1963, EC.

Koeleria Pers.

K. macrantha (Ledeb.) Schultes [K. cristata (L.) Pers.]
          Map 17.
Crested Hair-grass.   OWEE.   1899.
Native. Calcareous grassland, chalk pits. Locally frequent
on the Wolds.
Rare elsewhere:
U.D. Sand pit, Flixton 07, 1957, FEC; on sand, Ganton 97,
1982, FEC.
L.D. Cockle Pits, Brough 92, 1955, RG.
Also formerly noted on gravelly areas at Coneygarth 14,
1899 and near Driffield 05 (R. 1902).

Trisetum Pers.

T. flavescens (L.) Beauv. (*T. pratense* Pers.)   Map 457.
Yellow Oat-grass.
Native. Road verges, old pastures, chalk and sand pits.
Shows a preference for calcareous soils, but widely distrib-
uted. Common, particularly on the Wolds.

Avena L.

A. fatua L.
Wild-oat.   c.1845.
Naturalised alien. Weed of arable and waste places; often
abundant in corn fields. Common.
Var. **glabrata** Peterm. Roadside between Halsham East
End and Roos 22, 1949, RL, det. Dr C.E. Hubbard
(CEH); bombed site, Hull 12, 1951, FEC, det. CEH.

Var. **pilosa** Syme Bombed site, Wincolmlee, Hull 12,
1952, FEC, det. CEH.

Avenula (Dumort.) Dumort.

A. pratensis (L.) Dumort. [*Helictotrichon pratense* (L.)
Pilg.; *Avena pratensis* L.]   Map 5.
Meadow Oat-grass.   1896.
Native. Grassland on chalk and limestone. Infrequent.
Restricted to the grazed grassland belt of the Wolds.

A. pubescens (Huds.) Dumort. [*Helictotrichon pubescens* (Huds.) Pilg.; *Avena pubescens* Huds.]   Map 458.
Downy Oat-grass.   1897.
Native. On basic soils, often on damp soils as at the edge
of fen-marsh; chalk hillsides, roadside verges, chalk quarries. Locally frequent on the Wolds.
Uncommon in Holderness: by Hornsea Mere 14, 1960,
FEC; by roadside, near Arnold 13, 1969, FEC; along
disused railway, near Wassand station 14, 1980, FEC; in
meadows by the Lambwath stream, Withernwick 13 & 23,
1982, FEC.

Arrhenatherum Beauv.

A. elatius (L.) Beauv. ex J. & C. Presl (*A. avenaceum*
Beauv.)
False Oat-grass.
Native. Rough grassland, roadsides, waste places. Very
common.

Holcus L.

H. lanatus L.
Yorkshire-fog.
Native. Meadows, pastures, rough grassland, waste places
on a wide variety of soils. Very common.

H. mollis L.   Map 459.
Creeping Soft-grass.
Native. Open woodland, poor grassland, preferring moderately acid soils and often carpeting the ground. Common
in Lower Derwentland; absent from much of the Wolds,
otherwise infrequent.

Deschampsia Beauv.

D. cespitosa (L.) Beauv.   Map 460.
Tufted Hair-grass.
Native. On wet badly drained soils; rough grassland,
marshy areas, open woodland. Sometimes abundant in
marshy fields. Common.

D. flexuosa (L.) Trin.   Map 35.
Wavy Hair-grass.
Native. Usually on dry sandy soils; locally abundant on
heathland; also in open woodland. Infrequent; most
records for Lower Derwentland, but also locally in Upper
Derwentland as at Firby Wood 76, 1955, RG and Kenny-
thorpe Moor 76, 1970, ATD.
Other records:
Hold. Cutting, main road, east of Etton 94, 1955, RG;
Alexandra Dock, Hull 12, 1979, FEC, still there.

D. setacea (Huds.) Hack.
Bog Hair-grass.
Native. Peaty margins of pools and in boggy places on
heaths. Rare.
L.D. Skipwith Common 63, 1903, H.S. Thompson (Nat.
1904, 62).
Wolds Near Burton Fleming 07, 1909 (SYF). Extinct?

Aira L.

A. praecox L.　　　　　　　　　　　　　　　　　Map 29.
Early Hair-grass.
Native. Mainly on acid sandy soils; on heaths, commons and along railway tracks. On sand dunes at Spurn 41. Locally frequent in Lower Derwentland and occurs at several places at or near the coast between Flamborough and Filey.
Uncommon elsewhere:
U.D. Sand pit, Flixton 07, 1957, FEC; Kennythorpe Moor and sand pit 76, 1958, FEC; Sands Wood, Wintringham 87, 1964, FEC; near Potter Brompton 97, 1986, EC.
Hold. King George Dock, Hull 12, 1953, FEC; near Scorborough 04, 1970, MC; on railway sidings, Spring Head, Hull 02, 1978, FEC; on Alexandra Dock, Hull, 12, 1979 and Queen Elizabeth Dock, Hull 12, 1983, FEC.

A. caryophyllea L.　　　　　　　　　　　　　　Map 241.
Silver Hair-grass.
Native. On dry gravelly and sandy soils; on heaths and commons. Locally frequent in Lower Derwentland; also occurs on sand in the Vale of Pickering and at Spurn 41. Frequent along disused railway tracks in Holderness.
Other records:
U.D. Kennythorpe 76, 1958, FEC.
Wolds On railway tracks, Willerby 03, 1964, FEC, near Burdale 86, 1981, FEC and near Speeton 17, 1984, SMA. On steep knoll, Fordon Bank 07, 1968, FEC; on Flamborough Head 27, 1970, MC; near Foxholes 97, 1985, DRG.
Hold. Near shipyard, Hessle 02, 1951, FEC; near King George Dock, Hull 12, 1976, FEC; on Alexandra Dock, Hull 12, 1979, FEC; on Priory Yard railway sidings 02, 1977 and Spring Head Sidings, Hull 02, 1978, FEC.

Ammophila Host

A. arenaria (L.) Link　(A. arundinacea Host)　Map 201.
Marram.　　　　　　　　　　　　　　　　　　　　1798.
Native.　Sand dunes.
The main binder of sand at Spurn 41. Here and there on the Holderness coast: formerly at Hornsea 24 and Bridlington Quay 16 (Teesdale, 1800); also at Sand le Mere 33 (R. 1902) and 1970, ATD; at Barmston, Fraisthorpe and Wilsthorpe 16, 1970, MC. On the R. Humber bank, near Skeffling 31, 1973 and near Easington 31, 1983, FEC.

Calamagrostis Adans.

C. epigejos (L.) Roth　　　　　　　　　　　　Map 461.
Wood Small-reed.　　　　　　　　　　　　　　1890.
Native. Open places in damp woods, ditches; more rarely on roadsides and waste places. Infrequent.
Several localities in Lower Derwentland including Sutton Wood 74, 1958, FEC; Allerthorpe Common 74, 1958, FEC & 1984, YNU Excursion; Skipwith Common 63, 1970, FEC; near Hemingborough 63, 1981, DRG.
Other scattered localities include:
Wolds Pocklington Wood 85, 1950, RL; wood, Kilnwick Percy 84, 1957, RG; Hunmanby Gap 17, 1971, YNU Excursion.
Hold. Bentley Moor Wood 03, 1967, FEC; near Little Kelk 16, 1970, MC; Bygot Wood 04, 1971, FEC; Rise Park 14, 1971, FEC where it was known in 1890 (R. 1902); Priory Yard Sidings, Hull 02, 1972, FEC; Alexandra Dock, Hull 12, 1979, FEC; Queen Elizabeth Dock, Hull 12, 1986, FEC.

C. canescens (Weber) Roth　(C. lanceolata Roth)
　　　　　　　　　　　　　　　　　　　　　　　Map 138.
Purple Small-reed.　　　　　　　　　　　　　1843.
Native. Fens, wet open woodland. Locally frequent in the

R. Hull valley as along Leven Canal and by the R. Hull at Pulfin Bend 04 where it forms large beds.
Other localities are scattered including:
L.D. Heslington Fields 64, 1843, OAM & 1957, FEC; Black Plantation, Holme upon Spalding Moor 73, 1957, FEC; Allerthorpe Common 74, 1959, FEC & 1984, YNU Excursion; North Cliffe Wood 83, 1979, FEC; wood, Hasholme Carr 83, 1980, FEC.
Wolds Near Millington 85, 1952, RL; Flamborough Head 26 & 27, 1984, SMA.
Hold. Forms large beds at Hornsea Mere 14 and is abundant at Roos Bog 22, FEC; marsh by road, near Elstronwick 23, 1958, FEC; Alexandra Dock, Hull 12, 1979, FEC, still present.

A *C. canescens* introgressant population, derived from the hybrid with *C. stricta*, occurs by a dyke adjacent to Leven Canal 04 (Crackles, 1977).

C. canescens x **C. stricta** = **C. x gracilescens** (Blytt) Blytt
Leven Canal 04, 1951, F.E. Crackles, herb. FEC & herb. K; the only British locality. Hybrid populations at two chromosome levels, 2n = 28 and 2n = 56 still occur. The diploid is male sterile and infertile. The tetraploid produces good pollen and is slightly fertile and is unlike its Scandinavian counterpart which produces empty pollen and is apomictic (Crackles, 1975c & 1977).

C. canescens x **C. epigejos**
Two beds believed to be of this hybrid on Alexandra Dock, Hull 12, 1979, F.E.Crackles; both parental species are present in the area.

C. stricta (Timm) Koel.
Narrow Small-reed.　　　　　　NME.　　　　1951.
Native. A sub-arctic species of lake edges. One locality. Locally frequent at the edge of Leven Canal 04, 1951, F.E. Crackles, still present. The canal was cut through the site of former meres (Crackles, 1968).

Agrostis L.

A. canina L.
Velvet Bent.
Native. Damp or wet places. Distribution inadequately known.
L.D. Marshy ground, Heslington Fields 64, 1957, FEC, det. CEH; in several flood meadows by the R. Derwent in ten km squares 63, 64, 73 and 76, 1979 - 1981, NCC.
Wolds North Ferriby Ings 92, 1987, FEC.
Hold. Water-meadow, Withernwick 13, 1982, FEC.

A. vinealis Schreb. [*A. canina* subsp. *montana* (Hartm.) Hartm.]
Brown Bent.
Native. On dry soils on heaths, commons and roadsides. Recorded mainly for Lower Derwentland, sometimes in quantity as on Skipwith Common 63 and at Duck Nest 83. The distribution of the species requires further study.

A. capillaris L. (*A. tenuis* Sibth., *A. vulgaris* With.)
　　　　　　　　　　　　　　　　　　　　　　Map 462.
Common Bent.
Native. On a wide range of soils, particularly prevalent on sandy acid soils. On heaths, in pastures, on Wolds grassland, waste ground and roadsides. Common.

A. gigantea Roth   Map 463.
Black Bent.
Native. Cultivated and waste ground. Infrequent, but widely distributed.
On bombed sites in the Hull area 02 & 12, 1950-1953, FEC.

A. stolonifera L.
Creeping Bent.   1897.
Native. Grassland, roadsides, cultivated land, waste places, open woodland. Very common.
Var. *palustris* (Huds.) Farw.
Native. Wet places. Frequent.

A. scabra Willd.
Rough Bent.
Alien. A native of N. America. Rare.
Well established and in quantity on railway sidings near Spring Head, Hull 02, 1978, F.E. Crackles, det. CEH and on the Priory Yard Sidings, Hull 02, 1982, FEC.

Apera Adans.
A. spica-venti (L.) Beauv.   Map 30.
Loose Silky-bent.   CE.   1888.
Native and introduced. Mainly on dry sandy soils, on arable, on roadsides, on waste places. Locally frequent in Lower Derwentland. First record: near Market Weighton, 1888, YNU Excursion (R. 1902).
Other records:
U.D. Sand pit, Staxton 07, 1957, FEC.
Hold. Casual in the Hull area: refuse tip, Hessle 02, 1941, AKW; bombed site, High St, Hull 12, 1952, FEC; King George Dock, Hull 12, 1953 & 1986, FEC.

A. interrupta (L.) Beauv.
Dense Silky-bent.   1896.
Native. Dry sandy soils. Rare.
U.D. Sand pit, Flixton 07, 1896, W. Inverness & 1937, WAS (Nat. 1938, 27); sand pit, Staxton 07, 1956, RG; near Potter Brompton 97, 1986, EC; Wintringham 87, 1986, EC.

Polypogon Desf.
P. monspeliensis (L.) Desf.
Annual Beard-grass.   1896.
Alien. Waste land. Rare.
L.D. Casual at Barlby 63, WNC (R. 1902); Brough 92, 1939, AKW (Nat. 1940, 27).
Hold. Old brick pond, Hull, 1896, later built on, and Hull docks (R. 1902); King George Dock, Hull 12, 1935, AKW (W. 1938).

Phleum L.
P. pratense L.
Timothy, Cat's-tail.

Subsp. *pratense*
Native and introduced. Grown for grazing and hay; also on field margins, roadsides and waste places. Very common.

Subsp. *bertolonii* (DC.) Bornm. (*P. bertolonii* DC.)
                    Map 464.
Smaller Cat's-tail.
Native. Old pastures, chalk grassland, roadsides; on a wide range of soils, but showing a preference for calcareous soils. Common on the Wolds, infrequent elsewhere.

P. arenarium L.
Sand Cat's-tail.   c.1845.
Native. Open situations on sand dunes. Rare.
Now only known on Spurn Point 41; first recorded 1898, YNU Excursion (R. 1902); formerly at Atwick 15, c.1845, OAM.

Alopecurus L.
A. myosuroides Huds.   Map 223.
Black-grass, Slender Foxtail,   c.1845.
Native. Arable fields and waste places, mainly on heavy soils. Locally frequent in Holderness and near the R. Humber, in Lower Derwentland.
Also recorded recently for the Skirpenbeck, Bugthorpe area 75 and rarely on the southern wolds. Formerly recorded for Mowthorpe 86 and near Bridlington 16, 1909, FAL (SYF).

A. pratensis L.
Meadow Foxtail.
Native. Meadows and other grassland, waysides, waste places. Common.

A. geniculatus L.   Map 465.
Marsh Foxtail.
Native. Damp depressions in meadows, marshy ground, edges of ponds, ditches. Frequent.

A. geniculatus x *A. pratensis* = *A.* x *hybridus* Wimm.
Meadow by R. Derwent, near Sutton Wood 74, 1973, F.E. Crackles, det. CEH.

A. aequalis Sobol. (*A. fulvus* Sm.)
Orange Foxtail.
Native. Marshy places. Very rare.
L.D. Allerthorpe Common 74, 1953, RG.
Hold. Near Skidby Drain, between Hull and Beverley 03 (R. 1902); gravel pit, Brandesburton 14, 1969, MC.

Milium L.
M. effusum L.   Map 82.
Wood Millet.
Native. Woods on damp heavy soils with humus. Infrequent and local. Most records for the Cottingham, Beverley area and the southern part of the Wolds; it also occurs in the Kirkham area.
Other records:
L.D. North Cliffe Wood 83, 1954, FEC; Sutton Wood 74, 1958, FEC; Sutton Rush Wood 74, 1984, DMcCo.
Hold. Weldon's Plantation, Winestead 32, 1981, FEC.

Anthoxanthum L.
A. odoratum L.
Sweet Vernal-grass.
Native. Old pastures and meadows; on a variety of soils and in both dry and damp places. Frequent.

A. aristatum Boiss. (*A. puelii* Lecoq & Lamotte)
Annual Vernal-grass.   1935.
Introduced. Sandy fields. Rare.
L.D. Near Bielby 74, 1957, RG & 1978, GAN.
Hold. King George Dock, Hull 12, 1935, TS (W. 1938).

Phalaris L.
P. arundinacea L.   Map 129.
Reed Canary-grass.
Native. Wet places. Margins of rivers, streams, lakes and ponds; in dykes and marshes; often forming large beds. Common.
On Hull bombed sites 02 & 12, 1950-1953, FEC.

P. canariensis L.
Canary-grass.
A Mediterranean species, introduced with bird seed. Casual. Mainly in the Hull area: Marfleet 12, 1931, Hessle 02, 1932 and King George Dock, Hull 12, AKW (W. 1938); on bombed sites and other waste places in Hull's Old Town 12, 1950-1985, FEC; refuse tip, Leads Rd 13, 1962, FEC. Other records:
L.D. Near Elvington 64, 1973, RTh.
Wolds Near Langtoft 06, 1971, MC.
Hold. Thorngumbald 22, 1969, MC; Aldborough 23, 1975, EBM.

Parapholis C.E. Hubbard
P. strigosa (Dumort.) C.E. Hubbard (*Lepturus filiformis* auct.)   Map 213.
Hard-grass.   OSE.   1896.
Native. Salt and brackish marshes and on bare ground near sea or R. Humber. Locally frequent in salt-marshes along the R. Humber and on the R. Humber shore west to Brough 92.
Here and there on the sea coast: Hornsea Sands 24, 1938, RB (BEC *12*, 205); Barmston 15, 1970, KFPB.

P. incurva (L.) C.E. Hubbard
Curved Hard-grass.   OSE.
Native. On bare sandy ground, only covered by high spring tides. Rare.
Spurn Point 41, 1970, T. Dargie (Dargie, 1970), still present.

Nardus L.
N. stricta L.   Map 42.
Mat-grass.
Native. On poor dry to damp sandy and peaty soils; usually on heaths and commons. Uncommon, but sometimes in quantity.
Most records for Lower Derwentland: Market Weighton sandfield 84, JJM (R. 1902); Skipwith Common 63 (R. 1902) and 1951, FEC; Snake Hall Moor 83, 1953, FEC; Bunny Hill 83, 1953, RG; Heslington Common 64, 1957, FEC; Breighton Common 73, 1958, FEC; Allerthorpe Common 74, 1959, FEC; Ellerton Common 74, 1970, DWS; Duck Nest 83, 1981, FEC.
Rare elsewhere:
Wolds At foot of grassy slope, Wharram Quarry 86, 1959, FEC.
Hold. Swine Moor, Beverley 04, 1920, YNU Excursion.

Spartina Schreb.
S. anglica C.E. Hubbard
Common Cord-grass.
Introduced. Widely established along the lower reaches of the R. Humber covering large areas of mud flats as in Spurn Bight. In the early years of its introduction, it was erroneously recorded as *S.* x *townsendii*.
First recorded at Welwick 31, 1932, TS (W. 1938) where it is believed to have been deliberately introduced; arrived at Spurn 41, 1946, FEC. Locally dominant in several salt-marshes and frequent by the Kilnsea Canal 41. There has been a recession of the *Spartina* belt in some areas in very recent years as new salt-marshes have begun to form.

Echinochloa Beauv.
E. crus-galli (L.) Beauv. (*Panicum crus-galli* L.)
Cockspur.
Introduced.   Uncommon.
L.D. Olympia Oil Mill Sidings, Selby 63, 1932, WAS &

JK (W. 1938).
Hold. St Andrew's Dock, Hull 02 (R. 1902); Cottingham 03, 1944, RG; King George Dock, Hull 12, 1960, FEC; near dock, east Hull 12, 1982, FH.

Setaria Beauv.
S. viridis (L.) Beauv.
Green Bristle-grass.
Introduced.   Uncommon.
L.D. Olympia Oil Mill Sidings, Selby 63, 1931, WAS & JK (W. 1938); by A163, Bubwith, resulting from a lorry spill 73, 1983, CSVY.
Wolds Cucumber houses, Elloughton 92, 1972, JG.
Hold. St Andrew's Dock, Hull 02 (R. 1902); waste place, Little High St, Hull 12, 1975, FEC.

S. italica (L.) Beauv.
Foxtail Bristle-grass.
Introduced.   Uncommon.
Hold. Spring Head, Hull 02, 1939 and Hessle 02, 1955, AKW; near seed warehouse, High St, Hull 12, 1978, FEC.

S. pumila (Poiret) Schultes [*S. lutescens* (Weigel) F.T. Hubbard; *S. glauca* auct.]
Yellow Bristle-grass.
Introduced.   Uncommon.
L.D. Olympia Oil Mill Sidings 63, 1933, WAS & CMR (W. 1938).
Hold. St Andrew's Dock, Hull 02 (R. 1902); near seed warehouse, High St, Hull 12, 1980, FEC, conf. E.J. Clement.

Panicum L.
P. miliaceum L.
Common Millet.
Introduced.   Uncommon.
L.D. Olympia Oil Mill Sidings, Selby 63, 1932, WAS.
Hold. St Andrew's Dock, Hull 02 (R. 1902); King George Dock, Hull 12, 1933-1937, AKW (W. 1938); near seed warehouse, High St, Hull 12, 1981, EC; clearance site, Division Rd, Hull 02, 1984, MG.

SUPPLEMENT OF CASUAL ALIEN SPECIES

Included in this supplement are all those rare, introduced or adventive species, which have not become naturalised or established in the East Riding of Yorkshire. Casual species which have been recorded on three or more occasions, and at least once since 1950, are included in the main text.

RANUNCULACEAE
Adonis annua L. (*A. autumnalis* L.)
Bridlington Quay 16, HS (R. 1902).

Ceratocephalus falcatus (L.) Pers. (*Ranunculus falcatus* L.)
Hull docks, 1902, CW (W. 1938).

PAPAVERACEAE
Roemeria hybrida (L.) DC.
Hull docks, CW (W. 1938).

Glaucium corniculatum (L.) Rudolph (*G. phoeniceum* Crantz)
Hull docks, 1899-1900 (R. 1902).

Eschscholzia californica Cham. [*E. douglasii* (Hook. & Arn.) Walp.]
King George Dock, Hull 12, 1935, AKW (W. 1938).

Hypecoum pendulum L.
Hull docks, 1901, CW (W. 1938).

FUMARIACEAE
Fumaria densiflora DC. (*F. micrantha* Lag.)
Hull docks, 1902, CW (W. 1938).

CRUCIFERAE
Brassica tournefortii Gouan
Bombed site, Merrick St, Hull 12, 1951, FEC.

B. juncea (L.) Czern.
Bombed site, Jenning St, Hull 12, 1953, FEC.

Erucastrum gallicum (Willd.) O.E. Schulz
King George Dock, Hull 12, CMR (W. 1938); old chalk pit Hessle 02, 1970, EC.

Sinapis dissecta Lag.
West Dock, Hull, 1900, CW (W. 1938).

Hirschfeldia incana (L.) Lagr.-Foss.
Near dock, east Hull 12, 1982, FH.

Eruca sativa Mill.
Hull docks 02, 1902, CW (W. 1938); near dock, east Hull 12, 1982, FH.

Lepidium perfoliatum L.
Alexandra Dock, Hull 12, 1903, CW; King George Dock, Hull 12, 1933-1936, AKW (W. 1938).

L. virginicum L.
West Dock, Hull 02 (R. 1902).

L. densiflorum Schrad.
King George Dock, Hull 12, 1935, AKW (W. 1938).

Erucaria hispanica (L.) Dr.
West Dock, Hull 02, CW (W. 1938).

Cardaria chalepensis (L.) Hand.-Mazz.
Bank of R. Humber, Hessle 02, 1980, EC.

Neslia paniculata (L.) Desv. [*Vogelia paniculata* (L.) Hornem.]
Hull docks, 1904, CW (W. 1938); King George Dock, Hull 12, 1953, FEC.

Bunias orientalis L.
Spurn 41, 1946, AKW & 1952, RL, herb. HLU.

Berteroa incana (L.) DC.
Old mill site, Brough 92, 1939, AKW.

Barbarea verna (Mill.) Asch. [*B. praecox* (Sm.) R. Br.]
Driffield 05, MH, Hull docks (R. 1902).

B. intermedia Boreau
Hull docks, 1903, CW (W. 1938).

Malcolmia africana (L.) R.Br. [*Wilckia africana* (L.) F. von Muell.]
Hull docks, 1902, CW (W. 1938).

Matthiola sinuata (L.) R. Br.
Hull docks (R. 1902); near Hessle 02, GP (W. 1938).

Sisymbrium austriacum Jacq. [*S. pyrenaicum* (L.) Vill.]
Anlaby Common 02, 1937, AKW (W. 1938).

S. irio L.
Hull docks, 1902, CW (W. 1938).

S. loeselii L.
Hull docks (R. 1902).

CARYOPHYLLACEAE
Silene inaperta L.
Olympia Oil Mill Sidings, Selby, WAS (W. 1938).

Dianthus guttatus M. Bieb.
West Dock, Hull 02, 1902, CW (BEC. 2, 1910, 545).

Saponaria orientalis L.
Hull, CW (BEC 9, 1930, 337).

Gypsophila pilosa Huds. [*G. porrigens* (L.) Boiss.]
Hull docks, 1900, CW (W. 1938).

G. viscosa Murr.
Hull docks, 1902, CW (W. 1938).

PORTULACACEAE
Montia sibirica (L.) Howell
Birdsall House 86, 1933, RG.

Portulaca oleracea L.
Greenhouse weed, near Driffield 05, 1977, EC.

CHENOPODIACEAE
Chenopodium vulvaria L.
West Dock, Hull 02 (R. 1902).

C. berlandieri Moq. subsp. *zschackei* (Murr) Zobel
Skipwith 63, C.Druce (BEC, *9*, 1929, 36).

C. opulifolium Schrad. ex Koch & Ziz
West Dock, Hull 02 (R. 1902); Stoneferry, Hull 13, ABC
(BEC. *7*, 1923, 208).

C. hircinum Schrad.
Hull, MCo (BEC. *6*, 1922, 744).

C. glaucum L.
Hull docks (R. 1902).

C. leptophyllum Nutt.
Hull, ABC (BEC. *6*, 1922, 744); near the R. Humber shore,
Hessle 02, 1937, AKW (W. 1938).

C. aristatum L.
Olympia Oil Mill Sidings, Selby 63, 1932, WAS & JK
(W.1938).

C. striatum (Krasan) J.Murr
Hull, MCo (BEC. *6*, 1922, 744).

C. x *haywardiae* Murr (*C. hircinum* x *C. striatum*)
Oil works, Hull, MCo (BEC. *7*, 1923, 209).

Atriplex tatarica L.
Hull, MCo (BEC. *6*, 1922, 745).

A. hortensis L.
Springhead, Hull 02, AKW (BEC. *12*, 1939-1940, 292).

Axyris amarantoides L.
Hull tanneries, ABC (BEC. *6*, 1922, 745).

Kochia scoparia (L.) Schrad.
Olympia Oil Mill Sidings, Selby, 63, 1933, WAS & JK;
High St, Hull 12, 1978, FEC, det. E.J. Clement (EJC).

MALVACEAE
Malva pusilla Sm.
Hull docks (R. 1902); by Pocklington Canal 74, 1980,
RGu.

M. parviflora L.
Hull docks (R. 1902); King George Dock, Hull 12, 1933,
AKW (W.1938).

Lavatera thuringiaca L.
West Dock, Hull 02, CW (W. 1938).

L. trimestris L.
By seed warehouse, High St, Hull 12, 1984, EC.

Sida rhombifolia L.
Olympia Oil Mills Sidings, Selby 63, 1933, WAS &
JK(W.1938).

S cordifolia L.
Near oil mills, Hull, 1922, MCo (BEC. *6*, 1922, 604).

Althaea hirsuta L.
Bombed site, High St, Hull 12, 1952, FEC.

Abutilon theophrasti Med.
Olympia Oil Mill Sidings, Selby 63, WAS & JK (W 1938);
Skeffling 31, 1959, D. Wade, det. J.E. Lousley.

Hibiscus trionum L.
Olympia Oil Mill Sidings, Selby 63, 1933, WAS & JK (W.
1938).

LINACEAE
Linum bienne Mill.
Abundant along a short stretch of the A163, near Derwent
Bridge, Bubwith 73, 1983, CSVY.

GERANIACEAE
Geranium versicolor L. (*G. striatum* L.)
Roadside, Burton Constable 13 (R. 1902); by railway,
near Bridlington 16, 1977, railway survey, ITE.

G. nodosum L.
Wood, Londesborough 84, HI (Baker, 1854).

OXALIDACEAE
Oxalis europaea Jord.
Skipwith churchyard 63, 1972, TFM.

O. incarnata L.
Fulford 64, 1975, EB.

VITACEAE
Vitis vinifera L.
Bombed site, Naylor's Row 12 and Osborne St, Hull 02,
1952, FEC.

LEGUMINOSAE
Medicago laciniata (L.) Mill.
Hull, MCo (BEC. *6*, 1922, 723).

Trigonella hamosa L.
Hull dock (R. 1902).

Trifolium aureum Poll.
Staxton 07, 1940, HR (N.H. Scarb.).

Vicia villosa Roth
King George Dock, Hull 12, 1933-1937, AKW (W. 1938).

V. lutea L.
Hull docks, 1902, CW (W. 1938).

Lathyrus hirsutus L.
North cliff, Bridlington 16, RJF (BEC. *6*, 1921, 380).

L. latifolius L.
Hull docks, 1902, CW (W. 1938).

L. sativus L.
King George Dock, Hull 12, 1935, AKW (W. 1938).

Glycine soja S. and Z.
Olympia Oil Mill Sidings, Selby 63, WAS (W. 1938).

ROSACEAE
Potentilla argentea L.
Hull docks (R. 1902); King George Dock, Hull 12, 1933, AKW (W. 1938).

P. intermedia L.
King George Dock, Hull 12, 1937, WAS & AKW (W. 1938).

P. supina L.
Hull docks, JFR (W. 1938).

LYTHRACEAE
Lythrum hyssopifolia L.
King George Dock, Hull 12, 1937, AKW & WAS (W. 1938).

ONAGRACEAE
Oenothera laciniata Hill. (*O. sinuata* L.)
King George Dock, Hull 12, 1933, FS (W. 1938).

UMBELLIFERAE
Anethum graveolens L.
By seed warehouse, High St, Hull 12, 1975, FEC.

Scandix australis L.
Hull docks, CW (W. 1938).

Bupleurum lancifolium Hornem.
Fangfoss 75, 1963, MT; garden weed, Hunmanby 07, 1972, Mr Rowntree.

B. baldense Turra (*B. aristatum* auct.)
West Dock, Hull (R. 1902).

Apium leptophyllum (Pers.) Muell. ex Bentham
Hull, ABC (BEC. *6*, 1922, 728).

Ammi majus L.
Bombed site, High St, Hull 12, 1950, FEC; waste place, Stoneferry, Hull 13, 1987, RM.

A. visnaga (L.) Lam.
King George Dock, Hull 12, 1932, FS (W. 1938); by seed warehouse, High St, Hull 12, 1978, FEC.

Laserpitium latifolium L.
Bank of R. Hull, Wawne ferry 03, 1956, ESt, det. WAS, herb. FEC.

EUPHORBIACEAE
Mercurialis annua L.
Occasionally near the Hull docks, JWB (R.1902); King George Dock, Hull 12, 1931, AKW (W.1938).

Euphorbia esula L.
Gravel pit, Dunnington 65, 1928, HB; Hull docks, CW (W. 1938); Fangfoss 75, 1956, CT.

E. cuneifolia Guss.
King George Dock, Hull 12, 1932, FS (W. 1938).

POLYGONACEAE
Polygonum pensylvanicum L.
Olympia Oil Mill Sidings, Selby 63, WAS & JK (W. 1938).

P. bungeanum Turcz
Olympia Oil Mill Sidings, Selby 63, 1932, WAS & JK (W.1938).

Fagopyrum tataricum (L.) Gaertn.
Olympia Oil Mill Sidings, Selby 63, WAS & JK (W. 1938).

Rumex patienta L.
West Dock, Hull, CW (BEC. *10*, 1932, 110).

R. dentatus L.
King George Dock, Hull 12, 1937, CMR & WAS.

R. obovatus Danser
Hull, ABC (BEC. *6*, 1922, 746).

R. triangulivalvis (Danser) Rech. f.
Hull docks 02, 1922, MCo.

POLEMONIACEAE
Polemonium pauciflorum Watson
Garden weed, east Hull 13, 1979, B.Smart, det. J. Lewis, BM.

HYDROPHYLLACEAE
Phacelia ciliata Benth.
King George Dock, Hull 12, 1936, AKW (W. 1938).

P. parviflora Pursh.
King George Dock, Hull 12, 1934, AKW (W. 1938).

BORAGINACEAE
Heliotropium europaeum L.
Olympia Oil Mill Sidings, Selby 63, WAS & JK (W. 1938).

Lappula squarrosa (Retz.) Dumort., subsp. *squarrosa* [*Echinospermum lappula* (L.) Lehm.]
Near Hull docks (R. 1902); King George Dock, Hull 12, 1935, AKW (W.1938).

Asperugo procumbens L.
Hull docks and other waste ground, JWB (R.1902).

Amsinckia lycopsoides (Lehm.) Lehm.
King George Dock, Hull 12, 1933-1936, AKW (W.1938).

Anchusa undulata subsp. *hybrida* (Tenore) Coutinho.
(*A. hybrida* Tenore)
Hull docks (R. 1902).

Echium plantagineum L.
King George Dock, Hull 12, 1933, AKW (W. 1938).

CONVOLVULACEAE
Ipomoea hederacea (L.) Jacq.
Olympia Oil Mill Sidings, Selby 63, 1932, WAS & JK (W.1938).

I. sibirica Pers.
Olympia Oil Mill Sidings, Selby 63, 1933, WAS & JK (W. 1938).

Cuscuta suaveolens Ser.
Pearson's Park, Hull 03, CW (W. 1938).

C. campestris Yunck.
Herb seed garden, Cottingham 03, 1976, EC.

SOLANACEAE
Physalis alkekengi L.
Hull docks (R. 1902); garden weed, North Newbald 93, 1972, FEC.

Solanum sarrachoides Sendtn.
Spurn 31, 1977, EP.

S. rostratum Dunal.
Hull docks (R. 1902).

S. sisymbrifolium Lam.
Olympia Oil Mill Sidings, Selby 63, WAS & JK (W. 1938); bombed site, High St, Hull 12, 1953, FEC.

Nicotiana rustica L.
Garden weed, Sancton 93, M. Bleasdale, 1979, conf. EJC.

SCROPHULARIACEAE
Verbascum phlomoides L.
Near Fulford 64, 1981, EB.

Misopates calcynum Rothm.
Quay by R. Hull, High St, Hull 12, 1979, FEC, det. EJC.

Scrophularia vernalis L.
Londesborough Park 84, 1972, TFM.

Veronica longifolia L.
Rubbish tip, Hessle 02, AKW (BEC, *12*, 1939-1940, 283).

Melampyrum arvense L.
Fangfoss 75, 1956, MT.

Parentucellia viscosa (L.) Caruel
Elvington airfield 64, 1972, Miss Day; near Yedingham 87, 1972, EHW & PG.

OROBANCHACEAE
Orobanche ramosa L.
In quantity on tomato plants under glass, Thorngumbald 12, 1909, H. Knight (W. 1938).

LABIATAE
Elsholtzia ciliata (Thunb.) N. Hyl. (*E. cristata* Willd.)
Olympia Oil Mill Sidings, Selby 63, WAS & JK (W. 1938).

Salvia verticillata L.
Hull docks (R. 1902); King George Dock, Hull 12, 1933-1937, AKW (W. 1938).

S. pratensis L.
Hull docks (R. 1902).

S. reflexa Hornem.
By seed warehouse, High St, Hull 12, 1980, FEC.

S. controversa Ten.
Hull docks (R. 1902).

Stachys annua (L.) L.
Hull docks, CW (R. 1902); near oil mill by the R. Hull 12, 1934, HJD (W. 1938).

Lamium molucellifolium Fr.
Nursery, near Cottingham 03, 1955, RG, herb. HLU.

Leonurus cardiaca L.
Barlby 63, 1905, JWB; Cliffe Common station 63, 1909, JFR (W. 1938).

L. marrubiastrum L.
Hull docks (R. 1902).

Wiedemannia orientalis Fisch. & Mey.
West Dock, Hull, CW (W. 1938).

Amethystea caerulea L.
Olympia Oil Mill Sidings, Selby 63, 1931, JK (W. 1938).

PLANTAGINACEAE
Plantago indica L. (*P. arenaria* Waldst. & Kit.)
Hull docks (R. 1902).

CAMPANULACEAE
Campanula patula L.
King George Dock, Hull 12, 1933, FS (W. 1938).

C. rapunculus L.
Wressle 73, Archdeacon Pierson (O.B.G. 1805).

RUBIACEAE
Spermacoce verticillata L. [*Borreria verticillata* (L.) G.F. Meyer]
Olympia Oil Mill Sidings, Selby 63, 1933, WAS & JK (W. 1938).

Galium spurium L. var. *vaillantii* DC.
Hull docks, CW (W. 1938).

VALERIANACEAE

Valerianella eriocarpa Desv.
Hull docks, CW (W. 1938).

DIPSACACEAE

Dipsacus sativus (L.) Honck. [*D. fullonum* (L.) subsp.
sativus (L.) Thell.]
West Dock, Hull 02 (R. 1902); near seed warehouse, High
St, Hull 12, 1980, FEC.

Cephalaria gigantea (Ledeb.) Bobrov [*C. elata* (Hornem.)
Schrad.]
Roadside between South Cave and Elloughton, 1937, (W.
1938).

COMPOSITAE

Bidens pilosa L.
Near docks, east Hull 12, 1982, FH.

Helianthus decapetalus L. (*H. multiflorus* L.)
King George Dock, Hull 12, 1935, AKW (W. 1938).

H. giganteus L.
King George Dock, Hull 12, 1933, AKW (W. 1938).

H. annuus L.
Near seed warehouse, High St, Hull 12, 1981, FEC.

Ambrosia artemisiifolia L.
Olympia Oil Mill Sidings, Selby 63, WAS & JK (W. 1938).

A. trifida L.
Skeffling 31, 1959, D. Wade, det. J.E. Lousley (JEL).

Spilanthes decumbens (Sm.) Moore var. *leptophylla* (DC.)
Moore
King George Dock, Hull 12, 1933, AKW (W. 1938).

Siegesbeckia orientalis L.
Olympia Oil Mill Sidings, Selby 63, WAS & JK (W. 1938).

Hemizonia pungens Torr. & A.Gray
Hull docks (R. 1902); Endike Lane end, Beverley Rd, Hull
03, 1924, JFR; King George Dock, Hull 12, 1933, AKW,
(W. 1938).

Tagetes minuta L.
King George Dock, Hull 12, 1933, AKW (W. 1938).

Villanova dissecta DC.
Hull docks (R. 1902).

Senecio tanguticus Maxim.
Allotment, Sutton on Hull 13, 1952, FEC.

Inula helenium L.
Near Willerby 03, 1898, CW (R. 1902).

Parthenium hysterophorus L.
Hull docks (R. 1902).

Anaphalis margaritacea (L.) Benth.
Pit near Cottingham 03, 1960, FEC.

Anthemis austriaca Jacq.
Hull docks, CW (W. 1938).

A. ruthenica M. Bieb.
Hull docks, CW (W. 1938).

A. altissima L.
Hull, 1914, CW (BEC. *9*, 1917, 112).

Achillea alpina L.
King George Dock, Hull 12, 1934, AKW (W. 1938).

A. distans subsp. *tanacetifolia* Janchen. (*A. tanacetifolia*
All.)
West Dock, Hull 02, CW (W. 1938).

A. ligustica All.
Hull docks (R. 1902).

Matricaria decipiens Koch
Hull, CW (BEC. *9*, 1918, 384).

Artemisia campestris L.
Occasionally near the Hull docks (R. 1902).

A, macrantha Ledeb.
King George Dock, Hull 12, 1936, AKW (W. 1938).

Carduus pycnocephalus L.
Hull docks, CW; King George Dock, Hull 12, 1934, AKW
(W. 1938).

Centaurea calcitrapa L.
Hull docks (R. 1902).

C. aspera L.
Hull docks (R. 1902).

C. melitensis L.
Hull docks (R. 1902).

C. axillaris Willd. (*C. cheiranthifolia* Willd.)
Kelsey Hill 22, 1935, FS (W. 1938).

C. diluta Ait.
By seed warehouse, High St, Hull 12, 1979, FEC, det. EJC.

C. salmantica L.
Near seed warehouse, High St, Hull 12, 1975, FEC, det.
R.D. Meikle.

Rhagadiolus stellatus (L.) Gaertn. (*R. edulis* Gaertn.)
Hull docks (R. 1902).

Carthamus tinctorius L.
Rubbish tip, Brough 92, 1939, AKW (BEC. *12*, 1939-1940,
284); near seed warehouse, High St, Hull 12, 1981, EC and
by Humber Dock, Hull 02, 1982, FEC.

Tragopogon hybridus L.
Garden weed, Swanland 92, 1978, FEC, det. EJC.

T. porrifolius L.
Hull docks (R. 1902); cliffs near Bridlington 16, WLW (W. 1938).

Hieracium diaphanum Fr.
King George Dock, Hull 12, 1933, D.W. Toyne (W. 1938).

Crepis setosa Haller f.
North Cave 83, 1898, JFR (R. 1902).

LILIACEAE
Asparagus officinalis L.
Near Spurn 41, E.W. Wade (W. 1938) and 1961, A Vaughan; Humber foreshore, Ferriby 92, 1948, RL.

Lilium pyrenaicum Gouan
Spurn 41, RG, ((W. 1938).

Asphodelus fistulosus L.
West Dock, Hull 02, 1904, CW (BEC. *3*, 1911, 129); Salt End Common 12, 1915, JWB, herb. FEC.

Ornithogalum nutans L.
Between York and Heslington 64 (Baines, 1840); Kexby 75, 1900-1901, WB.

AMARYLLIDACEAE
Allium carinatum L.
Heslington Fields 64 (Baines, 1840); Barlby 63, WNC (R. 1902).

A. neapolitanum Cyr.
King George Dock, Hull 12, 1935, AKW (W. 1938).

A. moly L.
Near Fangfoss 75, 1961, MT (Nat. 1962, 26).

IRIDACEAE
Sisyrinchium montanum Greene var. *cerebrum* Fern.
Garden weed, east Hull 12, 1982, FEC.

Iris germanica L.
Wood, Wheldrake 64, 1965, YNU Excursion.

Gladiolus byzantinus Mill.
Southcoates, Hull 13, 1979, EC.

COMMELINACEAE
Commelina coelestis Willd.
Olympia Oil Mill Sidings, Selby 63, WAS (W.1938).

GRAMINEAE
Lolium remotum Schrank
In seed fields (R. 1902).

L. rigidum Gaud.
By seed warehouse, High St, Hull 12, 1981, FEC.

Puccinellia festuciformis (Host) Parl.
Hull, 1907-1908, CW (SYF).

Cynosurus echinatus L.
King George Dock, Hull 12, 1932, TS (W. 1938); Staxton 07, 1947, ERC.

Lamarckia aurea (L.) Moench
East Park, Hull 13, CW (W. 1938).

Briza maxima L.
Disused railway station, Ellerby 13, 1984, FEC.

Bromus madritensis L.
Hull docks (R. 1902); Bishop Wilton 75, 1957, RG.

B. tectorum L.
Hull docks (R. 1902).

B. arvensis L.
Cornfields, near Little Weighton 93 (Teesdale, 1800).

B. unioloides H.B.K.
Hull docks, CW (W. 1938).

B. rubens L.
Hull docks, CW (W. 1938).

B. scoparius L.
Hull docks (R. 1902).

B. macrostachys Desf.
Hull docks (R. 1902).

B. squarrosus L.
Hull docks (R. 1902).

Brachypodium distachyon (L.) Beauv.
Hull docks, CW (W. 1938).

Koeleria phleoides (Vill.) Pers.
Hull docks, CW (W. 1938).

Phalaris paradoxa L.
Hull docks, CW; King George Dock, Hull 12, 1934, AKW (W. 1938).

P. aquatica L. (*P. bulbosa* auct., non L.)
Hull, ABC (BEC. *6*, 1922, 752).

Sesleria capitata L. [*Panicastrella capitata* (L.) Moench]
Hull docks, CW (W. 1938).

Eragrostis pilosa (L.) Beauv.
Olympia Oil Mill Sidings, Selby 63, WAS & JK (SYF).

E. cilianensis (All.) F.T. Hubbard (*E. major* Host)
Olympia Oil Mill Sidings, Selby 63, WAS & JK (SYF).

Echinochloa utilis Ohwi & Yabuno
Near seed warehouse, High St, Hull 12, 1981, FEC.

Digitaria sanguinalis (L.) Scop. (*Panicum sanguinale* L.)
Olympia Oil Mill Sidings, Selby 63, 1933, WAS (W. 1938); near seed warehouse, High St, Hull 12, 1979, FEC.

Panicum capillare L.
St Andrew's Dock, Hull 02 (R. 1902).

Setaria verticillata (L.) Beauv.
St Andrew's Dock, Hull 02 (R. 1902); near seed warehouse, High St, Hull 12, 1979-1980, FEC, conf. EJC.

S. geniculata (Lam.) Beauv.
Near seed warehouse, High St, Hull 12, 1980, FEC.

Eleusine indica (L.) Gaertn.
Selby 63, 1956, DM.

DISTRIBUTION MAPS

An open square (□) indicates a pre-1950 record.

A black square (■) indicates a post-1950 record.

Letter symbols used on the maps indicate the type of habitat occupied by each species and the specific conditions required and are as follows:

ac	=	acid conditions	**pg**	=	poor grassland
alk	=	alkaline conditions	**pl**	=	plantation
ar	=	arable	**ps**	=	pond side
b	=	bog	**pt**	=	peaty soil
bm	=	brackish marsh	**pw**	=	primary woodland
c	=	canal	**r**	=	river
ca	=	calcareous soil	**rb**	=	river bank
cg	=	calcareous grassland	**rb(H)**	=	bank of R. Humber
cl	=	cliff	**rd**	=	roadside verge
cn	=	cornfield	**RH**	=	by the R. Hull
cp	=	chalk pit	**rs**	=	shore of the R. Humber
cy	=	clay	**rsd**	=	railway siding
d	=	dyke or drain	**rsw**	=	reedswamp
da	=	damp place	**rt**	=	railway track
db	=	drain bank	**s**	=	stream
dg	=	damp grassland	**sa**	=	sand
ds	=	dyke or drain side	**sb**	=	stream bank
dw	=	damp wood	**sc**	=	scrub
f	=	fen	**sg**	=	grassland on sand
fd	=	field edge	**SI**	=	on Sunk Island
g	=	grassland	**sl**	=	saline conditions
gd	=	garden	**sm**	=	salt-marsh
gr	=	gravel	**sp**	=	sand pit
grp	=	gravel pit	**ss**	=	stream side
gw	=	gateway	**ssh**	=	sea shore
h	=	hedge	**w**	=	wood
hb	=	hedge bank	**wc**	=	wood clearing
hth	=	heath	**wds**	=	well-drained soils
l	=	lake	**we**	=	wood edge
ld	=	large drain	**wem**	=	wet meadow
ln	=	lawn	**wep**	=	wet place
ls	=	lake side	**wl**	=	wall
m	=	marsh	**wm**	=	water-meadow
mg	=	marshy ground	**wp**	=	waste place
nb	=	near buildings	**wr**	=	wood ride
ng	=	neutral grassland	**ww**	=	wet wood
o	=	open community			
op	=	old pasture			
p	=	pond (incuding water-filled gravel pit)			
pa	=	path			

1 Acinos arvensis

2 Anacamptis pyramidalis

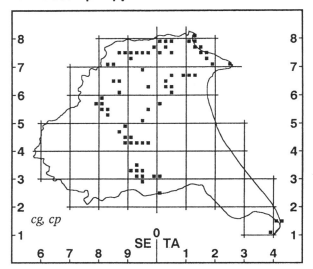

3 Arabis hirsuta

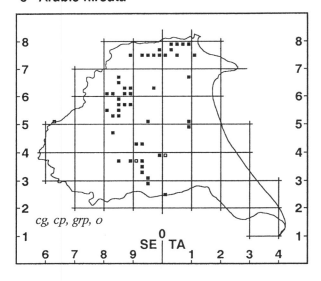

4 Astragalus danicus

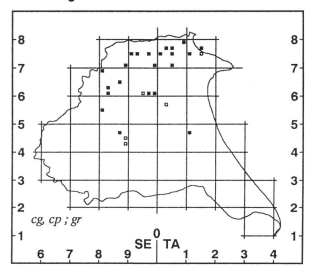

5 Avenula pratensis

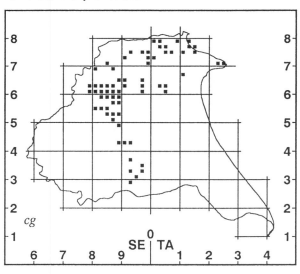

6 Brachypodium pinnatum

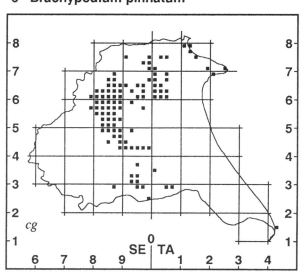

7 Bromus erectus

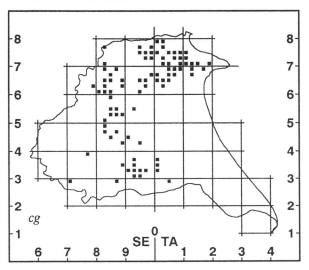

cg

8 Campanula glomerata

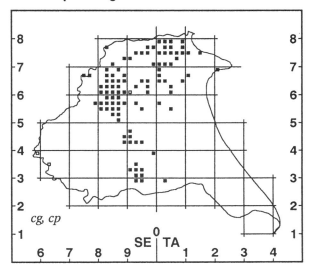

cg, cp

9 Carex caryophyllea

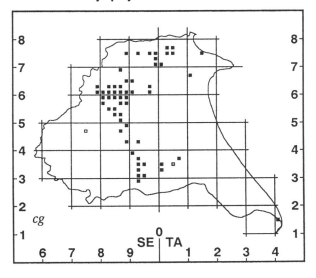

cg

10 Carlina vulgaris

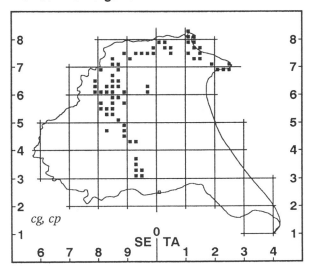

cg, cp

11 Centaurea scabiosa

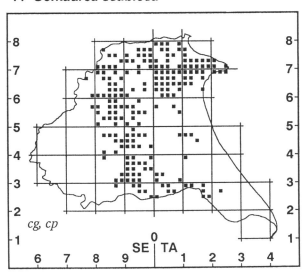

cg, cp

12 Cirsium eriophorum

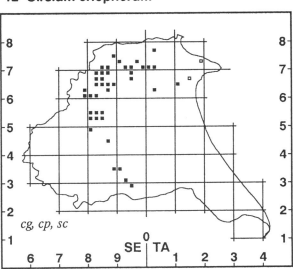

cg, cp, sc

13 Filipendula vulgaris

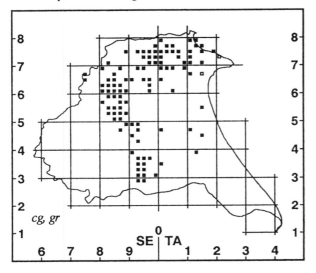

cg, gr

SE | TA

14 Galeopsis angustifolia

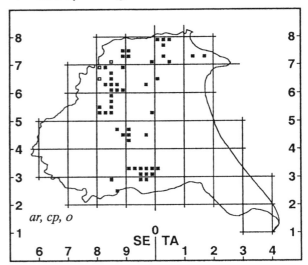

ar, cp, o

SE | TA

15 Gentianella amarella

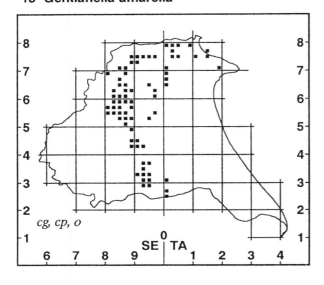

cg, cp, o

SE | TA

16 Helianthemum nummularium

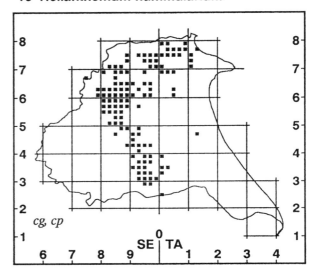

cg, cp

SE | TA

17 Koeleria macrantha

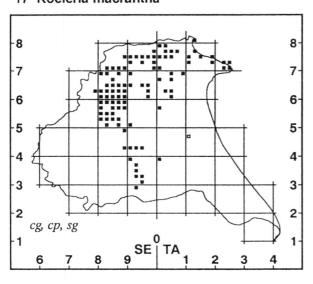

cg, cp, sg

SE | TA

18 Ophrys apifera

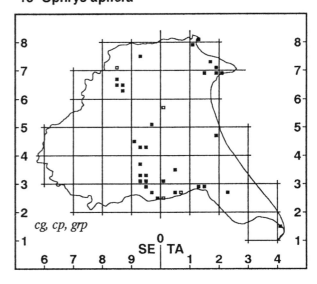

cg, cp, grp

SE | TA

19 Origanum vulgare

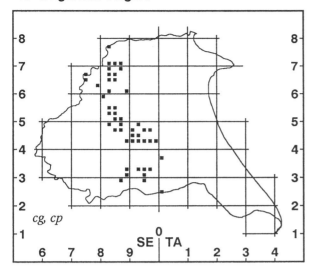

cg, cp

20 Picris hieracioides

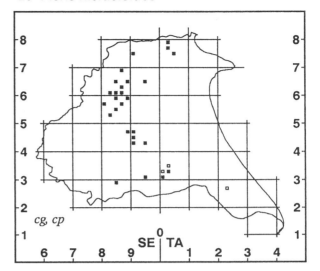

cg, cp

21 Pimpinella saxifraga

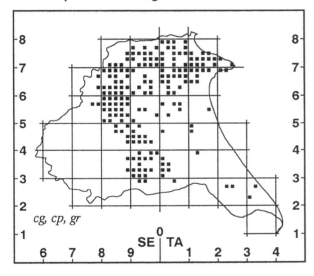

cg, cp, gr

22 Plantago media

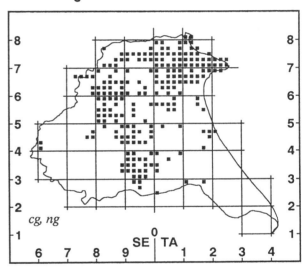

cg, ng

23 Polygala vulgaris

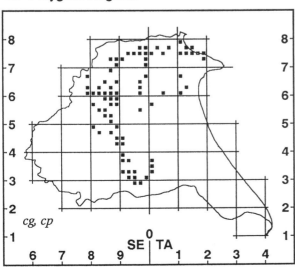

cg, cp

24 Sanguisorba minor ssp. minor

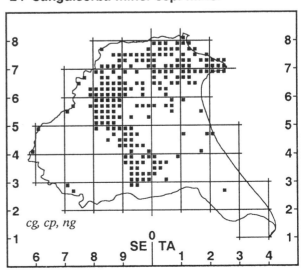

cg, cp, ng

25 Scabiosa columbaria

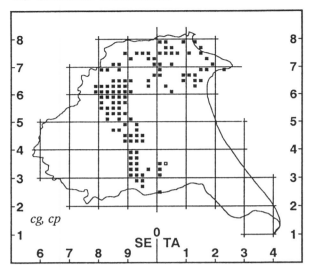

cg, cp

26 Thymus praecox ssp. arcticus

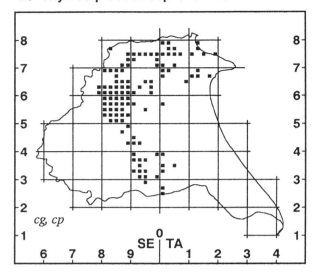

cg, cp

27 Thymus pulegioides

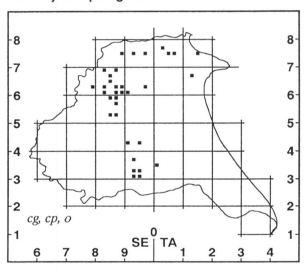

cg, cp, o

28 Viola hirta

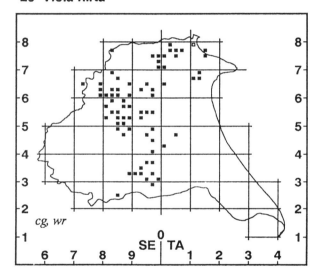

cg, wr

29 Aira praecox

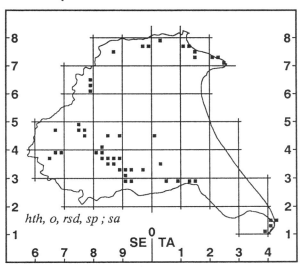

hth, o, rsd, sp ; sa

SE | TA

30 Apera spica-venti

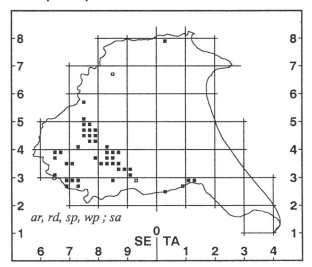

ar, rd, sp, wp ; sa

SE | TA

31 Calluna vulgaris

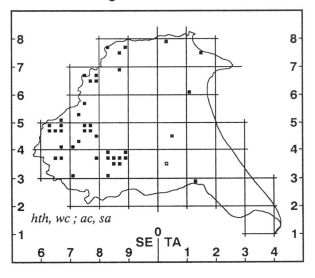

hth, wc ; ac, sa

SE | TA

32 Carex binervis

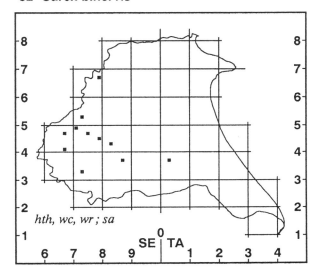

hth, wc, wr ; sa

SE | TA

33 Carex pilulifera

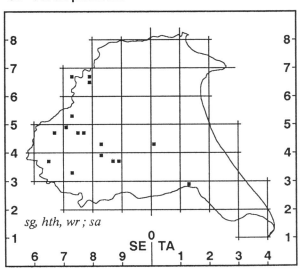

sg, hth, wr ; sa

SE | TA

34 Cerastium semidecandrum

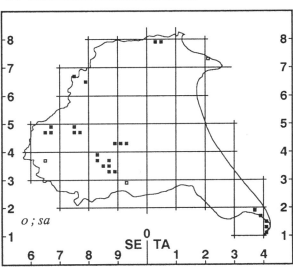

o ; sa

SE | TA

179

35 Deschampsia flexuosa

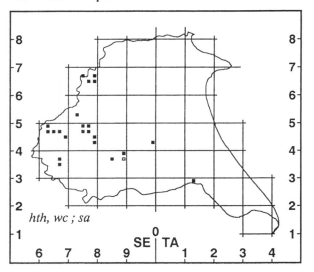

hth, wc ; sa

36 Erica tetralix

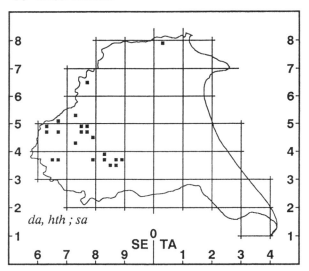

da, hth ; sa

37 Erodium cicutarium

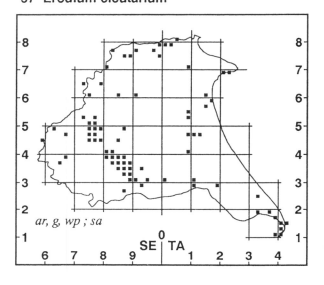

ar, g, wp ; sa

38 Filago minima

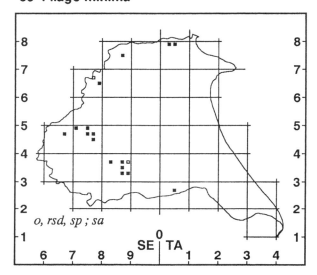

o, rsd, sp ; sa

39 Galium saxatile

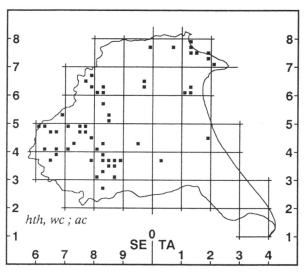

hth, wc ; ac

40 Hypericum humifusum

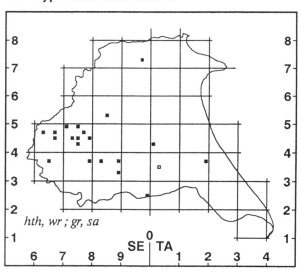

hth, wr ; gr, sa

41 Juncus squarrosus

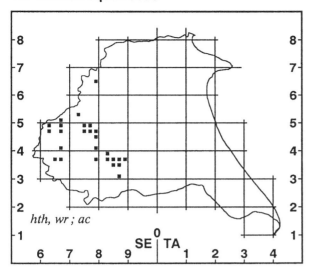

hth, wr ; ac

SE | TA

42 Nardus stricta

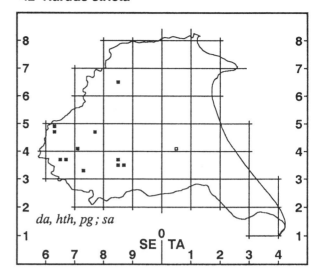

da, hth, pg ; sa

SE | TA

43 Ornithopus perpusillus

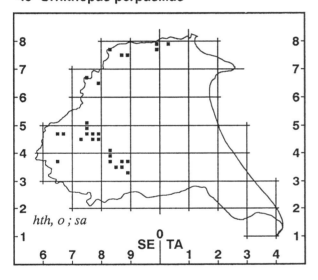

hth, o ; sa

SE | TA

44 Polygala serpyllifolia

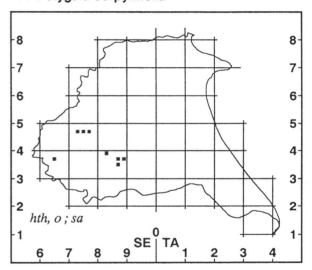

hth, o ; sa

SE | TA

45 Salix repens

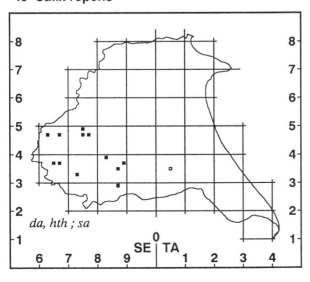

da, hth ; sa

SE | TA

46 Scleranthus annuus

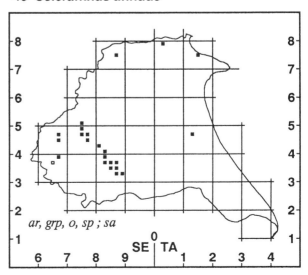

ar, grp, o, sp ; sa

SE | TA

47 Senecio sylvaticus

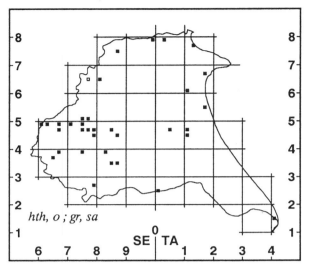

hth, o ; gr, sa

48 Spergularia rubra

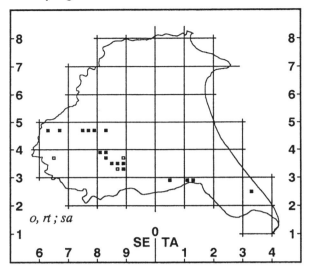

o, rt ; sa

49 Teesdalia nudicaulis

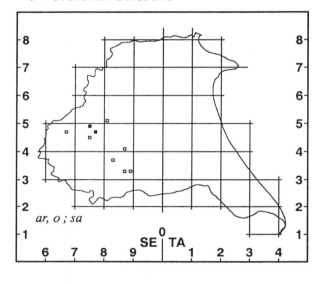

ar, o ; sa

50 Trifolium arvense

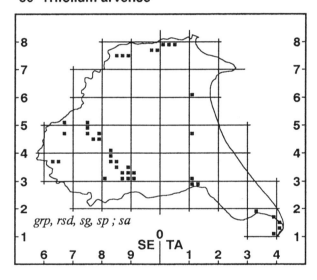

grp, rsd, sg, sp ; sa

51 Equisetum telmateia

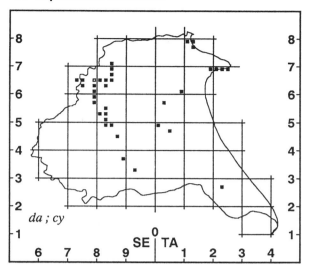

da ; cy

52 Geranium pratense

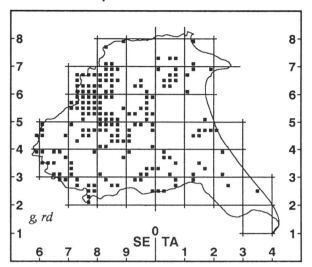

g, rd

53 Hordeum secalinum

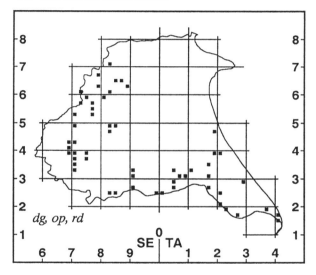

dg, op, rd

54 Picris echioides

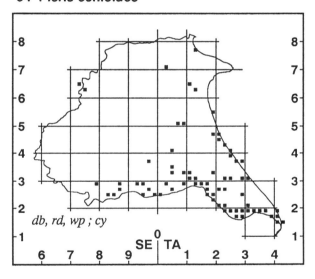

db, rd, wp ; cy

55 Sanguisorba officinalis

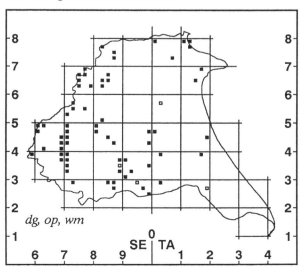

dg, op, wm

56 Senecio erucifolius

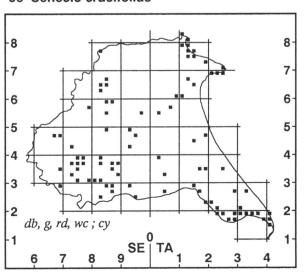

db, g, rd, wc ; cy

57 Silaum silaus

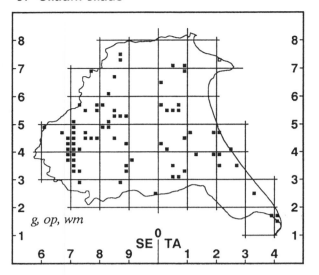

g, op, wm

58 Trifolium medium

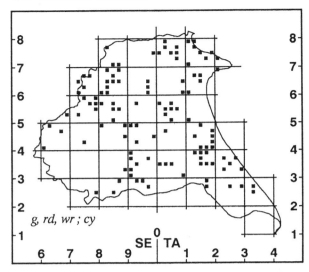

g, rd, wr ; cy

59 Allium ursinum

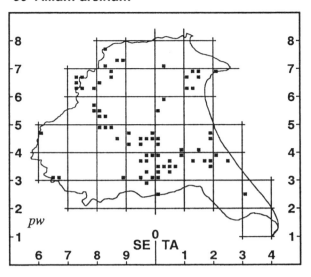

pw

60 Anemone nemorosa

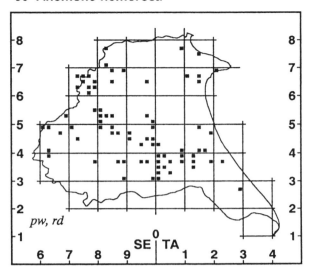

pw, rd

61 Arum maculatum

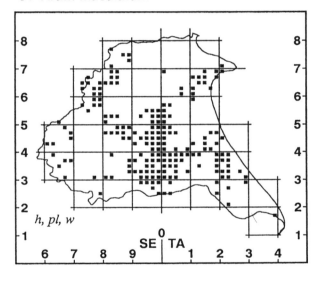

h, pl, w

62 Athyrium filix-femina

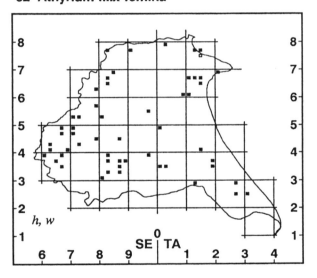

h, w

63 Atropa belladonna

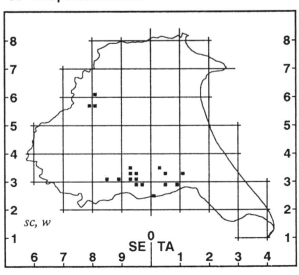

sc, w

64 Bromus ramosus

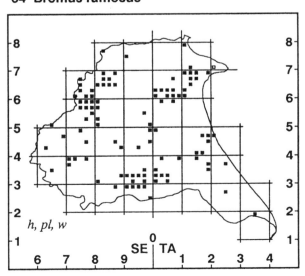

h, pl, w

65 Bryonia dioica

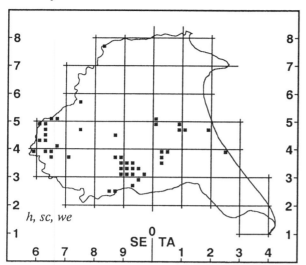

h, sc, we

66 Carex sylvatica

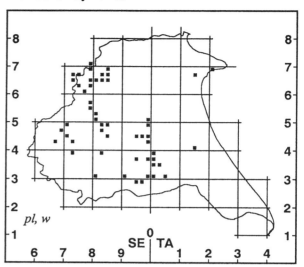

pl, w

67 Chrysosplenium oppositifolium

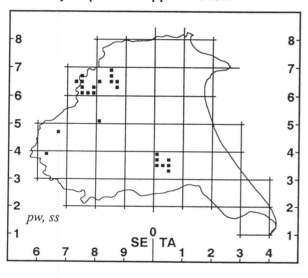

pw, ss

68 Circaea lutetiana

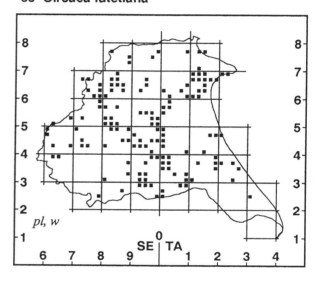

pl, w

69 Cornus sanguinea

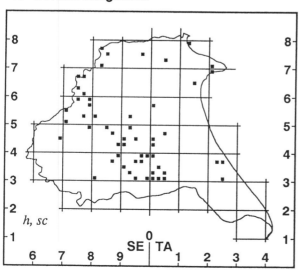

h, sc

70 Corydalis claviculata

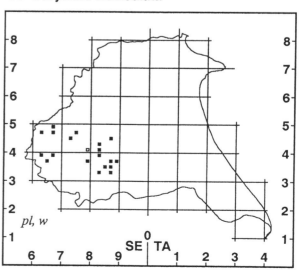

pl, w

71 Daphne laureola

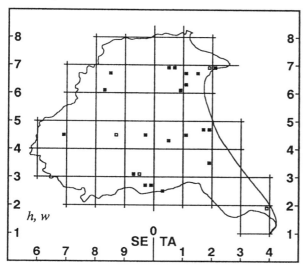

72 Dryopteris carthusiana

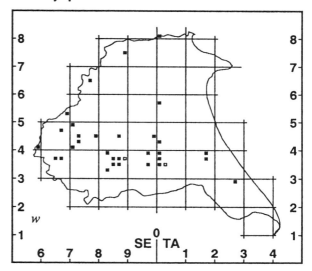

73 Dryopteris dilatata

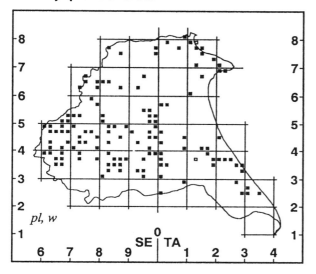

74 Elymus caninus

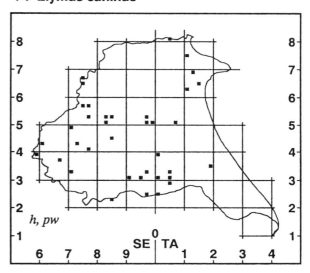

75 Festuca gigantea

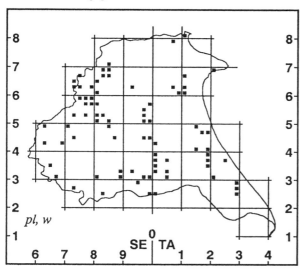

76 Hyacinthoides non-scripta

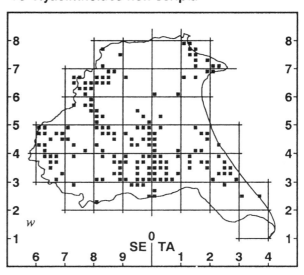

77 Ligustrum vulgare

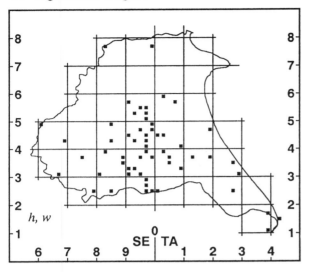

78 Lonicera periclymenum

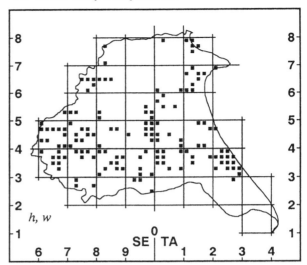

79 Luzula pilosa

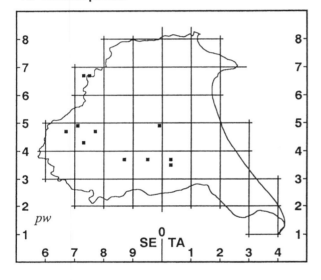

80 Lysimachia nemorum

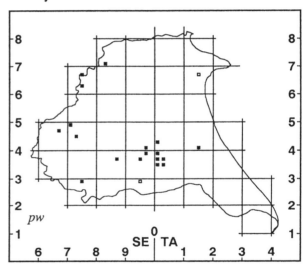

81 Mercurialis perennis

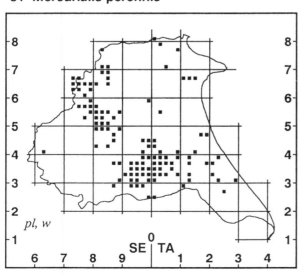

82 Milium effusum

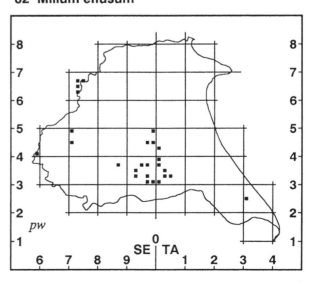

83 Moehringia trinervia

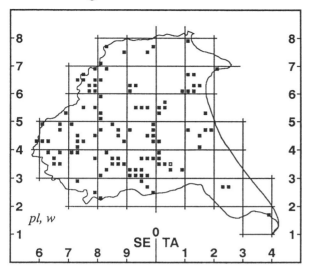

84 Oxalis acetosella

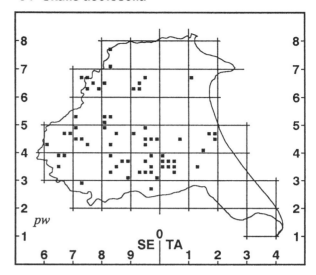

85 Poa nemoralis

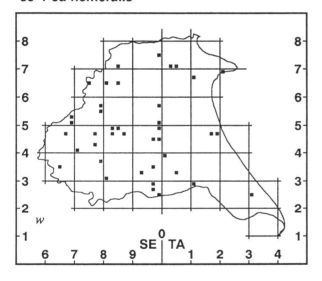

86 Primula vulgaris

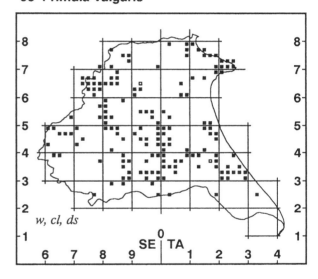

87 Ranunculus auricomus

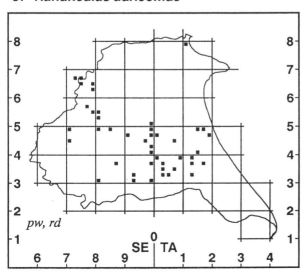

88 Sanicula europaea

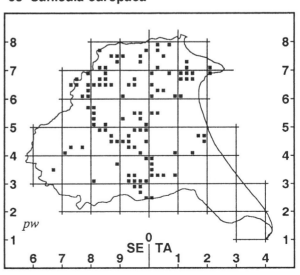

89 Scrophularia nodosa

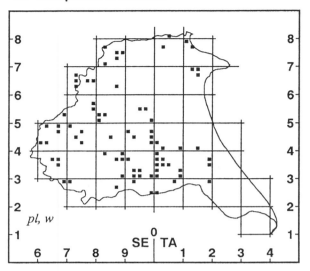

pl, w

SE | TA

90 Silene dioica

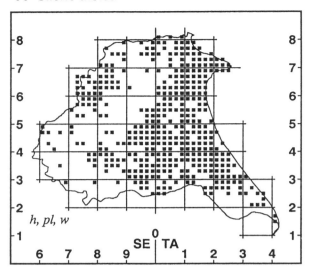

h, pl, w

SE | TA

91 Tamus communis

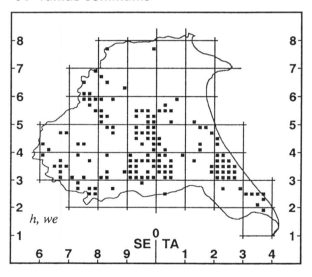

h, we

SE | TA

92 Veronica montana

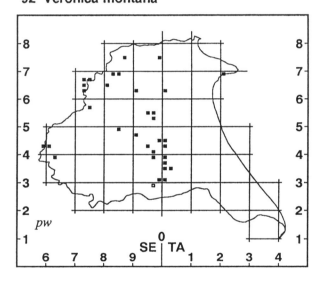

pw

SE | TA

93 Viburnum opulus

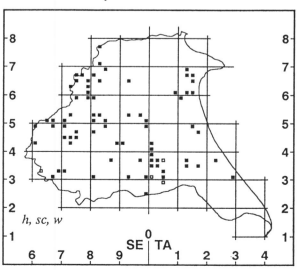

h, sc, w

SE | TA

94 Viola reichenbachiana

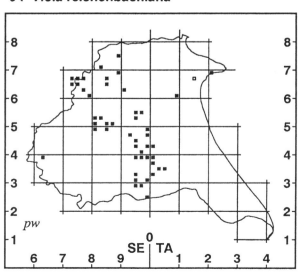

pw

SE | TA

95 Berula erecta

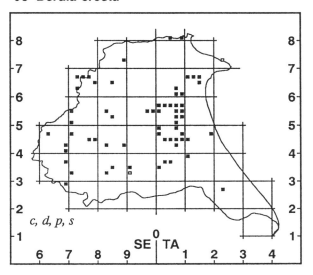

c, d, p, s

96 Catabrosa aquatica

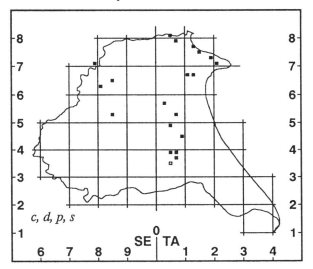

c, d, p, s

97 Ceratophyllum demersum

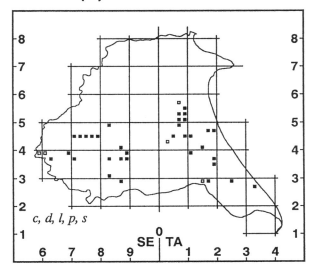

c, d, l, p, s

98 Elodea canadensis

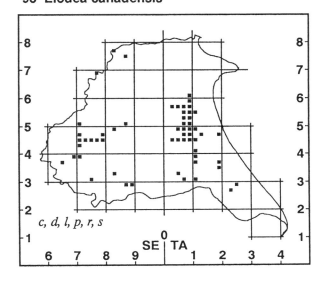

c, d, l, p, r, s

99 Groenlandia densa

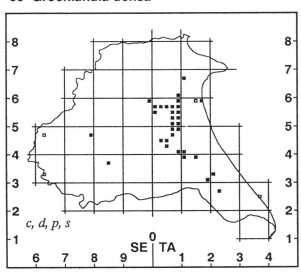

c, d, p, s

100 Hippuris vulgaris

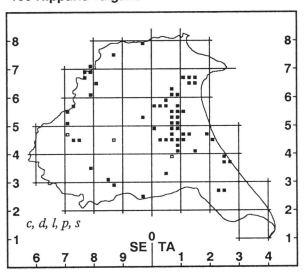

c, d, l, p, s

101 Hottonia palustris

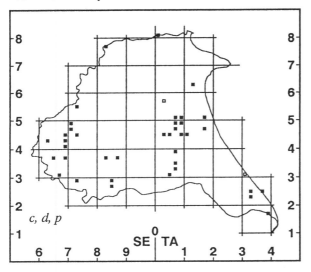

c, d, p

102 Lemna minor

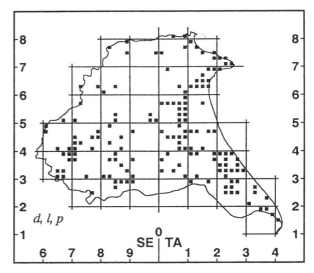

d, l, p

103 Lemna trisulca

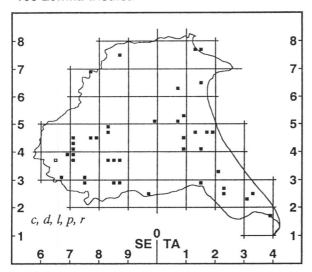

c, d, l, p, r

104 Myriophyllum spicatum

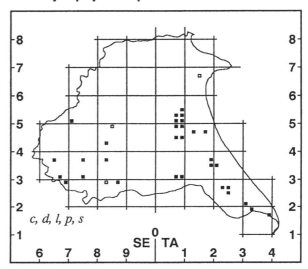

c, d, l, p, s

105 Nuphar lutea

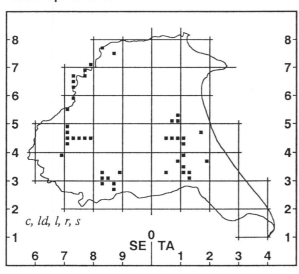

c, ld, l, r, s

106 Oenanthe aquatica

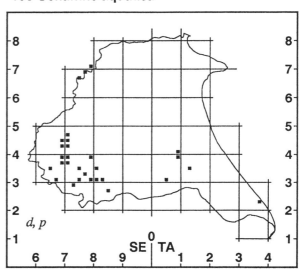

d, p

107 Oenanthe fluviatilis

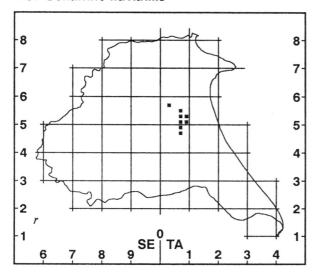

108 Potamogeton crispus

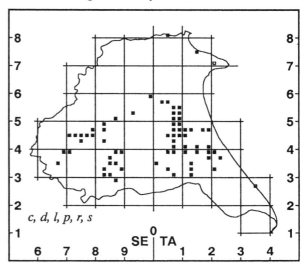

109 Potamogeton lucens

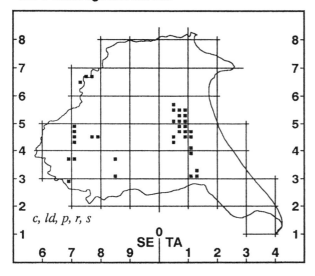

110 Potamogeton natans

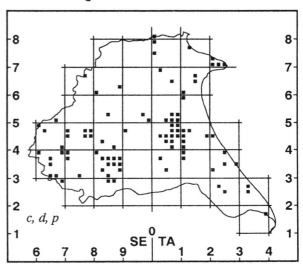

111 Potamogeton pectinatus

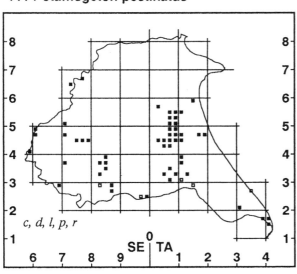

112 Potamogeton polygonifolius

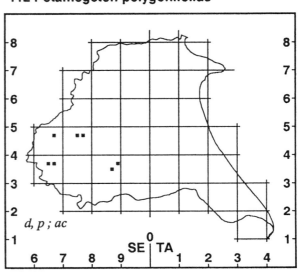

113 Ranunculus circinatus

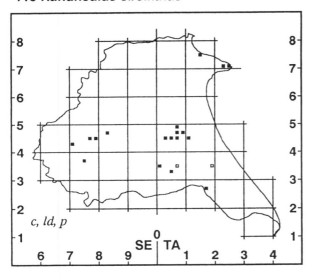

c, ld, p

114 Ranunculus peltatus

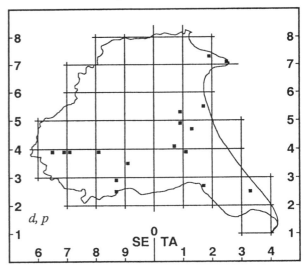

d, p

115 Ranunculus trichophyllus

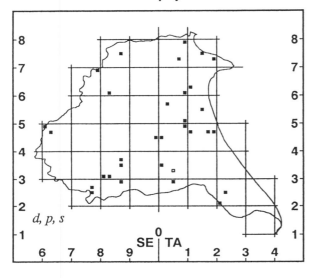

d, p, s

116 Sagittaria sagittifolia

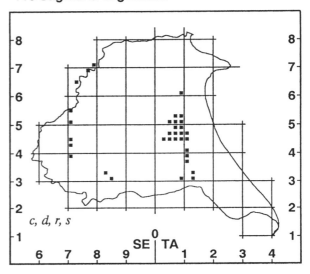

c, d, r, s

117 Sparganium emersum

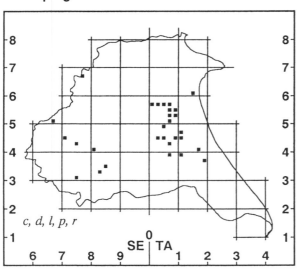

c, d, l, p, r

118 Zannichellia palustris

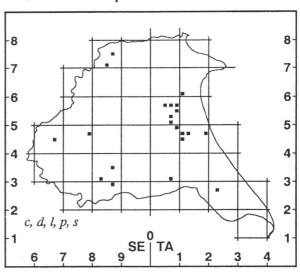

c, d, l, p, s

119 Alisma plantago-aquatica

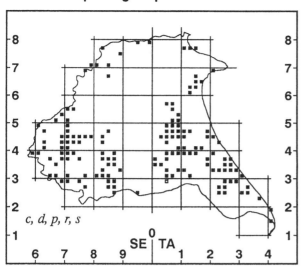

c, d, p, r, s

120 Carex acuta

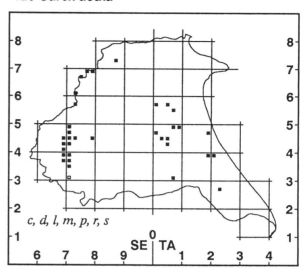

c, d, l, m, p, r, s

121 Carex acutiformis

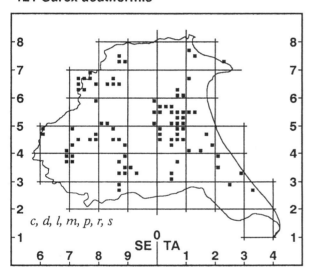

c, d, l, m, p, r, s

122 Carex elata

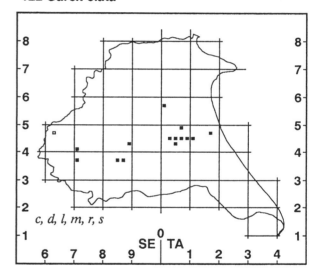

c, d, l, m, r, s

123 Carex riparia

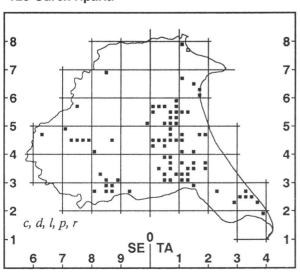

c, d, l, p, r

124 Carex rostrata

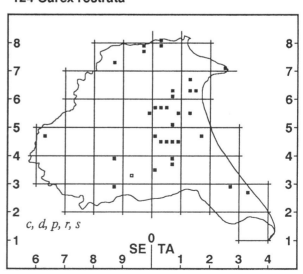

c, d, p, r, s

125 Eleocharis palustris

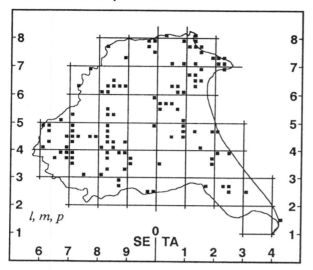

l, m, p

126 Equisetum fluviatile

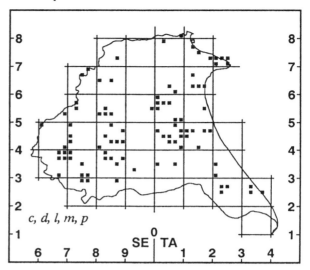

c, d, l, m, p

127 Glyceria maxima

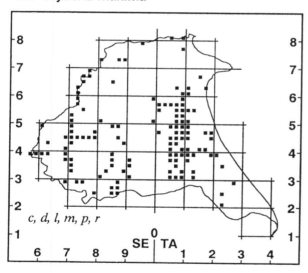

c, d, l, m, p, r

128 Iris pseudacorus

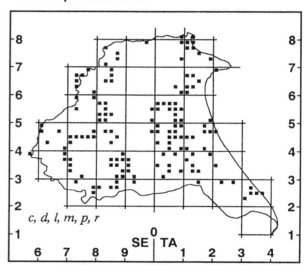

c, d, l, m, p, r

129 Phalaris arundinacea

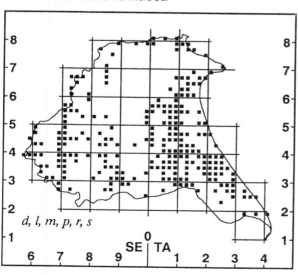

d, l, m, p, r, s

130 Phragmites australis

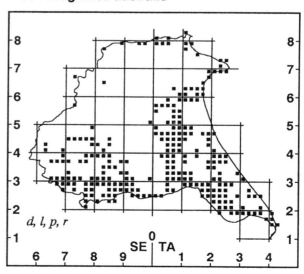

d, l, p, r

131 Rumex hydrolapathum

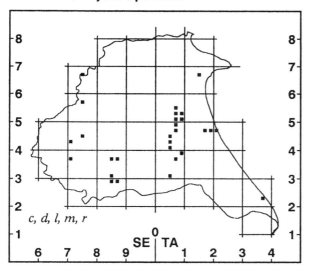

c, d, l, m, r

132 Schoenoplectus tabernaemontani

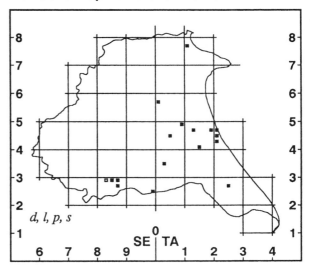

d, l, p, s

133 Sparganium erectum

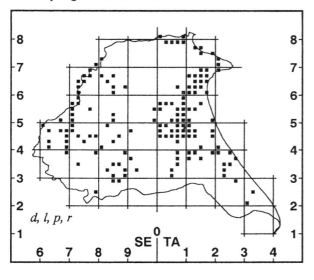

d, l, p, r

134 Typha latifolia

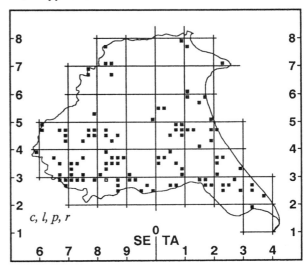

c, l, p, r

135 Apium nodiflorum

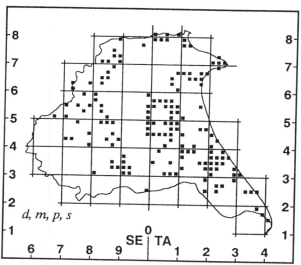

d, m, p, s

SE TA

136 Barbarea stricta

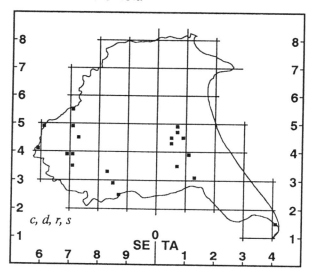

c, d, r, s

SE TA

137 Butomus umbellatus

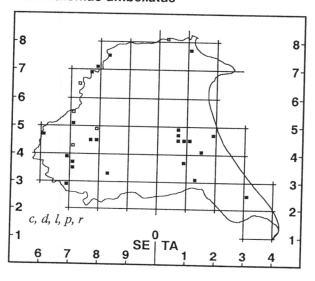

c, d, l, p, r

SE TA

138 Calamagrostis canescens

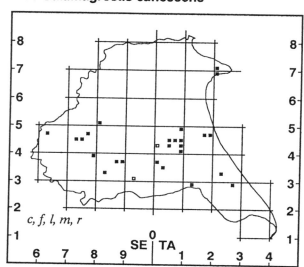

c, f, l, m, r

SE TA

139 Caltha palustris

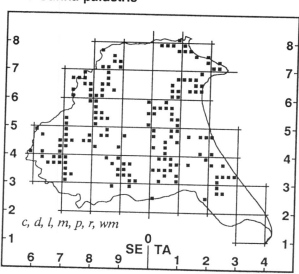

c, d, l, m, p, r, wm

SE TA

140 Carex paniculata

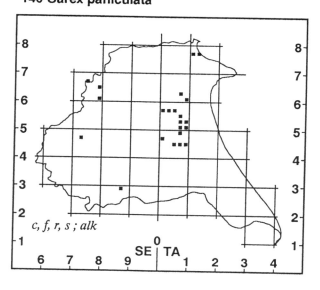

c, f, r, s ; alk

SE TA

198

141 Carex vesicaria

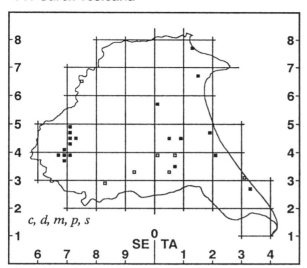

c, d, m, p, s

142 Eupatorium cannabinum

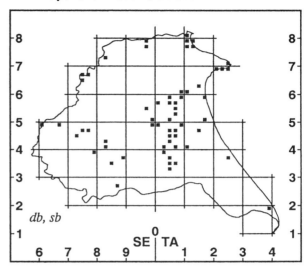

db, sb

143 Galium palustre

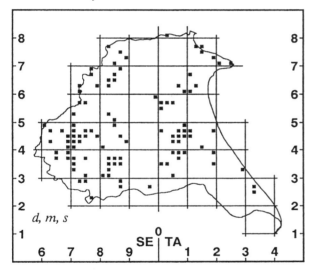

d, m, s

144 Glyceria declinata

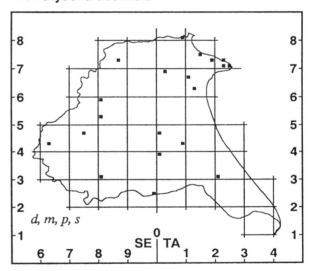

d, m, p, s

145 Glyceria fluitans

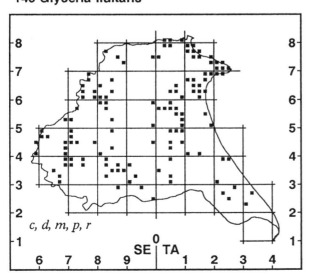

c, d, m, p, r

146 Glyceria plicata

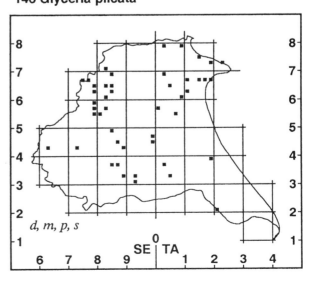

d, m, p, s

147 Hypericum tetrapterum

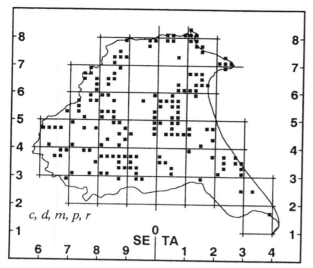

c, d, m, p, r

148 Juncus acutiflorus

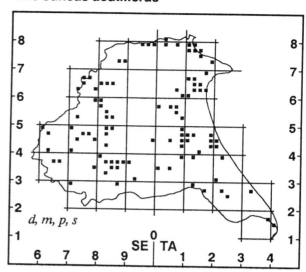

d, m, p, s

149 Juncus articulatus

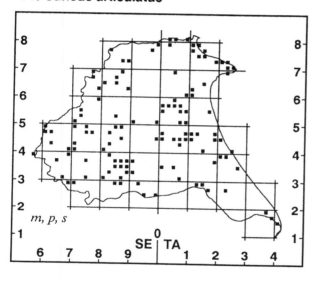

m, p, s

150 Juncus subnodulosus

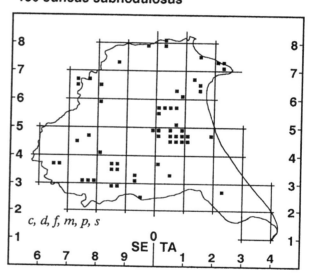

c, d, f, m, p, s

151 Lycopus europaeus

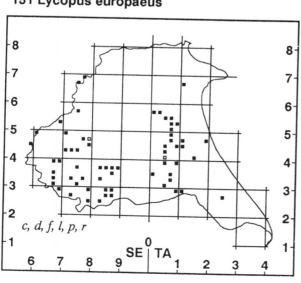

c, d, f, l, p, r

152 Lysimachia vulgaris

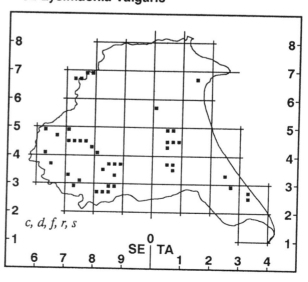

c, d, f, r, s

153 Lythrum salicaria

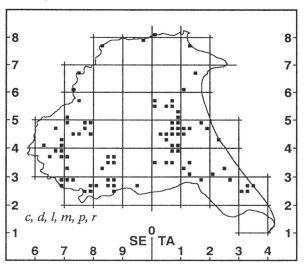

154 Mentha aquatica

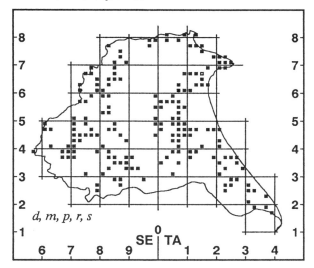

155 Myosotis laxa ssp. caespitosa

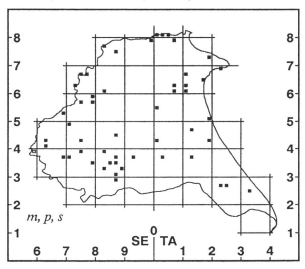

156 Myosotis scorpioides

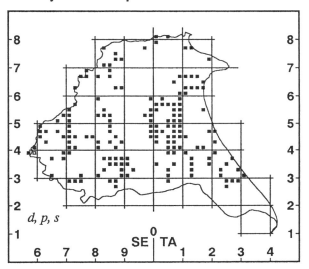

157 Myosoton aquaticum

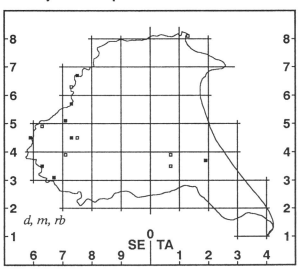

158 Nasturtium officinale s.l.

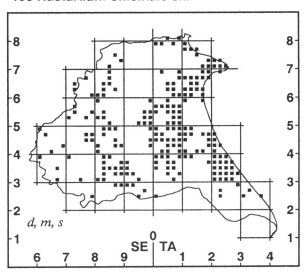

201

159 Ranunculus flammula

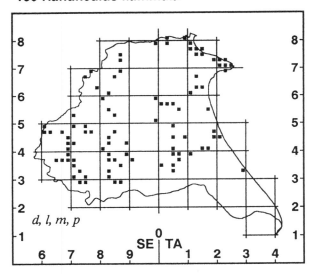

d, l, m, p

160 Ranunculus lingua

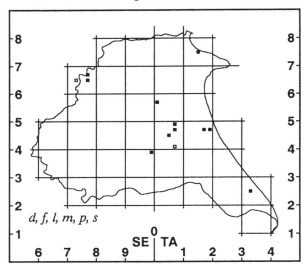

d, f, l, m, p, s

161 Ranunculus sceleratus

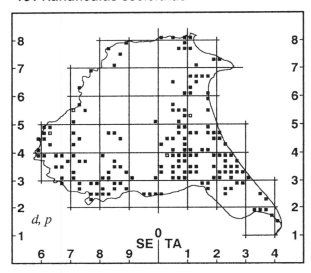

d, p

162 Rorippa amphibia

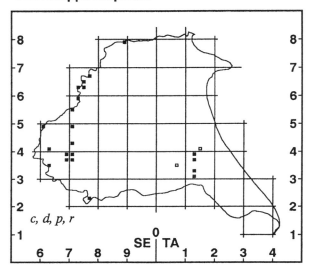

c, d, p, r

163 Rorippa sylvestris

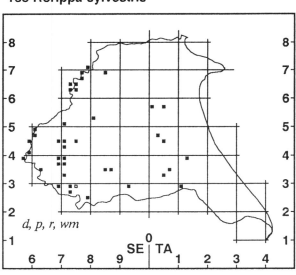

d, p, r, wm

164 Scutellaria galericulata

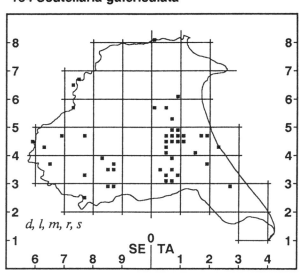

d, l, m, r, s

165 Stachys palustris

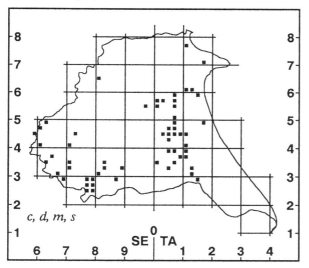

c, d, m, s

166 Stellaria uliginosa

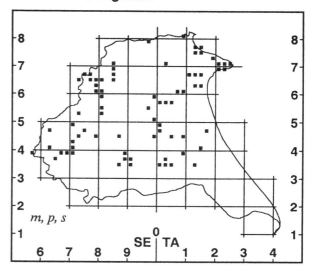

m, p, s

167 Thalictrum flavum

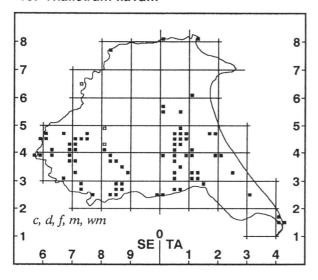

c, d, f, m, wm

168 Valeriana officinalis

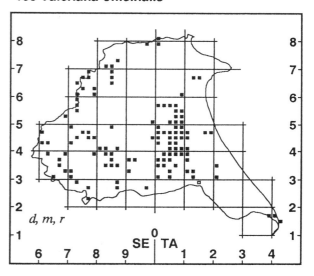

d, m, r

169 Veronica anagallis-aquatica

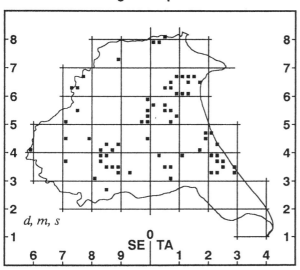

d, m, s

170 Veronica beccabunga

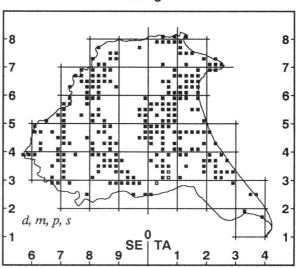

d, m, p, s

203

171 Veronica catenata

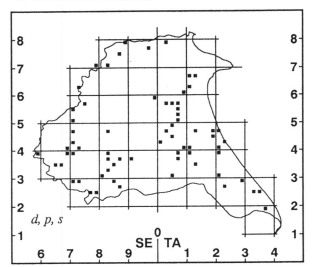

d, p, s

172 Veronica scutellata

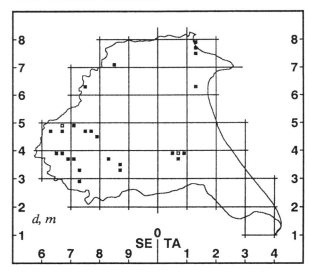

d, m

204

173 Anagallis tenella

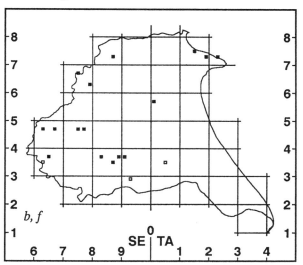

b, f

174 Blysmus compressus

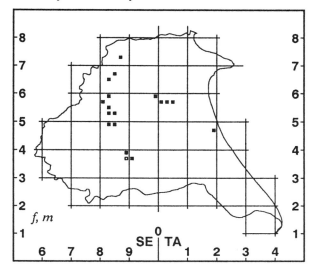

f, m

175 Carex disticha

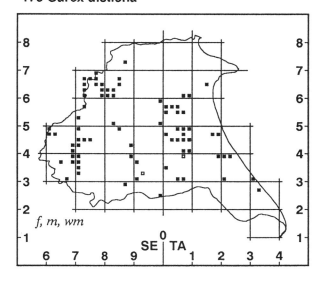

f, m, wm

176 Carex echinata

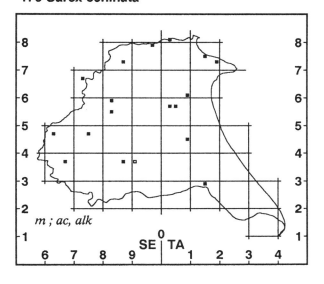

m ; ac, alk

177 Carex nigra

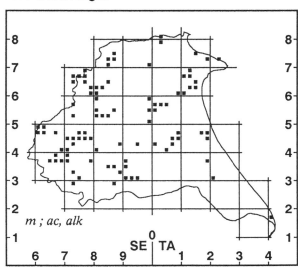

m ; ac, alk

178 Carex panicea

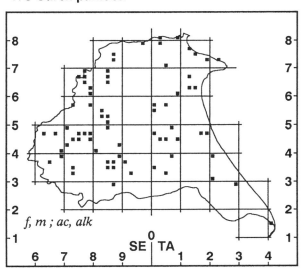

f, m ; ac, alk

179 Carex viridula ssp. brachyrrhyncha

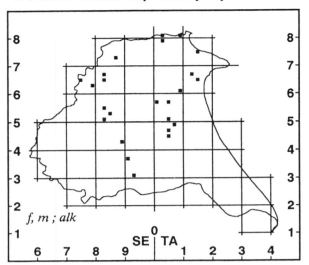

f, m ; alk

180 Carex viridula ssp. oedocarpa

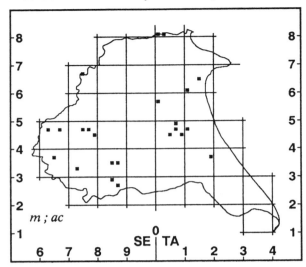

m ; ac

181 Dactylorhiza incarnata

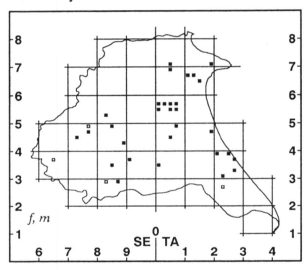

f, m

182 Epilobium palustre

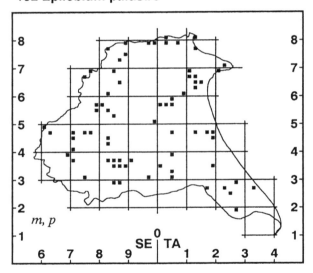

m, p

183 Equisetum palustre

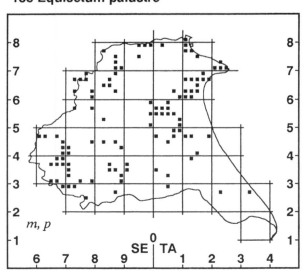

m, p

184 Eriophorum angustifolium

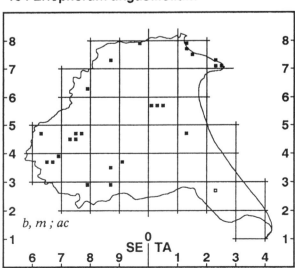

b, m ; ac

185 Galium uliginosum

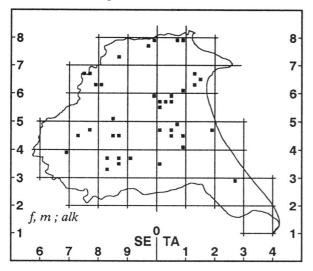

f, m ; alk

186 Hydrocotyle vulgaris

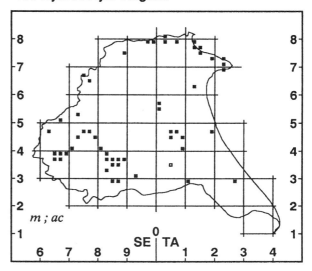

m ; ac

187 Juncus bulbosus

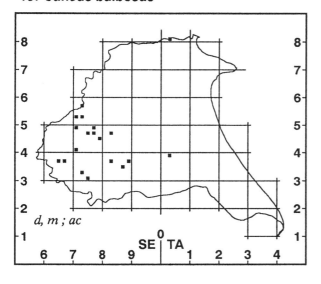

d, m ; ac

188 Lychnis flos-cuculi

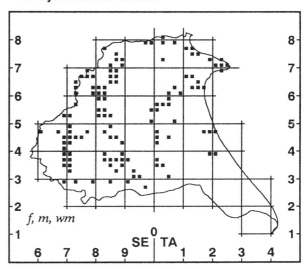

f, m, wm

189 Menyanthes trifoliata

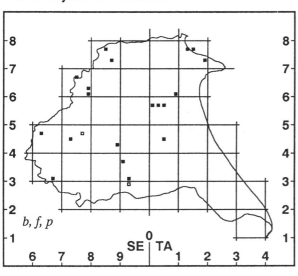

b, f, p

190 Oenanthe fistulosa

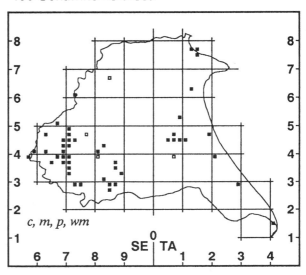

c, m, p, wm

191 Oenanthe silaifolia

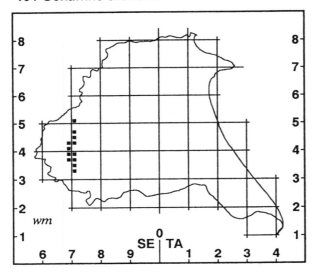

wm

192 Pedicularis palustris

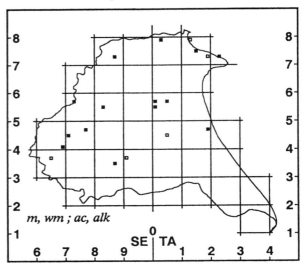

m, wm ; ac, alk

193 Polygonum hydropiper

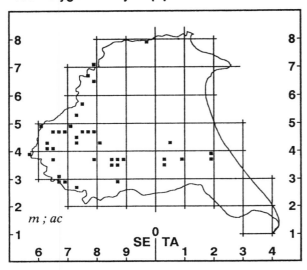

m ; ac

194 Potentilla palustris

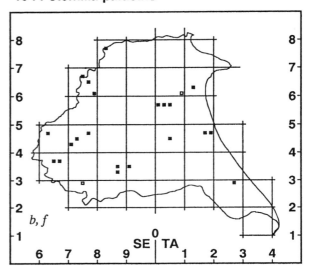

b, f

195 Samolus valerandi

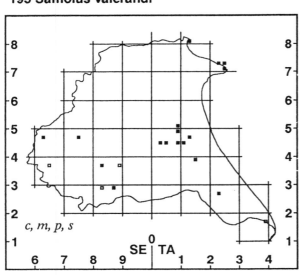

c, m, p, s

196 Senecio aquaticus

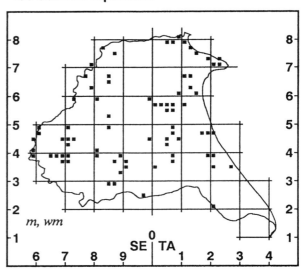

m, wm

197 Stellaria palustris

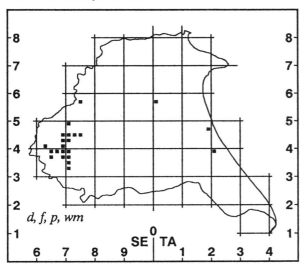

d, f, p, wm

198 Triglochin palustris

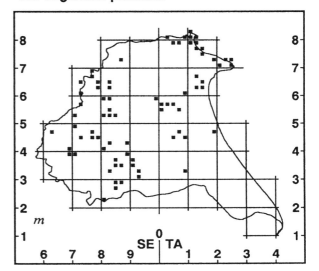

m

199 Valeriana dioica

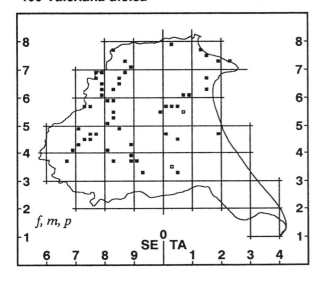

f, m, p

200 Viola palustris

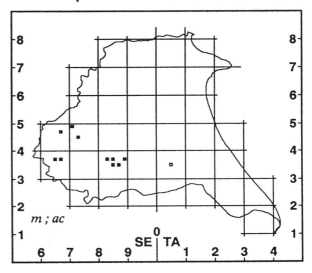

m ; ac

209

201 Ammophila arenaria

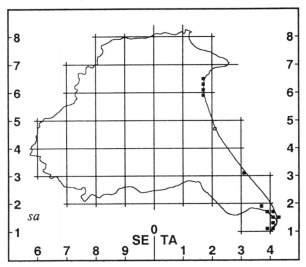

sa

202 Apium graveolens

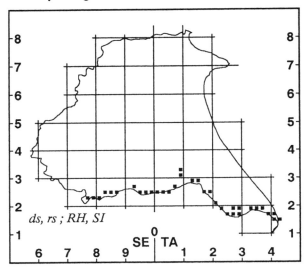

ds, rs ; RH, SI

203 Armeria maritima

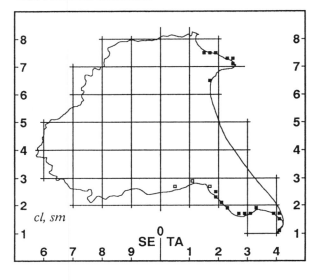

cl, sm

204 Artemisia maritima

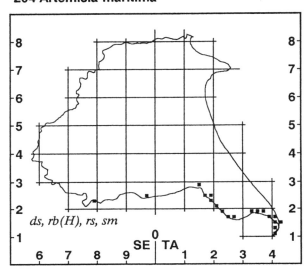

ds, rb(H), rs, sm

205 Aster tripolium

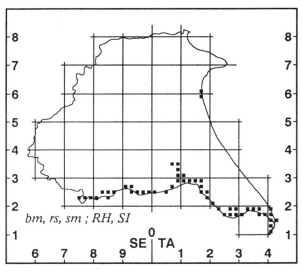

bm, rs, sm ; RH, SI

206 Atriplex littoralis

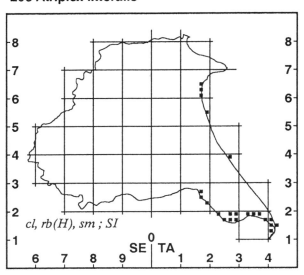

cl, rb(H), sm ; SI

207 Cochlearia officinalis

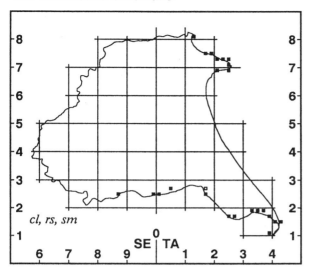

cl, rs, sm

208 Elymus farctus

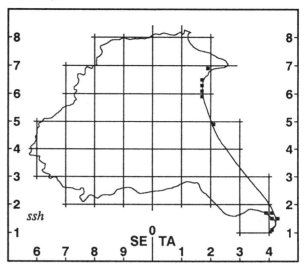

ssh

209 Elymus pycnanthus

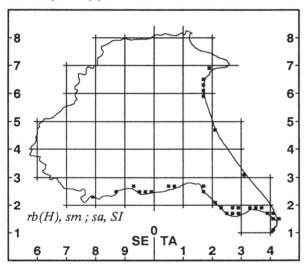

rb(H), sm ; sa, SI

210 Glaux maritima

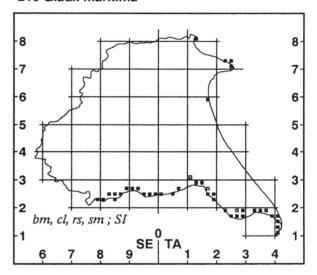

bm, cl, rs, sm ; SI

211 Halimione portulacoides

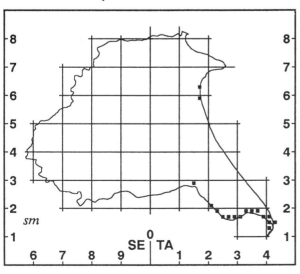

sm

212 Juncus gerardi

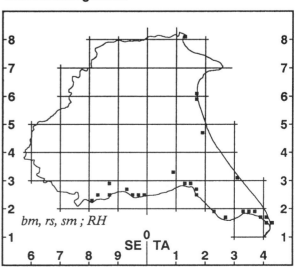

bm, rs, sm ; RH

213 Parapholis strigosa

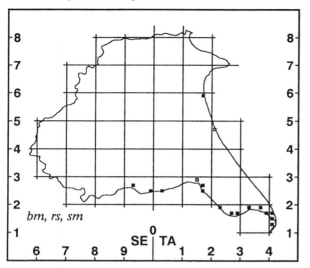

bm, rs, sm

SE TA

214 Plantago coronopus

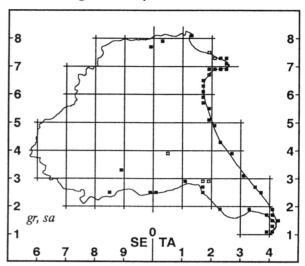

gr, sa

SE TA

215 Plantago maritima

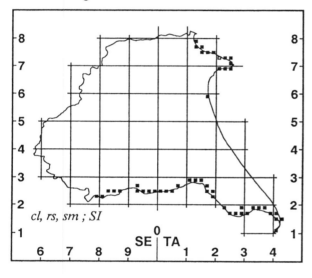

cl, rs, sm ; SI

SE TA

216 Puccinellia distans

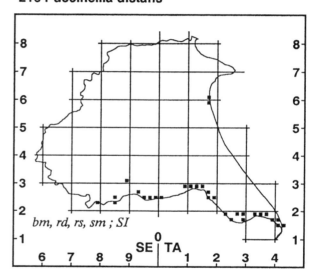

bm, rd, rs, sm ; SI

SE TA

217 Puccinellia maritima

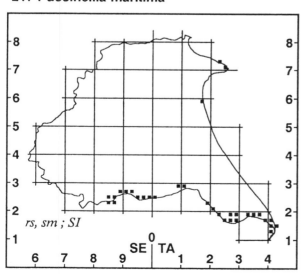

rs, sm ; SI

SE TA

218 Scirpus maritimus

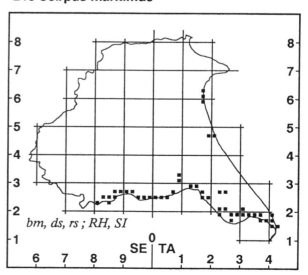

bm, ds, rs ; RH, SI

SE TA

219 Spergularia marina

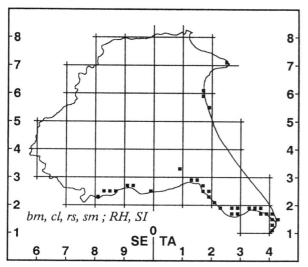

bm, cl, rs, sm ; RH, SI

220 Spergularia media

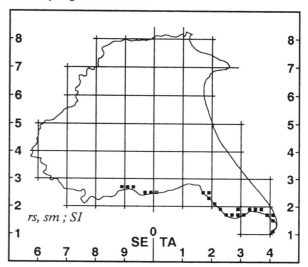

rs, sm ; SI

221 Suaeda maritima

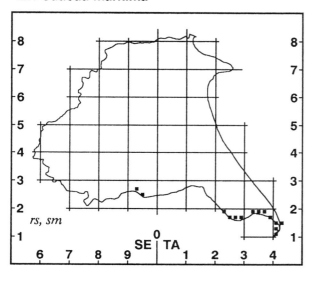

rs, sm

222 Triglochin maritima

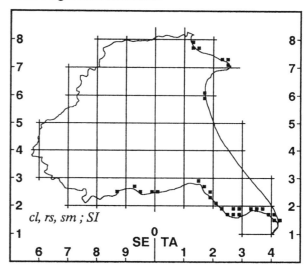

cl, rs, sm ; SI

223 Alopecurus myosuroides

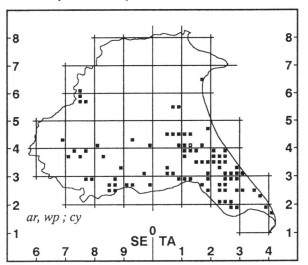

ar, wp ; cy

224 Amsinckia intermedia

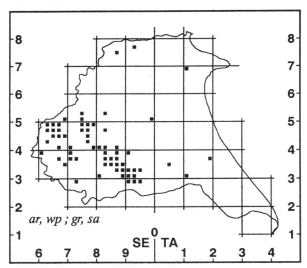

ar, wp ; gr, sa

225 Anchusa arvensis

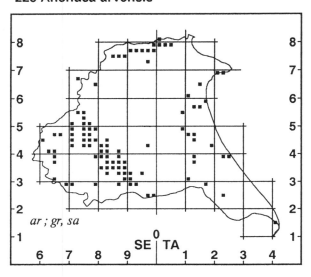

ar ; gr, sa

226 Chrysanthemum segetum

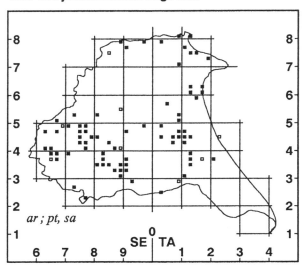

ar ; pt, sa

227 Euphorbia exigua

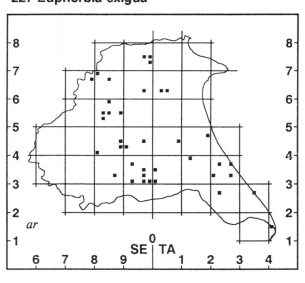

ar

228 Fumaria parviflora

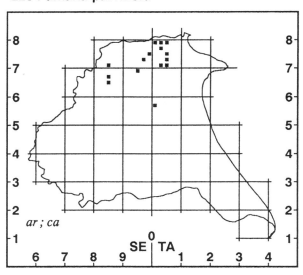

ar ; ca

229 Galeopsis speciosa

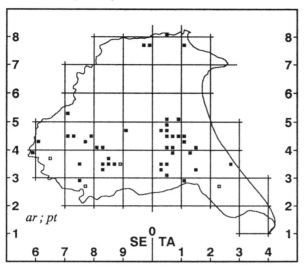

ar ; pt

SE 0 TA

230 Lamium amplexicaule

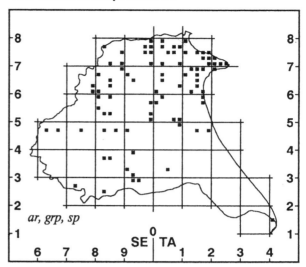

ar, grp, sp

SE 0 TA

231 Lamium hybridum

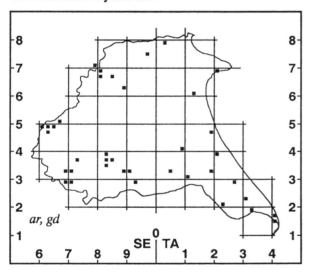

ar, gd

SE 0 TA

232 Legousia hybrida

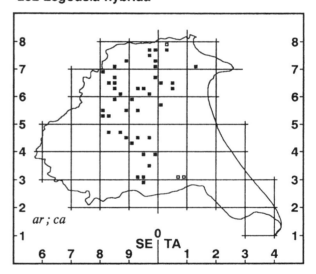

ar ; ca

SE 0 TA

233 Papaver lecoqii

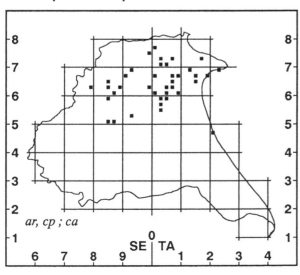

ar, cp ; ca

SE 0 TA

234 Ranunculus arvensis

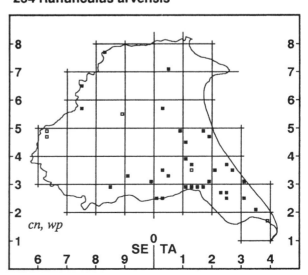

cn, wp

SE 0 TA

235 Silene noctiflora

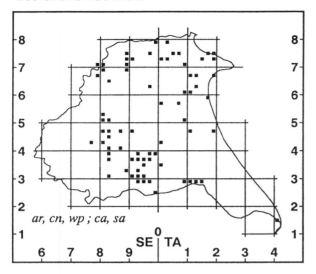

ar, cn, wp ; ca, sa

236 Spergula arvensis

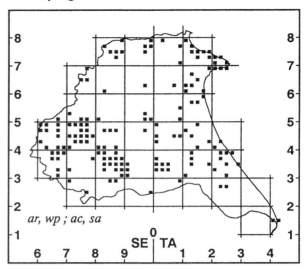

ar, wp ; ac, sa

237 Stachys arvensis

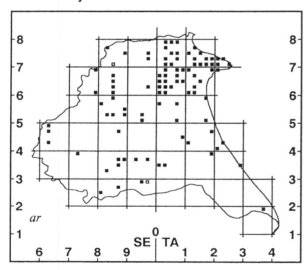

ar

238 Valerianella dentata

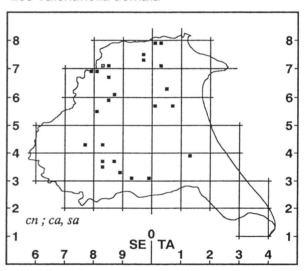

cn ; ca, sa

239 Veronica agrestis

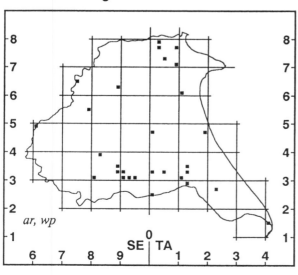

ar, wp

240 Viola tricolor ssp. tricolor

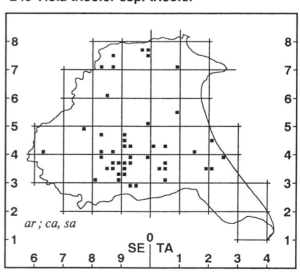

ar ; ca, sa

241 Aira caryophyllea

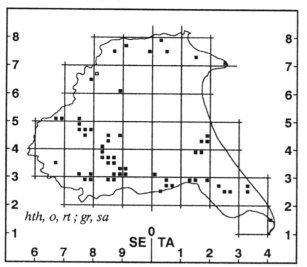

hth, o, rt ; gr, sa

242 Anthyllis vulneraria

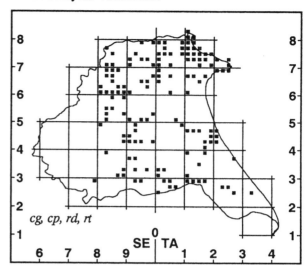

cg, cp, rd, rt

243 Chaenorhinum minus

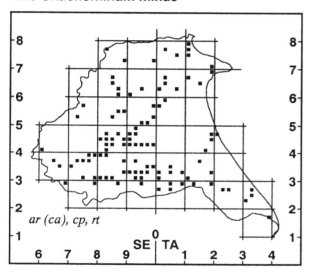

ar (ca), cp, rt

244 Hieracium pilosella

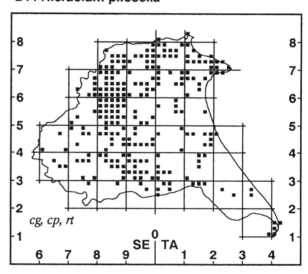

cg, cp, rt

245 Hypericum perforatum

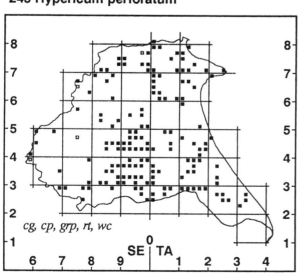

cg, cp, grp, rt, wc

246 Sedum acre

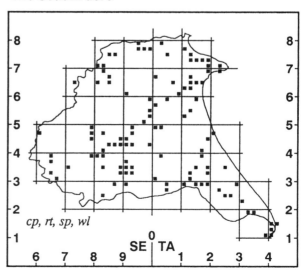

cp, rt, sp, wl

217

247 Asplenium ruta-muraria

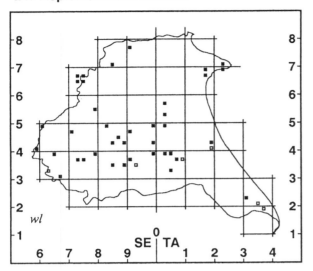

248 Asplenium trichomanes

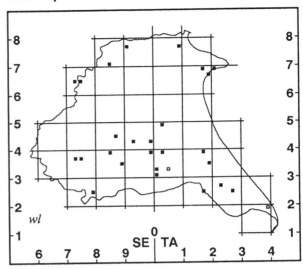

249 Cymbalaria muralis

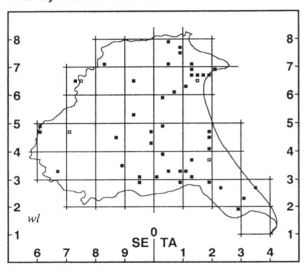

250 Parietaria judaica

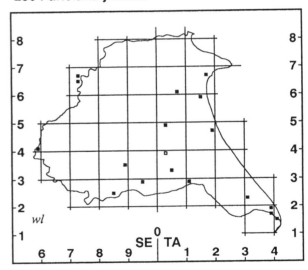

251 Calystegia silvatica

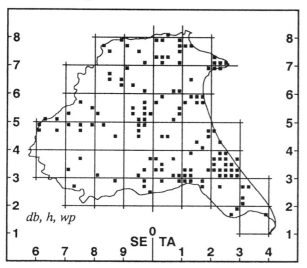

db, h, wp

252 Cardaria draba

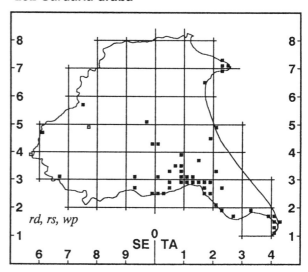

rd, rs, wp

253 Crepis vesicaria ssp. haenseleri

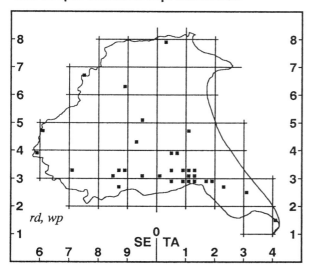

rd, wp

254 Diplotaxis muralis

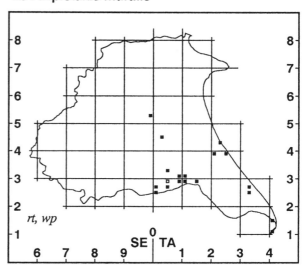

rt, wp

255 Epilobium ciliatum

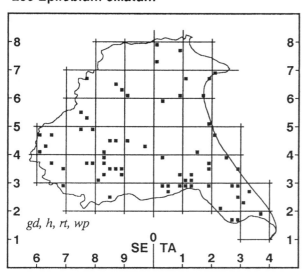

gd, h, rt, wp

256 Impatiens glandulifera

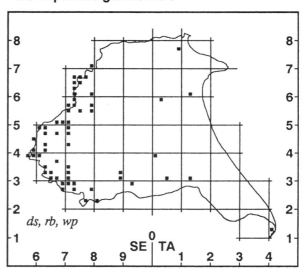

ds, rb, wp

257 Melilotus alba

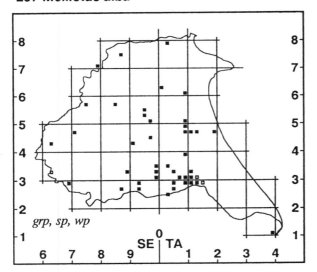

grp, sp, wp

258 Melilotus altissima

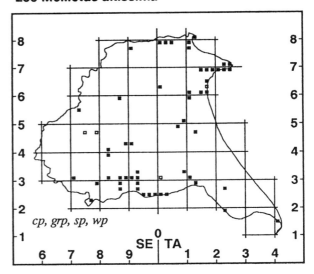

cp, grp, sp, wp

259 Melilotus officinalis

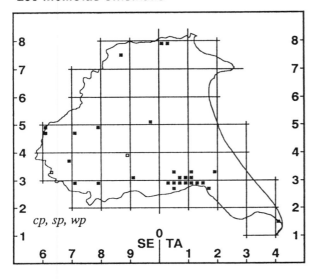

cp, sp, wp

260 Reynoutria japonica

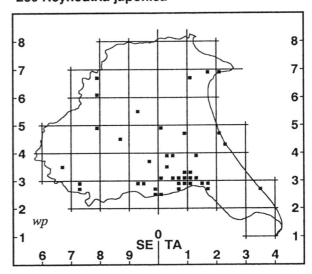

wp

261 Senecio squalidus

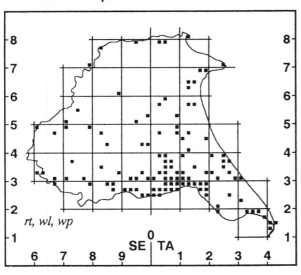

rt, wl, wp

262 Sisymbrium altissimum

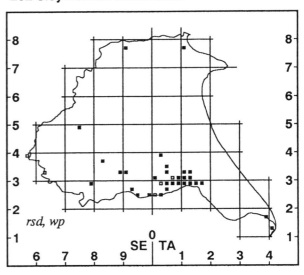

rsd, wp

263 Sisymbrium orientale

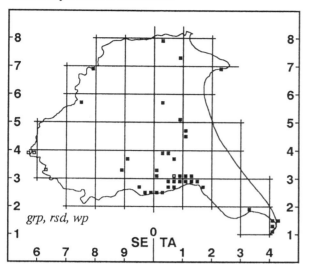

grp, rsd, wp

264 Veronica filiformis

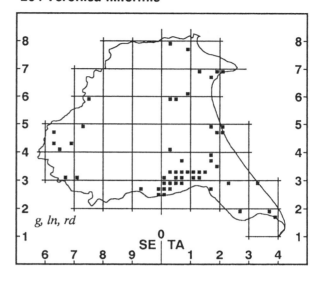

g, ln, rd

265 Equisetum arvense

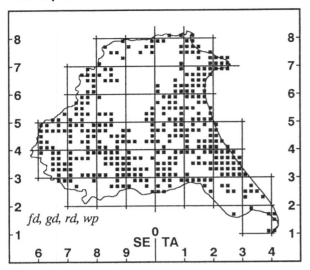

fd, gd, rd, wp

266 Pteridium aquilinum

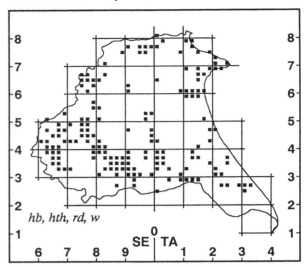

hb, hth, rd, w

267 Blechnum spicant

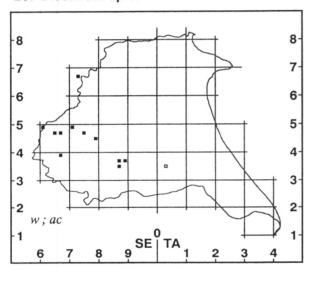

w ; ac

268 Phyllitis scolopendrium

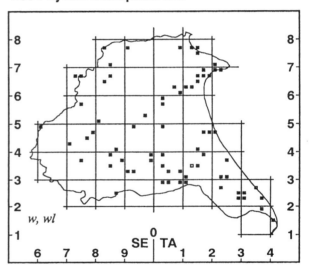

w, wl

269 Dryopteris filix-mas

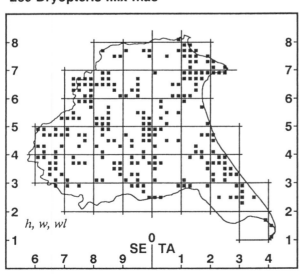

h, w, wl

270 Ophioglossum vulgatum

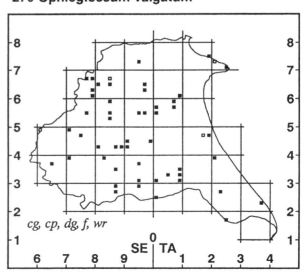

cg, cp, dg, f, wr

271 Eranthis hyemalis

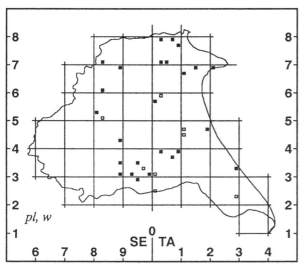

pl, w

272 Ranunculus sardous

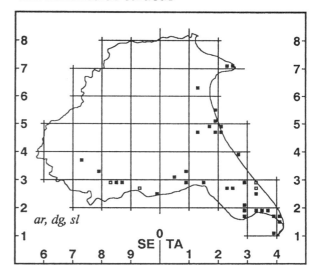

ar, dg, sl

273 Ranunculus ficaria

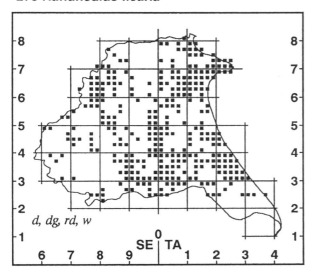

d, dg, rd, w

274 Papaver rhoeas

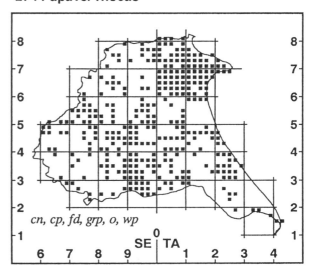

cn, cp, fd, grp, o, wp

275 Papaver dubium

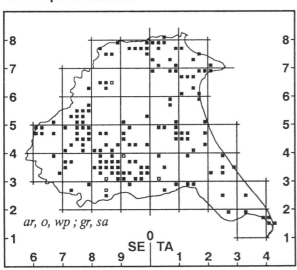

ar, o, wp ; gr, sa

276 Papaver argemone

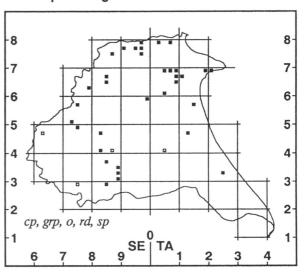

cp, grp, o, rd, sp

277 Chelidonium majus

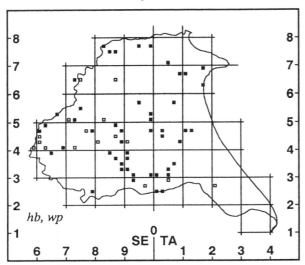

hb, wp

SE 0 TA

278 Fumaria officinalis

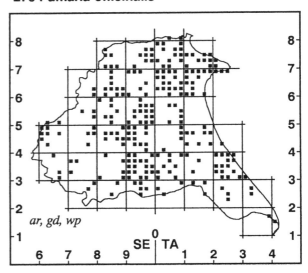

ar, gd, wp

SE 0 TA

279 Coronopus squamatus

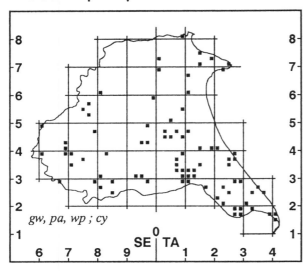

gw, pa, wp ; cy

SE 0 TA

280 Thlaspi arvense

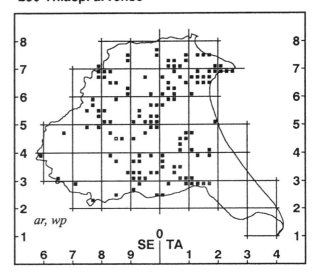

ar, wp

SE 0 TA

281 Erophila verna

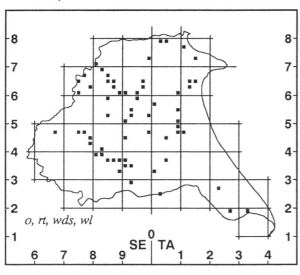

o, rt, wds, wl

SE 0 TA

282 Cardamine pratensis

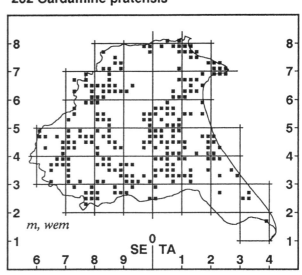

m, wem

SE 0 TA

283 Cardamine amara

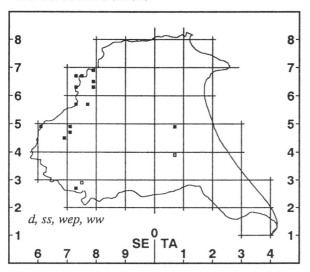

d, ss, wep, ww

284 Cardamine flexuosa

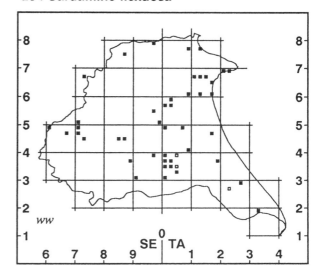

ww

285 Cardamine hirsuta

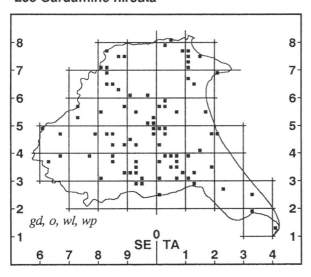

gd, o, wl, wp

286 Barbarea vulgaris

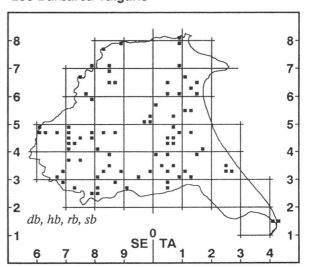

db, hb, rb, sb

287 Rorippa palustris

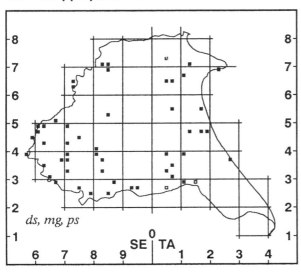

ds, mg, ps

288 Alliaria petiolata

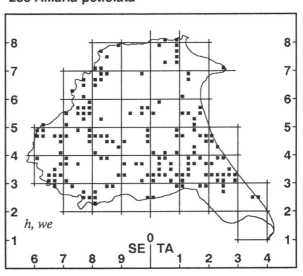

h, we

289 Arabidopsis thaliana

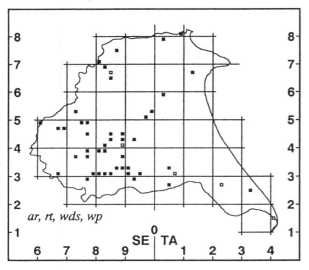

ar, rt, wds, wp

290 Reseda luteola

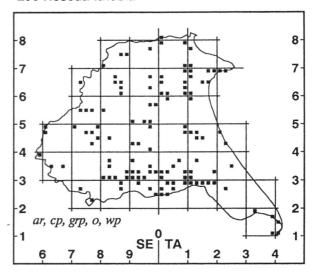

ar, cp, grp, o, wp

291 Reseda lutea

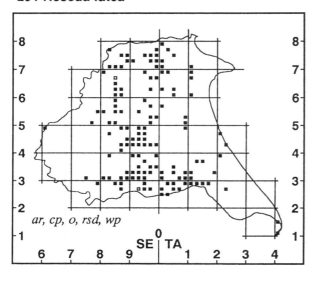

ar, cp, o, rsd, wp

292 Viola odorata

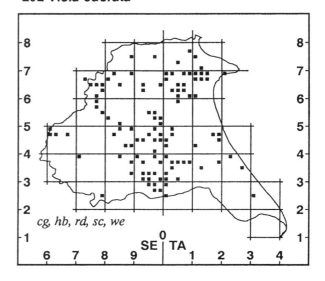

cg, hb, rd, sc, we

293 Viola riviniana

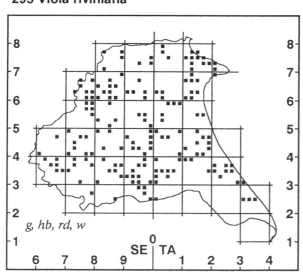

g, hb, rd, w

294 Viola arvensis

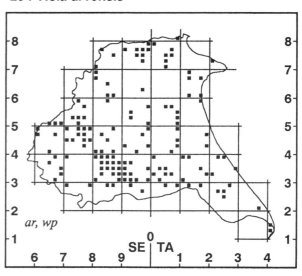

ar, wp

295 Hypericum pulchrum

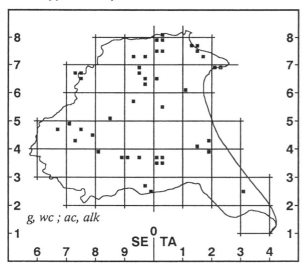

g, wc ; ac, alk

301 Stellaria holostea

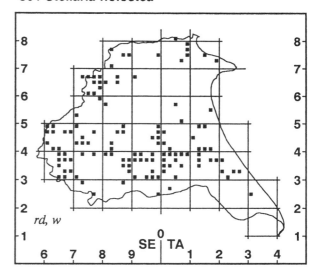

rd, w

297 Silene vulgaris

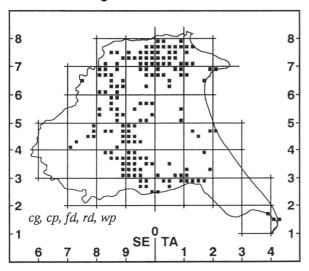

cg, cp, fd, rd, wp

303 Sagina apetala ssp. erecta

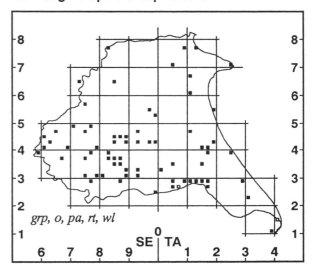

grp, o, pa, rt, wl

299 Cerastium arvense

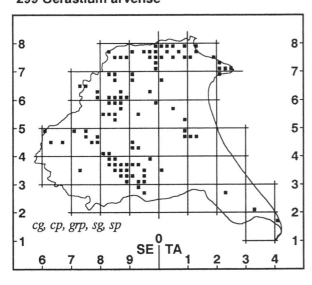

cg, cp, grp, sg, sp

305 Arenaria leptoclados

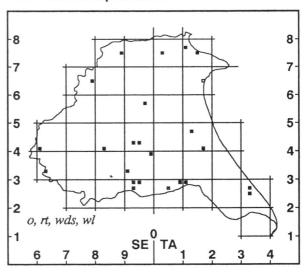

o, rt, wds, wl

296 Hypericum hirsutum

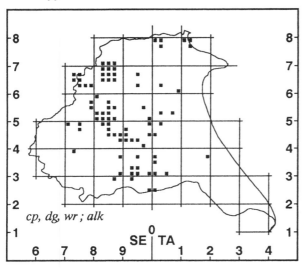

cp, dg, wr ; alk

302 Stellaria graminea

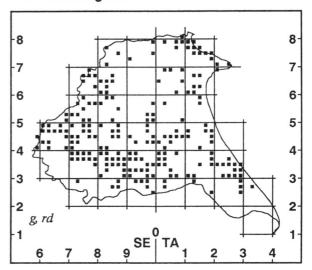

g, rd

298 Silene latifolia ssp. alba

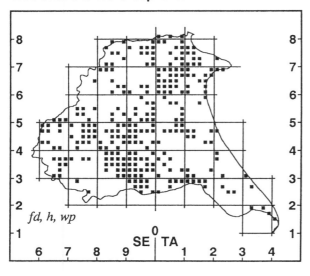

fd, h, wp

304 Arenaria serpyllifolia

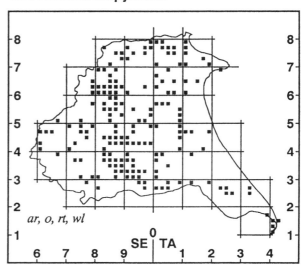

ar, o, rt, wl

300 Cerastium glomeratum

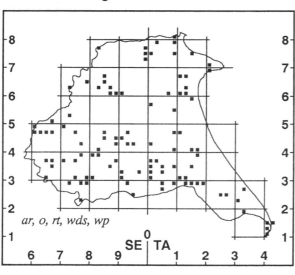

ar, o, rt, wds, wp

306 Chenopodium rubrum

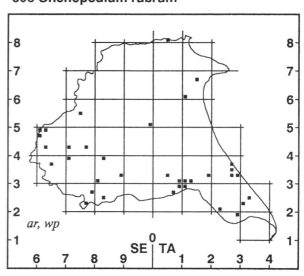

ar, wp

307 Atriplex prostrata

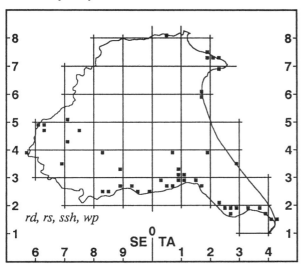

rd, rs, ssh, wp

SE 0 TA

308 Malva moschata

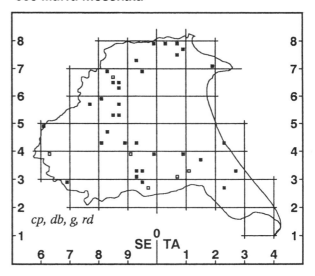

cp, db, g, rd

SE 0 TA

309 Malva sylvestris

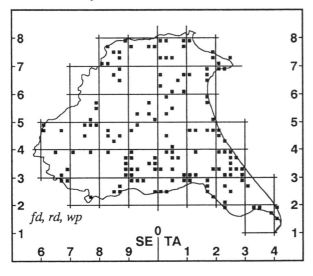

fd, rd, wp

SE 0 TA

310 Malva neglecta

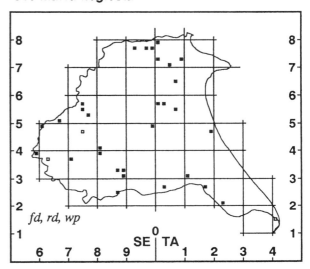

fd, rd, wp

SE 0 TA

311 Linum catharticum

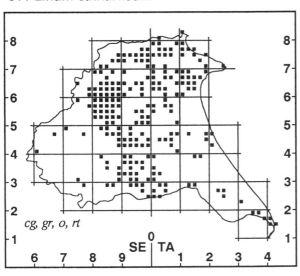

cg, gr, o, rt

SE 0 TA

312 Geranium dissectum

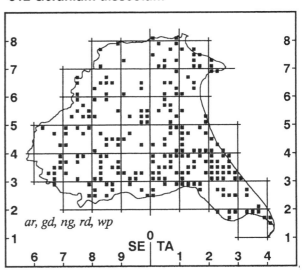

ar, gd, ng, rd, wp

SE 0 TA

313 Geranium pusillum

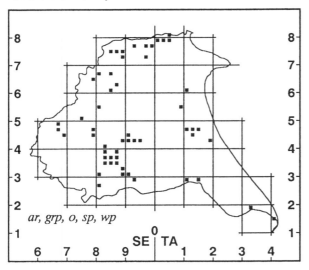

ar, grp, o, sp, wp

314 Geranium robertianum

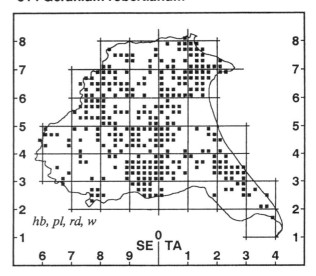

hb, pl, rd, w

315 Acer campestre

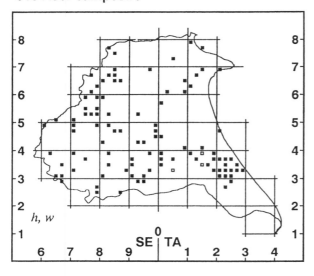

h, w

316 Ulex europaeus

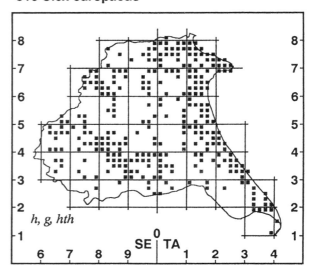

h, g, hth

317 Cytisus scoparius

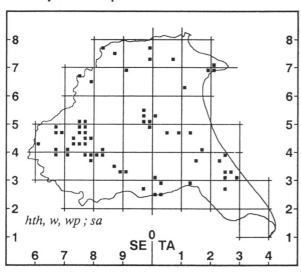

hth, w, wp ; sa

318 Ononis repens

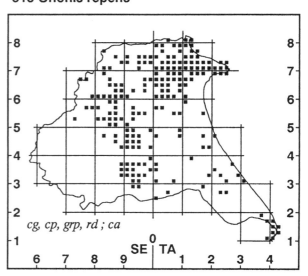

cg, cp, grp, rd ; ca

319 Trifolium fragiferum

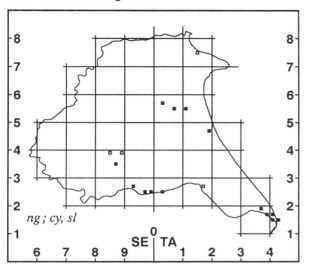

ng ; cy, sl

320 Trifolium campestre

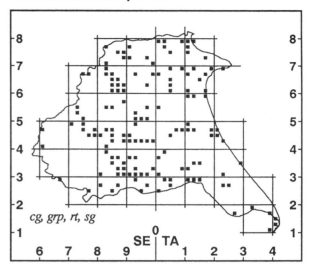

cg, grp, rt, sg

321 Lotus uliginosus

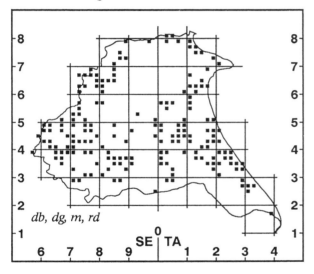

db, dg, m, rd

322 Vicia hirsuta

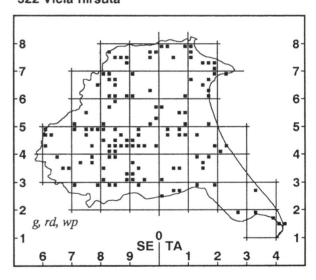

g, rd, wp

323 Lathyrus montanus

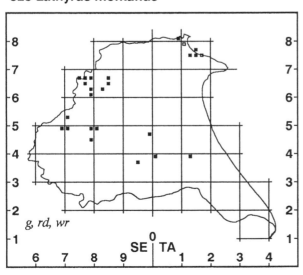

g, rd, wr

324 Filipendula ulmaria

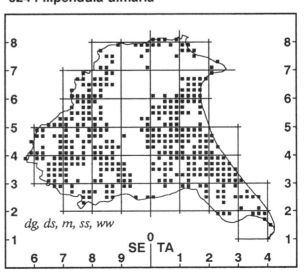

dg, ds, m, ss, ww

231

325 Potentilla sterilis

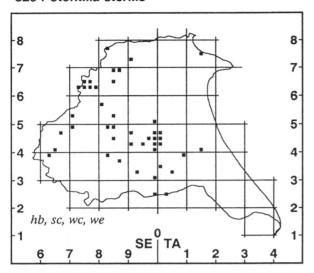

hb, sc, wc, we

326 Potentilla erecta

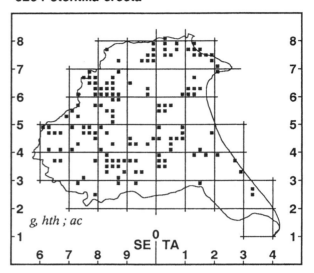

g, hth ; ac

327 Fragaria vesca

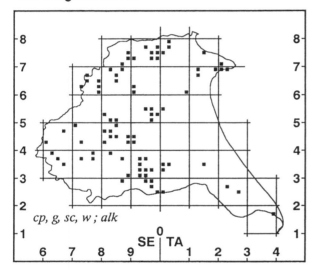

cp, g, sc, w ; alk

328 Geum urbanum

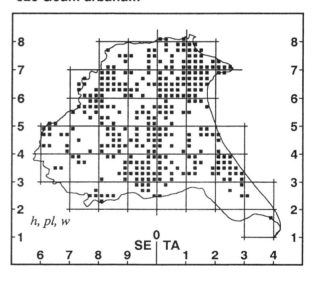

h, pl, w

329 Geum rivale

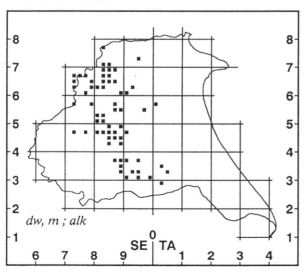

dw, m ; alk

330 Geum urbanum x G. rivale

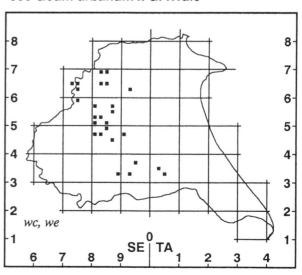

wc, we

331 Agrimonia eupatoria

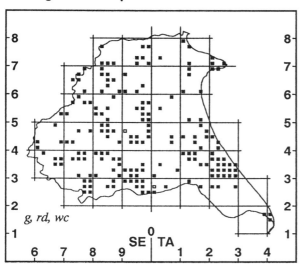

g, rd, wc

SE 0 TA

332 Aphanes arvensis s.l.

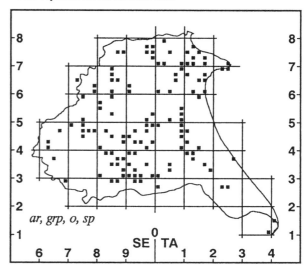

ar, grp, o, sp

SE 0 TA

333 Epilobium hirsutum

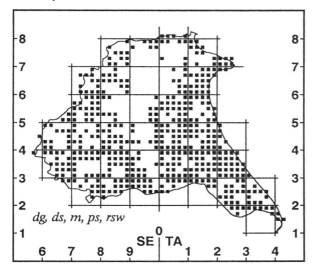

dg, ds, m, ps, rsw

SE 0 TA

334 Epilobium parviflorum

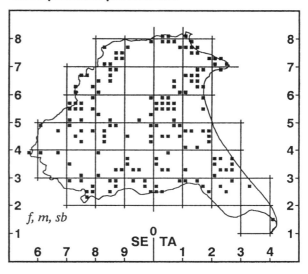

f, m, sb

SE 0 TA

335 Epilobium obscurum

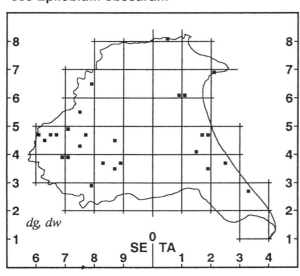

dg, dw

SE 0 TA

336 Chaerophyllum temulentum

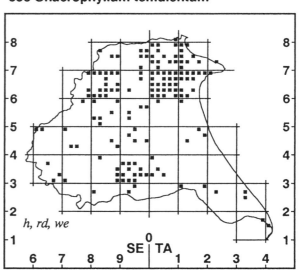

h, rd, we

SE 0 TA

337 Torilis nodosa

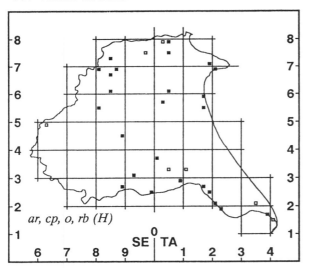

ar, cp, o, rb (H)

338 Conium maculatum

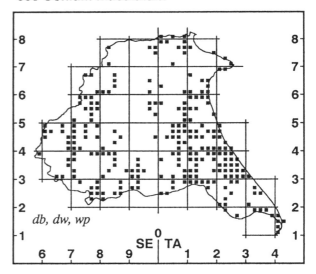

db, dw, wp

339 Conopodium majus

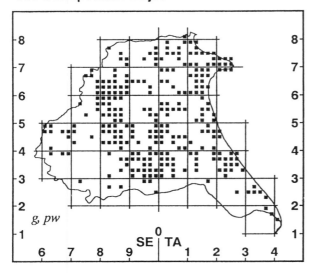

g, pw

340 Pimpinella major

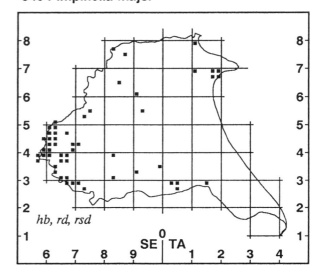

hb, rd, rsd

341 Aegopodium podagraria

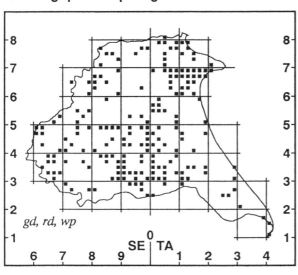

gd, rd, wp

342 Aethusa cynapium

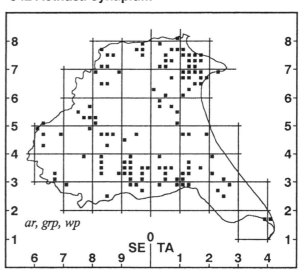

ar, grp, wp

343 Angelica sylvestris

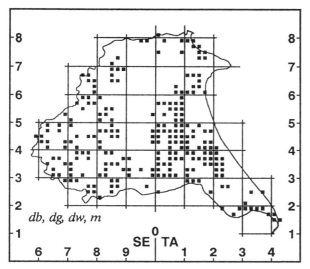

db, dg, dw, m

344 Daucus carota

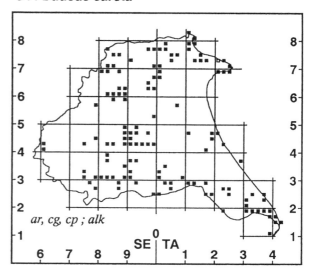

ar, cg, cp ; alk

345 Euphorbia helioscopia

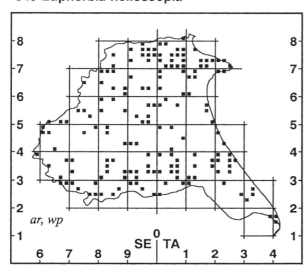

ar, wp

346 Euphorbia peplus

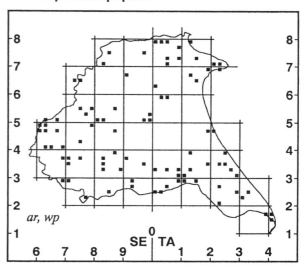

ar, wp

347 Polygonum amphibium

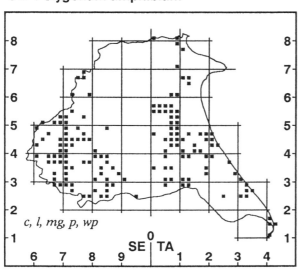

c, l, mg, p, wp

348 Rumex acetosella

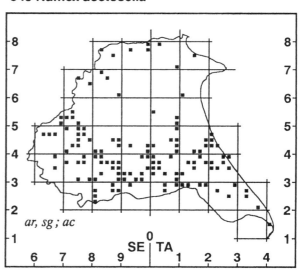

ar, sg ; ac

349 Rumex sanguineus

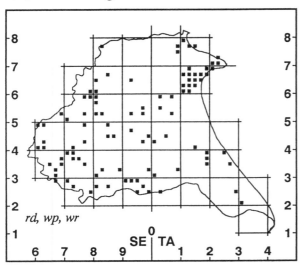

rd, wp, wr

350 Rumex conglomeratus

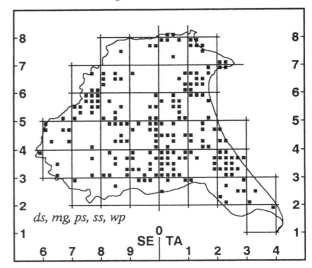

ds, mg, ps, ss, wp

351 Urtica urens

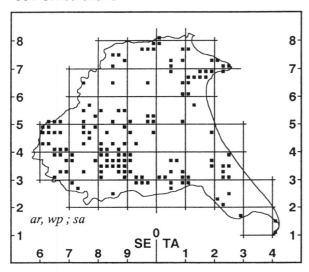

ar, wp ; sa

352 Humulus lupulus

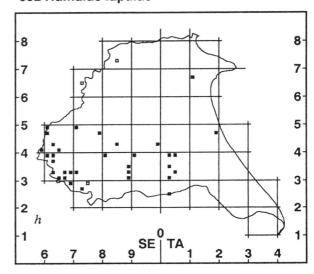

h

353 Betula pendula

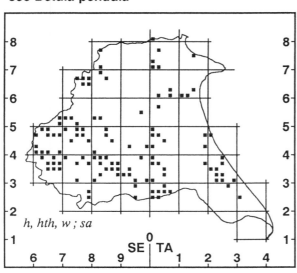

h, hth, w ; sa

354 Alnus glutinosa

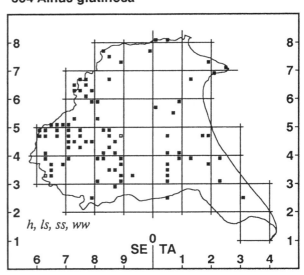

h, ls, ss, ww

355 Corylus avellana

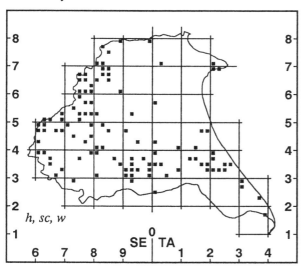

h, sc, w

356 Salix alba

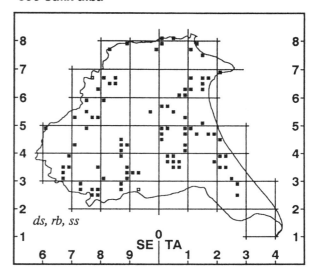

ds, rb, ss

357 Salix fragilis

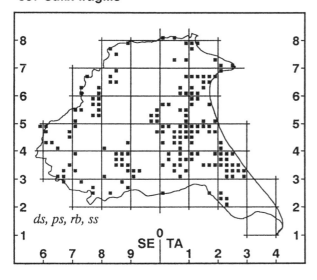

ds, ps, rb, ss

358 Salix viminalis

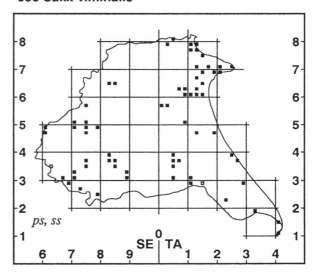

ps, ss

359 Salix caprea

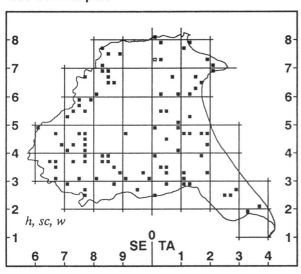

h, sc, w

360 Salix cinerea

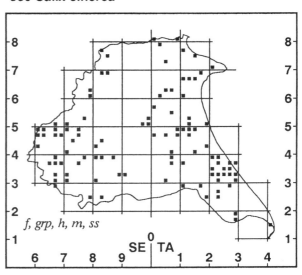

f, grp, h, m, ss

361 Primula veris

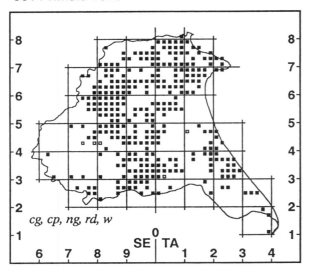

cg, cp, ng, rd, w

362 Lysimachia nummularia

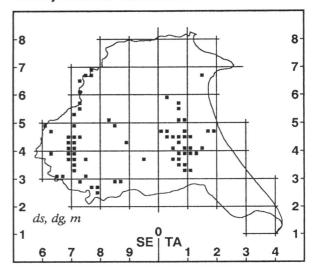

ds, dg, m

363 Centaurium erythraea

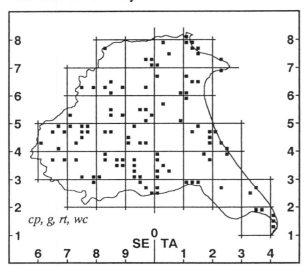

cp, g, rt, wc

364 Symphytum x uplandicum

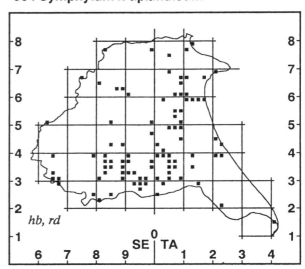

hb, rd

365 Echium vulgare

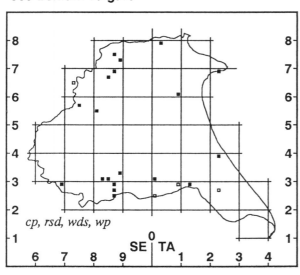

cp, rsd, wds, wp

366 Calystegia sepium

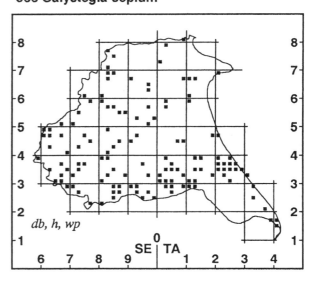

db, h, wp

367 Solanum dulcamara

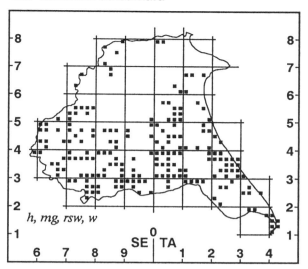

h, mg, rsw, w

368 Solanum nigrum

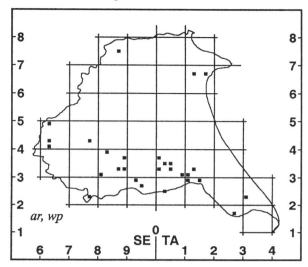

ar, wp

369 Verbascum thapsus

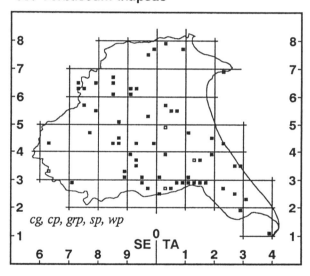

cg, cp, grp, sp, wp

370 Linaria vulgaris

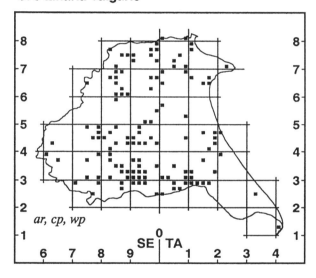

ar, cp, wp

371 Scrophularia auriculata

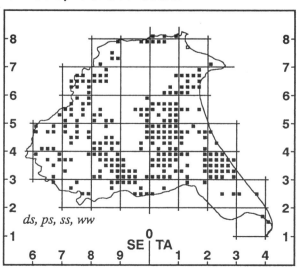

ds, ps, ss, ww

372 Digitalis purpurea

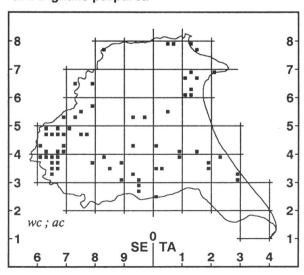

wc ; ac

373 Veronica officinalis

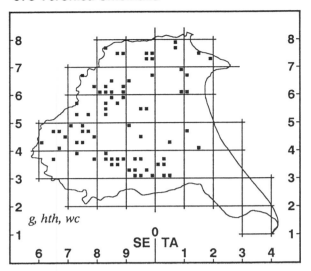

g, hth, wc

374 Veronica serpyllifolia

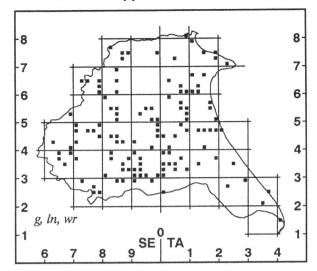

g, ln, wr

375 Veronica arvensis

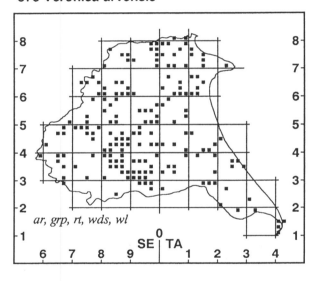

ar, grp, rt, wds, wl

376 Veronica hederifolia

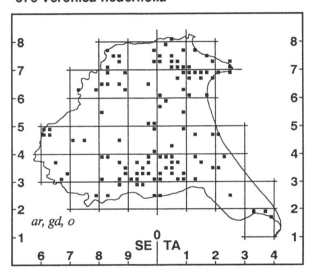

ar, gd, o

377 Pedicularis sylvatica

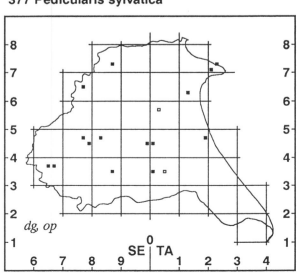

dg, op

378 Rhinanthus minor

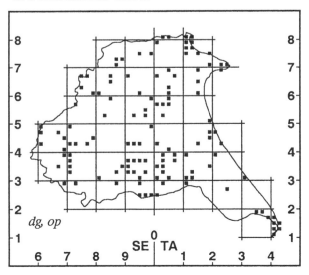

dg, op

379 Euphrasia officinalis s.l.

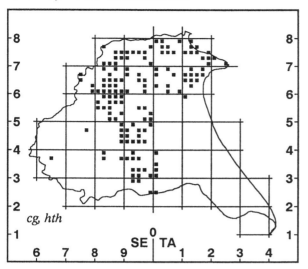

cg, hth

380 Odontites vernus

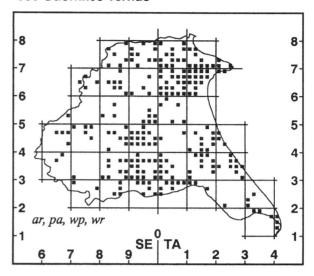

ar, pa, wp, wr

381 Mentha arvensis

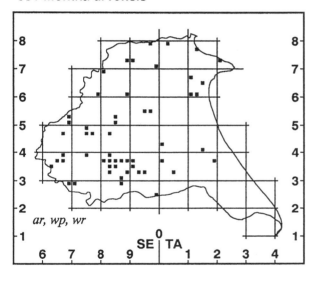

ar, wp, wr

382 Clinopodium vulgare

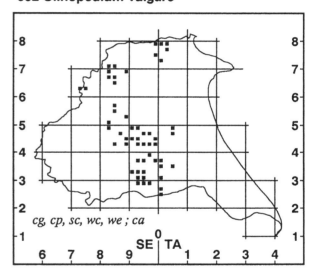

cg, cp, sc, wc, we ; ca

383 Stachys officinalis

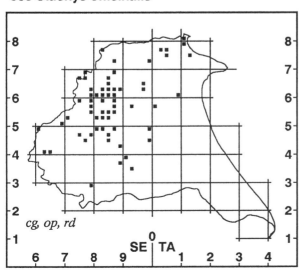

cg, op, rd

384 Ballota nigra

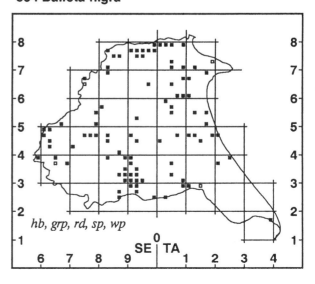

hb, grp, rd, sp, wp

385 Galeopsis tetrahit s.l.

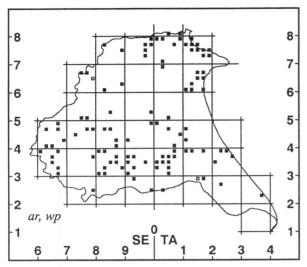

ar, wp

386 Glechoma hederacea

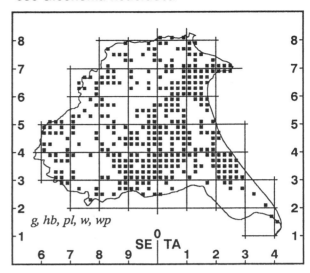

g, hb, pl, w, wp

387 Teucrium scorodonia

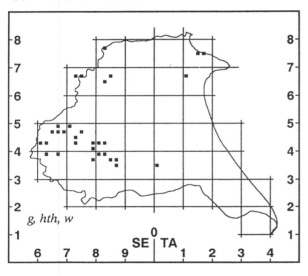

g, hth, w

388 Ajuga reptans

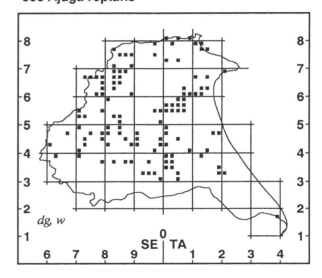

dg, w

389 Campanula latifolia

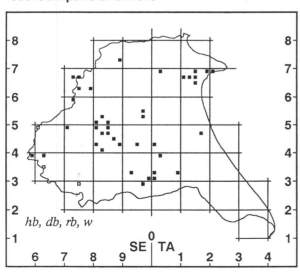

hb, db, rb, w

390 Campanula rotundifolia

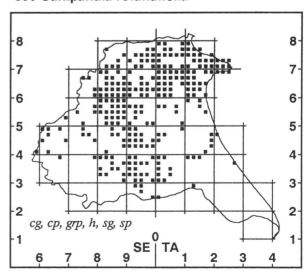

cg, cp, grp, h, sg, sp

391 Sherardia arvensis

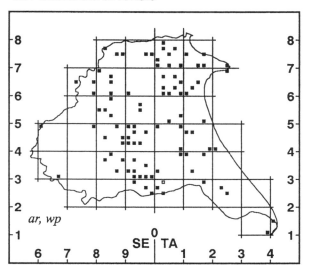

ar, wp

392 Galium cruciata

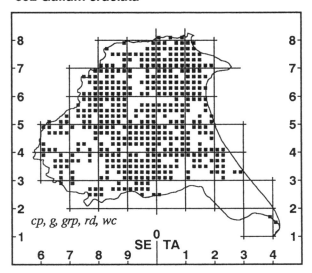

cp, g, grp, rd, wc

393 Galium mollugo

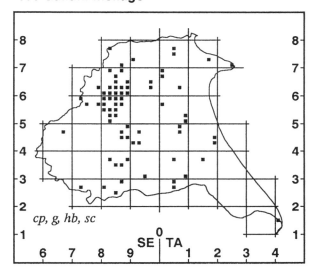

cp, g, hb, sc

394 Galium verum

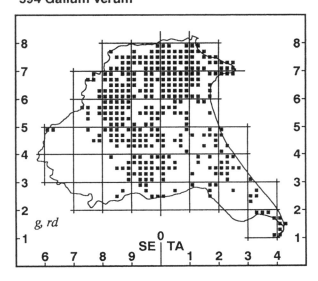

g, rd

395 Valerianella locusta

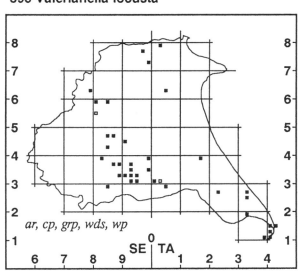

ar, cp, grp, wds, wp

396 Dipsacus fullonum ssp. sylvestris

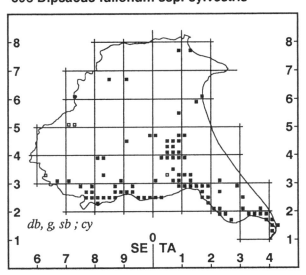

db, g, sb ; cy

397 Knautia arvensis

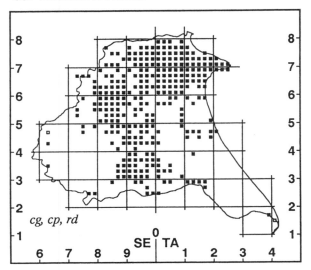

cg, cp, rd

398 Succisa pratensis

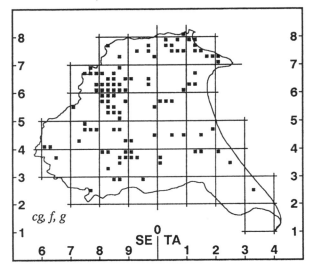

cg, f, g

399 Senecio viscosus

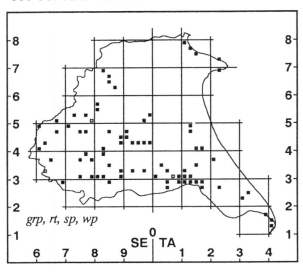

grp, rt, sp, wp

400 Tussilago farfara

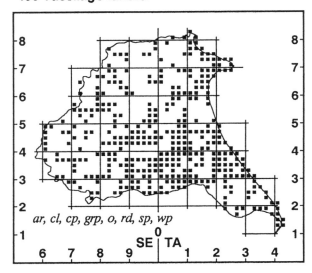

ar, cl, cp, grp, o, rd, sp, wp

401 Petasites hybridus

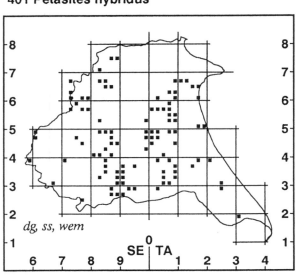

dg, ss, wem

402 Inula conyza

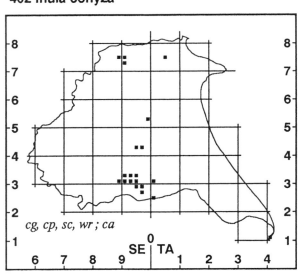

cg, cp, sc, wr ; ca

403 Pulicaria dysenterica

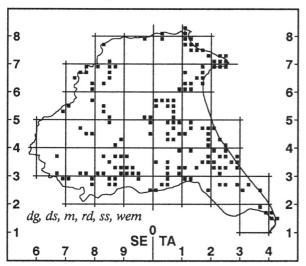

dg, ds, m, rd, ss, wem

404 Filago vulgaris

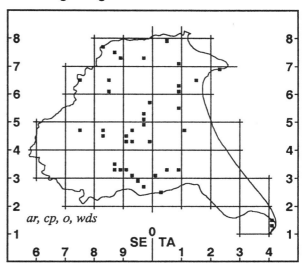

ar, cp, o, wds

405 Gnaphalium sylvaticum

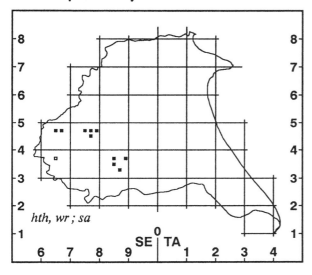

hth, wr ; sa

406 Gnaphalium uliginosum

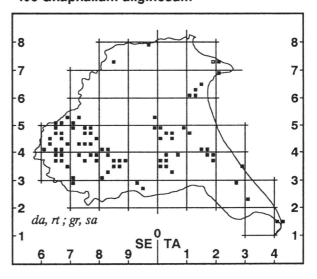

da, rt ; gr, sa

407 Erigeron acer

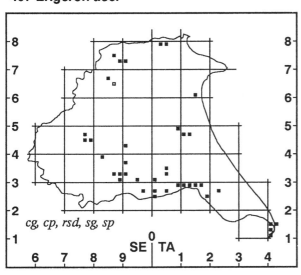

cg, cp, rsd, sg, sp

408 Achillea ptarmica

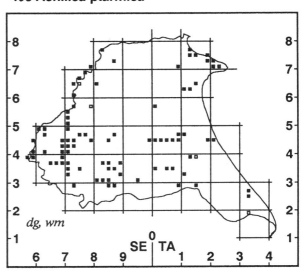

dg, wm

409 Matricaria recutita

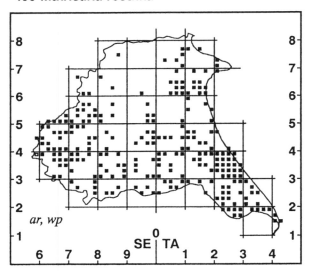

ar, wp

410 Leucanthemum vulgare

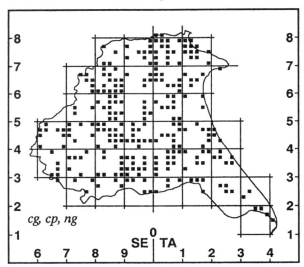

cg, cp, ng

411 Tanacetum parthenium

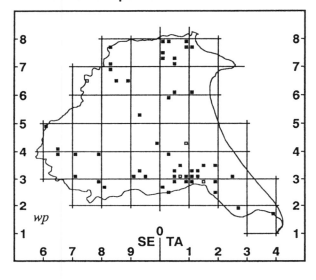

wp

412 Tanacetum vulgare

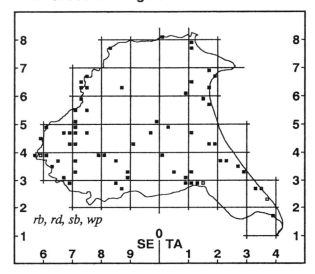

rb, rd, sb, wp

413 Artemisia vulgaris

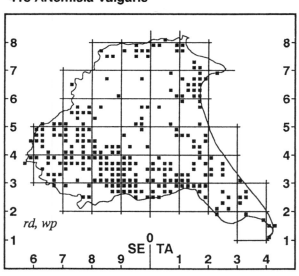

rd, wp

414 Carduus nutans

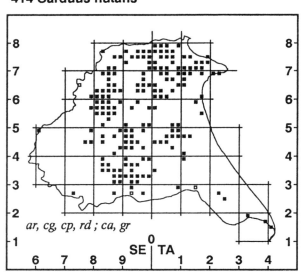

ar, cg, cp, rd ; ca, gr

415 Carduus acanthoides

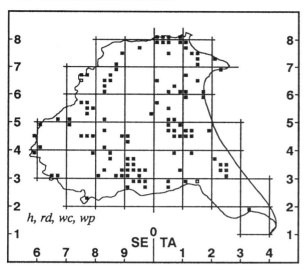

h, rd, wc, wp

SE | TA

416 Cirsium palustre

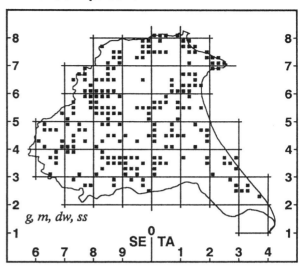

g, m, dw, ss

SE | TA

417 Serratula tinctoria

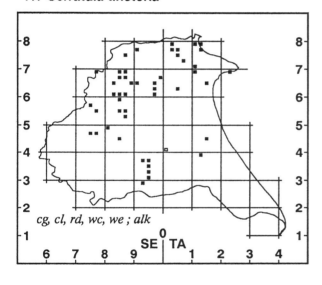

cg, cl, rd, wc, we ; alk

SE | TA

418 Hypochoeris radicata

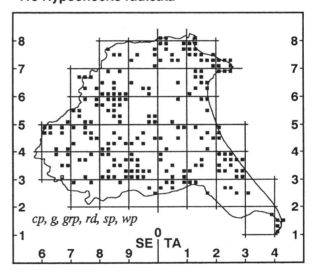

cp, g, grp, rd, sp, wp

SE | TA

419 Leontodon hispidus

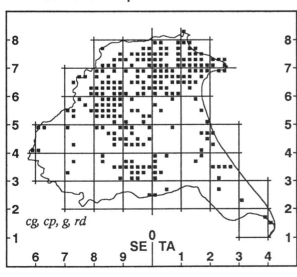

cg, cp, g, rd

SE | TA

420 Leontodon taraxacoides

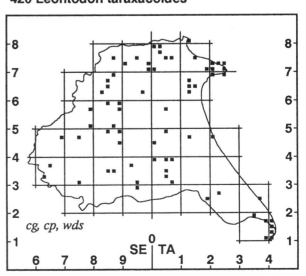

cg, cp, wds

SE | TA

421 Mycelis muralis

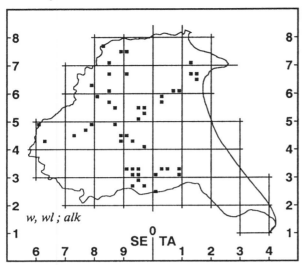

w, wl ; alk

422 Crepis capillaris

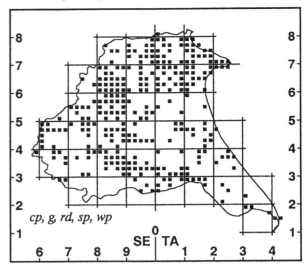

cp, g, rd, sp, wp

423 Crepis paludosa

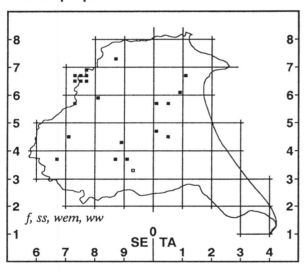

f, ss, wem, ww

424 Juncus bufonius

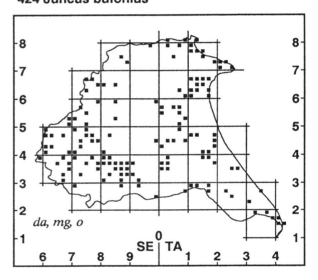

da, mg, o

425 Juncus inflexus

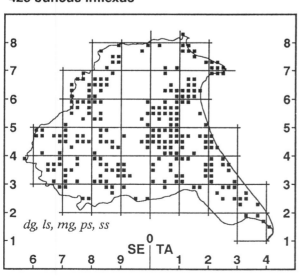

dg, ls, mg, ps, ss

426 Juncus effusus

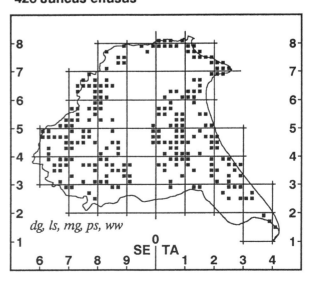

dg, ls, mg, ps, ww

427 Luzula campestris

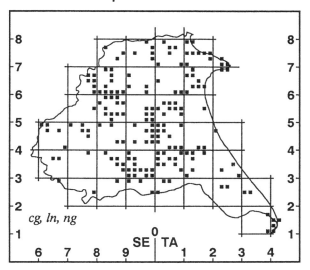

cg, ln, ng

SE 0 TA

428 Luzula multiflora

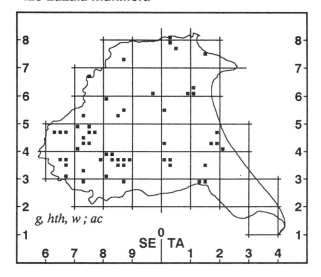

g, hth, w ; ac

SE 0 TA

429 Listera ovata

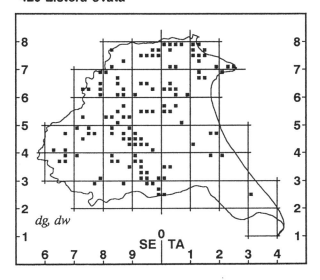

dg, dw

SE 0 TA

430 Coeloglossum viride

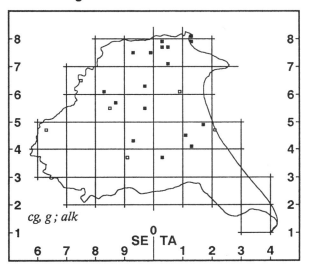

cg, g ; alk

SE 0 TA

431 Orchis morio

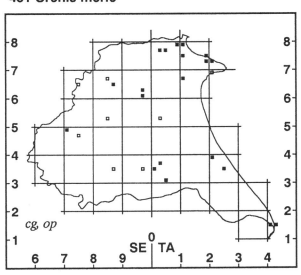

cg, op

SE 0 TA

432 Orchis mascula

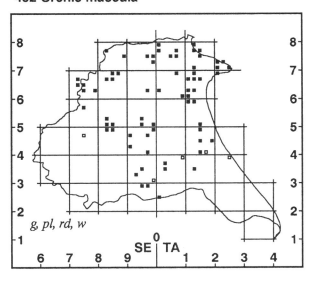

g, pl, rd, w

SE 0 TA

433 Dactylorhiza fuchsii

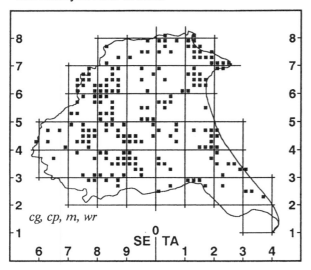

cg, cp, m, wr

434 Dactylorhiza maculata

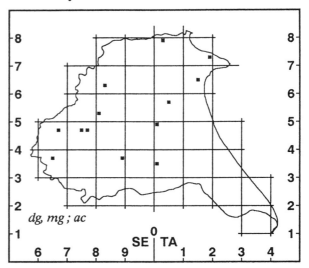

dg, mg ; ac

435 Dactylorhiza praetermissa

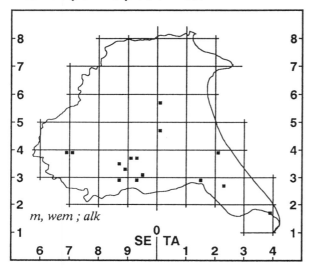

m, wem ; alk

436 Dactylorhiza purpurella

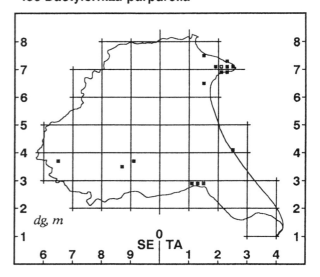

dg, m

437 Isolepis setacea

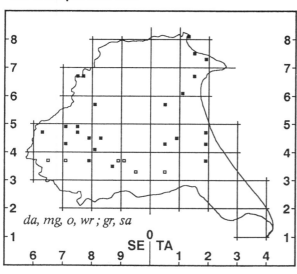

da, mg, o, wr ; gr, sa

438 Carex flacca

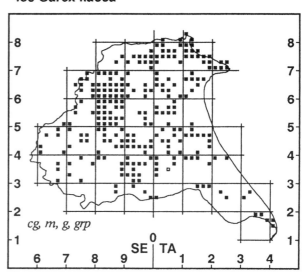

cg, m, g, grp

439 Carex hirta

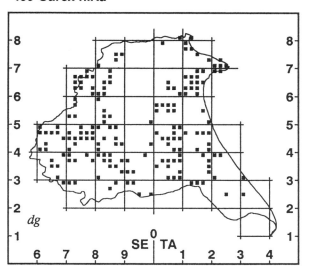

dg

440 Carex otrubae

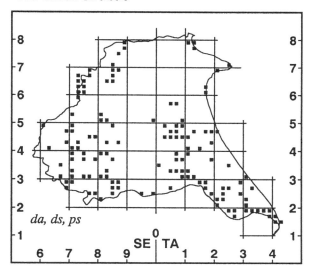

da, ds, ps

441 Carex spicata

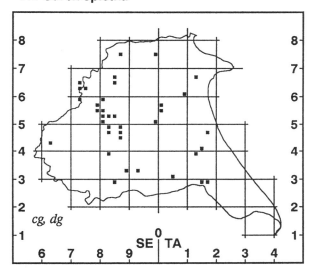

cg, dg

442 Carex remota

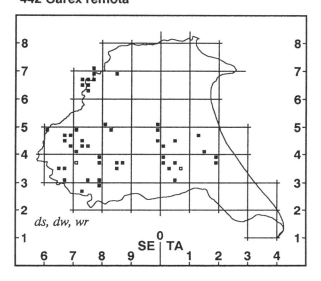

ds, dw, wr

443 Carex ovalis

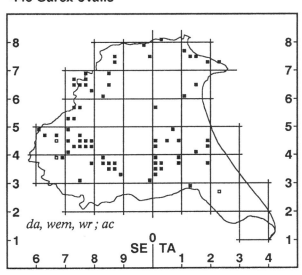

da, wem, wr ; ac

444 Molinia caerulea

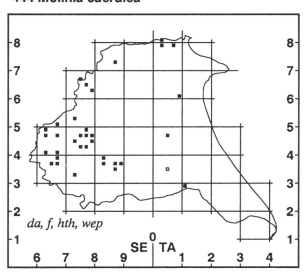

da, f, hth, wep

445 Danthonia decumbens

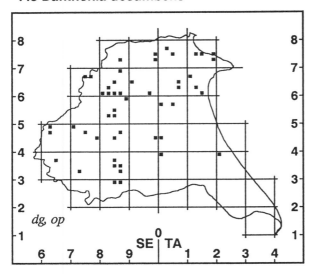

446 Festuca pratensis

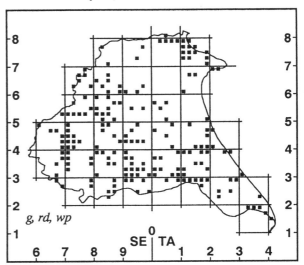

447 Festuca elatior

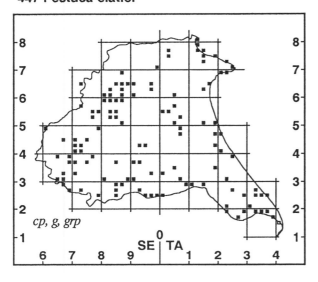

448 Festuca rubra

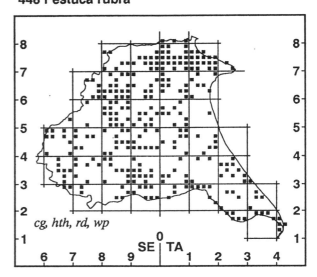

449 Festuca ovina

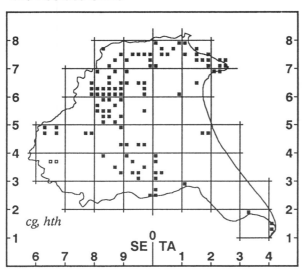

450 Vulpia bromoides

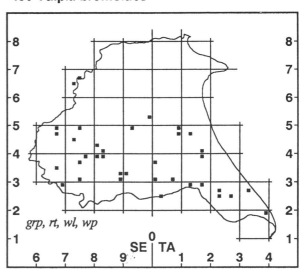

451 Catapodium rigidum

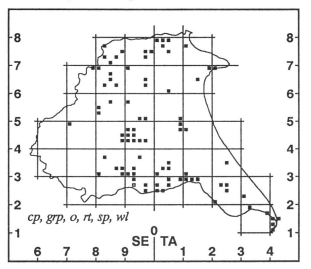

cp, grp, o, rt, sp, wl

452 Poa compressa

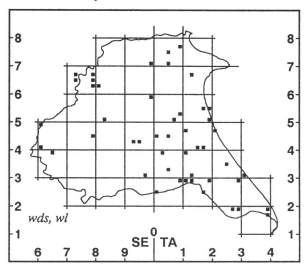

wds, wl

453 Cynosurus cristatus

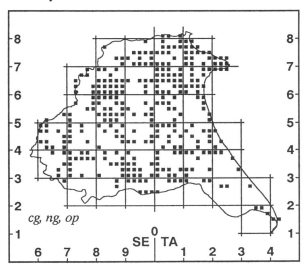

cg, ng, op

454 Briza media

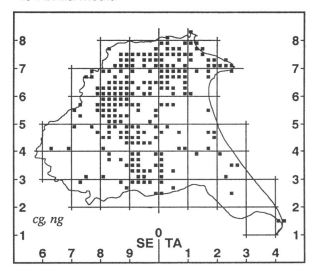

cg, ng

455 Brachypodium sylvaticum

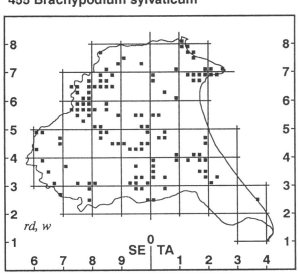

rd, w

456 Hordeum murinum

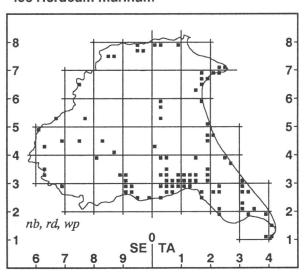

nb, rd, wp

457 Trisetum flavescens

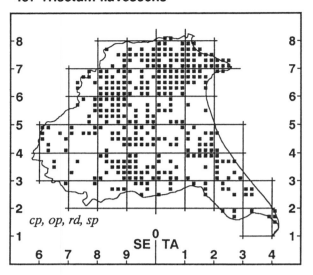

cp, op, rd, sp

458 Avenula pubescens

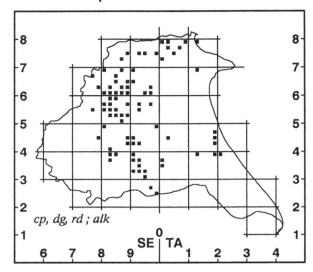

cp, dg, rd ; alk

459 Holcus mollis

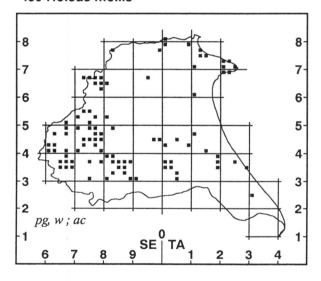

pg, w ; ac

460 Deschampsia cespitosa

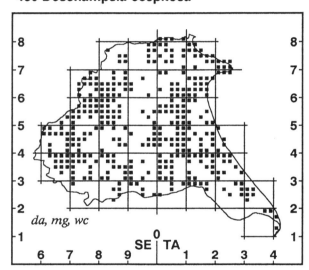

da, mg, wc

461 Calamagrostis epigejos

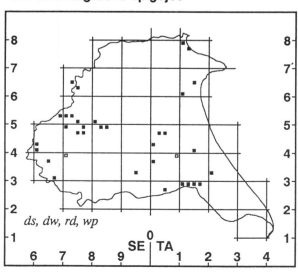

ds, dw, rd, wp

462 Agrostis capillaris

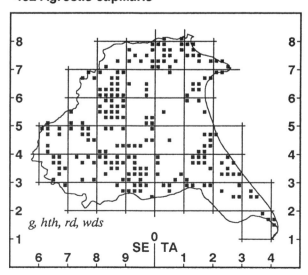

g, hth, rd, wds

463 Agrostis gigantea

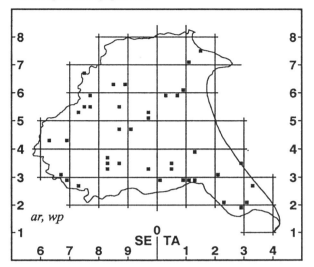

ar, wp

464 Phleum pratense ssp. bertolonii

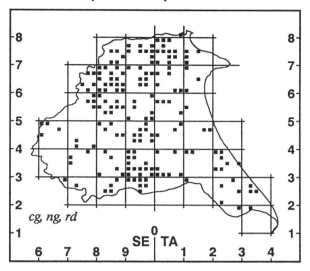

cg, ng, rd

465 Alopecurus geniculatus

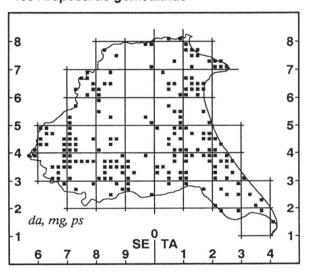

da, mg, ps

BIBLIOGRAPHY

AINSCOUGH, M.M., BARKER, C.M. and STACE, C.A. (1986). Natural hybrids between *Festuca* and species of *Vulpia* section *Vulpia*. *Watsonia*, **16**: 143-151. Bot. Soc. Brit. Isles.

ALLISON, K.J. (1976a). *The East Riding of Yorkshire Landscape*. London.

ALLISON, K.J., ed. (1976b). *The Victoria History of the County of York*, vol. **3**: 9. O.U.P.

ALLISON, K.J., ed. (1979). *The Victoria History of the County of York*, vol. **4**: 160. O.U.P.

ARMSTRONG, P. (1977). Excavations in Sewer Lane, Hull 1974. *East Riding Archaeologist*, vol.**3**. Hull Old Town Report Series No. 1.

ARMSTRONG, P. (1980). Excavations in Scale Lane / Lowgate 1974. *East Riding Archaeologist*, vol. **6**. Hull Old Town Report Series No. 4.

AVERY, B.W.(1980). *Soil Classification of England and Wales (Higher Categories)*. Soil Survey Technical Monograph No.**14**. Soil Survey of England and Wales. Harpenden.

AYERS, B. (1979). Excavations at Chapel Lane Staith 1978. *East Riding Archaeologist*, vol. **5**. Hull Old Town Report Series No. 3.

BAINES, H. (1840). *The Flora of Yorkshire*. London.

BAKER, J.G. (1854). *A Supplement to Baines' Flora of Yorkshire*. London.

BANGERTER, E.B. and KENT, D.H. (1957). *Veronica filiformis* Sm. in the British Isles. *Proc. Bot. Soc. Brit. Isles*, **2**, pt 3: 201.

BANGERTER, E.B. and KENT, D.H. (1962). Further notes on *Veronica filiformis*. *Proc. Bot. Soc. Brit. Isles*, **4**, pt 4: 392.

BECKETT, S.C. (1981). Pollen diagram from Holderness, North Humberside. *J. Biogeog.*, **8**: 177-193.

BOATMAN, D.J. (1971). Burton Bushes: an ecological view. *Bulletin, Hull Natural History Society*, vol. **3**, No. 2: 8-14.

BOATMAN, D.J. (1975). Hedges and roadside scrub of Walkington Parish. *Naturalist*, 1975: 91-95. Leeds.

BOATMAN, D.J. (1980). Mixed hedges of the former East Riding of Yorkshire. *Naturalist*, 1980: 41-44. Leeds.

BOLAM, G. (1913). Notes on the natural history of Hornsea Mere. *Naturalist*, 1913: 1-39. Hull.

BRAY, E. (1985). Hybrid Willows. *Naturalist*, 1985: 38. Leeds.

BUTCHER, R.W. (1960). Notes on Water Buttercups. *Naturalist*, 1960: 123-125. Hull.

CAMDEN, W. (1695). *Britannia*. Ed. Gibson, E. London.

CAMDEN, W. (1789). *Britannia*. Ed. Gough, R. London.

CATT, J.A. (1982). The Quaternary deposits of the Yorkshire Wolds. *Proc. North of England Soils Discussion Group.* **18**: 61-67.

CATT, J.A. (1987). The Quaternary of East Yorkshire and adjacent areas in Ellis, S., ed. *East Yorkshire - A Field Guide*: 1-14. Quaternary Research Association.

CHICKEN, E. (1986). A first look at the genus *Taraxacum* in South-east Yorkshire (v.c. 61). *Naturalist*, 1986: 87-90. Leeds.

CLAPHAM, A.R., TUTIN, T.G. and MOORE, D.M. (1987). *Flora of the British Isles.* Edn 3. Cambridge.

CLAPHAM, A.R., TUTIN, T.G. and WARBURG, E.F. (1981). *Excursion Flora of the British Isles.* Edn 3. Cambridge.

CLARK, J.G.D. (1971). *Excavations at Star Carr.* C.U.P.

COPE, T.A. and STACE, C.A. (1978). The *Juncus bufonius* L. aggregate in western Europe. *Watsonia*, **12** : 113-128. Bot. Soc. Brit. Isles.

CRACKLES, F.E. (1966). Three Umbellifers at the northern edge of their range. *Naturalist*, 1966: 49-51. Leeds.

CRACKLES, F.E. (1967). Some plant records by Robert Teesdale with special reference to the East Riding flora. *Naturalist*, 1967: 37-47. Leeds.

CRACKLES, F.E. (1968). Some plant associations of the River Hull valley. *East Yorkshire Field Studies*, **1**: 13-24. Hull.

CRACKLES, F.E. (1970). Arable weeds in East Yorkshire. *East Yorkshire Field Studies*, **3**: 1-14. Hull.

CRACKLES, F.E. (1974a). Seeking to understand the flora of the East Riding of Yorkshire. *Naturalist*, 1974: 1-17. Leeds.

CRACKLES, F.E. (1974b). A rush called the Dumbles. *The Local Historian*, vol. **11**, No. 2: 63-67. London.

CRACKLES, F.E. (1975a). The Monkey Orchid in Yorkshire. *Naturalist*, 1975: 25-26. Leeds.

CRACKLES, F.E. (1975b). The flowering plants of Spurn Point. *Naturalist*, 1975: 59-65. Leeds. Reprinted as a separate and updated 1986, 10pp.

CRACKLES, F.E. (1975c). *Calamagrostis canescens* (Weber) Roth x *C. stricta* (Timm) Koel. in Stace, C.A., ed. *Hybridization and the flora of the British Isles*: 578-579. London.

CRACKLES, F.E. (1976). *Apium repens* (Jacq.) Lag. and *A. nodiflorum* (L.) Lag. x *A. repens* (Jacq.) Lag. in the East Riding. *Naturalist*, 1976: 74. Leeds.

CRACKLES, F.E. (1977). Biosystematic and taxonomic studies of populations of *Calamagrostis stricta* (Timm) *Koel.*, *Calamagrostis canescens* (Weber) Roth and their hybrids. Unpublished M.Sc. thesis, University of Hull.

CRACKLES, F.E. (1982). *Stratiotes aloides* L. in the East Riding of Yorkshire. *Naturalist*, 1982: 99-101. Leeds.

CRACKLES, F.E. (1983a). Dumbles or Bumbles. *Lore and Language*, 1983: 53-55. University of Sheffield.

CRACKLES, F.E. (1983b). *Ruppia spiralis* L. ex Dumort. and *R. maritima* L. in S.E. Yorkshire. *Watsonia*, **14**: 274-275. Bot. Soc. Brit. Isles.

CRACKLES, F.E. (1983c). *Carex diandra* Schrank x *C. paniculata* L. in S.E. Yorkshire. *Watsonia*, **14**: 275-276. Bot. Soc. Brit. Isles.

CRACKLES, F.E. (1984). *Carex acuta* L. x *C. acutiformis* Ehrh. in S.E. Yorkshire. *Watsonia*, **15**: 33. Bot. Soc. Brit. Isles.

CRACKLES, F.E. (1986a). *Dactylorhiza majalis* (Reichb.) P.F. Hunt & Summerhayes subsp. *cambrensis* (R.H. Roberts) R.H. Roberts in S.E. Yorkshire. *Watsonia*, **16**: 78-80. Bot. Soc. Brit. Isles.

CRACKLES, F.E. (1986b). *Juncus ambiguus* Guss. (*J. ranarius* Song. & Perr.) in Yorkshire. *Naturalist*, 1986: 23. Leeds.

CRACKLES, F.E. (1986c). Botanical Comment 3. Vanishing arable weeds. *Yorks. Nat. Union Bulletin*, **5**: 10-12.

CRACKLES, F.E. (1986d). Botanical Comment 4. How came they? *Yorks. Nat. Union Bulletin*, **6**: 5-7.

CRACKLES, F.E. (1988). Botanical Comment 6. Converging interests. *Yorks. Nat. Union Bulletin*, **9**: 5-8.

CRACKLES, F.E. (1990). *Hypericum* x *desetangsii* Lamotte nm. *desetangsii* in Yorkshire, with special reference to its spread along railways. To be published in *Watsonia*, **18**. Bot. Soc. Brit. Isles.

CRACKLES, F.E. and GARNETT, P.M. (1967). *Bupleurum tenuissimum* L. *Naturalist*, 1967: 32. Leeds.

DANDY, J.E. (1958). *List of British Vascular Plants*. London.

DARGIE, T. (1970). *Parapholis incurva* on Spurn Head. *Naturalist*, 1970: 131. Leeds.

DE BOER, G. (1968). *A history of the Spurn Lighthouses*. East Yorkshire Local History Society, York. (East Yorkshire Local History Series, 24).

DENT, J. (1987). Later prehistory of East Yorkshire. *Archaeology and Landscape History of East Yorkshire*. Summary of papers, Univ. of Hull.

FENTON, K. (1977). *Salicornia* at Spurn. *Naturalist*, 1977: 33-34. Leeds.

FENTON, K. (1978). On the occurrence of *Zostera angustifolia* (Hornem.) Rchb. in the Humber. *Naturalist*, 1978: 156. Leeds.

FLENLEY, J. (1987a). Effects of the Ice Age on the landscape of East Yorkshire, and the first human arrivals. *Archaeology and Landscape History of East Yorkshire*. Summary of papers, Univ. of Hull.

FLENLEY, J.R. (1987b). The meres of Holderness in Ellis, S., ed. *East Yorkshire - A Field Guide*: 73-81. Quaternary Research Association,

FLINT, J.H. (1979).   *Azolla filiculoides* Lam. and its weevil *Stenopelmus rufinasus* Gyll. in Yorkshire. *Naturalist*, 1979: 112. Leeds.

FLINTOFF, R.J. (1931).   Some plants of the East Riding of Yorkshire. *Naturalist*, 1931: 229-232 and 261-263. Hull.

FLINTOFF, R.J. (1934).   *Crepis biennis* L. in Yorkshire. *The North Western Naturalist*, 1934: 30-34. Arbroath.

FOSTER,S.W. (1985).   The late Glacial history of the Vale of Pickering and northern Yorkshire Wolds. Unpublished Ph.D. thesis, University of Hull.

FOSTER,S.W. (1987).   The Sherburn Sands of the southern vale of Pickering in Ellis, S., ed. *East Yorkshire - A Field Guide*: 31-35. Quaternary Research Association.

FURNESS, R.R. (1985).   Soils in Humberside I. Sheet TA 14 (Brandesburton). *Soil Survey Record* 82. Soil Survey of England and Wales. Harpenden.

GARNETT, P.M. and SLEDGE, W.A. (1967).   The distribution of *Actaea spicata* L. *Naturalist*, 1967: 75-76. Leeds.

GAUNT,G.D. (1976).   The Devensian maximum ice limit in the Vale of York. *Proc. Yorks. Geol. Soc.* **40**: 631-637.

GAUNT, G.D. (1981).   Quaternary history of the southern part of the Vale of York. In Neale J. and Flenley J.R., eds *The Quaternary of Britain*: 81-97. Pergamon Press. Oxford.

GAUNT, G.D., JARVIS, R.A. and MATTHEWS, B. (1971).   The late Weichselian sequence in the Vale of York. *Proc. Yorks. Geol. Soc.*, **38**: 281-284.

GERARD, J. (1633).   *The Herball*. Edn 2, ed. Johnson, T.   London.

GODWIN, Sir H. (1975).   *The history of the British Flora*. Edn 2. C.U.P.

GOOD, R. (1944).   On the distribution of the Primrose. *Naturalist*, 1944: 41-46. Hull.

GOOD, R. (1959).   Some old East Riding plant records. *Naturalist*, 1959: 99-100. Hull.

GRUBB, P.J., GREEN, H.E. and MERRIFIELD, C.J. (1969).   The ecology of chalk heath; its relevance to the calcicole-calcifuge and soil acidification problems. *J. Ecol.*, **57**, No. 1: 175-211. Oxford.

HARRIS, A. (1961). *The Rural Landscape of the East Riding of Yorkshire, 1700 - 1850*. O.U.P.

HARRIS, A. (1971).   Burton Bushes: the historical evidence. *Bulletin, Hull Natural History Society*, vol. **3**, No. 2: 3-8.

HARRIS, A. (1987).   The post-medieval landscapes of the Yorkshire Wolds. *Archaeology and Landscape History of East Yorkshire*. Summary of papers, Univ. of Hull.

HASLAM, S., SINKER, C. and WOLSELEY, P. (1975).   British water plants. *Field Studies*, **4**, No. 2. Field Studies Council.

HEATHCOTE, W.R. (1951).   A soil survey of warpland in Yorkshire. *J. of Soil Science*, **2**: 144-162.

HENREY, B., ed. CHATER, A.O. (1986). *No ordinary gardener, Thomas Knowlton, 1691-1781*. British Museum (Nat. Hist.). London.

HUBBARD, C.E. (1968). *Grasses.* Edn 2. Penguin. Harmondsworth.

JARVIS, R.A. (1973). Soils in Yorkshire II. Sheet SE 60 (Armthorpe). *Soil Survey Record* **12**. Soil Survey of England and Wales. Harpenden.

JARVIS, R.A. *et al.* (1984). *Soils and their use in northern England.* Bulletin **10**. Soil Survey of England and Wales. Harpenden.

JEFFERSON, R.G. (1984). The vascular flora of disused chalk pits and quarries in the Yorkshire Wolds. *Naturalist*, 1984: 19-22. Leeds.

JERMY, A.C. *et al.* eds (1978). *Atlas of Ferns of the British Isles.* London.

JERMY, A.C., CHATER, A.O. and DAVID, R.W. (1982). *Sedges of the British Isles.* Bot. Soc. Brit. Isles. London.

KENT, D.H. (1956). *Senecio squalidus* L. in the British Isles 1. Early records (to 1877). *Proc. Bot. Soc. Brit. Isles*, **2**, pt 2: 115-118.

KENT, D.H. (1959). *Corrigiola litoralis* in 'Plant Notes'. *Proc. Bot. Soc. Brit. Isles*, **3**, pt 3: 283-284.

KENT, D.H. (1960). *Senecio squalidus* L. in the British Isles 2. The spread from Oxford (1879 - 1939). *Proc. Bot. Soc. Brit. Isles*, **3**, pt 4: 375-379.

KENT, D.H. (1964). *Senecio squalidus* L. in the British Isles 6. Northern England (1940 ->). *Proc. Bot. Soc. Brit. Isles*, **5**, pt 3 : 217-219.

KENT, P. (1980). *Eastern England from the Tees to the Wash.* British Regional Geology. H.M.S.O. London.

KEW, H.W. and POWELL, H.E. (1932). *Thomas Johnson, botanist and royalist.* London.

LANKESTER, E., ed. (1846). *Memorials of John Ray.* Ray Society.

LEES, F.A., ed. CHEETHAM, C.A. and SLEDGE, W.A. (1941). *A Supplement to the Yorkshire Floras.* Hull.

LEWIN, J. (1969). The Yorkshire Wolds: A study in geomorphology. *Hull University Occasional Papers in Geography*, **11**. University of Hull.

LOUSLEY, J.E. (1976). *Flora of Surrey.* David & Charles. Newton Abbot.

MADGETT, P.A. and CATT, J.A. (1978). Petrography, stratigraphy and weathering of late Pleistocene tills in East Yorkshire, Lincolnshire and North Norfolk. *Proc. Yorks. Geol Soc.*, **42**: 55-108.

MARSHALL, J.J. (1892). Are *Crocus vernus* and *C. nudiflorus* natives of England? *Naturalist*, 1892: 55. London.

MATTHEWS, B. (1971). Soils in Yorkshire I. Sheet SE 65 (York East). *Soil Survey Record* **6**. Soil Survey of England and Wales. Harpenden.

MATTHEWS, J.R. (1955). *Origin and distribution of the British Flora*. London.

MERRYWEATHER, J. (1984). The ecology of British Rail in North Humberside. *Pteridologist*, **1**: 9.

NICHOLSON, G.G. (1983). Studies on the distribution and the relationship between the chromosome races of *Ranunculus ficaria* L. in S.E. Yorkshire. *Watsonia*, **14**: 321-328. Bot. Soc. Brit. Isles.

PALMER, J. (1966). Landforms, drainage and settlement in the Vale of York. In Eyre, S.R. and Jones, G.R.J. eds *Geography as Human Ecology*: 91-121. Arnold. London.

PALMER, L.S. (1939). Holderness in the making. *The History of the East Riding of Yorkshire*: 7-11. Hull.

PASHBY, B.S. (1977). Brent Geese and *Zostera* at Spurn. *Naturalist*, 1977: 85-90. Leeds.

PENNY, L.F. (1964). A review of the last glaciation in Great Britain. *Proc. Yorks. Geol. Soc.*, **34**, pt 4, No. 20: 387-411.

PERRING, F.H. and WALTERS, S.M., eds (1962). *Atlas of the British Flora*. London.

PERRING, F.H., ed. (1968). *Critical Supplement to the Atlas of the British Flora*. London.

PETCH, T. (1901). The Sea Lavender (*Statice limonium*) in Holderness. *Trans. Hull Sci. and Field Nat. Club*, **1**: 233-235.

PETCH, T. (1903). The marine fauna of the Humber District and the Holderness Coast. *Trans. Hull Sci. and Field Nat. Club*, **3**: 27-41.

PETCH, T. (1905a). Notes on the reclaimed land of the Humber District. *Trans. Hull Sci. and Field Nat. Club*, **3**: 221-231.

PETCH, T. (1905b). Notes on *Aster tripolium*. *Naturalist*, 1905: 50-54.

PHILIP, G. (1936). An Enalid plant association in the Humber Estuary. *J. Ecol.*, **24**: 205-219.

PRESTON, C.D. (1985). *Ruppia spiralis* L. ex Dumort. in Yorkshire. *Watsonia*, **15**: 274-275. Bot. Soc. Brit. Isles.

PRINGLE, A.W. (1985). Holderness coast erosion and the significance of ords. *Earth Surface Processes and Landforms*, **10**: 107-124.

PYRAH, M. (1959). *Corrigiola litoralis* in the Castleford area. *Naturalist*, 1959: 6. Hull.

RATCLIFFE, D.A., ed. (1977). *A Nature Conservation Review*. C.U.P. London.

RAYNER, D.H. and HEMINGWAY, J.E. (1974). *The Geology and Mineral Resources of Yorkshire*. Yorkshire Geol. Soc. Leeds.

RICHARDS, A.J. (1972). The *Taraxacum* flora of the British Isles. *Watsonia*, Supp. to vol. **9**. Bot. Soc. Brit. Isles.

RIDDELSDELL, H.J. (1902). North of England plants in the Motley herbarium at Swansea. *Naturalist*, 1902: 343-354. London.

ROBINSON, J.F. (1902). *The Flora of the East Riding of Yorkshire*. Hull.

ROSE, J. (1985). The Dimlington stadial / Dimlington chronozone; a proposal for naming the main glacial episode of the late Devensian in Britain. *Boreas,* **14**: 225-230.

SARGENT, C. (1984). *Britain's railway vegetation.* Institute of Terrestrial Ecology: Huntingdon.

SARGENT, C., MOUNTFORD, O. and GREENE, D. (1986). The distribution of *Poa angustifolia* L. in Britain. *Watsonia,* **16**: 31-36. Bot. Soc. Brit. Isles.

SCHADLA-HALL, R.T. and CLOUTMAN, E.W. (1985). The eastern vale of Pickering and the archaeology of a buried landscape in Haselgrove, C., ed. *Archaeology from the Ploughsoil*: 77-86. Sheffield University. Sheffield.

SHEPPARD, J.A. (1956). The draining of the marshlands of East Yorkshire. Unpublished Ph.D. thesis. University of London.

SHEPPARD, J.A. (1957). The medieval meres of Holderness. *Trans. Inst. Brit. Geogrs* 23: 75-86.

SHEPPARD, J.A. (1958). *The draining of the Hull valley.* East Yorkshire Local History Society, York. (East Yorkshire Local History Series, 8).

SHEPPARD, J.A. (1966). *The draining of the marshlands of South Holderness and the Vale of York.* East Yorkshire Local History Society, York. (East Yorkshire Local History Series, 20).

SMITH, A.H. (1937). *The place-names of the East Riding of Yorkshire and York.* C.U.P.

SOIL SURVEY OF ENGLAND AND WALES (1983). *1:250,000 Soil Map of England and Wales.* Sheet 4. Soil Survey of England and Wales. Harpenden.

STACE, C.A., ed. (1975). *Hybridization and the flora of the British Isles.* Bot. Soc. Brit. Isles. London.

STRICKLAND, H. (1812). *General view of the agriculture of the East Riding of Yorkshire.* London.

TEESDALE, R. (1794). *Plantae Eboracenses* or A catalogue of the more rare plants which grow wild in the neighbourhood of Castle Howard in the North Riding of Yorkshire disposed according to the Linnean system. *Trans. Linn. Soc.,* **2**: 103-125. London.

TEESDALE, R. (1800). A supplement to the *Plantae Eboracenses. Trans. Linn. Soc.* **5**: 36-93. London.

VERSEY, H.C. (1971). Geology and Topography in Sledge,W.A., ed. *The Naturalists' Yorkshire.* Dalesman Pub. Co. Ltd. Clapham.

WALSH, G.B. and RIMINGTON, F.C., eds (1953). *The natural history of the Scarborough District,* vol. **1**.

WARBURTON, S. (1978). *The Yorkshire Derwent; a case for conservation.* The Derwent Trust. York.

WILSON, A.K. (1938). *The adventive flora of the East Riding of Yorkshire.* Occasional Paper of the Hull Scientific and Field Naturalists' Club.

YOUNG, D.P. (1955). *Epipactis phyllanthes* in Yorkshire. *Naturalist,* 1955: 65.

INDEX

Names of families are printed in capitals. All other names are printed in ordinary roman type except for synonyms which are in italics. Only synonyms of names of genera in use until recently are given. Specific epithets are given only for those species for which there is a distribution map. Figures with the prefix 'M' refer to the distribution maps (pages 174-255).

264

Honkenya 82
Hop 109
Hop Trefoil 89
Hordeum 162
    murinum 162, M456
    secalinum 162, M53
Horehound 125, 126
Hornbeam 110
Horned Pondweed 144
Horned-poppy 72
Hornwort 71
Horse-chestnut 86
Horse-radish 75
Horseshoe Vetch 90
Horsetail 65
Hottonia
    palustris 113, M101
Hound's-tongue 116
House-leek 97
Humulus
    lupulus 109, M352
Huperzia 65
Hyacinthoides 145
    non-scripta 145
Hydrocharis 141
HYDROCHARITACEAE 141
Hydrocotyle
    vulgaris 102, M186
HYDROPHYLLACEAE 168
Hyoscyamus 118
Hypecoum 166
HYPERICACEAE 78
Hypericum 78-79
    hirsutum 79, M296
    humifusum 78, M40
    perforatum 78, M245
    pulchrum 78, M295
    tetrapterum 78, M147
Hypochoeris 136
    radicata 136, M418

Iberis 74
Ilex 87
Impatiens 86
    glandulifera 86, M256
Inula 131-132, 170
    conyza 132, M402
Ipomoea 169
IRIDACEAE 147, 171
Iris 147-148, 171
    pseudacorus 148, M128
ISOETACEAE 65
Isoetes 65
Isolepis
    setacea 153, M437
Ivy 102
Ivy-leaved Toadflax 120

Jacob's-ladder 116
Japanese Knotweed 108
Jasione 127
JUNCACEAE 145
JUNCAGINACEAE 142
Juncus 145-146
    acutiflorus 146, M148
    articulatus 146, M149
    bufonius 146, M424
    bulbosus 146, M187
    effusus 146, M426
    gerardi 146, M212
    inflexus 146, M425
    squarrosus 145, M41

subnodulosus 146, M150

Kickxia 120
Kidney Vetch 90
Knapweed 135, 136
Knautia
    arvensis 129, M397
Knawel 82
Knotgrass 107
Knotweed 108
Kochia 167
Koeleria 162, 171
    macrantha 162, M17

LABIATAE 123, 169
Lactuca 137
Lady-fern 66
Lady's Bedstraw 128
Lady's-mantle 95
Lady's-tresses 148, 149
Lagarosiphon 142
Lamarckia 171
Lamb's Lettuce 129
Lamb's Succory 136
Lamiastrum 125
Lamium 125, 169
    amplexicaule 125, M230
    hybridum 125, M231
Lappula 168
Lapsana 136
Larch 68
Larix 68
Larkspur 68
Laserpitum 168
Lathraea 122
Lavatera 167
Lathyrus 91, 168
    montanus 91, M323
Legousia
    hybrida 127, M232
LEGUMINOSAE 87, 167
Lemna 152
    minor 152, M102
    trisulca 152, M103
LEMNACEAE 152
Lemon-scented Fern 67
LENTIBULARIACEAE 123
Leontodon 136
    hispidus 136, M419
    taraxacoides 136, M420
Leonurus 169
Leopard's-bane 131
Lepidium 73-74, 166
Lesser Celandine 70
Lettuce 137
Leucanthemum
    vulgare 134, M410
Leymus 162
Ligustrum
    vulgare 114, M77
LILIACEAE 144, 171
Lilium 145, 171
Lily-of-the-valley 144
Lime 84
Limestone Fern 67
Limonium 113
Limosella 120
LINACEAE 85, 167
Linaria 119
    vulgaris 119, M370
Linum 85, 167
    catharticum 85, M311

Listera 148-149
    ovata 148, M429
Lithospermum 117
Littorella 127
Lobularia 75
Lolium 159, 171
London Plane 110
Londonpride 97
Lonicera
    periclymenum 129, M78
Loosestrife 113, 114
LORANTHACEAE 101
Lords-and-Ladies 151
Lotus 90
    uliginosus 90, M321
Lousewort 121
Lucerne 88
Lunaria 74
Luronium 141
Luzula 146-147
    campestris 147, M427
    mulitflora 147, M428
    pilosa 146, M79
Lychnis 80
    flos-cuculi 80, M188
Lycium 118
LYCOPODIACEAE 65
Lycopodiella 65
Lycopodium 65
Lycopsis 116
Lycopus
    europaeus 124, M151
Lyme-grass 162
Lysimachia 113-114
    nemorum 113, M80
    nummularia 113, M362
    vulgaris 113, M152
LYTHRACEAE 99, 168
Lythrum 99, 168
    salicaria 99, M153

Mahonia 71
Maianthemum 144
Maiden Pink 80
Malcolmia 166
Male-fern 66
Mallow 84-85
Malus 97
Malva 84-85, 167
    moschata 84, M308
    neglecta 85, M310
    sylvestris 85, M309
MALVACEAE 84, 167
Maple 86
Mare's-tail 101
Marigold 131, 134
Marjoram 124
Marram 163
Marrubium 126
Marsh-bedstraw 128
Marsh Cinquefoil 94
Marsh Fern 67
Marsh-marigold 68
Marsh-orchid 151
Marsh Pea 91
Marsh Pennywort 102
Marsh Samphire 84
Marshwort 104
MARSILEACEAE 67
Martagon Lily 145
Mat-grass 165

267